THE ARRL
UHF/MICROWAVE
EXPERIMENTER'S
MANUAL

ANTENNAS,
COMPONENTS
AND DESIGN

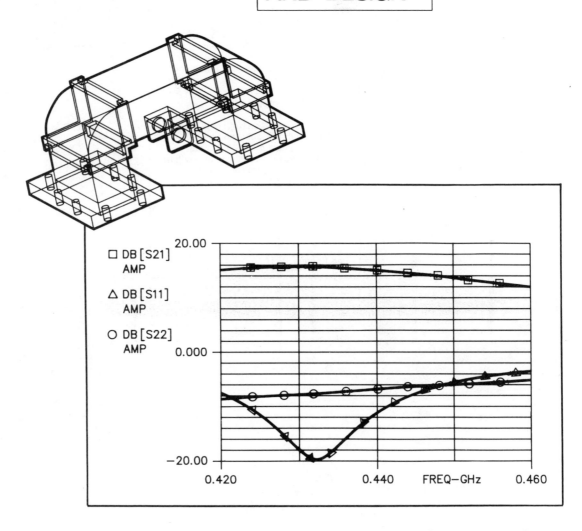

PUBLISHED BY THE AMERICAN RADIO
RELAY LEAGUE

225 Main Street
Newington, CT 06111 USA

Foreword

There have always been two types of people: Those content to follow in the footsteps of others, and those who have an innate desire to break new ground, to work at the cutting edge of an endeavor, whatever it may be.

Guglielmo Marconi, the "Father of Wireless," is certainly a member of the latter group. In 1922, he prophesied: "...the study of short electric waves, although sadly neglected practically all through the history of wireless, is still likely to develop in many unexpected directions, and open up new fields of practical research."

Several generations of experimenters, many of them Amateur Radio operators, have brought the UHF and microwave state of the art to a point that Marconi could only have dreamt of. The first chapter of this book provides an overview of the history of microwave experimentation, work that continues to reap practical benefits and expand our knowledge of the world.

About This Book: This book is written for those who populate the Amateur Radio frequencies at 420 MHz and above, those working in the UHF and microwave realm, and those who want to learn what the excitement is all about. *The ARRL UHF/Microwave Experimenter's Manual* provides a great deal of theoretical and practical information about the devices, equipment and antennas that make UHF and microwave communication possible. The great majority is original material, written by the authors expressly for this book. Some of it, however, appeared previously in the League's monthly journal, *QST*. The ARRL is planning to publish a companion volume containing construction projects. With these two books, you'll have the tools you need to make your mark in the ever-expanding world of UHF and microwave communications.

David Sumner, K1ZZ
Executive Vice President
Newington, Connecticut
August 1990

Acknowledgments

Thanks to the following individuals and manufacturers: ICOM America, Inc, for donating equipment used in preparing this volume; Microwave Modules, Ltd, for special consideration; Everett L. Gracey, WA6CBA (KLM Electronics, Inc); M. I. Wood (Microwave Modules, Ltd); John E. Magnusson, WØAGD (Times Fiber Communications, Inc); Bob Richardson, W4UCH (Richcraft Engineering); Tom Snellings, WB7ONU (ICOM America, Inc); Dana Atchley, Jr, W1CF and Marc Goldfarb, WB2ELF (M/A-COM); California Eastern Laboratories, Inc; James A. McGregor (Microtech); Claus Neie, DL7QY (*DUBUS*); Juergen Dahms, DCØDA (*Der SHF Amateur*); Karl Weiner, DJ9HO (*The UHF Compendium*), Barry Manz, WB2TSY (*Microwaves & RF*) and Julius Madey, K2KGJ (Applied Invention).

This project could not have been possible without the hard work and dedication of a large number of individuals. Although it would not be feasible to list them all, special words of thanks are due the following: Charles L. Hutchinson, K8CH, Dennis Lusis, W1LJ, Mark Wilson, AA2Z, Kirk Kleinschmidt, NTØZ, and Joel P. Kleinman, N1BKE, who served as editors; Geoffrey H. Krauss, WA2GFP, who reviewed parts of the manuscript; Robert Schetgen, KU7G, Larry Wolfgang, WR1B, Bruce Hale, KB1MW, Jeffrey Kilgore, KC1MK, and Robert Stein, W6NBI, who assisted the editors; Michelle Chrisjohn, WB1ENT, Leslie K. Bartoloth, KA1MJP, and Deborah Strzeszkowski, who were responsible for typesetting and layout; David Pingree, Mark Kajpust and Dianna Roy, who rendered the drawings; and Steffie Nelson, KA1IFB who proofread the typeset manuscript.

Cover: Sue Fagan, Graphic Design; David Pingree, Illustrations; Meyers Studio, Photography

Contents

Chapter 1

A Brief History

By Dr H. Paul Shuch, N6TX,   and   Maureen A. Thompson, KA1DYZ
Professor of Electronics   84 Pentlow Ave
Pennsylvania College of Technology   New Britain, CT 06053
1 College Ave
Williamsport, PA 17701

Microwave—the very term conjures up images of some futuristic laboratory filled with incomprehensible apparatus, the lair of the mad scientist straight from a horror movie. And in a sense, this strange technology deserves its image of a bottled genie just recently uncorked. The abilities of microwave radiation to cook a burger in record time, relay a TV program across a continent, nail a speeding motorist a mile down the turnpike, and survey our galactic neighbors from across the gulf of space have all emerged within the lifetime and memory of most radio amateurs.

Although most of us think only of the modern applications of microwaves, they are literally as old as the universe. And their application by man predates what we commonly call the Electronic Age. Thus, the study of microwaves must really begin with a journey back in time.

THE MICROWAVE REGION

The substance of electronic communication is the electromagnetic wave, an ever-expanding sphere of intersecting electrostatic and magnetic lines of force traveling at the speed of light. Mathematically, these waves are all alike, whether emanating from sunlight, searchlight or satellite. Their behavior was predicted by James Clerk Maxwell, a professor of experimental physics at Cambridge University, England, as far back as 1865. Maxwell developed a set of four equations, and they form the basis of most classical studies of microwaves. Shown in Fig 1, these equations involve the symbols and terminology of calculus. Fortunately for those not so mathematically inclined, we neither have to understand nor apply these equations in order to experiment with microwaves.

Electromagnetic waves vary in length from the very short to the very long, from X rays to ultraviolet to visible light to infrared—to name a few. Fig 2, a chart of the electromagnetic spectrum, displays the wavelength and frequency for several different types of electromagnetic waves. The right side of the chart shows the nonamateur allocations in the lower portion of the microwave region. Letter designators are used to denote sections of the microwave region (Fig 3).

$$\nabla \cdot E = p$$

$$\nabla \cdot H = 0$$

$$\nabla \times E + \frac{\delta H}{\delta t} = 0$$

$$\nabla \times H = \frac{\delta E}{\delta t} + I$$

where

 E = electronic field vector
 H = magnetic field vector
 I = electric current vector
 p = electric charge

Fig 1—Maxwell's equations for electromagnetic propagation in free space. The first equation (Divergence of E equals p) is simply Gauss' Law for electricity. It describes the shape of an electric field caused by a charge. The second equation (Divergence of H equals zero) is Gauss' Law for magnetism. It describes the shape of a magnetic field caused by a magnet. Maxwell's third equation (Curl of E plus the partial time derivative of H equals zero) is a statement of Faraday's Law, which describes an electric field caused by a time-varying magnetic field. The fourth equation (Curl of H equals I plus the partial time derivative of E) is Ampere's Law, describing the shape of a magnetic field caused by a current.

The actual boundaries of the microwave region are somewhat arbitrary, but frequencies between 1 and 250 gigahertz (10^9 Hz, abbreviated GHz) are generally considered to be in the region. These frequencies correspond to wavelengths of 30.5 cm to 1.27 mm. Table 1-1 shows the Amateur Radio Service and Amateur Satellite Service allocations in the microwave region.

You can readily simulate electromagnetic waves by dropping a stone into a pool of water. Notice that the waves generated by this action spread out from the point of origin, propagating equally in all directions. Notice also that you can count the number of waves passing a fixed point in a given time (frequency), and measure with a ruler the physical distance between successive crests, or peaks, of the waves (wavelength). The term *wavelength*, then, refers to the distance the wave travels during the time of one complete cycle (crest to crest). In free space, these waves travel 300 million meters per second, a velocity we

A Brief History   1-1

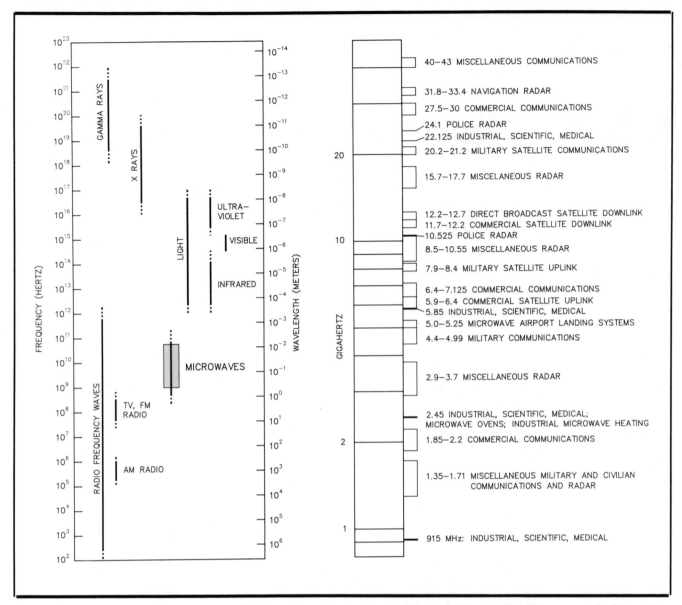

Fig 2—The electromagnetic spectrum, with the microwave region highlighted. (From ''The Microwave Problem,'' by Kenneth R. Foster and Arthur W. Guy. Copyright © 1986 by Scientific American, Inc. All rights reserved.)

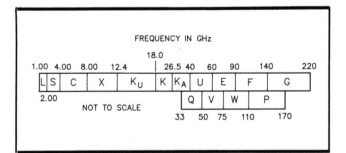

Fig 3—The microwave bands are divided into sub-bands, which are given letter designations.

call the ''speed of light.'' The equation for calculating this is

$$c = f \lambda \qquad \text{(Eq 1)}$$

where

c = the speed of light (3.00×10^8 meters/second)
f = the frequency in hertz and
λ = the wavelength in meters.

In the microwave realm, frequency is commonly measured in gigahertz and wavelength is expressed in centimeters (cm). Solving Eq 1 for wavelength and frequency,

Table 1-1

Amateur Radio UHF and Microwave Allocations

Updated to January 1990

US amateurs holding at least a Technician class license may operate on the following frequencies:

Freq	Notes
MHz	
1240-1300	1-4
2300-2310	1,5-7
2390-2450	1,5,7,8
3300-3500	1,5,9,10
5650-5925	1,5,11-13
GHz	
10.00-10.50	1,3,14,15
24.00-24.25	1,3,5,16,17
47.00-47.20	
75.50-81.00	1,3,14
119.98-120.02	9,18
142-149	1,3,9,14
241-250	1,3,14,19
above 300	9

Notes

[1] 1240-1300, 2300-2310, 2390-2450, 3300-3500 and 5650-5925 MHz, 10-10.5, 24.05-24.25, 76-81, 144-149 and 241-248 GHz: secondary allocation; Government radiolocation service primary

[2] 1240-1260 MHz: secondary allocation; foreign radionavigation-satellite service primary

[3] 1240-1300 MHz, 10-10.5, 24.05-24.25, 76-81, 144-149 and 241-248 GHz: secondary allocation; foreign radiolocation service primary

[4] 1270-1295 MHz: US Novices are permitted all authorized modes, 5 W output maximum

[5] Stations of different services of the same category in one ITU region or subregion must not interfere with services in other regions or subregions.

[6] In the US, co-secondary allocation with Government fixed and mobile services.

[7] Secondary allocation in all ITU regions; in Regions 2 and 3, foreign fixed, mobile and radiolocation services primary

[8] 2400-2450 MHz: secondary allocation; industrial, scientific and medical (ISM) primary

[9] 3332-3339, 3345.8-3352.5 MHz, 119.98-120.02, 146.82-147.12 and 343-348 GHz: secondary allocation; radioastronomy service primary

[10] In the US, co-secondary with nongovernment radiolocation service

[11] 5650-5725 MHz: co-secondary in all ITU Regions with space research service. 5725-5850 MHz: secondary allocation in all ITU Regions. 5650-5850 MHz: secondary allocation; foreign radiolocation service primary. 5850-5925 MHz: co-secondary allocation in Region 2 with radiolocation service; foreign fixed, fixed-satellite and mobile services primary.

[12] 5850-5925 MHz: in the US, secondary allocation; nongovernment fixed satellite service primary

[13] 5725-5875 MHz: secondary allocation; ISM primary

[14] 10.45-10.5, 76-81, 144-149 and 241-248 GHz: secondary allocation; nongovernment radiolocation service primary

[15] Co-secondary allocation with nongovernment radiolocation service

[16] 24.05-24.25 GHz: in the US, co-secondary allocation with nongovernment radiolocation, and government and nongovernment earth-exploration-satellite services

[17] 24-24.25 GHz: secondary allocation; ISM on 24.125 GHz primary

[18] Secondary allocation; fixed, inter-satellite and mobile services primary

[19] 244-246 GHz: Secondary allocation; ISM on 245 GHz primary

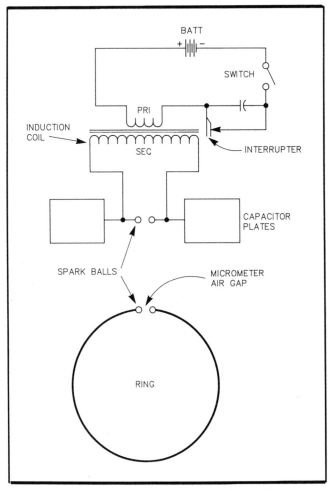

Fig 4—Hertz's first transmitting setup. It confirmed Maxwell's theory that electric and magnetic components of a wave were perpendicular to the direction of motion of the wave. Hertz also confirmed that electromagnetic radiation propagated as waves and that it traveled with the speed of light. (Adapted from *Encyclopaedia Britannica*, 14th edition, 1973.)

and substituting the value for the speed of light, we have:

$$\lambda = 30 \ / \ f \qquad \text{(Eq 2)}$$

$$f = 30 \ / \ \lambda \qquad \text{(Eq 3)}$$

where

λ = wavelength in cm and

f = frequency in GHz.

Physicists measuring the wavelength of microwaves often find the meter and centimeter difficult to work with, so many electromagnetic spectrum charts of the microwave region use the unit of angstrom (Å). One angstrom is equal to 1/10,000,000,000 (that's 1×10^{-10}) meter.

HARNESSING THE WAVES

The usefulness of electromagnetic radiation lies in its ability to carry information from point A to point B. That ability was first demonstrated by the German physicist

Heinrich Rudolph Hertz, a professor of physics at what is now the Technical University of Karlsruhe, Germany. In 1888 he succeeded in generating radio waves and receiving them a short distance away.

His first transmitting and receiving setup is shown in Fig 4. Hertz used an induction coil connected to a pair of metal rods. A flat metal plate was attached on one end of each rod, while the other end had a metal ball. He could adjust the spacing between the metal balls to control the air gap between them. When the switch was closed, battery current flowed through the primary winding of the induction coil. The iron core of the coil served as an electromagnet, attracting the iron "interrupter." This would break the circuit, allowing the magnetic field to decay. The interrupter would then spring back to the closed position, completing the circuit again. In this way a pulsed direct current was produced in the induction coil primary. The changing primary current then induced a voltage (and current) in the secondary coil.

An induction coil is really a transformer, except that it uses direct current and a magnetic circuit interrupter to produce the changing primary current. When the voltage induced in the induction coil secondary was large enough, a spark would jump across the air gap between the two metal balls. Hertz found that the spark from the induction-coil "transmitter" caused a small spark to jump across the air gap between the metal balls of his "receiving" loop. He had detected electromagnetic waves, only 23 years after Maxwell had predicted them! It may be even more astonishing to realize that Hertz's 1888 experiments involved the radiation and detection of *microwave* energy. Man's first use of radio waves was in the microwave spectrum.

In later experiments, Hertz focused his microwaves into a directed beam, through the use of a metal mirror in the shape of a parabola. He wrote: "As soon as I had succeeded in proving that the action of an electric oscillation spreads out as a wave in space, I planned experiments with the object of concentrating this action and making it perceptible at greater distances by putting the primary conductor in the focal line of a large concave parabolic mirror." Today the parabolic reflector, or dish, is the most commonly used microwave antenna.

FROM HERTZ TO MARCONI

Some significant experiments parallel Hertz's pioneering work. Ernst Werner von Siemens, best remembered for having built an extensive network of telegraph lines across Europe, received a German patent for coaxial cable in 1884. At the time of his death in 1892, no practical use of his invention had yet been made. The first commercial application of coaxial cable as a transmission line was probably in carrying live television images of the Berlin Olympic Games, over a 93-mile path to Leipzig, in 1936. The unit for conductance is the siemens, in honor of the father of coaxial cable.

In 1894, Oliver Lodge first demonstrated the use of waveguide transmission lines at London's Royal Institu-

tion. At the University of Calcutta, in 1897, J. C. Bose developed the waveguide horn antenna. This is basically the same design that Arno Penzias and Robert W. Wilson of Bell Labs were to use 68 years later to detect the background radiation left over from the formation of the universe (the "Big Bang" theory of the Universe) perhaps 18 billion years ago. This work earned Penzias and Wilson a Nobel Prize in 1978.

Lord Rayleigh (an English physicist) also presented the theory of electromagnetic wave propagation through hollow conducting tubes in 1897. His idea, however, lay dormant for over 30 years until the development of microwave generators.

Guglielmo Marconi, a name familiar to every amateur, is credited with being the "father of wireless" for his December 12, 1901 success of bridging 2000 miles of space between Newfoundland and England. But in 1897 he had transmitted and received modulated *microwave* signals over a four-mile path, in a demonstration for the British Post Office. He also employed a parabolic reflector to extend the range of his first station.

Just after World War I, Marconi delved into the 150-MHz range, and built an AM transmitter using a V-24 tube. His antenna was a dipole and parabolic reflector. The matching receiver used a semiconductor diode (crystal) detector. Around 1930, Marconi used improved tubes and beam antennas to demonstrate communication up to 168 miles over a sea path at frequencies above 500 MHz.

From this auspicious beginning, microwave experimentation suffered a 20-year dormancy when Marconi and others discovered that lower-frequency radio waves could propagate over greater distances. In 1922, Marconi wrote in a paper presented to the Institute of Radio Engineers: "...the study of short electric waves, although sadly neglected practically all through the history of wireless, is still likely to develop in many unexpected directions, and open up new fields of profitable research."

In retrospect, the "unexpected directions" and "new fields" of which Marconi spoke must certainly be said to include radio astronomy and radar (developments of the 1930s); microwave telephone and television relay techniques of the '40s; the aviation electronics advances of the '50s; the birth of space communications in the '60s; the biomedical electronics and personal communications revolutions of the '70s; the earth resources management activities of the '80s; and quite possibly the eventual colonization of space. But all of these developments awaited the perfection of microwave active devices—vacuum tubes and semiconductors optimized for the generation, amplification and control of microwave signals.

RADIO BECOMES REGULATED

In the 19th century, the major commercial wireless companies from Germany, Britain, Russia, Spain, France, Hungary, Austria, Italy and the United States were in stiff competition with each other. If a coastal station used a certain make of wireless equipment, it was not allowed to handle communications to or from a ship using another company's model, except in times of distress. To organize this mishandling of affairs, regulatory rules had to be introduced to all involved.

In 1903, the first conference between these nations was held in Berlin. Another Berlin conference that followed in 1906 was important in that it was the first time ever that specific frequencies were assigned to certain services. By 1908, commercial wireless was well established.

These meetings laid the foundation for the present-day series of World Administrative Radio Conferences (WARCs). Representatives from around the globe meet every 20 years or so to allocate frequencies among their many and varied users. But what about Amateur Radio? (*Radio* is the term the participants of the 1906 Conference agreed on to describe communication through space without the use of wires.)

The amateur population was increasing by the early part of 1917 when the United States became entangled in World War I. During April 1917, all licensed radio amateurs, numbering around 10,000, were ordered off the air. Equipment was donated to the government and many radiomen were employed for military communications and as technicians. The ban on receiving signals was lifted in April 1919, and by November amateurs could once again transmit Morse code freely.

SHORT WAVES, LONG DISTANCE

In the '20s, amateur experimenters were kept busy proving that short waves could be used for long distance communication. This view hindered progress in the VHF area. It was thought that frequencies above 30 MHz could only follow line-of-sight paths. Experiments were performed in the 50- to 70-MHz range as tubes for this band were more readily available. Amateurs moved lower in frequency as 5-meter gear became popular, and by the late '20s, the world above 50 MHz was inhabited mainly by experimenters rather than communicators.

During the '30s, it was noticed that 5-meter signals did not always travel in a line-of-sight path. Under the direction of Ross Hull, a native of Australia who had joined the ARRL Headquarters staff in 1926, experiments employing new "acorn tubes" and Yagi directive antennas broke much new ground. In the summer of 1934, W1AL, at ARRL HQ in West Hartford, Connecticut, was heard at Mount Desert Island, Maine, 292 miles away, using the 5-meter directive array shown in Fig 5. Further experimentation with newly designed transmitters, receivers and antennas on the 56- and 224-MHz bands laid the groundwork for others. Hull's work was cut short by his untimely death in 1938.

The acorn tube was an important part of the practical microwave oscillator circuit Hull used (Fig 6). One of the first in the high-frequency range, it was top choice for those wanting maximum power output. But the compromise here was between stability and efficiency, and stability was poor. The acorn assisted Hull in his breakthrough discovery of tropospheric bending of UHF waves, later described in a *QST* article appropriately titled,

Fig 5—The directive array at W1AL enabled ARRL's Ross Hull to broaden the VHF communications range of Amateur Radio from 10 to 20 miles to over 200 miles!

"The New Tube and Directive Antennas Reveal a World of Possibilities."

Star Light, Star Noise

A few years before Hull's discovery of the bending of UHF signals in the lower atmosphere, Karl Jansky, a 26-year-old Bell Labs employee at Holmdel, New Jersey, spawned the science of radio astronomy. In August 1931, he employed an aerial and receiver to discover what he called "Star Noise."

Jansky's aerial consisted of a wooden frame, rotatable about a vertical axis, on which was mounted an array of dipoles with reflectors. A horizontal aperture of 2 wavelengths at the operational frequency of 20 MHz provided a rather broad-beam radiation pattern, but with useful suppression of the back lobe. At the time, Jansky was involved in a project documenting sources of static on transatlantic telephone radio circuits (2 through 30 MHz). He was able to identify three: local thunderstorms, distant thunder-

Fig 6—The acorn detector tube and its tuning equipment, as used by Ross Hull and others in 1934 to further the state of the art on the 224-Mc band.

The insides of a 12-cavity 3-cm. magnetron shown actual size. The two rings inside the structure strap alternate cavities. The two fins are part of the cooling surfaces.

A "package-type" magnetron, in which the magnet is integral with the tube. The 2J55 operates at 9400 megacycles (3.2 centimeters). The over-all height of the tube is six inches.

The local oscillator tube used in 3000-Mc. radar receivers, the 2K28 reflex klystron. The resonant cavity makes connection to the copper discs midway along the glass part of the tube. The other half of the disassembled cavity also is shown in this view.

The real "works" of a 10-cm. magnetron, showing the eight cavities surrounding the cathode and the "strapping" of alternate cavities. The cathode is supported only by the heater leads coming in on either side of the cavities.

A 300-kilowatt magnetron, the 2J26. The output connection projects from the seal in the foreground. The pyrex bowl on top protects the cathode and heater leads and provides a mounting for the terminal jacks.

The 2J38 is a compact lower-powered magnetron of the package type that was used extensively in aircraft radar. The output fitting is for coaxial line.

Fig 7—A variety of magnetron and reflex klystron tubes that were manufactured by Raytheon during the 1940s. Photos and captions from December 1945 *QST*.

storms and what he described as "a steady weak hiss from an unknown origin."

This new science was not called radio astronomy until the 1950s because few astronomers were familiar with radio technology and its potential. It wasn't until the 1940s that Bell Labs started building exquisitely sensitive microwave radio receivers for radar, and this work was based on microwave radio and waveguide technology from the 1920s and 1930s. Jansky directed his studies to radar during World War II. After the war ended, he became involved in microwave repeater technology.

BIRTH OF A NEW ERA

The term *microrays* (microwaves), was coined during the early 1930s, probably by Andre Clavier of the

Laboratorie Central de Telecommunications in Paris. In 1931, Clavier participated in the first trans-English Channel microwave contact. The 1.7-GHz AM contact used 3-meter parabolic dish antennas. (In 1941, he used 3 GHz for tests on tropospheric scatter.)

The magnetron was developed during this time as well. The British Admiralty assigned the task of developing a microwave generator to a research group at the University of Birmingham, England. When the group established a practical form of obtaining satisfactory power output at extremely short wavelengths, Sir Henry Tizard demonstrated the cavity magnetron to American scientists.

In 1940, the US government assigned the Raytheon facility to work with the Massachusetts Institute of Technology to develop experimental microwave-type tubes.

The 4J38 is a high-power "maggie" capable of a peak power output of 850 kilowatts at 3600 megacycles (8.3 centimeters). A pick-up loop in one of the anode cavities connects to a coaxial line which terminates in an antenna in the wave-guide section at the left. The ring at the top of the glass tube enclosing the cathode leads is a corona shield, required because of the high potential (30,000 volts) at which this tube operates. The over-all height is slightly over ten inches.

This type of package magnetron uses direct coupling from one of the magnetron cavities to a section of wave guide. The glass window on this section of guide acts as a matching transformer into the external wave guide.

The glass boot around the heater leads is cut away to provide for forced cooling of the heater leads and seal.

The metal tube is the 2K25, a receiver local oscillator of the reflex-klystron type that tunes from 8700 to 9550 Mc. The cavity is built in and is adjusted by the square nut on the side. Small variations of about 40 Mc. are obtained by changing the repeller voltage a small amount. What looks like an extension of one of the socket pins is a small length of coaxial line and antenna used for outgoing coupling.

The glass tube is the 721A, a duplexing tube. Used in an external resonant cavity, it serves as an instantaneous switch to short the input of the receiver when the transmitter is on and hence protects the small crystal used as a mixer in the receiver. The cap on the side is for a "keep-alive" voltage which maintains some ions in the tube at all times and decreases the break-down time when the transmitter power is applied.

Fig 7 shows some of Raytheon's successful line of magnetrons and reflex klystrons, many of which were employed in World War II.

After the US entered the war in December 1941, communication on the airwaves came to a halt. With rag-chewing and experimenting on the frequencies suspended, the government asked qualified amateurs to assist the armed forces in learning Morse code and electronic technology. Other amateurs with appropriate educational background assisted in laboratory experiments and new techniques associated with the microwave region. Radar and pulse communication developed rapidly during this period.

The klystron was developed in the '30s, but its widespread use didn't come about until the '50s. As George Badger, W6RXW, wrote in 1961, "Klystrons come in all sizes, capable of handling anything from milliwatts to megawatts, at frequencies from about 200 MHz up." Its usefulness stemmed from the fact that conventional VHF tubes suffered from frequency and power-handling limits. Transit time (the finite time of flight of an electron between electrodes in a vacuum tube) was the major reason equipment designers investigated newer microwave tube designs. Klystrons were used most widely in high-power amplifier service.

Amateur communication on the microwave bands became popular right after World War II ended, in the fall of 1945. There were two reasons: (1) Surplus radar equipment, manufactured and used during the war, was being sold at affordable prices, and (2) frequencies and techniques utilized by the military in the VHF and microwave range were opened to radio amateurs. Every experimenter of the day longed to get hold of surplus equipment when several bands of superhigh frequencies—2300-2450 and 5250-5650 MHz, and 10.0-10.5 and 21.0-22.0 GHz—became available for amateur use on November 15, 1945.

On that very day, Reuben Merchant, W2LFG, and

A. E. Harrison, W6BMS, opened the 5300-MHz band using surplus equipment (Fig 8). The first contact spanned 5 miles. The heart of their transmitter and receiver was a Sperry 2K43 reflex klystron tube, and it fit nicely into this frequency range. The receiver worked in conjunction with a crystal mixer into a 30-MHz IF in the form of an FM receiver. Highly directive antennas eliminated interference between the transmitter and receiver.

Fig 8—W2LGF and W6BMS were the first two amateurs to open the 5300-MHz band. The transmitter, with a blower for cooling the klystron, is mounted in front of the upper dish. The receiver local oscillator and mixer similarly are mounted in front of the lower parabolic reflector.

Fig 9—W9WHM/2 and W6OJK/2 bridged the communications gap on 2300 MHz. An electric heater was used for one of their reflectors. The feed for the antenna was a half-wave radiator backed by a parasitic reflector.

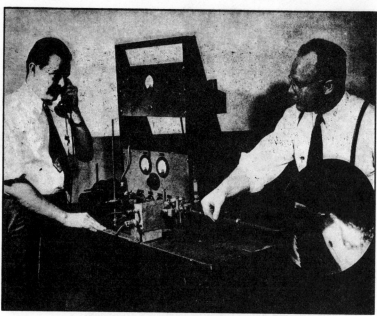

Fig 10—W1NVL/2 and W9SAD/2 are shown with their 21-GHz gear. This station opened the 21.9-GHz band.

The success of Merchant and Harrison spawned new interest in microwave firsts. A. R. Koch, W9WHM/2, and G. H. Floyd, W6OJK/2, bridged the gap on the 2400-MHz amateur assignment. The new 2C40 lighthouse tube was chosen for their transceivers, and the antenna system was a parabolic reflector. One reflector was made of wire screening attached to a wooden frame, and the other was simply an electric-heater assembly with the microwave dipole substituted for the heater element (Fig 9). A 0.7-mile QSO was finally established on April 29, 1946, after prior unsuccessful attempts.

Postwar, the highest frequency band allotted to amateur use was 21.9 GHz. On May 18, 1946, A. H. Sharbaugh, W1NVL/2, and R. L. Watters, W9SAD/2, conducted the first two-way contact on this band. Their one-hour voice QSO spanned a distance of 800 feet. The RF generator used for transmitting and receiving was a developmental reflex tube designated Z-668, developed by the General Electric Co during the war. Their setup is shown in Fig 10.

Earlier that same month, James A. McGregor, W2RJM, and Charles K. Atwater, W2JN, made the first 3-cm contact, spanning a distance of 2 miles on 10.3 GHz. They used modified 723A/B klystrons (also known as 2K25), for permitted operation in the amateur band. A 30-inch parabaloid fed with waveguide and a Hallicrafters S-29 receiver were employed with the aid of a gasoline-driven generator. Fig 11 shows part of their equipment. The oscillator and preamplifier are built into one small unit, which is mounted directly on the waveguide at the rear of the parabolic reflector. The 723A/B, mounted horizontally with its output probe projecting into the waveguide, serves as transmitting oscillator and local oscillator. The device on the right is a 3-cm wavemeter.

A similar arrangement was used by D. L. Thompson, W6IFE/3, and W. F. Kennedy, W4HPJ/3, who stretched the distance record on the same band to 7.65 miles. Their

Fig 11—This oscillator and preamplifier unit assisted W2RJM and W2JN in setting a record on the 10.3-GHz band. A 3-cm wavemeter is on the right.

advice to any interested amateur in September 1946 was to "first head for the nearest surplus dealer in your area!"

W6IFE went on to open the 3300-MHz band using a 707B with an external cavity. He upgraded his record by reaching new distances on two other bands—2300 and 3300 MHz (contact was established at 20.2 and 21 miles, respectively). Finding no one else interested in building this type of equipment, he built two units. One served as a fixed station (using a 707B), the other as a portable (using a 446B lighthouse). His waveguide was home-made from tin cans soldered together.

In May 1947, it was reported that the last microwave band, 1215 MHz, had been occupied. The lowest in frequency, it was receiving attention as B. W. Bates, W1BBM, Cape Cod, Massachusetts, completed a two-way contact with H. K. Hentz, W1ARC, over a distance of 0.4 mile using two 2C40 transceivers and parabolic reflectors. Later that year, Bates discovered that a 2C40 lighthouse tube performed on 1275 MHz as efficiently as ordinary tubes do on the VHF band.

A new world had been opened to the microwave frequencies by these experimenters. Equipment could now be modified to work better and longer distances. Microwave pioneers found there was no turning back, and they turned their attention to setting new records.

THE FABULOUS '50s

By 1951, amateur activity on the microwave bands had reached new heights. Information on buying or building equipment for each band was readily available, and those already involved were sharing their valuable hints to recruit new operators.

The maser (*m*icrowave *a*mplification by *s*timulated *e*mission of *r*adiation) was invented in the spring of 1951. Charles H. Townes's device consisted of a small metal box containing excited ammonia molecules. With microwaves radiating into the cavity tuned to 24 GHz, a highly coherent beam of high-frequency microwaves was emitted. To obtain the required electron behavior for Amateur Radio applications, it was necessary for the maser to not only be in a strong magnetic field, but its electrons had to be those of certain gases, or substances, such as ruby or garnet. This could get expensive. The largest drawback, however, was in the area of low-noise operation. The maser had to be cooled to a very low temperature by liquid nitrogen, a commodity not found in the everyday ham shack!

Distance records were still being broken and new ones set, but not until October 1954 was a new 10-GHz record set—this time by R. L. Harris, W7OKV, and L. F. Garrett, W7JIP, both of Oregon. With considerably improved equipment and high-powered klystrons, they communicated over a 109-mile path. Fig 12 shows the rear view of the antenna mount, the 723A/B klystron, a 3-cm wavemeter and the IF preamplifier. A plug-in IF system was used at W7JIP.

In February 1957, it was announced that a new solid-state oscillator for microwave use had been developed by Bell Laboratories. The device, called a spin oscillator, would operate as an amplifier, and exhibited very low noise. It was in its development stage, but was said to have the potential for extending the boundaries of microwave communications and radio astronomy. It also had one drawback for amateurs: It was operated while immersed in liquid helium!

The first amateur communication at 36.5 GHz occurred during July 1957 on the roof of the Hughes Aircraft Company building in Culver City, California. Richard G. Somers, W6NSV, and William J. Odlum, K6YYF, set their gear for amateur two-way communication on a frequency in the unassigned territory above 30 GHz (Fig 13). The building size limited communication to 500 feet.

A Hughes-built transmitter, equipped with automatic frequency control circuits and its own regulated supply,

was used. Duplex operation was conducted on the same frequency—a system somewhat different from that normally used.

Band limits were changed by the FCC in June 1958 from 3.3-3.5 GHz to 3.5-3.7 GHz—and then back again early in 1962. New and inviting articles on microwave sta-

Fig 12—Rear view of the antenna mount used by W7JIP/7 for his 10-GHz contact. The 3-cm wavemeter and 723A/B klystron is mounted on the waveguide. The IF preamplifier is to the left.

Fig 13—In July 1957, W6NSV communicated with K6YYF on 36.5 GHz from the roof of the Hughes Aircraft Company building. A Hughes-built transmitter, equipped with automatic frequency control circuits and its own regulated supply, was used in the operation.

tions and operation appeared, including one that showed the San Bernardino Microwave Society's beer-can *polaplexer*, which could be used with a parabolic reflector, or by itself as an antenna for distances up to a few hundred feet (Fig 14). Parts for many kinds of microwave stations were unavailable at the time some of the articles were published, but this did not discourage experimenters.One of these was W8DDR, who conducted successful experiments on the 5650-MHz band using largely homebuilt equipment (see Fig 15).

Fig 14—The San Bernardino Microwave Society's beer-can polaplexer, mounted on its parabolic reflector.

Sharbaugh and Watters returned to the spotlight in October 1958 as they set two new DX records: 14 miles on 21 GHz (14 mm wavelength) and 150 feet on 50 GHz (6 mm wavelength)—believed to be the highest frequency ever used at the time for two-way voice communication. An estimated RF power of 1 microwatt was the limiting factor in the transmission range.

During the 21-GHz experiment, horn antennas were aimed visually with field glasses. Later, 15-inch-diameter parabolic reflectors were tried at both ends with a significant improvement. The equipment used in the 50-GHz test was similar to that used 13 years earlier when they had set their 21-GHz DX record. Two types of klystrons were used: the General Electric Z-668 and the 2K33A. With the tremendous growth of television by 1958, IF amplifiers with improved noise figures were now available. Sharbaugh's and Watters's calculations showed that their distance record could be extended greatly with the use of this improved receiving equipment.

Six years later, A. Harry Sharbaugh, W2UKL, would reappear in amateur headlines. In October 1964, and still interested in pioneering amateur microwave communication techniques, he broke his own record on 21 GHz with a QSO distance of slightly over 27 miles.

The 1959 June VHF Party presented an ideal opportunity for W6DQJ and K6AXN to set a record of 400 miles on 1296 MHz. On June 14, they set their stations at the extreme northern and southern ends of the San Joaquin Valley in California, far beyond line of sight. Because the contact was made at 0850, signals over this path were at their peak; they exchanged reports of 569 and 559. The equipment used on each end consisted of a crystal-controlled 2C39 transmitter delivering 10-W output, and a crystal-controlled converter feeding narrow-band receivers. CW was used exclusively. Antennas were 4-foot parabolas with vertically polarized dipoles.

The team of Leonard Garrett, W7JIP, and Ernest

Fig 15—Microwave transceivers built by C. J. Prechtel, W8DRR, for 5650 MHz. The FM receiver (right photo) was built from readily available TV components, and the horn antennas were made from hardware-store funnels.

Manly, W7LHL, extended the 10-GHz record on July 25, 1959. The contact covered a distance of 187 miles, from Oregon to Washington. CW was first heard at 1825, but improved signal conditions at 2005 enabled them to use voice with S9 signals.

The station setup at W7JIP/7 consisted of a Varian X-13 transmitter oscillator, followed by a double-stub tuner and a 20-dB directional coupler, for frequency and power measurement. The receiver was a surplus short-slot hybrid mixer, using a pair of 1N23E crystals, followed by a cascode stage at 30 MHz and a surplus radar IF strip. Noise figure was 6.5 dB. Antennas were surplus 30-inch parabolas, with Cutler (slot) feed. These were originally designed for 9375 MHz, but Len was able to modify them to get an SWR of 1.03:1 at 10 GHz. Similar equipment was used at the other end, except for the 58-inch mesh dishes. W7JIP and W7LHL went on to extend communication distance on this band even further—to 265 miles—on July 31, 1960.

SPACE: THE FINAL FRONTIER

Ever since man has inhabited the earth, he has focused his attention on what still remains much of a mystery today—the Universe. What possibilities does it hold for amateur communications? For those experimenting during October 1946, comet Giacobini-Zinner would be a prime testing ground. Though the basic idea of meteor-trail reflection of radio waves had been known for some time, the brush between the comet and earth was probably the first time meteor trails were used for actual communications purposes by anyone. Contacts on 50 MHz were made over distances of 200 to 1200 miles, with a continuous but fluttery quality never before observed. Voice and CW were both usable, though the flutter tended to break up CW keying. The second encounter with the comet came on October 9, 1959, but the results were disappointing to many amateurs who spent whole-night vigils in search of their rare DX.

The first successful launch of Operation Shotput (similar to the ECHO experimental satellites) occurred on October 28, 1959. There were four in this series, with the last one launched April 1, 1960. Its purpose was to place a large (90- to 125-foot diameter) "balloon" into orbit. The balloon had aluminized Mylar surfaces for reflecting VHF and UHF signals. A handful of amateurs were ready to bounce 15-second transmissions, in sequence, at the 100-foot sphere, which was launched from Wallops Island, Virginia. Some heard nothing, while others achieved positive results.

As the 1960s rolled in, mysteries of the moon and universe captured the public's interest. The search for different worlds using radio telescopes began with Frank Drake's Project Ozma. The moon also captured amateurs' interest on both sides of the USA— notably Sam Harris, W1FZJ, a member of the Rhododendron Swamp VHF Society, W1BU, in Medfield, Massachusetts, and the Eimac Radio Club of San Marcos, California, W6HB. Sam's first

attempt to contact the club via the Earth-Moon-Earth (EME) path was on 144 MHz. Echoes were recorded several times, but they were discouragingly weak and sporadic. It was decided to make that prospective QSO on a higher frequency—1296 MHz. That frequency was chosen because Faraday polarization shift becomes negligible, galactic and solar noise are at a minimum, receiver noise figures of less than 1 dB are possible and tubes are capable of a kilowatt of input.

W1BU's antenna system was an 18-foot parabolic reflector with an ingenious automatic system for tracking the moon. The club also employed a Microwave Associates 1296-MHz parametric amplifier and the Eimac kilowatt klystron amplifier (Fig 16). With this equipment and plenty of human labor, W1BU was successfully receiving its own echoes in May 1960. Now, who could match them?

The challenge was answered by O. H. Brown, W6HB, from the Eimac Radio Club. On July 17, 1960, faint signals were heard from W6HB to W1BU, and on July 21, signals exchanging reports and calls were heard coast-to-coast, via the moon. The first lunar QSO had made amateur history! Fig 17 shows the distances involved.

It was not until two years later, August 9, 1962, that the second moonbounce contact, between W1BU (W1FZJ, operator) and KH6UK (W2UK, operator) on Oahu, took

Fig 16—The kilowatt klystron amplifier used in the 1296-MHz EME station at W1FZJ/W1BU. It delivered 350 to 400 watts output. Receiving gear is in the rack in the left foreground. The entire station is housed in a tent directly below the dish antenna, and is remotely controlled.

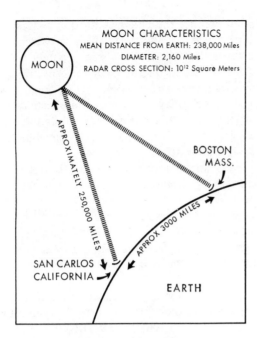

Fig 17—The 1296-MHz signal path of W1BU/W1FSJ-W6HB.

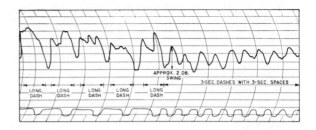

Fig 18—A reproduction of a chart recording made by W4HHK of the 2304-MHz signal from W3GKP. The echo charted was received via the lunar surface. Reading from right to left, we see one minute of dots and one minute of dashes, all showing, in varying degrees above the receiver noise threshold. Maximum signal level, some 3 to 4 dB above noise, was achieved by using high selectivity, a very slow sending rate and visual readout. The signal transmitted by W3GKP is shown in the lighter trace across the bottom.

place on 1296 MHz. Harris's 1296-MHz gear was in a school bus. Both stations used Eimac 1-kW klystrons. That same year, the first 1296-MHz moonbounce signals were received from Europe via Dr Hans-R. Lauber, HB9RG, and Hans Raetz, HB9RF.

The first of a successful series of OSCAR (Orbiting Satellite Carrying Amateur Radio) satellites was launched on December 12, 1961. It carried a 100-mW telemetry beacon in the 144-MHz band and its friendly Morse code greeting of HI lasted approximately two weeks. Launched with the Discoverer XXXVI satellite at no cost to the government, OSCAR I was built and tested entirely by radio amateurs.

In the early part of 1963, a four-part article on "Pulse: A Practical Technique for Amateur Microwave Work," suggested that amateur experimenters familiarize themselves with the 2300, 3300, 5650 and 10,000-MHz bands. This range would be best suited for tracking, controlling and communicating with space vehicles. How right authors Robert F. Guba, W1QMN, and John T. Zimmer, W2BVU, were.

Through their articles, W1QMN and W2BVU introduced pulse to amateurs using microwave communication. Previously, amateurs were using AM or FM gear with receiver bandwidths many times wider than optimum. Pulse is inherently a wide-band mode and consists of short bursts of RF carrier lasting millionths of a second. It had been used mainly for radar during World War II.

On the morning of January 10, 1969, Mike Staal, K6MYC, and Dick Hart, KØMQS, scored another first when their 144-MHz signals reached the moon. What made this contact different from the rest were the antennas—previous EME efforts used small dishes of amateur con-

struction. K6MYC's antenna was a 160-element collinear, while KØMQS sported an eight-wire rhombic stack over 700 feet long on a nearby hilltop.

The first EME work on 2.3 GHz resulted in echoes heard from the moon in early 1969. The terrestrial distance was 750 miles, from Spencerville, Maryland, to Collierville, Tennessee. William Smith, W3GKP, transmitted while Paul Wilson, W4HHK, received not only signals, but recorded charts of their work (Fig 18). Their antennas, obtained through MARS surplus channels, were adapted from monitoring solar noise for 432 MHz for their EME work. W4HHK received with an 18-foot dish installation and W3GKP transmitted through a 28 footer.

On October 19, 1970, Project 2300 became a reality for W4HHK and W3GKP. Three and a half years earlier, they had gotten together in an attempt to communicate with voice signals bounced off the moon on 2300 MHz. This was the highest frequency ever used for moonbounce. The 1970 DX record for that band is likely to be an all-time record for man-hours expended to achieve a single QSO!

Louis Anciaux, WB6NMT, and "Lucky" Whitaker, W7CNK, successfully completed the first 220-MHz moonbounce contact on March 15, 1970. Their EME first covered a terrestrial distance of 650 miles. This record lasted less than 26 hours, however, as WB6NMT went on to contact Jud Snyder, K2CBA—a distance of 2650 miles. Contact was made on CW.

The first amateur communication using packet techniques over a path supported by meteor-induced ionization occurred on August 5, 1983 between 1415 and 1605Z. Ralph Wallio, WØRPK near Des Moines, Iowa, contacted Robert Carpenter, W3OTC near Rockville, Maryland. FM was used on 50.505 MHz. On the Iowa end, the rig was a converted commercial land-mobile base station, running about 250-W output to a 5-element Yagi. W3OTC's station consisted of an FT-726R with a 150-W Mirage amplifier. At times, a 4-250A power amplifier delivered approximately 500 W to a 6-element Yagi. The TAPR board operated at 1200 bauds. Interestingly, W3OTC had participated in the development (around 30 years earlier) of the meteor-burst communications system now in use on many government and commercial communications circuits.

The first SSTV picture believed to be transmitted using meteor scatter was achieved by two UK amateurs on May 7, 1985. Jeremy Royle, G3NOX, in Essex, England, transmitted a composite, high-definition, single-frame color SSTV signal to Chris Tran, GM3WOJ, in Ross-shire, Scotland, on 50 MHz. GM3WOJ received the single burst of the G3NOX test signal at 5-9+.

AMATEURS EXPERIMENT WITH LIGHT WAVES

On May 14, 1960, Dr Theodore H. Maiman, an employee of the Hughes Aircraft Company in California, developed the first ruby laser (*l*ight *a*mplification of *s*timulated *e*mission of *r*adiation). It was an optically pumped model, which means that it emits pulses at a relatively low repetitive rate in the infrared region and its output is visible.

Research on other forms of laser systems continued once Dr Maiman's model was accepted. During 1961, Ali Javan, William R. Bennett and D. R. Herriott of Bell Laboratories invented the gas laser. The combination of helium and neon gases in a continuous-wave oscillator would prove to be a favorite for Amateur Radio communications. The injection laser was created in 1961, using gallium-arsenide diodes that emit infrared radiation. Three individuals, Robert H. Rediker, Marshall I. Nathan and Robert N. Hall, each of different companies, are credited with its invention.

A notable Amateur Radio laser demonstration took place on May 3 and 4, 1963. The Radio Club at Electro-Optical Systems, Inc, of Pasadena, transmitted a voice message 118 miles across the California desert using a helium-neon laser and a pair of confocal (having the same focus) mirrors. This event claimed a new record for communication on 474.100 terahertz (mega-megahertz)! The laser used in "Operation Red Line" is shown in Fig 19. It was excited and modulated by a Viking II operating on 28.62 MHz. At the receiving end, a beam was collected through a 12½-inch telescope that fed an S-20 photomultiplier tube and its associated translation equipment. An audio amplifier was connected to a loudspeaker and a tape recorder.

The first two-way laser QSO took place at the Air Force Academy in Colorado on February 25, 1971. Raymond Thomas Jr, WA8WEJ/Ø and William Schrader, W4UDS/Ø are credited with establishing point-to-point contact over a 950-foot path on 475 THz.

Fig 19—The helium-neon laser used in "Operation Red Line." The message sent began, "This is W6POP operating portable in the San Gabriel Mountains... The transmitter is operating on a wavelength of 6328 Angstroms with a radiated output power of 1/8 milliwatt (125 microwatts)."

MICROWAVES IN TRANSIT

In 1976, the Mount Airy VHF Club, based in Philadelphia, mounted an ambitious moonbounce DXpedition to Barranquilla, Colombia. Their station, HK1TL, worked 16 different EME stations, including club member Allen Katz, K2UYH, who thus became the first to earn the Worked All Continents award on 432 MHz and moonbounce.

The group used only homebuilt equipment that included a 432-MHz kW amplifier, a power supply and exciter employing a 4X150 exciter to a 4CX250 driver. The antenna was a system of 16 13-element K2RIW-style Yagis designed to fit into 6-foot shipping crates.

By the early '60s, the Gunn diode oscillator (named after its inventor, John Gunn of IBM) had become popular in the area of low-power microwave generation. As if to accommodate VHF/UHF DXpeditioners, Microwave Associates began marketing a 10-GHz transceiver with a 17-dB-gain horn in 1977. This compact, affordable unit brought the 3-cm band closer to reality for many. It was soon labeled the Gunnplexer®, and British amateurs experimenting with a similar unit were reaching up to 70 miles. The Gunnplexer reduces the problem of handling large amounts of equipment for portable operation, as it fits into the hand and is operated from a single 12-V power supply (ac or batteries). See Fig 20.

Commercial mobile transceivers became available dur-

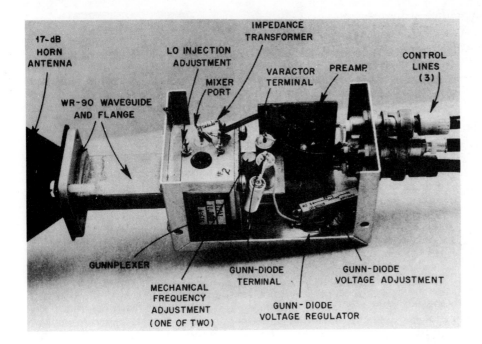

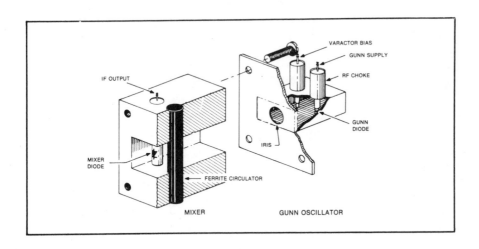

Fig 20—The Gunnplexer, introduced in the late 1970s, made portable 10-GHz experimentation a breeze.

ing the late 1970s, engendering new interest in the 1200-MHz and 10-GHz bands.

Recent Microwave Experimentation: North America

In June 1970, the San Bernardino Microwave Society mounted an assault on distance records for the 3300- and 5650-MHz amateur bands. The Society was chartered solely to promote amateur communication on frequencies above 1000 MHz, and had an unwritten rule that the club's record activity be strictly with amateur-owned equipment to avoid unfair advantage over amateurs not having access to government- or company-owned gear.

A 214-mile QSO, well beyond line of sight, was the group's goal. This mission was accomplished on June 18, 1970, with a 6-foot dish at Mt Breckenridge, California, to a 4-foot tripod on Mt Hamilton, site of the Lick Observatory. Crystal-stabilized klystrons were used at both ends, with provisions for both narrow- and wide-band reception. The rigs, designed by D. L. Thompson, W6IFE, and other SBMS members, used a ROCLOC (Relative Or Crystal Local Oscillator Control) system. This design allowed the klystron oscillator to be frequency-locked to either the incoming signal (relative) or to a harmonic of a stable crystal oscillator (crystal). Use of a tunable AFC receiver allowed the klystron oscillator to be moved accurately in frequency without losing frequency lock. The ROCLOC system was full duplex through use of the polaplexer approach.

During the late 1970s, Robert M. Richardson, W4UCH/2, designed and operated an experimental 10-GHz fast-scan television system. See Fig 21. The signal was sent over a 4-mile path across Lake Chautauqua, New York, using Gunnplexers for transmission and reception.

Richardson resurfaced in 1980 to demonstrate his new Gunnplexer video system (plus subcarrier audio) at a

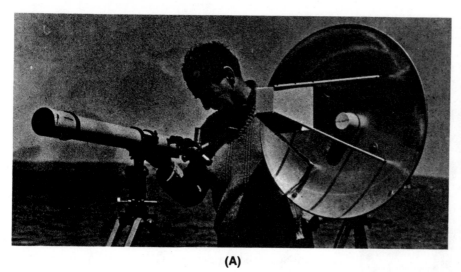

(A)

(B)

Fig 21—At A, W4UCH/2 prepares to align the 10-GHz Gunnplexer terminal with the aid of a small telescope on the shore of Lake Chautauqua, New York. The received 10-GHz operation fast-scan television signal is displayed at B. The signal traveled over a four-mile path and appears on a TRS-80 microcomputer (one of the operation formats pioneered by Bob at 10 GHz).

national Amateur Radio convention. W4UCH/2 created a 4.5-MHz carrier for FM modulating with his audio source and mixed that with a baseband video signal. The two were then directly applied to the Gunnplexer. The receive Gunnplexer was adjusted so that its local oscillator was offset from the transmitter oscillator by 55.25 MHz. This IF signal was then fed directly into a standard NTSC television receiver (FM video into an AM television receiver). Bob called this the "Richardson Effect." The color appeared without smear or ringing and could be sent over a 1/8- to 1/4-mile range, or 5.5 miles with a 2-foot dish.

The 1980s got off to a good start with record achievements in the mid-to-upper GHz ranges. Most of the work was done with the Gunn-diode transceivers. Challenged by European achievements on 10 GHz, Charles D. Martin, WA1KPS, and Wayne Green, W2NSD/1, established new records from a New Hampshire mountaintop. Not one of their contacts was under 50 miles and only the longest (106 miles) required a parabolic antenna. The other contacts were made with Gunnplexers and the "standard" 17-dB-gain horn antenna.

The first reported contact using solid-state gear on 1296 MHz took place on September 20, 1981, as Andy Furlong, WA2FGK, Al Katz, K2UYH, and Bill Ashby, K2TKN, worked Peter Blair, G3LTF. A new transistor marketed by the Microwave Semiconductor Corp in New Jersey introduced a new L-band 100-W pulse, enabling them to output 85 to 90 watts on CW, with a 50% duty cycle (5 seconds on and 5 seconds off). Andy coupled a pair of these devices for approximately 160-W output. K2UYH's 28-foot dish antenna was used. Although there were some feed-line losses, they caused no difficulty.

About this time, Paul Wilson, W4HHK, and Lewis Munford, W8YIO, made a 590-mile contact on 2304 MHz. W4HHK was running 1-kW klystron amplifiers with about 300 W RF output, to an 18-foot dish.

Meanwhile, Jim Hagan, WA4GHK, at Hilton Head, South Carolina, worked Jack Ross, K4NTD, at Sebastian Inlet, Florida, on 10 GHz, a distance of 294 miles. Gunnplexers (10 mW) were phase-locked at 10.2500 and 10.2799 GHz. Dish antennas were 2.5 feet and 4 feet. Received signals were down converted to 29.9 MHz and fed to an HF communications receiver, permitting use of NBFM (5-kHz deviation) or CW (500-Hz bandwidth). The contact lasted for 30 minutes. During August 1984, Hagan conducted a series of 300-mile contacts with Todd Roberts, WD4NGG, of Palm Bay, Florida, using 10-mW Gunnplexers to produce narrow-band FM to 1-m dishes on 10.2500 and 10.2799 GHz.

A new 1296-MHz DX record of 2472 miles was recorded on June 24, 1984, as Chip Angle, N6CA, contacted Paul Leib, KH6HME. N6CA's portable setup near Palos Verdes, California (1100-foot elevation) included a 44-element loop Yagi up 20 feet on a van with about 100 W of RF available at the antenna. At KH6HME, four 25-element Yagis on a 30-foot tower driven by a 25-W air-cooled power amplifier provided the signal. Leib was located on the east side of the Mauna Loa volcano, at an elevation of 8000 feet. 1.5-dB-noise-figure preamps were used at both ends. The QSL card confirming this contact was an engraved coconut!

After two weeks of trying, a new 24-GHz record was achieved by US amateurs on August 24, 1985. Lauren D. Libby, KXØO and Philip H. Bergeson, WØMXY, were sta-

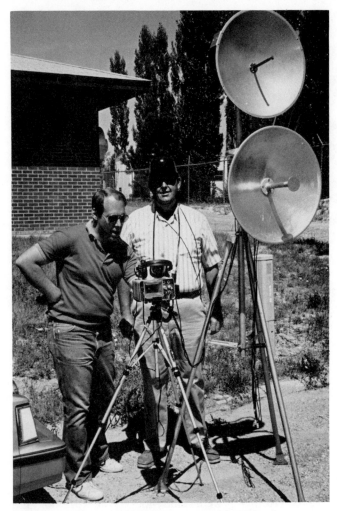

Fig 22—Lauren, KXØO (left) and Phil, WØMXY, with some of the gear they used to contact stations as far away as Texas and Kansas during several productive mountaintopping expeditions.

tioned in Northglen, Colorado, and Douglas P. Wilson, WAØVSL and NKØO, were stationed at the summit of Pikes Peak. The distance covered was 74.077 miles. A 65-mW Gunnplexer and a 2-foot dish were used at each end. The 30-MHz wideband IF transceiver, manufactured by Advanced Receiver Research, provided broadcast-quality duplex audio. Signals were 8 to 12 dB above noise. See Fig 22.

During early July 1986, KXØO, AAØL and WØMXY traveled to the summit of Pikes Peak, 14,110 feet ASL. Best DX, on 1296.1, was a 653-mile contact with WB5LUA on July 4. Equipment included an ICOM-1271 with a GaAsFET preamp and a 3CX100A7 amplifier running about 80 W to a 55-element F9FT single Yagi. They returned to Pikes Peak in July and September 1987 to study long-range propagation paths on 1.2, 2.3 and 10 GHz. Their efforts culminated in a 450-mile 2.3-GHz contact with WB5AFY. KXØO ran 30 W to a 60-element loop Yagi, while WB5AFY ran 400 W to a 4-foot dish.

Another DXpedition culminated in a new North American 3456-MHz record in August 1986. WA5TNY, KA5JPD and N5MP traveled to a location south of Fort Worth, Texas and worked W7CNK at Oklahoma City. The 228-mile SSB and CW QSOs were the result of several attempts by the North Texas Microwave Society (NTMS) to break the long-standing 3456 record. Both stations used homebuilt transverters, and WA5TNY used a 6-foot-diameter TVRO dish with a TVRO low-noise amplifier.

In October, WB5LUA and two other NTMS members, KD5RO and N5GEJ, traveled to Mena, Arkansas, where they set several DX records on 3456 MHz. Best DX was with WA5TNY in Fairy, Texas, a distance of 288 miles. WB5LUA was perched on a 60-foot fire tower on a 2600-foot-ASL hill.

In November, a new 5.7-GHz North American DX record of 286 miles was set by K5PJR and WA5ICW, members of the Northeast Oklahoma Microwave Society.

Late that same month, an excellent opening led to a new US DX record on 1296 MHz—1286 miles—between KD5RO and WB3CZG.

A noteworthy 47-GHz contact was completed between WA3RMX and WB7UNU/W7TYR in early March 1987. The 13.92-mile path was barely visible using a 30-power telescope.

In May, a group of New Jersey amateurs using the club call sign WA2WEB made several 2304-MHz EME contacts using a 100-W solid-state transmitter final that required only 100-mW of drive and weighed only 6 pounds.

The North American 10-GHz DX record fell by the wayside following an all-out assault by members of the San Diego Microwave Group and other California microwave enthusiasts in July 1987. The 414-mile QSO between N6GN, on Ball Rock, Tehama County, and W6SFH on Mt Frazier, took nearly an hour to complete.

In July 1988, a North American DX record for wideband FM on 10 GHz was established when XE2GDK (Terry, N6CW, op) near San Quintin, Mexico, worked Gary, NN6W/6, near Santa Barbara, a distance of 358 miles. XE2GDK used a 10-mW Gunnplexer and a 4-foot dish, and NN6W ran 15 mW to a 19-inch dish. On Aug 6, that record was extended to 479 miles, as Bruce Erikson, WBØHLC/6, on Frazier Mountain (8000 feet above sea level) completed CW and SSB contacts with Rich Rhymes, WB7ABP/6 on Bonanza King Mountain (7000 feet ASL).

Also in July, a record-breaking 5760-MHz contact was completed between WA5ICW near Boise City, Oklahoma and N5JJZ at Broken Arrow, Oklahoma, a distance of 404 miles.

A new 3456-MHz record of 454 miles was set in August between KXØO on Pikes Peak and WB5AFY in Vernon, Texas. The equipment at KXØO consisted of a transverter with 1296-MHz IF, 13.5 W and a 32-inch dish with soup-can feed. WB5AFY used a 275-W TWT amplifier and 6-foot dish with soup-can feed. Both receiving systems had 1-dB noise figures.

The ARRL UHF Contest in early August was the

Fig 23—Crater Lake, Oregon, was the site from which Tom Hill, WA3RMX/7, made a record-breaking 65.37-mile 47-GHz contact in August 1988. The photo shows his 28.5-inch dish and 3.5-mW transmitter.

setting for a new world DX record on 47 GHz between Tom Hill, WA3RMX/7 and K7AUO (Tektronix Employees' ARC). The 65.37-mile QSO nearly doubled the previous record. WA3RMX was at Crater Lake, Oregon, and K7AUO was on Mt Ashland. WA3RMX built the two linear transverters used in the QSO from new, surplus and homebuilt parts. See Fig 23.

In September, N6XQ/XE2GFH and WA5LIG/XE2GBO set three consecutive North American DX records on 10 GHz. Operating from Guerrero Negro, Baja California, with an 80-mW wideband-FM Gunnplexer system and a 4-foot dish, they contacted NN6W (15 mW and a 30-inch dish) near Santa Ynez Peak, a distance of 595.3 miles.

At about the same time, a new lightwave distance record was set between WA7LYI on Mt Lemmon, Arizona (near Tucson) and KY7B on South Mountain (near Phoenix). Both stations used 20-mW helium-cadmium lasers, 19- × 22-inch Fresnel lenses and the MCW mode for the 95-mile QSO.

Recent Microwave Experimentation: Other Than North America

On July 12, 1980, Nicola Sanna, IØSNY/7, set a new DX record of 470 miles on 10 GHz. (This distance was later increased to 534 miles.) His signal reached from Brindisi, southern Italy to IW3EHQ/3 and I3SOY/3 at Col Visenti in the Italian Alps. One end of the path was at a high-altitude inland location, but it had a line-of-sight path, at grazing incidence, to the sea. This presumably allowed the 10-GHz signal to fire into the northern end of the duct at sea level, the other end of the path. Wideband 10-mW FM

Gunnplexers feeding 1-meter dishes were used by all stations. Signals were Q5 and S5-8.

Sanna made headlines again during July 1982, when he set new records that included sending his signal across the Adriatic Sea, from Spain to Italy (Fig 24). With calm surface conditions and warm Mediterranean temperatures, IØSNY/EA5, stationed near Valencia, Spain, first worked Pietro Blasi, IØYLI, near Rome, a distance of 684 miles, on July 3. The record gradually increased as IØSNY worked Bruni Schiavoncini, IWØBFZ, at 694 miles on July 6. Not content with this, he again contacted IWØBFZ at 724 miles on July 10. All these contacts were made using 30-mW Gunnplexer systems and 1-m dishes. Sanna was also active on 1296 MHz. Using a 17-element Yagi and a 4-W transmitter, he contacted I2KSX/8 in Calibria, southern Italy, 867 miles away, for a new European DX record.

The following year, Sanna positioned himself and his 10-GHz unit in Ceuta (Spanish Morocco) while IØSNY/EA9 worked Capo San Vito (Western Sicily), a 1000-mile span across the Mediterranean. A duct formation and unusually hot weather conditions enabled him to set this new record on July 18, 1983. After this QSO, Sanna set a new 1296-MHz European record, working the southern tip of Italy, a distance of 1189 miles. On 10 GHz, a 50-mW Gunnplexer was used with a 30-MHz IF and a 200-kHz bandwidth, with a 1-m dish antenna. On 1296 MHz, a Kenwood TS-700G was used to drive a Microwave Modules transverter. A 40-W amplifier using a 3CX100 on transmit and a 20-element Yagi antenna assisted this endeavor. It's no wonder that Sanna received the Microwave Associates 10-GHz DX Award and 24-GHz transceiver prize later that year.

Using his new 24-GHz Gunnplexers and a 2-foot parabolic dish, Sanna created another first over a 206-mile path on August 11, 1984. The modulated CW QSO took place between the island of Ischia and southern Italy. The transceiver consisted of a varactor-tuned, 30-mW Gunn oscillator, a waveguide circulator and a Shottky detector mount. On July 8, 1985, Sanna used 24 GHz to make a Europe-to-Africa QSO.

In 1980, a 23-cm record was set over a 1422-mile path, as Dr Walter J. Howse, VK6KZ, contacted Chris Skeer, VK5MC, across the Australian Bight, a body of water located at the southern part of the continent. Equipment used was a modified Kenwood TS-120V transceiver for 144 and 432 MHz, and 10-W power levels on these bands. Power output on 1296 MHz was about 4-W fed to a 1-m parabolic dish mounted above the car. The receive converter was comprised of two BFR 91 RF amplifiers ahead of a Microwave Modules converter. Antennas were 5- and 7-element Yagis for 144 and 432 MHz, respectively. Howse and Skeer were to hold the 23-cm world record until Sanna extended it in 1983.

On July 11, 1981, a new world record for the 10-GHz band was set by Gianni Pirazzini, I4QIG. The distance was 515 miles, and 10-mW Gunnplexers and 1-m dishes were used at both ends.

(A)

Fig 24—(A) Nicola Sanna, IØSNY, shown during a DXpedition to Spain, where he set distance records on two different bands. **(B)** The diagram shows the "standard" 10-GHz station used in Italy during the late 1970s and early 1980s. The availability of this complete system, extensively tested, refined and debugged, is one of the reasons microwave activity has prospered in Italy and elsewhere in Europe.

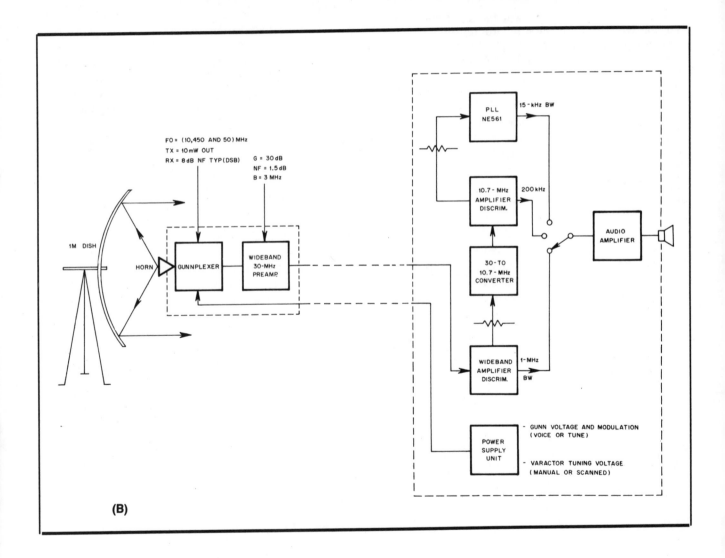

(B)

(A)

(B)

Fig 25—HB9MIN's operating site is shown at A; a rear view of the dish is displayed at B. The transceiver, complete with dial thermometer, confirms the sub-zero temperature. (photos from *Radio Communication*, RSGB)

Fig 26—This radio telescope was used as a receiving system by a group of amateur experimenters from the First Physical Institute of the University of Cologne. Their split-frequency QSO was on the 75.5- to 81.0-GHz band.

On January 13, 1985, a new amateur world distance record was established on 47 GHz. Erich Zimmermann, HB9MIN/P, and Arnold Sporbeck, HB9AMH/P, set the mark with a 33-mile QSO. Zimmermann was about 3300 feet above sea level, and the temperature was 12° F. Falling snow scattered the signals, enabling the antennas to be moved plus or minus 3° without a significant change in signal strength. Their station is shown in Fig 25.

Zimmermann used a 25-mW, 23.5-GHz M/A-COM Gunn oscillator, a homebuilt doubler and a GaAs Schottky-diode mixer. The antenna was a 0.6-meter dish with a slotted-radiator feed, offering 45-dB gain. Sporbeck ran a 10-mW, 47-GHz Gunn oscillator and an MA-40406 mixer, similar to Zimmermann's, to a 0.4-meter dish with a slotted-radiator feed. His 40-cm parabola was actually a lamp shade purchased at a furniture store. A complete description of HB9MIN's homebuilt 47-GHz equipment is described in another section of this book.

In late 1985, several West German amateur experimenters ventured where no other amateurs had gone before. On December 10, Manfred Bester, DL5KR, Karl Jacobs, Rudolf Scheider, DL6KAM, and Tom Pauls, N4CDS/DJØKP, completed a QSO on the 75.5-81.0 GHz band. This group of experimenters from the First

Physical Institute of the University of Cologne made a split-frequency QSO over 29 miles using 77 GHz and 430 MHz. The battery-powered transmitting system used a 10-mW output, PLL-stabilized Gunn oscillator coupled to a 30-cm portable dish antenna. Their return link was the 70-cm Cologne repeater, DBØSK. The receiving system was a radio telescope shown in Fig 26. The battery-powered transmitting system used a 10-mW output, PLL-stabilized Gunn oscillator coupled to a 30-cm portable dish antenna.

In January 1986, a new world record was set on the 3456-MHz band by two Australians, as Reg Galle, VK5QR, and Wally Green, VK6WG, closed the communications gap across the Australian Bight. Contact was first established over this 1171-mile path on 144 MHz, then on 432, 1296, 2304 and finally on 3456 MHz.

They used two identical 19.964-MHz crystal oscillators fed into a pair of Microwave Modules 28/432-MHz transverters and mixed with the LO chain at 404 MHz to produce 384 MHz. The module was lined up on 384 MHz to produce 10 watts. VK6WG fed his 10 watts to a tripler to 1152 MHz through a filter to another tripler to 3456 MHz and through another filter to a 3- to 4-watt amplifier. VK5QR fed his 10 watts at 384 to an amplifier for 30 watts reduced to about 20 and into a tripler to produce 12 watts on 1152 MHz. This was then fed into another tripler through a filter to get another 2 watts on 3456, and then fed to a 10-foot dish through another filter. The dish was equipped with a log periodic for 1296/2304/3456, replacing the three-turn helix used for Mode L work.

Amateur microwave experimentation has come a long way from its roots in Hertz's spark-gap rig of 1888. Technology that will enable you to become a part of this communications revolution is detailed in the chapters that follow. Welcome to the exciting world of microwave Amateur Radio!

BIBLIOGRAPHY

Bronwell, A. B., and R. E. Beam, *Theory and Application of Microwaves*, First edition (New York: McGraw-Hill Book Company, 1947).

Carroll, J. M., *The Story of the LASER* (New York: E. P. Dutton & Co, 1964).

Davidoff, M. R., *The Satellite Experimenter's Handbook* (Newington: ARRL, 1985).

Davis, H. B. O., *Electrical and Electronic Technologies: A Chronology of Events and Inventors From 1940 to 1980* (New Jersey: Scarecrow Press, 1985).

Fox, R. W., *Optoelectronics Guidebook—with tested projects*, First edition (Blue Ridge Summit, PA: TAB Books, 1977).

Kaufman, M., and A. H. Seidman, *Handbook for Electronics Engineering Technicians*, Second edition (New York: McGraw-Hill Book Company, 1984).

Leinwoll, S., *From Spark to Satellite* (New York: Charles Scribner's Sons, 1979).

Marsh, K., *The Way The New Technology Works* (New York: Simon and Schuster, 1982).

Pearson, K., "Collecting the Calls of the Cosmos," *Bell Laboratories Record*, vol 61, no. 4, April 1983.

Chapter 2

RF Safety Practices

By Dr David Davidson, W1GKM (SK)

The *ARRL Handbook* and some *QST* articles stress safety precautions in the ham shack during equipment alignment and maintenance, and while erecting or adjusting antennas. These admonitions concern preventing contact with electrical voltages and currents.

Another important safety concern is radio-frequency (RF) protection. This involves minimizing human exposure to strong RF fields that might occur near or around antenna structures. At VHF and above, this includes antenna feed systems and waveguide openings.

The biological effects of RF exposure have been studied for more than two decades. We now know a great deal about these effects in animals, particularly where the RF energy produces detectable tissue heating. There has been progress in translating these results to the case of human exposure, although there remain questions about bioeffects at lower RF field intensities.

Since 1979 there has been much activity in advancing RF-protection guides (RFPG) or standards. The US government has never had a formal RF-protection standard, either for occupational exposure or for exposure of the general population, although an advisory RFPG did exist for the work place until 1983.

In 1979 the Federal Communications Commission (FCC) initiated an inquiry into how RF protection should be provided through its licensing procedures. The National Environmental Protection Act (NEPA) requires the Commission to consider environmental issues. Since 1970, the FCC has been pursuing its NEPA obligation in the licensing of satellite Earth stations with antenna diameters of 30 feet or more.

By 1982, the American National Standards Institute (ANSI) had adopted a RFPG that recommended maximum permissible exposure levels (MPELs) for frequencies between 0.3 MHz and 100 GHz (Fig 1).[1] This RFPG recognized that in a uniform RF field, the human body absorbs RF energy more effectively at a frequency where body length is about 0.4 λ and the body's long axis is aligned with the incoming electric-field polarization. This condition is known as "whole-body resonance."

The ANSI guide aims to provide RF safety by limiting whole-body RF rate-of-energy uptake to no more than 0.4 watt per kilogram (W/kg), which provides a safety factor of 10 over the consensus threshold of RF hazard at >4 W/kg.[2] Additionally, the guide states that any "spatial peak value of the SAR would not exceed 8 W/kg over any one gram of tissue and over any time period of 0.1 hour." (ANSI C95.1-1982, paragraph 6.6, p 13; paragraph 6.11, p 15.) The ANSI guide also notes "Measurements...shall be made at distances 5 cm or greater from any object." (paragraph 4.3, p 10.) For example, for an average male adult weighing about 70 kilograms, and about 1.75 meters tall, the maximum RF energy uptake would be at about 60 MHz, close to TV channel 2, and not far removed from the 6-meter amateur band.

There is also a special ANSI exclusion for hand-held radios: "At any frequency between 300 kHz and 100 GHz, the protection guides may be exceeded if the radio frequency input power of the radiating device is seven watts or less." (paragraph 4.2(2), p 10.)

Most organizations commenting in the FCC inquiry recommended that ANSI's 1982 RFPG be followed until the US Environmental Protection Agency (EPA) issues a

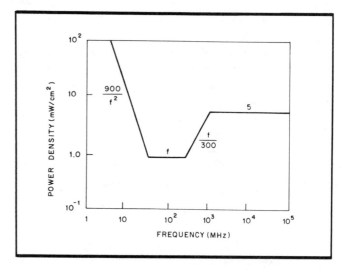

Fig 1—Maximum permissible RF power density (ANSI, 1982) for far-field exposure of human beings or animals, averaged over any six-minute period, and well insulated or isolated (more than 10 cm) from ground.

guideline for protection of the general population from RF energy. An EPA guideline would likely become obligatory for agencies of the federal government; it would likely become a *de facto* national standard. In the meantime, many states or localities have been proposing or enacting RF regulations, some of which are more stringent than ANSI's.[3] The ARRL has consistently maintained that Amateur Radio should be excluded from these regulations because of the intermittent nature of amateur transmissions; modulation or keying varies the instantaneous power, there are frequent pauses, much time is spent listening, and the RF power is low compared to the levels used in the broadcasting services. This thesis has not been accepted by all regulators, however.

In 1985, the FCC decided to accept the majority's recommendation by promulgating the ANSI RFPG as an *interim* standard, effective January 1986 for processing applications for broadcasting, satellite Earth stations and experimental stations. In early 1987, the FCC exempted Amateur Radio stations from "routine evaluation of their environmental impact due to human exposure to radio-frequency radiation."

The EPA pointed out that some amateur operations involve relatively high effective radiated power (ERP). The ARRL acknowledged that amateurs sometimes use high ERP, but recommended that amateurs comply by becoming "RF aware"—learning about the subject during preparation for FCC license exams, and by practicing self-regulation. ARRL recommended this course owing to (a) administrative reasons, (b) the long licensing term (10 years), and (c) the impossibility of predicting 10 years in advance which frequency bands amateurs would use.

Other countries, such as Canada, the Federal Republic of Germany, Sweden, and the USSR, all have protection guides (standards, or codes)—each of which is different—concerning the application, exclusions and MPELs at various frequencies. Many of the foreign standards have been undergoing changes. None of these countries seem to be concerned yet about amateur operation, possibly because the legal power limits are generally much lower than in the USA.

Regardless of US regulations and the practice abroad, it is prudent and responsible to examine those situations where high-level RF fields occur. The radio amateur must determine if access should be controlled, whether RF power should be limited or not, and what precautions need be taken—including a knowledge of what the RF power density levels are, should questions ever be raised. On this basis, a radio amateur can, and preferably should, choose to use more conservative RF power density levels than those in the ANSI RFPG.

Our knowledge of RF bioeffects will grow as more studies are made. Regulations may be changed accordingly. For example, in April 1986 a non-governmental body, the National Council on Radiation Protection and Measurements (NCRP), recommended that an RF-protection standard for public exposure be set at a power-density level 1/5 that of ANSI 1982. NCRP calculated this safety factor by noting that a worker spends 1/5 of his life on the job. However, NCRP allows an averaging period of one-half hour for the general public. The idea was to allow brief high RF exposure of the general public while passing a "civil telecommunications system."[4] And, in December 1986 the EPA solicited comments on three options for regulating the public's exposure. One is like ANSI's, a second like NCRP's, and the third is twice as stringent as NCRP's. Most respondents have urged adoption of option 2 or one close to it. Amateurs should know where they stand on this issue, so they can understand the consequences of changes in equipment, modes of operation, and antenna configurations with respect to levels of an adopted RFPG. More importantly, amateurs must realize the consequences of changes in RF exposure-protection standards.

Near- and Far-Field Antenna Zones

A convenient place to begin to appreciate the actual RF fields is well away from a transmitting antenna, in the *far-field* zone. Close to an antenna is the *near-field* zone, in which complicated RF fields exist. Beyond that zone in the far field, it is possible to estimate the magnitudes of the electric and magnetic fields, or the power density they develop, and relate these to the MPELs of an RFPG or standard. *If the estimate is lower than the MPEL, one knows that from that point outward, at the same bearing to the source, levels are of no concern.* A maximum limit can be computed by assuming: (1) the highest transmitter power level allowed, or that the licensee expects to employ, and (2) the highest antenna gain that might be used.

Power Density and Field Strength

A radio emitter in free space appears to be sending out a spherical wavefront. Radiated RF power is spread over the area of this imaginary sphere, centered on the source. Power measured per unit area (for example, per m^2) decreases as the distance increases (Fig 2). This reduction is proportional to the square of the distance from the source. If the source has a directional antenna, then at a constant radial distance the power-density level will depend on the bearing from the source. For examining a worst case, let's consider levels along the direction of maximum antenna gain.

The power density, S (in W/m^2), at an observation point, is proportional to the square of the electric field, E (in V/m). The proportionality constant in this relationship is the impedance of free space (377 ohms):

$$S = \frac{E^2}{Z_0} = \frac{E^2}{377} \qquad \text{(Eq 1)}$$

This relation between S and E (its RMS value) holds only in the far field, because $Z_0 = 120\pi = 377$ ohms is uniformly true there, being independent of position.

Similarly, the associated RMS magnetic field strength, H, is also related to S:

$$S = Z_0 H^2 \qquad \text{(Eq 2)}$$

because $Z_0 = E/H$ everywhere. This relationship characterizes transmission in free space, far from a source. Propagation of the E and H fields away from a source, therefore, represents a power flow outward. For RF-protection purposes in the far field at VHF, UHF and above, the quantity of interest is S, the average power flow per unit area, which we can compute if we know either E or H.

Near-Field Region

In the near field, the distances between an observing point and various parts of a source antenna differ greatly

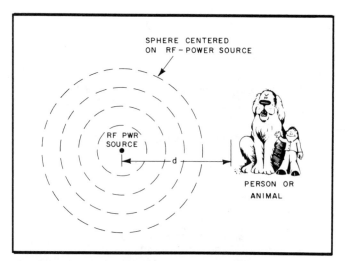

Fig 2—Radiation sphere that is centered on an RF-power source. If the source is isotropic, then at distance d the entire RF power, P, is distributed uniformly over the spherical surface $(4\pi d^2)$, so the power density is $P/(4\pi d^2)$. If the source is not isotropic, the power density at d is $PG/(4\pi d^2)$, where G is the power gain in the direction of measurement.

from each other in terms of wavelength. The distance from the antenna to that point where the near field ends, or the far field begins, varies according to antenna type. When estimating power densities for RF-protection purposes, the nominal far-field boundary is a useful reference location. Within this distance, however, the E and H fields of the antenna are geometrically complicated; their size and spatial disposition relate to energy storage in and around the radiating system, and depend on how the voltages and currents are distributed on the antenna structure, too. In the near field the ratio, Z, of an E-field to an associated H-field component, no longer is equal to the impedance Z_0 of free space, but takes on values that vary markedly over relatively short distances near the antenna. In the near field, it is not always possible to uniquely define a power flow and hence a real power density.

As an example, the electric field in the far-field region of a $\frac{1}{2}$-λ dipole is polarized in a direction parallel to the dipole axis, when viewed from a position on the perpendicular bisector. In the near-field region, the electric field

strength having the same polarization as found in the far field is very small, while the magnetic field strength is large. Thus, the wave impedance $Z = E/H$ there is much lower than 377 ohms. (The H field can be calculated accurately for a point on the bisector by assuming it is caused by the antenna current flowing in a very long wire coincident with the dipole axis.)

Near the tips of a dipole antenna, the current is approximately zero. The magnetic field just outside the tips is very small, but the E field is very high, because this is the part of the antenna where electric charge is stored. Thus the wave impedance, Z, near the tips, can be high. The E field near the tip depends on shape. A thin, wire dipole will have high E fields near the ends, but if the antenna is thick or the ends have large knobs or spheres, the E field can be reduced dramatically, by a factor of 10 or more.[5] Thus, while the far-zone E field can be predicted without having much detail of the antenna structure, in the near-field zone specific information is required to achieve relatively accurate results, and advanced mathematical methods of evaluation must be employed.[6,7,8]

For amateurs working at VHF and above, it is interesting to compare the near fields of a simple straight-wire dipole and that of a helical dipole (comprising many turns of small diameter).[6,7] Although both would have equivalent far fields for the same radiated power, the near fields will be very different. Even two helical dipoles (or grounded helical monopoles), each with a different number of turns and diameter, will have different near-field configurations, and thus different local energy storage configurations.

Power Density

At UHF and above, RF power is often fed to the antenna by means of a waveguide. A waveguide appropriate for 10 GHz (WR90) has an inside cross section of 1.0×2.3 cm (0.4×0.9 in). From the open end of such a waveguide the average power density emerging, S, if power P is supplied, is

$$S = \frac{P}{ab} \qquad \text{(Eq 3)}$$

where a and b are the waveguide inner dimensions. The result for P = 1 W is

$$S = 4347 \text{ W/m}^2, \text{ or } 435 \text{ mW/m}^2$$

Although a mismatch would cause reflection of power back to the source, this is a very high power density—one that could cause a tissue burn close to the opening! This example illustrates why the care and handling of RF energy in the ham shack has to be taken seriously, and why with even a low-power source, dangerous levels can be developed if RF power flow is concentrated in a small area.

An open waveguide end is often used as a rudimentary antenna or feed system. Far from the opening, the power density falls off as the square of the distance (discussed earlier), but the region near such an opening should be made inaccessible during operation.

Far-Field Power Density

In the far-field region in free space, power density, S, falls off as the square of the distance.

$$S = \frac{PG}{4\pi R^2} = \frac{(EIRP)}{(\text{Area of sphere at R})} \qquad (Eq\ 4)$$

where

P = RF power supplied to the antenna

G = far-field, free-space antenna gain (numeric value), relative to an isotropic antenna

R = distance from the antenna

The product PG is called EIRP (effective isotropic radiated power), and is the term used at frequencies above 1 GHz. [Below this frequency, antenna gain is often referred to as the gain of a ½-λ dipole, which is 1.64 times the isotropic gain. In this case, the FCC uses the abbreviation ERP instead of EIRP.] For P we would use the *average power* supplied over some period, usually the averaging period found in the RFPG, which for the ANSI 1982 RFPG is six minutes. For CW keying *throughout an averaging period,* P would be around 50% of the average RF power supplied per RF cycle, because of the on/off duty cycle. For SSB, the average power would be much less because of the peak-to-average characteristic, including speech pauses. Together, these come to about 7 dB, or an average power of about 1/5 of the peak envelope power (PEP). For FM or RTTY, the carrier is always present during the sending interval and the power P to be used is 50% of PEP.

Most amateurs don't know the actual gain of their antennas. For RF protection we want an upper-bound or worst-case estimate, so we can use a textbook value for G for the type of antenna being used.[9] Generally this value is given in a table or a figure, and refers to the ideal case of a lossless antenna far from the influences of structures or ground. (Examples of how to use G in Eq 4 are given below.) In calculating power density for RF-protection assessment, one should start by determining the far-field power density associated with the main lobe.

Since all real antennas are elevated above Earth, reflections can occur through reinforcement by the image in the ground plane, via nearby reflective surfaces, or by field enhancements near metal objects. Although complete reinforcement would double the RF field and thus quadruple the power density, the FCC and EPA

RF Awareness: Protection Rules for the Radio Amateur

The following protection rules are suggested as a matter of prudence and good practice. They are worth observing whether or not a particular Amateur Radio operation is covered in the RF regulations enacted by the government.

1) Respect RF power.

2) Know the RF power input to your antenna.

3) Know approximately the directional properties of your antenna (for example, the gain, and the gain pattern).

4) If in doubt about how much power density you are generating nearby, reduce power output. Note, that for US amateurs, FCC rules require that "amateur radio stations shall use the minimum power necessary to carry out the desired communications."† Thus, if your signal is being received as 20 dB over S9, you can and should reduce power.

5) When using high power and high antenna gain, keep transmissions short, especially with high-duty-cycle modes (RTTY, FM, and so on), unless the antennas are isolated.

6) Keep the antenna parts away from people, especially if you are using full legal power or close to it, or are using a high-duty-cycle mode.

7) At high power levels, be sure the entire antenna is at least several meters away from persons who might be present for the RFPG averaging period. This is most important for vertical antennas!

8) With mobile rigs of 10 W or more, *do not* transmit if a person is standing one-half meter or less from the car antenna.

9) When using hand-held units, maintain at least 2.5 to 5 cm separation between your forehead and the antenna, especially if the RF power is close to 7 W. Observe the manufacturer's recommendations on use and placement.

10) Be sure RF power is *off* (and stays off) before climbing a tower to make antenna adjustments. Also, make certain all neighboring antennas are deactivated. *Never assume* RF power is off—check, and re-check!

11) In the SHF bands:

• Never look into the open end of a waveguide that is carrying power.

• Never direct the end of such a waveguide toward a person or animal.

• Never direct a powered horn or "dish" toward people or animals.

• Know the power being fed into your waveguide.

• Make sure all waveguide flanges and transitions are tightly secured, preferably with a torque wrench, to specifications. If in doubt, wrap the junction in metallic foil. Household foils may be used, but for this purpose several high-shielding, conductive foils are available commercially. (3M/Electrical Products Division, 225-4N 3M Center, St Paul, MN 55144.)

12) Make certain that all RF-power-stage-compartments in transmitters are closed tightly before operating the transmitter.

13) The lids or covers for RF-power-stage compartments or cavity panels should be secured tightly with numerous screws to prevent leakage at UHF and higher.

14) Never install an antenna so that the radiating elements can be reached by human beings, or so that the near-field radiation can be directed at people or animals.

15) Never work around radiating antennas in bare feet or flimsy footwear or permit others to do so.

†FCC Rules and Regulations, Part 97, Amateur Radio Service, Section 97.313(a). Government Printing Office, Washington, DC. Part 97 is reproduced in the ARRL publication, *The FCC Rule Book.*

recommend using 2.5S, where S is the power density calculated in Eq 4.[10]

Where Does the Far Field Begin?

Since S is highest for the least distance R, we need to know where the far field begins. The hint about where the far field begins is contained in Eq 4. This critical distance is the smallest for which the inverse-square law in that formula is still valid. It is determined for the kind of antenna used, by considering where, as the antenna is approached, the increase in S begins to slow down (the rate of change decreases), and the power density is no longer inverse-square-law dependent.

Table 1 lists the distances R_{ff} at which the far field can be considered to begin (for the purposes of this chapter).[11] The distance (column 3) is expressed in terms of some maximum or characteristic antenna dimension, such as the diameter. Column 2 identifies the characteristic dimension.

The formulas given here are to be used with practical units: power in watts, distances in meters, E fields in volts/meter and H fields in amperes/meter. Then S comes out in watts/square meter (W/m^2). [Some RFPGs express the MPEL in milliwatts/square centimeter (mW/cm^2). To convert a value in W/m^2 to one in mW/cm^2, simply divide by 10. Wavelength (λ) should also be in meters.]

To assure an upper-bound estimate, the free-space antenna gain should be used if the actual value is not known. A textbook value, as noted, will be useful because, among other things, antenna-system losses are either neglected or underestimated. Column 4 in Table 1 lists suggested antenna gains for each entry.

Column 5 gives the desired power density at R_{ff} for the antennas listed, expressed as the ratio, P/S, of the RF power P, applied to the antenna to achieve a specified power density S, such as the MPEL of an RFPG. (The dimension of P/S is area in m^2, being the hypothetical area through which the RF energy appears to flow at the point of observation.)

Example 1

A Yagi, $G' = 20$ (13 dBi), is mounted atop a 30-foot (9-meter) tower. The frequency is 430 MHz, $\lambda = 0.7$ meter. According to Table 1, the far-field reference location, measured along the axis of the beam (the "boresight"), is located at a distance R_{ff} from the Yagi end element

$$R_{ff} = \frac{2 \times (0.35)^2}{0.7} = 0.36 \text{ m} \qquad \text{(Eq 5)}$$

With the antenna 30 feet above local ground and the main lobe pointed into the right half-plane, let us find the maximum power density that could occur for RF power P, at a radius of 9 meters or 30 feet. According to Eq 4, the power density will be

Table 1

Far-field Location and RF Protection Parameters

Antenna Type	Characteristic Dimension	R_{ff}	Antenna Gain	P/S at R_{ff}
Parabolic dish	Diameter, D	$2D^2/\lambda$	$2\pi(D/\lambda)^2$	$8D^2$
Broadside array	Width, w Height, $\lambda/2$	$2w^2/\lambda$	$4\pi A/\lambda^2$ $A = w\lambda/2$	$8w^3/\lambda$
Waveguide (open end) Sides a, b $(a \geq b)$	a	$2a^2/\lambda$	$10ab/\lambda^2$	$5a^3/b$
Pyramidal horn, 60° angle, all edges L equal, $L = 2\lambda$	L	$2L^2/\lambda$	Gain $\cong 25$ (14 dBi)	$32\lambda^2$
Axial-mode helix	Turn diameter, D Circumference, $C \cong 1\lambda$ Spacing, s Turns, n	$2D^2/\lambda$	$15ns/C$	$\cong \lambda^3/(\pi ns)$
End-fire types:				
Yagi Boom length, B	$L = \lambda/2$; length of driven element	$2L^2/\lambda$	$G' = 5.8 + 11.1B$ $(0.3 \leq B \leq 2.5 \lambda)$	$\cong \pi\lambda^2/G'$
Loop (quad)-Yagi Boom length, B	Max width, L, of loop (quad)	$2L^2/\lambda$	ditto	ditto
Stacked Yagi (vertically)	Stack spacing, W	$2W^2/\lambda$	2 (Yagi gain)	$4\pi W^4/(\lambda^2 G')$

Notes

Gains are numeric values; gain (dBi) = 10 log gain (numeric).
Waveguide & horn gains are based on text notes 12 and 13.
Axial-mode helix design formulas are taken from Kraus.[14]
G' is an approximation from the Yagi curves of Greenblum,[15] and is given with respect to an isotropic antenna, to be useful in Eq. 4.
   (The following approximation fits values given in the *ARRL Handbook*, Chapter 33, for boom lengths between 0.4 λ and 4.2 λ:
   $G' = 3.8 + 12.25B - 0.687B^2$)
Parabolic dish gain is based on 64% efficiency.
All dimensions are in meters.

$$S = \frac{PG'}{4\pi R^2}$$

where $R = 9$ meters (30 feet) and $G' = 20$.

Since Eq 4 is for free space, we must figure in the possible contribution of the antenna image in the ground plane. At some positions above the ground plane there will be reinforcement and at others there will be almost complete cancellation.[12] At any maximum, the electric field will be no more than doubled, quadrupling the power density. Thus, a factor of 4 needs to be applied

$$P/S = \frac{4\pi R^2}{4G'} = \frac{9^2 \pi}{20} = 12.86 \text{ M}^2$$

For protection in accordance with the ANSI standard, S should not exceed 1.4 mW/cm^2, or 14 W/m^2. Thus, the allowed RF power to the antenna would be

$$P = 12.86 \times 14 = 180 \text{ W}$$

This is allowed power expressed as the average over *any* six-minute transmission period. Notice, this is a worst-case estimate because a factor of 4, rather than 2.5, was used.

Suppose a future general-population standard is promulgated that follows NCRP's recommendations, in which all ANSI MPELs have been lowered by a factor of 5, while the averaging period has been lengthened by a factor of 5, to 30 minutes.[4,13] In the above example, P would come out as $180/5 = 36$ W, to be the average over *any 30-minute period*. In Amateur Radio practice, the end result might be the same as with the ANSI standard when the type of modulation is taken into account. For example, if SSB is used a factor of 7 dB (numeric value of five) relates PEP to average power. In a six-minute transmission period under the ANSI standard, we could allow 5×180 W $= 900$ W PEP. Under the more stringent standard, 5×36 W $= 180$ W would seemingly be the limit. However, *provided* that each transmission never lasts more than six minutes and there are silent periods in between, the same 900-W PEP could be employed.

Example 2

The frequency of operation, f, is 10 GHz, so $\lambda = 3$ cm $= 0.03$ meter. A parabolic "dish" antenna is employed, diameter, D, $= 2$ feet $= 0.6$ meter. The start of the far field is

$$R_{ff} = \frac{2D^2}{\lambda} = \frac{2 \times 0.6^2}{0.03} = 24 \text{ m}$$

At R_{ff} the P/S ratio (from Table 1) is

$$P/S = 8D^2 = 8 \times 0.6^2 = 2.9 \text{ m}$$

Let us assume that the dish illumination is tapered, in order to minimize diffraction of the RF energy over the dish circumference. Fig 3 shows there is a location of axial reinforcement, or an RF "hot spot" located on axis at a point $R' = 0.1R_{ff} = 2.4$ meters from the dish aperture. For a tapered dish illumination, the power density at R' is *42 times* the value at R_{ff}. It is not necessary to invoke

the RFPG for the hot spot *if* we know that *location R' is inaccessible* when the RF power is on.

For $f = 10$ GHz, the ANSI MPEL is 5 mW/cm^2 = 50 W/m^2 for whole-body exposure. The maximum allowed RF power (six-minute averaging) without access to the area within a 24-meter radius of the antenna is

$$P = 2.9 \times 50 = 145 \text{ W}$$

The dish antenna has a half-power beamwidth of about 3.5°. Thus, at the distance R_{ff} from the aperture, but off-axis by 1.75°, the power density would be 25 W/m^2 = 2.5 mW/cm^2.

Example 3

The frequency remains at 10 GHz, but the antenna is open-ended, WR90 waveguide. Assume that the area between the waveguide end and a point 1 meter distant is inaccesible. At a distance 1 meter from the antenna, RF-energy protection is desired according to the ANSI standard; therefore, S is not to exceed 5 mW/cm^2 or 50 W/m^2. What is the maximum power permissible under these conditions?

From Table 1, the gain of this antenna is

$$G = \frac{10 \text{ ab}}{\lambda^2} = 2.56$$

where a, b are the inside waveguide dimensions for WR90.

The far field begins at 4.5 cm, so Eq 4 can be used to compute the allowed RF power. Because the antenna is located near some flat surfaces, this time we include the EPA/FCC factor of 2.5 to protect spatially. Thus, at 1 meter

$$S = \frac{2.5 \text{ PG}}{4\pi R^2}, \text{ and } P = \frac{4\pi \times 1^2 \times 50}{2.5 \times 2.56} = 98 \text{ W}$$

This is the maximum average power that can be applied for any six-minute period.

Example 4

In this case, $f = 1296$ MHz, so $\lambda = 23$ cm $= 0.23$ meter. The antenna is an "optimum horn" with considerable flare-out, so that the edges are greater than 1 λ long. Let the dimensions for L be 46 cm (18 inches) and 51 cm (20 inches), so that one side is exactly 2 λ long. The gain of this horn, G, $= 28$, or 14.4 dBi.[14] Here,

$$R_{ff} = \frac{2 \times 0.51^2}{0.23} = 2.26 \text{ m}$$

ANSI's MPEL at this frequency is 5 mW/cm^2 = 50 W/m^2. From Eq 4 we have

$$S = \frac{GP}{4\pi R_{ff}^2} = \frac{28 \text{ P}}{4\pi \times 2.26^2} = 0.44 \text{ P}$$

and $P = 50/0.48 = 115$ W maximum average for any six-minute exposure. A similar result would be obtained for a 60° pyramidal horn, 46 cm (18 inches) on each edge.

In Westman,[15] the 10-dB beamwidth of the above

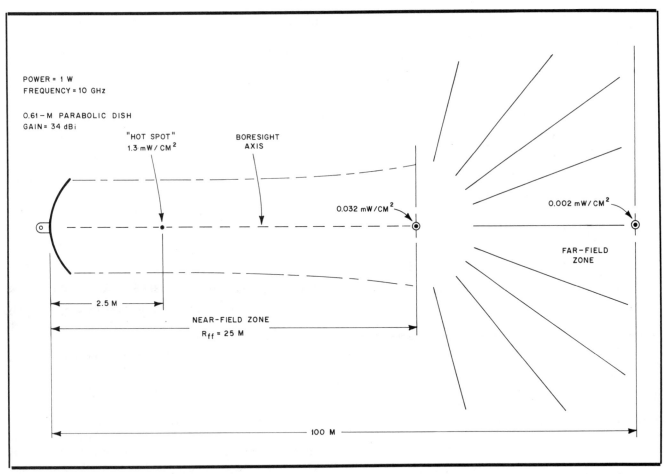

POWER = 1 W
FREQUENCY = 10 GHz

0.61 - M PARABOLIC DISH
GAIN = 34 dBi

"HOT SPOT"
1.3 mW/CM²

BORESIGHT AXIS

0.032 mW/CM²

0.002 mW/CM²

FAR-FIELD ZONE

2.5 M

NEAR-FIELD ZONE
R_{ff} = 25 M

100 M

Fig 3—The zones around a parabolic antenna, showing RF power density levels at various positions along the boresight axis. Note that the R′ "hot spot" is located 2.5 meters from the antenna.

horn (0.1 the power density) is given as 40°. If no access is possible at R_{ff} through an angle 20° above or below the boresight of this horn, the averaged RF power could be raised to 10 × 104 W/2.5 = 416 W, while safety is maintained as close as 2.26 meters from the antenna. Here the EPA/FCC factor of 2.5 was used.

In the above examples, the initial location of interest was R_{ff}, the start of the far field in the direction of maximum radiation. For antennas such as the parabolic dish, broadside array, and pyramidal horn, an upper limit of the power density can be found for distances as close as $0.3R_{ff}$ by increasing the power density found for R_{ff} by a factor of $(1/0.3)^2$, or approximately 10. At distances closer than $0.3R_{ff}$, scaling by the inverse square of the distance will lead to a gross overestimate of power density.

The National Bureau of Standards has provided the details of the power density levels in front of typical microwave circular parabolic antennas.[16] Fig 4 shows the results for one with diameter D = 16.2 λ, fed with 1 W RF power. (For f = 10 GHz, D = 1.6 feet.) The horizontal scale is distance away from the aperture in units of D^2/λ, or $R_{ff}/2$. The vertical scale is in units of the diameter. Tapered illumination by the feed was assumed.

Contours, separated by 2.5 dB, are in dB below 1 mW/cm² for 1 W input. Thus, if the RF power supplied is 10 W, the level 1 mW/cm² would be found approximately 2.4 meters (8 feet) in front of the aperture along the boresight axis.

Vertical Monopole and Polarization

In the VHF region (30 to 300 MHz), the human body may be close to 0.4 to 0.5 λ long, depending on age and build; at this wavelength the uptake of RF energy is greater than at others, particularly if the polarization (orientation) of the electric field is aligned parallel to the body axis. Radio-protection guides recognize this "resonance effect" by generally setting the lowest permissible maximum power density level in this frequency range. For amateurs, this suggests that the case of vertically polarized antennas, fed at the highest power levels, should be reviewed for power-density estimates. Tower-mounted, horizontally polarized antennas produce very little vertically polarized field at ground level near the antenna, assuming flat terrain around the antenna support.

For a vertical monopole over perfect ground, fed for more than six minutes with 1 kW of FM or RTTY at

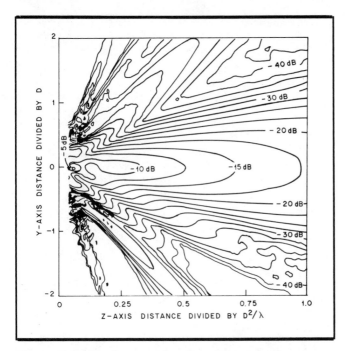

Fig 4—Calculated power density contours in the near-field zone of a parabolic antenna with diameter D = 16.2 λ. The contours are spaced 2.5 dB, and the levels are shown in dB below 1 mW/cm² for 1 W RF power input. The horizontal axis is in front of the aperture. This figure was adapted from reference 16.

30 MHz, the distance at which the power density meets the ANSI protection level of 1 mW/cm² is 5.2 meters. During transmissions, access should be denied within this radius.

Near-Field Exposure

As noted, the fields close to an antenna are complex and there are more spatial field components than in the far field. For a dipole there is not only an electric field oriented parallel to the antenna, but also a radially polarized field that may be the stronger, close to the antenna.[8] In this region, the parameter for checking RF-energy protection as provided in the ANSI standards (and most foreign standards) is the sum-squared electric field strength

$$(E_s)^2 = (E_1)^2 + (E_2)^2 + (E_3)^2 \qquad \text{(Eq 6)}$$

where E_1, E_2, and E_3 are three orthogonal E-field components, such as the x, y, and z components. A similar summing applies to the H field. This is the method used in most commercial RF-exposure meters.

Experiments have been performed at VHF/UHF using full-size models of human beings, known as phantoms, which have been filled with material simulating the electrical properties of tissue, muscle and bone at the chosen radio frequencies.[17] The results of one experiment at 350 MHz can be directly applied to Amateur Radio practice at 430 MHz. The energy-rate uptake, or SAR, was measured in the model by an internal field probe. In the

far field of a dipole, with polarization aligned with the body upright (antenna axis parallel to body length), the measured SAR was in accord with the ANSI-intended SAR limit. This held true for both whole- and partial-body exposure, when the ambient power density was held to 1.2 mW/cm² (the ANSI MPEL for 350 MHz).

With the dipole center placed 2 to 3 inches from the neck and shoulder region, 6 W produced the same whole-body SAR as measured in the far-field exposure. However, for partial-body exposure, only 2 W produced the same SAR in the model's head as found in the far-field case. (In this test the dipole center was adjacent to the head.) Note that the far-field (MPEL) power density of 1.2 mW/cm² could be produced in free-space at a distance, d, of 1 meter, by feeding the dipole with 92 W of RF power.[18]

Making Measurements in the Far Field

As mentioned previously, the near field is extremely complex. This makes power-density measurement difficult in the near field.[19] A field-strength meter can be used to check far-field estimates. The meter's antenna should be oriented parallel with the ambient E field, which can be achieved by looking for the highest reading as the antenna is slowly rotated. A good meter is self-contained (battery operated) and well-shielded, and does not have drift problems or zero-setting errors. The reading is best taken without human presence near it, which is accomplished by setting the meter on an insulated stand, backing away and reading the indicator from a distance. A pair of binoculars can be helpful. (Some amateurs may be able to borrow a commercial power-density monitor for a short time.)

The power density, S, is represented by

$$S = \frac{E^2}{377}$$

where E is in V/m. A reading with transmitter off should also be taken, to assure no contamination from unidentified sources.

Notes

[1]American National Standards Institute (ANSI) paper C95.1, "American National Standard Safety Levels with Respect to Human Exposure to Radio Frequency Electromagnetic Fields, 300 kHz to 100 GHz," Institute of Electrical and Electronic Engineers, Inc, 345 East 47th St, New York, NY 10017. This text includes the rationale for the RFPG.

[2]The rate of energy uptake is known as the *specific absorption rate,* or SAR. To relate SAR to the body's use of energy, note that for a resting adult the body's metabolic rate is about 1.3 W/kg, while for swimming, the rate is about 11 W/kg, and for running, about 18 W/kg. Rates in certain parts of the body (head, heart) are considerably higher. See: US Environmental Protection Agency, Health Effects Research Laboratory, "Biological Effects of Radio Frequency Radiation," *EPA-600/8-23/026F,* Sep 1984.

[3]The trend to more stringent protection levels has the following basis: The ANSI RFPG (Appendix) states, "Because of the limitations of the biological effects database, these guides are offered as upper limits of exposure, particularly for the population at large." There is also the problem of possible electric shock or startle effects with exposure to the full ANSI level below about 50 MHz, upon touching metallic objects without the feet being adequately insulated from ground.

[4]Commonwealth of Massachusetts, Department of Public Health, "Regulations Governing Fixed Facilities which Generate Electromagnetic Fields in the Frequency Range of 300 kHz to 100 GHz, and Microwave Ovens," *105 CMR 122.000,* Oct 1983. Department of Public Health, Boston, MA 02111. See also NCRP Report No. 86, "Biological Effects and Exposure Criteria for Radiofrequency Electromagnetic Fields," Apr 6, 1986, by the National Committee on Radiation Protection and Measurement, 7910 Woodmont Av, Bethesda, MD 20814. The Canadian government is considering promulgating a standard similar to these for public protection.

[5]R. King, *The Theory of Linear Antennas* (Cambridge, MA: Harvard University Press, 1956), Chapter 5, pp 575-576.

[6]Q. Balzano, et al, "The Near Field of Omnidirectional Helical Antennas," *IEEE Transactions on Vehicular Technology,* Vol VT-31, Nov 1982, pp 173-185.

[7]Ibid, "The Near Field of Dipole Antennas, Part 2: Experimental Results," *IEEE Transactions on Vehicular Technology,* Vol VT-30, Nov 1981, pp 175-181.

[8]A. Adams, et al, "Near Fields of Wire Antennas by Matrix Methods," *IEEE Transactions on Antennas and Propagation,* AP-21(5), Sep 1973, pp 602-610.

[9]See Chapter 16. Some useful references are: *The ARRL Antenna Book, The ARRL Handbook,* and Kraus (note 14). Gains measured by amateurs for a number of antennas at 1296 and 2304 MHz are given in *QST,* Jan 1986, p 96.

[10]"Evaluating Compliance with FCC-Specified Guidelines for Human Exposure to Radio-Frequency Radiation," *OST Bulletin 65,* Oct 1985. Office of Science and Technology, Federal Communications Commission, Washington, DC 20554.

[11]Transition from the near field to the far field is not sharp. The value of R_{ff} given here is based on a fairly strict phase criterion, so that conventional far-field gains (G) may be used in Eq 4.

With many antennas, such as the parabolic dish and broadside array, the inverse-distance-squared law (Eq 4) holds well for distances as small as $0.3R_{ff}$ for RF-protection estimating. See the later discussion.

[12]G. Hall, ed, *The ARRL Antenna Book,* 15th edition (Newington, CT: ARRL, 1988), Chapter 3.

[13]D. Cahill, "A Suggested Limit for Population Exposure to Radio-Frequency Radiation," *Health Physics,* Vol 45, Jul 1983, pp 109-126.

[14]H. Jasik, *Antenna Engineering Handbook* (New York: McGraw-Hill, 1961), Chapter 10, or E. C. Jordan, editor, *Reference Data for Engineers: Radio, Electronics, Computers and Communications,* 7th edition (Indianapolis, IN: Howard W. Sams Co, 1985) p 32-21, or J. Kraus, *Antennas,* 2nd edition (New York: McGraw-Hill, 1988).

[15]H. Westman, ed, *Reference Data for Radio Engineers,* 5th edition, (Indianapolis, IN: Howard W. Sams Co, 1969) pp 25-37.

[16]R. L. Lewis, A. C. Newell, "An Efficient and Accurate Method for Calculating and Representing Power Density in the Near-Field-Zone of Microwave Antennas," National Bureau of Standards, Dec 1985. Available as PB86-181963, from NTIS, Dept of Commerce, Springfield, VA 22161.

[17]M. Stuchly, et al, "Exposure of Human Models in the Near and Far Field—a Comparison," *IEEE Transactions on Biomedical Engineering,* BMI-12(8), Aug 1985, pp 609-615.

[18]The E field of a ½ λ dipole in free-space is E = P/d, where P is the power, and d the distance along the boresight. If E corresponds to the MPEL power density S_0, we must have $E^2 = 377S_0$. Therefore, the transmitter power, P, must be no more than $P = S_0 d^2/0.13$.

[19]J. Coppola and D. Krautheimer, "Environmental Monitoring for Human Safety, Part 2: Radiation Monitors," *RF Design,* Apr 1987, pp 48-53.

Chapter 3

UHF and Microwave Propagation

By Emil Pocock, W3EP
625 Exeter Rd
Lebanon, CT 06249

Amateur experimentation in the ultrahigh frequencies (300 to 3000 MHz) and microwave frequencies (3000 MHz and higher) has a relatively recent history. Prior to 1941, the "ultra highs" referred to the two bands at 56 and 112 MHz! Knowledge of ultrahigh frequency propagation was limited to sporadic-E and tropospheric refraction, both described extensively in *QST* during the 1930s. Amateurs generally assumed that the region above 112 MHz was strictly limited to line-of-sight distances. Although no specific UHF assignments existed in the frontier above 112 MHz, on September 14, 1941, W6IOJ and W6MYJ made what was probably the first true UHF contact when they spanned nearly 100 km on 400 MHz.

When amateurs returned to the airwaves after the World War II ban was lifted, they were greeted with specific UHF and microwave bands at 420 MHz and higher. Taking immediate advantage of the new assignments, W6BMS/2 and W2LGF recorded an historic first when they completed a 5.3-GHz contact on November 15, 1945, the day the FCC released the new bands. Within a year of that pioneering event, contacts were made on the 2.4, 10, and 24-GHz bands as well. Distance records were broken monthly as the new microwave frequencies were explored. By the end of 1947, distance records had been made and broken many times on all bands between 420 MHz and 24 GHz. As workable paths continued to lengthen, it became obvious that microwaves were not limited to line-of-sight distances, as once thought.

Propagation experimentation and distance records continued to inspire activity on the UHF and microwave bands. In recent years, tropospheric ducting between California and Hawaii have supported 432- and 1296-MHz paths of over 4000 km, and similarly favorable atmospheric conditions over the Mediterranean Sea have enabled contacts on the 10-GHz band to exceed 1600 km. Table 1 lists current world UHF and microwave distance records. Table 2 lists records by mode and band made from the United States and Canada. No doubt these records will be exceeded in the coming years.

Tropospheric ducting has been responsible for the most spectacular UHF and microwave distance records, but it is not the only means of propagation. During the forty years since the first forays into the UHF region and beyond, amateurs have discovered and explored a variety of propagation modes. Aurora, meteor scatter, and transequatorial spread-F, all familiar to the VHF amateur, have been observed in the UHF spectrum. Reflections from buildings, airplanes, and other man-made objects often extend the range of UHF and higher frequency signals beyond line-of-sight distances. With careful choice of location, UHF and microwaves can be refracted over and around mountains, scattered by the atmosphere, rain, and snow, and be reflected by lightning strokes. Other modes of propagation perhaps still await discovery. Familiarity with propagation is essential for successful use of UHF and microwaves.

This chapter reviews current knowledge and amateur practices in terrestrial propagation between 420 MHz and 300 GHz. Earth-moon-earth communications is treated in other chapters. The following discussions of UHF and microwaves are both descriptive and quantitative. Descriptive discussions provide a general overview of each means of propagation, distances that might be expected, and hints on how to make best use of each propagation mode. Relevant equations are provided for those who want to make more precise estimates of path loss, station performance, and probability of completing contacts. The equations used herein assume ideal geographic, propagation, and equipment conditions. Because ideal conditions are rarely ever fully met in actual practice, all calculations must be assumed to represent the most optimistic performance estimates. For those readers who would rather skip the mathematics, solutions to most of the common propagation problems are also provided in graphic and tabular form. Sources for equations, tables, and graphs, along with detailed discussions of various aspects of UHF and microwave propagation, can be found in standard technical works provided in the list of references at the end of the

Table 1

Claimed World UHF and Microwave Terrestrial Distance Records

Band (λ)	Most-used Frequency	Propagation Mode	Distance (km)	Stations	Date
70 cm	432 MHz	Tropo*	4151	XE2GXQ-KH6HME	1989 July 15
33 cm	903 MHz	Tropo	1003	WB5LUA-W4ODW	1988 Mar 22
23 cm	1296 MHz	Tropo*	4151	XE2GXQ-KH6HME	1989 July 15
13 cm	2304 MHz	Tropo	1883	VK5QR-VK6WG/p	1978 Feb 17
9 cm	3456 MHz	Tropo	1885	VK5QR-VK6WG	1986 Jan 25
6 cm	5760 MHz	Tropo	981	G3ZEZ-SM6HYG	1983 July 12
3 cm	10 GHz	Tropo	1660	I0SNY/EA9-I0YLI/IE9	1983 July 8
12 mm	24 GHz	Tropo	331	I0SNY/IC8-I8YZO/8	1984 Aug 11
6 mm	47 GHz	Line-of-sight	105	WA3RMX/3-K7AUO	1988 Aug 6
4 mm	76 GHz	Line-of-sight	0.5	HB9AGE/p-HB9MIN/p	1985 Dec 30
3 mm	120 GHz	No Reports			
2 mm	142 GHz	No Reports			

Source: *QST* and other published reports. Tropo includes tropospheric scattering and ducting.
Tropo* indicates paths primarily over water.

Table 2

Claimed American UHF and Microwave Terrestrial Distance Records, by Propagation Mode

Band (λ)	Most-used Frequency	Propagation Mode	Distance (km)	Stations	Date
70 cm	432 MHz	Tropo*	4151	XE2GXQ-KH6HME	1989 July 15
		Tropo	2121	WA5VJB-WB3CZG	1986 Nov 29
		Aurora	1901	WB5LUA-W3IP	1986 Feb 8
		Meteor scatter	1994	WB55LUA-KD5RO/2	1988 Dec 13
33 cm	903 MHz	Tropo	1003	WB5LUA-W4ODW	1988 Mar 22
23 cm	1296 MHz	Tropo*	4151	XE2GXQ-KH6HME	1989 July 15
		Tropo	2070	KD5RO-WB3CZG	1986 Nov 29
13 cm	2304 MHz	Tropo	1513	KD5RO-W8YIO	1986 Nov 29
9 cm	3456 MHz	Tropo	987	XE2GXQ-N6CA/N6SNA	1989 July 23
6 cm	5760 MHz	Tropo	987	XE2GXQ-N6CA/N6SNA	1989 July 23
3 cm	10 GHz	Tropo	987	XE2GFH-NN6W	1989 July 23
12 mm	24 GHz	Line-of-sight	186	WA3RMX/7-WB7UNU/7	1986 Aug 23
6 mm	47 GHz	Line-of-sight	105	WA3RMX/3-K7AUO	1988 Aug 6
4 mm	76 GHz	No Reports			
3 mm	120 GHz	No Reports			
2 mm	142 GHz	No Reports			

Souce: *QST* and other published reports. Tropo includes tropospheric scattering and ducting.
Tropo* indicates paths primarily over water.

chapter. References to more accessible amateur publications are provided in the notes.

LINE OF SIGHT

Radio waves, like light and other forms of electromagnetic radiation, travel in straight lines through the unobstructed vacuum of space. It is convenient to think of light waves traveling in straight lines through the Earth's atmosphere as well, but this is not precisely accurate. Small variations in the temperature, pressure, and water vapor content of the atmosphere slightly bend, or refract, light and radio waves—usually toward the Earth's surface. Even so, the visual line-of-sight distance to the horizon can be approximated as a straight line, assuming normal atmospheric conditions and a smooth, spherical Earth.

$$d_1 = \sqrt{12.75h} \qquad \text{(Eq 1)}$$

where

d_1 = visual distance to the horizon, kilometers
h = elevation of the observer, meters

In most practical applications, the horizon is terrain at some elevation above sea level, and therefore somewhat closer than the distance the equation yields. A more accurate estimate of the distance to the actual horizon can be made if the elevation of the observer is given in terms of elevation above average terrain or the elevation above the presumed horizon (Fig 1). Care must be taken to be sure that no intervening high ground obscures the more distant horizon.

A large portion of microwave communication is accomplished over line-of-sight distances, but the equation for the distance to the visual horizon is not accurate at radio frequencies. Under standard atmospheric conditions, radio waves are usually refracted earthward somewhat more than light. The distance to the radio horizon appears approximately 1.15 times further distant (equivalent to an Earth with a radius 1.33 times greater than it is) caused by atmospheric refraction. This multiplier is known as the *effective Earth radius factor*, or *k*, and may vary from less than 1.0 to near infinity.[1] The distance to the sea-level radio horizon, therefore, is given by

$$d_r = \sqrt{12.75h_s k} \qquad \text{(Eq 2)}$$

where

d_r = distance to the radio horizon, kilometers
h_s = elevation of the station above sea level, meters
k = effective Earth radius factor

For standard atmospheric conditions (k = 1.33), Eq 2 may be reduced simply to

$$d_r = \sqrt{17h_s} \qquad \text{(Eq 3)}$$

The maximum line-of-sight radio path between two stations is the sum of the distances of the two stations' view of the same horizon. This is shown schematically in Fig 2. A graphic solution to line-of-sight problems in provided in Fig 3. If the horizon is not at sea level, then elevations must be stated with reference to the presumed elevation of the horizon, as was done for calculating the distance to the visual horizon. A more precise analysis of the location, elevation, and distance to the horizon involves drawing a profile of the topography of the Earth from observer to horizon. Some specific guidelines in making such path analyses are provided in the section at the end of this chapter.

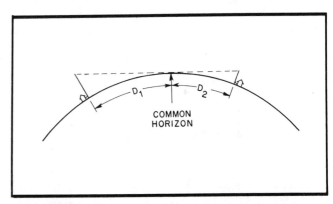

Fig 2—Maximum line-of-sight path distance between two stations is the sum of d₁ and d₂, the distances to a common horizon of each station.

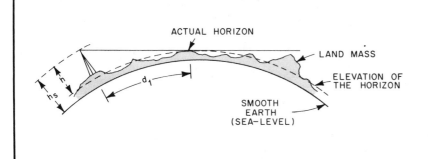

Fig 1—Distance to the visual horizon (d₁), taking into account topographical variations. The elevation of the tower (h) is given with reference to the approximate elevation of the horizon, rather than elevation above sea level (hₛ). In many applications, the elevation h may be approximated as elevation above average terrain.

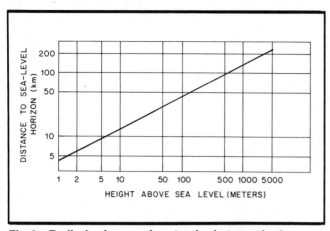

Fig 3—Radio horizon under standard atmospheric conditions for various elevations above sea level.

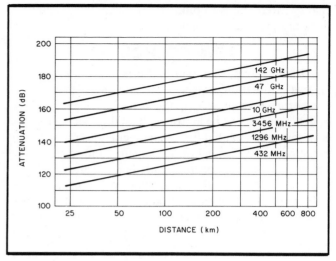

Fig 4—Free-space path loss.

FREE-SPACE AND ATMOSPHERIC LOSSES

All radio signals undergo losses, or attenuation, as they travel through space, whether it is in the near vacuum of extraterrestrial space or within the Earth's atmosphere. In addition, certain UHF and microwaves may be attenuated further by atmospheric gases, rain, snow, hail, fog, smog, and clouds. Attenuation considerations rarely limit high-frequency communications (3 to 30 MHz), and all but free-space losses can be ignored for most modes of terrestrial propagation in the VHF range (30 to 300 MHz). In the UHF range and higher, both atmospheric and free-space losses must be considered in deriving a realistic estimate of received signal strength in terrestrial paths.

Free-Space Losses

Radio signals radiated by an ideal isotropic antenna (one that radiates equally well in all directions) weaken with the square of the distance the signals travel through unobstructed space. This exponential attenuation with distance is caused by the gradual dispersal of energy in all directions from its source. Attenuation also increases with frequency, because the physical size of a theoretical isotropic antenna varies directly with wavelength. As wavelength decreases, the isotropic antenna becomes smaller, and it absorbs proportionally less radio energy from space. Free-space attenuation, measured as the ratio of received power to transmitted power, at a given frequency and distance by isotropic antennas, is given by

$$\frac{P_r}{P_t} = \left(\frac{300}{4\pi f d}\right)^2 \qquad \text{(Eq 4)}$$

where
  P_r = power received by an isotropic antenna, watts
  P_t = transmitted power from an isotropic antenna, watts
  f = frequency, MHz
  d = distance in meters between transmitter and receiver

The basic equation for free-space path loss is usually written in a more convenient form that expresses attenuation in terms of decibel (dB) loss

$$L_{fs} = 32.45 + 20 \log d + 20 \log f \qquad \text{(Eq 5)}$$

where
  L_{fs} = path loss, dB
  d = distance, kilometers
  f = frequency, MHz

Fig 4 provides the free-space path loss in decibels for a number of amateur bands at various distances. The decibel, basic to path-loss and station performance calculations, requires further discussion.

Measurement of Path Loss

The decibel is defined as 10 times the logarithm (base 10) of the ratio of two power measurements. The general equation for calculating decibel power gain or loss is

$$dB = 10 \log \frac{P_1}{P_2} \qquad \text{(Eq 6)}$$

where P_1 and P_2 are two power measurements in watts. From the general equation for calculating power relationships in decibels, a more specific equation for path-loss can be derived. The path-loss equation usually assumes transmitted power from an isotropic antenna to a receiver with an isotropic antenna

$$L_p = 10 \log \left(\frac{P_r}{P_t}\right) \qquad \text{(Eq 7)}$$

where
  L_p = total path loss, dB
  P_r = received power, watts
  P_t = transmitted power, watts

In typical path-loss applications, attenuation is considerable, and received power is correspondingly very small. For example, the free-space path loss over a 100-km

Table 3

Comparison of Power Measurements

Power (watts—W)	Power (dB relative to 1 watt—dBW)
10,000	40
1,000	30
100	20
10	10
1	0
0.1	− 10
0.01	− 20
.001	− 30
.0001	− 40
10^{-10}	− 100

$$dBW = 10\log W$$

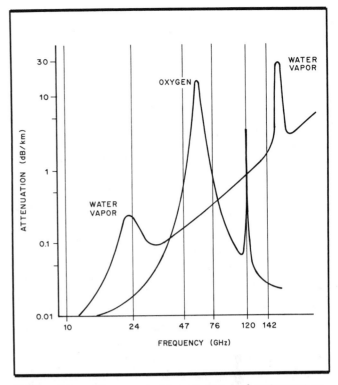

Fig 5—Attenuation caused by oxygen and water vapor at 10 grams per cubic meter. This is equivalent to 40% relative humidity at 25°C. Popular amateur microwave frequencies are indicated. There is very little attenuation caused by atmospheric gases at 10 GHz and lower. Note that the 24-GHz band lies near the center of a peak of water vapor absorption and the 120-GHz band is near a peak of oxygen absorption!

path at 10 GHz, calculated using Eq 5, is

$$L_{fs} = 32.4 + 20 \log 100 + 20 \log 10{,}000 = 152.4 \text{ dB}$$

A path loss of 152 dB, not uncommon in UHF and microwave work, means that the received signal is 152 dB weaker than the transmitted signals. If it is assumed that the transmitter has an output of 1 W to an isotropic antenna, the received power at an isotropic antenna 100 km away would be $10^{-15.2}$ W, or written in more convenient form, 6.3×10^{-16} W.[2]

Although the decibel is the expression of a relation between two power measurements, it can also be thought of as a measure of absolute power when taken with reference to some standard, such as 1 W used in the previous example. Because both 1 W and 1 mW (0.001 watt) are commonly employed in propagation work, care must be taken as to the standard being used. In this chapter, dBW indicates a power measurement with reference to 1 W and isotropic antennas. Positive values of power expressed in dBW are thus greater than 1 W, and negative values for dBW are less than 1 W. Using Eq 6, the general statement for calculating decibels, and substituting 1 W for P_2 in all calculations, it can be shown that 10 mW (0.01 W) can be expressed as − 20 dBW.

$$-20 \text{ dBW} = 10 \log \frac{0.01}{1}$$

Similarly, 1000 W can be expressed as + 30 dBW, and 6.3×10^{-16} W can be written as − 152 dBW. Table 3 provides some typical power measurements in watts and decibels.

Losses From Atmospheric Gases

At frequencies below 10 GHz, free-space path loss accounts for nearly all the attenuation in signal strength over completely unobstructed paths. At 10 GHz and higher, absorption by atmospheric oxygen and water vapor play an increasingly significant role in total attenuation. Fig 5 shows the relative absorption by oxygen and water vapor in the microwave portion of the radio spectrum.

Note that absorption by the two gases peaks around a few discrete frequency bands. Water vapor absorption continues to increase well into the infrared region until it decreases at the visible range.

The changeable composition of the atmosphere complicates the calculations of gaseous attenuation. The actual amount of oxygen and water vapor in the atmosphere normally declines with increasing altitude, caused primarily by the gradual decrease in atmospheric pressure. While the oxygen content of air within a few kilometers of the Earth does not change with the weather, the amount of water vapor varies dramatically. Several assumptions can be made to simplify attenuation calculations over terrestrial paths without introducing unacceptable distortions. First, only the lowest kilometer of the atmosphere normally need be considered, because the largest part of most terrestrial signal paths is limited to that region. Second, oxygen content in the lowest kilometer of the atmosphere can be approximated with a single average figure. Third, average temperature and humidity measurements can be used to describe the weather within the lowest kilometer. With these assumptions in mind, calculation of atmospheric attenuation is relatively straightforward.

Attenuation from oxygen and water vapor is a function of the actual amount of gas present, the distance through which the signal must pass, and the frequency. Empirical investigations have shown that attenuation varies linearly with distance. A simple attenuation factor may be used to calculate oxygen absorption because it has been assumed oxygen content does not vary either with weather or altitude within the first kilometer. Table 4 provides oxygen attenuation factors for various frequencies. To calculate attenuation caused by oxygen absorption, simply multiply the appropriate factor times the total path length in kilometers.

$$L_o = K_o d \qquad \text{(Eq 8)}$$

where

L_o = loss caused by oxygen absorption, dB
K_o = attenuation factor (from Table 4), dB/km
d = distance, kilometers

Water vapor does vary significantly with the weather. The actual water vapor content, or absolute humidity measured in grams of water per cubic meter, must be determined before the water vapor attenuation factor can be applied. Absolute humidity can be determined from the more common measurements of temperature and relative humidity. The maximum amount of water that a given volume of air can hold in the gaseous state is known as the saturation vapor content, equivalent to 100% relative humidity. Fig 6 shows the saturation vapor content for air at a wide range of temperatures. Absolute humidity is found by multiplying the saturation water vapor content in grams per cubic meter (g/m^3) by the relative humidity expressed as a decimal. The absolute humidity of air at 22 °C and 60% relative humidity is

$$20 \text{ g/m}^3 \times 0.60 = 12 \text{ g/m}^3$$

It should be noted that warm air can hold significantly more water vapor than cold air. Air at 22 °C and 60% relative humidity holds more water (12 g/m^3) than air at 10 °C and 100% relative humidity (10 g/m^3). The absolute humidity figure must then be multiplied by the water vapor attenuation factor, obtained from Table 4. The modified factor can then be multiplied by the total path length to obtain the attenuation caused by water vapor.

$$L_w = H K_w d \qquad \text{(Eq 9)}$$

where

L_w = loss caused by water vapor absorption, dB
H = absolute humidity, g/m^3
K_w = attenuation factor (from Table 4), dB/km per g/m^3
d = distance, kilometers

The total attenuation at any microwave frequency through an unobstructed atmosphere is the sum of the free-space loss, attenuation caused by oxygen, and attenuation caused by water vapor. The total attenuation of a 24-GHz signal over a 100-km path on a day with 25 °C temperature and 60% relative humidity can be figured easily. The free-space loss from Eq 4 is

Table 4

Attenuation Caused by Water Vapor and Oxygen

Frequency (GHz)	Oxygen (K_o, dB/km)	Water Vapor (K_w, dB/km per gram/m^3)
10	0.007	0.0004
24	0.018	0.024
47	0.3	0.014
76	0.7	0.036
120	3.0	0.09
142	0.03	0.13

Note: Authorities disagree about the magnitude of water vapor and attenuation above 10 GHz. No attempt has been made to reconcile the differences. The values presented here agree with several sources and are consistent with Fig 5.

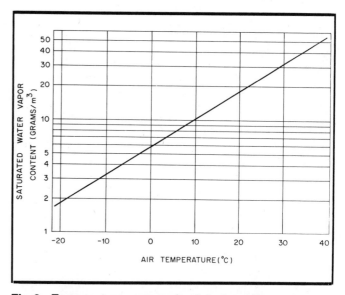

Fig 6—Temperature versus absolute humidity, measured in grams of water vapor per cubic meter, under saturated conditions. To calculate actual water vapor content for any temperature and humidity, multiply the relative humidity (in decimal form) by the saturated water-vapor content for the given temperature.

$$L_{fs} = 32.45 \times 20 \log 100 + 20 \log 24{,}000 = 160 \text{ dB}$$

The loss caused by oxygen, from Table 4 and Eq 8 is

$$L_o = 0.018 \times 100 = 1.8 \text{ dB}$$

The loss caused by water vapor, from Table 4 and Eq 9 is

$$L_w = (23.5 \times 0.60) \times 0.024 \times 100 = 33.84 \text{ dB}$$

The total path loss is 193.8 dB. Greater than one-sixth of the losses along this path are attributable to water-vapor absorption. By choosing a day with low atmospheric water vapor content (a cold and dry day), those losses could be reduced considerably. Fig 7 contrasts water-vapor

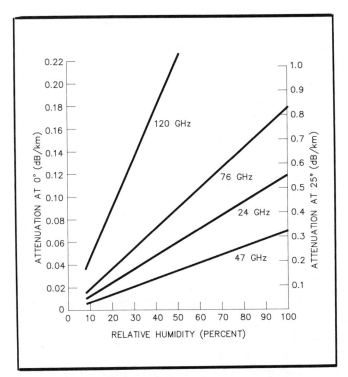

Fig 7—Attenuation due to water vapor absorption depends on the actual water vapor content of the air. This, in turn, is a function of temperature and relative humidity. Attenuation factors at two representative air temperatures (0° and 25°) for various frequencies may be read from the left and right scales respectively.

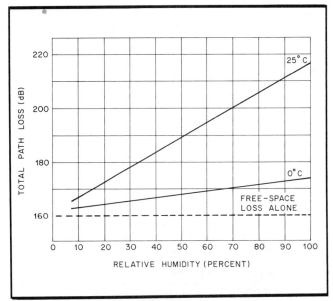

Fig 8—Free-space and atmospheric absorption at 24 GHz along a 100-km path varies considerably with the water vapor content of the air. The dashed line shows only the free-space losses. The two solid lines include oxygen and water vapor losses at 0° and 25° over a wide range of humidity. The lowest path losses can be expected on cool, dry days.

attenuation factors at various frequencies and relative humidities for cold- (0 °C) and warm-temperature (25 °C) conditions. The effect of water-vapor attenuation along a 100-km path at 10 GHz is shown in Fig 8.

Rain Attenuation

Absorption by rain increases path losses significantly at 10 GHz and higher. A 3.3-GHz signal passing through an intense thunderstorm region 20 km wide with rainfall of 25 millimeters per hour (mm/hr) experiences less than 0.2-dB loss. A 10-GHz signal traversing the same thunderstorm would lose 13 dB. Rain attenuation increases with frequency and the total amount of water suspended in droplet form at any moment. The amount of water in the path is a function of rainfall intensity and the geographic extent of the rain. The larger the area of rain along a radio path, the greater the losses. Normally, rain covers only a portion of a total path length. Attenuation caused by rainfall can be calculated from available data, as with oxygen and water vapor. Fig 9 provides attenuation factors, in dB

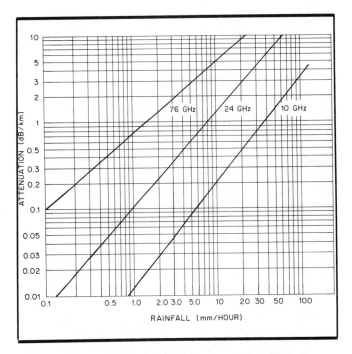

Fig 9—Rain attenuation at 18°C. These factors may vary by 20% over a temperature range of 0 to 40°C.

Table 5

Precipitation Rates in Temperate Climates

Rain (mm/hr)	Description
Less than 1	Drizzle
1 to 4	Light rain
4 to 16	Moderate rain
16 to 25	Heavy rain
25 to 50	Intense thundershower

per km, for various frequencies and rainfall intensities. Table 5 provides a general guide for estimating rainfall rates. Multiply the appropriate attenuation factor by the distance the signal must travel through rain to calculate losses.

$$L_r = K_r d \qquad (Eq\ 10)$$

where

L_r = attenuation due to rain, dB

K_r = rainfall attenuation factor (from Table 5), dB/km

d = distance of radio path in rain, kilometers

The attenuation of a 24-GHz signal caused by a 20-km region of light rain is determined as follows. From Table 5, assume a light shower produces about 2.5 mm/hr of rain. From Fig 9, the attenuation factor for 2.5 mm/hr of rain is 0.3 dB/km. Total attenuation from Eq 10 is

$$L_r = 0.3 \times 20 = 6\ dB$$

A rain attenuation of 6 dB must be added to the free-space and atmospheric loss figures to derive the total path loss.

In most practical cases, rainfall rates must be estimated, as weather reports rarely provide such information for current conditions in specific areas. In temperate climates, the descriptions in Table 5 can be used as a guide. Severe thunderstorms may produce rain at the rate of 25 mm/hr for up to 30 minutes. A thunderstorm of 50 mm/hr is seen on average once a year at any particular place in the midwestern United States. Individual thunderstorm cells average 8 to 10 km in diameter. Light rains and drizzles often cover much larger areas. Weather maps and current weather reports might be helpful in estimating rainfall coverage.

Rain attenuation is also affected by temperature. Attenuation figures given in Fig 9 are calculated for an air temperature of 18 °C. These figures may vary by as much as 20% over a temperature range of 0 to 40 °C. Generally, attenuation is near its peak at 18 °C over most of the frequencies affected for a wide range of rainfall rates. The given attenuation factors may overestimate actual rainfall losses slightly.

Snow and Hail

Snow and hail attenuation ranges from negligible to greater than that from rain of the equivalent precipitation rate, for frequencies of 10 GHz and higher. The attenuation factor for dry (completely frozen) hail is 1 to 10% of an equivalent amount of rain. The rates for partially melted hail approach the attenuation rates for an equivalent amount of rain. Empirical investigations have shown that hail that is as much as 20% melted may actually exceed the rain attenuation factor. Losses caused by snow are likely to be small, because snowfall precipitation rates, in terms of an equivalent amount of melted water, rarely exceeds 5 mm/hr. Attenuation caused by dry snow is so small that it can be ignored at all frequencies, but attenuation caused by partially melted snow may also exceed the attenuation rate for the equivalent amount of rain.

Fog and Clouds

Fog and clouds are composed of very fine water droplets, or sometimes ice crystals, suspended in air. As might be expected, fog and cloud attenuation becomes significant above 10 GHz and increases with frequency, fog density, and distance. Visibility is a good approximation of water droplet density, the governing factor in fog attenuation. Visibility is defined as the distance at which is is possible to see a dark object against the sky. Fig 10 provides for attenuation factors at 15 °C for various visibilities

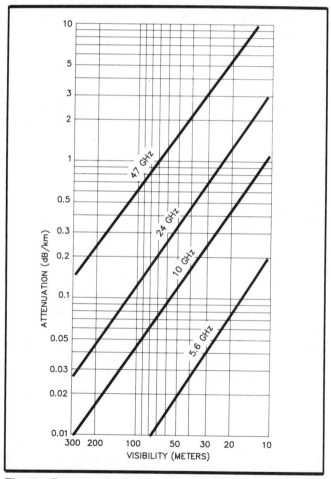

Fig 10—Fog attenuation at 15 °C. Losses are one-third less at 25° and two-thirds more at 0 °C.

and frequencies. Attenuation caused by fog can be estimated by multiplying the appropriate fog attenuation factor by the distance through which the signal must travel.

$$L_f = K_f d \qquad \text{(Eq 11)}$$

where

L_f = fog attenuation, dB
K_f = attenuation factor (from Fig 10), dB/km
d = path distance in fog, kilometers

For complex and not fully understood reasons, fog attenuation decreases slightly with increasing temperature. The fog attenuation factors must be adjusted for temperatures that vary significantly from the nominal 15 °C used in Fig 10. For an air temperature of 0 °C, multiply the appropriate factor by 1.67. Multiply by 0.67 for a temperature of 25 °C. The loss caused by a widespread area of dense fog, 50 km in depth on a freezing day, with visibility of 40 meters, at 10 GHz, can be easily estimated. The attenuation factor for 40-meter visibility, 0.17 dB/km, must be adjusted for temperature by multiplying by 1.67. The calculation based on Eq 11 is

$$L_f = (0.17 \times 1.67) \times 50 = 14.2 \text{ dB}$$

A 14.2-dB loss must be added to free-space and atmospheric gas losses to derive the total path loss.

The values for fog can also be used to estimate cloud attenuation. Clouds and fog composed entirely of ice crystals could be expected to have a negligible effect on path loss. Calculations of fog attenuation may also provide an approximation of attenuation caused by urban smog, which is composed primarily of small dust and soot particles, various exhaust gases, and water vapor.

PATH LOSS AND TOTAL SYSTEM PERFORMANCE

The concept of path loss has already been introduced in relation to free-space and atmospheric losses. Path loss is simply a measure of the attenuation a radio signal undergoes in traveling a given distance from transmitter to receiver. The total loss over a particular path is a sum of all the losses that are encountered. Attenuation may be caused not only by free-space losses, absorption by atmospheric gases, and absorption by precipitation and fog, but also by scattering, refraction, and reflection (discussed later). Total calculated path loss can be compared directly to transmitter and receiver station gain to assess the probability of completing a contact. For a contact to take place, path losses must be overcome by the combined gain of the transmitting and receiving stations. Receiver and transmitter station performances are evaluated in terms of decibels relative to 1 W and isotropic antennas and can be compared directly with path loss.

Total System Performance

Total system performance is a combined evaluation of transmitting and receiving stations. Transmitter station performance is simply transmitter effective radiated power, which takes into account power output and gain realized by the antenna. Receiver station performance is measured in terms of the weakest signal the receiving system can detect. The receiver system noise power, as the measurement of receiver station performance is called, takes into account receiver noise figure, bandwidth, and antenna gain. Transmitter performance is generally given in terms of positive values of dBW, a reflection of the relatively large amounts of power generated by transmitting stations. Receiver noise power is always given as large negative values of dBW, a measure of the strength of the weakest signal that can be detected. Total system performance is the difference between these two values.

$$P_s = P_{erp} - P_n \qquad \text{(Eq 12)}$$

where

P_s = total system performance, dBW
P_{erp} = transmitter station performance, dBW
P_n = receiver system noise power, dBW

Total system performance must overcome path loss for any signal to appear stronger than the background noise, and thus be discernible by the human ear. The difference between the two is called the signal-to-noise ratio and is easily calculated from

$$S = P_s - P_l \qquad \text{(Eq 13)}$$

where

S = signal-to-noise ratio, dB
P_s = total system performance, dBW
P_l = total path loss, dB

Transmitter Effective Radiated Power

Transmitter effective radiated power (ERP) can be calculated from transmitter power output, antenna gain, and feed-line loss. The required equation is

$$P_{erp} = P_t + G_{ta} - L_{tf} \qquad \text{(Eq 14)}$$

where

P_t = transmitter power, dBW
G_{ta} = transmitter antenna gain, dBi
L_{tf} = transmitter feed-line loss, dBW

The effective radiated power of a station with 50 watts output, a feed-line loss of 3 dB, and an antenna gain of 17 dB over a dipole can be calculated after the variables are put into the proper units. Transmitter power must be expressed in terms of dBW, and this can be accomplished directly with an equation derived from Eq 6, by assuming that P_2 is 1 W:

$$P_t = 10 \log P_w \qquad \text{(Eq 15)}$$

where

P_t = transmitter power, dBW
P_w = transmitter power, watts

Substituting into Eq 15:

$$10 \log 50 = 17 \text{ dBW}$$

Thus, 50 watts is equivalent to 17 dBW. Antenna gain must be expressed in dB gain over an isotropic antenna (dBi). Antenna gain can be measured, but it is more common to accept manufacturers' claims or to make a theoretical calculation.[3] The isotropic antenna is used as the standard reference for comparing antenna performance in path loss calculations (just as 1 W was the standard in power measurements), although the dipole is often used as well. The dipole has a gain of 2.14 dB compared to an isotropic antenna, so 2.14 dB must be added to any antenna gain figures cited with reference to a dipole. The revised antenna gain in this example is therefore 19.14 dBi. Feed-line loss is also stated in terms of dB and is an expression of the ratio of the power leaving a feed line compared to the power that entered at the other end. Feed-line losses can also be measured, but more commonly manufacturers' claims are accepted. Feed-line loss is already given in dB, so no further modification is required. Substituting all the variables into Eq 14, effective radiated power can be calculated:

$$P_{erp} = 17 + 19.17 - 3 = 33.17 \text{ dBW}$$

Effective radiated power in dBW can be converted to watts, if desired, by taking the antilog of one-tenth the value of dBW. Thus, 33.17 dBW is equivalent to 2075 watts.

Receiver System Noise Power

The receiver system noise power involves a slightly more complex set of calculations that take into consideration receiver noise figure (a measure of the additional noise created by the receiver itself), bandwidth, antenna gain, and feed-line loss.[4] The basic equation is

$$P_n = 10 \log (kBT_s) - G_{ra} \qquad \text{(Eq 16)}$$

where

P_n = receiver system noise power, dBW
k = Boltzmann's constant (1.38×10^{-23})
B = bandwidth, hertz
T_s = receiver system noise temperature, kelvins ($°C + 273.2$)
G_{ra} = antenna gain, dBi

This equation can be rewritten for greater ease of calculation as

$$P_n = 10 \log B + 10 \log T_s - 228.6 - G_{ra} \qquad \text{(Eq 17)}$$

The receiver system noise temperature requires another calculation that takes into consideration receiver noise temperature, feed-line loss, plus the additional thermal noise contributed by the feed line and antenna. The equation for calculating receiver system noise temperature is

$$T_s = T_a + T_l (R_l - 1) + L_r T_r \qquad \text{(Eq 18)}$$

where

T_a = effective antenna temperature, kelvins
T_l = physical temperature of the feed line, kelvins
R_l = feed-line loss, expressed as a ratio
T_r = receiver noise temperature, kelvins

These additional terms are not difficult to determine. The effective temperature that an antenna pointed at the horizon "sees" can be taken as ambient temperature, or 290 K. In some cases, especially in the millimeter bands, it may be considerably less. Antennas pointed above the horizon may see an equivalent temperature as low as 10 K, although terrestrial communications rarely involves elevated antennas. The feed-line loss must be given as a ratio, but this can be calculated directly from the more usual loss figure in dB:

$$R_l = \text{antilog} \left(\frac{L_{dB}}{10} \right) \qquad \text{(Eq 19)}$$

where L_{dB} = feed-line loss in dB. The physical temperature of the feed line may be considered as 290 K. The receiver noise temperature can be derived directly from the noise figure of the first receiver stage, usually the first RF amplifier, but sometimes it might be the mixer. This can be measured (although the equipment necessary is expensive), or manufacturers' claims can be accepted. The required conversion when the noise figure is known in dB only is

$$T_r = 290 \left[\text{antilog} \left(\frac{NF}{10} \right) - 1 \right] \qquad \text{(Eq 20)}$$

where NF = noise figure of the first receiver stage, dB.

By retracing the steps of Eq 16 through Eq 20, the total receiver system noise power can be calculated. Consider a 10-GHz receiving system with a 10-dB noise figure, a bandwidth of 100 kHz, a line loss of 1 dB, and a horn antenna with a gain of 17 dBi. The receiver noise power can be calculated systematically. From Eq 20, the receiver noise temperature is calculated

$$T_r = 290 \left[\text{antilog} \left(\frac{10}{10} \right) - 1 \right] = 2610 \text{ K}$$

The feed-line loss must be converted to a ratio using Eq 19.

$$L_r = \text{antilog} \left(\frac{1}{10} \right) = 1.26$$

The receiver system noise temperature can then be figured from Eq 18.

$$T_s = 290 + 290 (1.26 - 1) + 1.26 (2610) = 3650 \text{ K}$$

And finally the receiver system noise power is calculated from Eq 17.

$$P_n = 10 \log 100,000 + 10 \log 3650 - 228.6 - 17$$
$$= -160 \text{ dBW}$$

Small adjustments can be made for some of the assumptions used to calculate receiver system noise power. Actual ambient temperature could be substituted in place of the nominal 290 K for the feed-line temperature. Antenna temperature could be lowered to as little as 100 K under certain conditions for antennas pointed at the horizon. In practice, these fine tunings do not significantly affect the overall calculated receiver system noise power.

Using an ambient temperature of 270 K, slightly below freezing, and an antenna temperature of 100 K, the noise power improves by just 0.3 dBW. Dramatic improvements are made by reducing receiver bandwidth, reducing receiver noise figure, and increasing antenna size.

Calculation of the noise power of an ideal (but not perfect) receiver has some interesting applications. The bandwidth would be 100 Hz, about as narrow as can be used in a practical communications system. The receiver noise figure would be near zero, and there would be no feed-line loss. Ambient antenna temperature would remain at 290 K. Ignoring antenna gain, such an ideal receiver would have a noise power of -184 dBW. This base figure can be used as a standard by which to judge the performance of all other receivers. In addition, it can also be used as the starting point for a simplified method of determining the noise power of a receiver system without making the tedious calculations of Eq 14 through Eq 20.

A Simple Method for Calculating Receiver System Noise Power

An easy method to derive the noise power of a receiving system used in terrestrial communications (assumes an antenna temperature of 290 K) begins with the noise power of the ideal receiver, -184 dBW. Add the noise figure of the actual receiver, feed-line loss, and bandwidth factor, and subtract antenna gain. The result is the receiver system noise power. Expressed as an equation, it is

$$P_n = NF + L_f + B_{dB} - G_a - 184 \qquad \text{(Eq 21)}$$

where

P_n = receiver system noise power, dBW
NF = receiver noise figure, dB
L_f = feed-line loss, dB
B_{dB} = bandwidth adjustment factor, dB
G_a = antenna gain, dBi

The bandwidth factor adjusts for the deterioration in performance that comes with bandwidths greater than 100 Hz. It can be taken directly from Table 6 for commonly used bandwidths, or calculated using Eq 22.

$$B_{dB} = 10 \log B_{Hz} - 20 \qquad \text{(Eq 22)}$$

where B_{Hz} = receiver bandwidth in hertz. Using the same parameters as the previous example, that is a receiver with a noise figure of 10 dB, a 100-kHz bandwidth, a line loss of 1 dB, and a 17-dBi horn antenna, the receiver system noise power can be determined quickly using Eq 21.

$$P_n = 10 + 1 + 30 - 17 - 184 = -160 \text{ dBW}$$

The result is the same calculated by both methods, -160 dBW.

Total System Performance Example

Here is a practical problem that can be solved using the path loss and total system performance analysis. Can a pair of 10-GHz Gunn-diode stations complete a 100-km contact? Assume the stations have the following charac-

Table 6

Bandwidth Factors Used for Calculating Receiver System Noise Power

Receiver Bandwidth	Bandwidth Factor
100 Hz	0
500 Hz	7
2.3 kHz	13.6
100 kHz	30
250 kHz	34
1 MHz	40

Note: Use this Table for adjusting bandwidth factor in Eq 21.

teristics: 10-dB receiver noise figure; 100-kHz bandwidth; 10-mW output power (FM); 17-dBi horn antennas for receiving and transmitting; no feed-line loss. The chosen 100-km path is essentially line of sight from two mountaintops. It is a clear spring day, 10°C and 50% relative humidity.

From Eq 5, the free-space path loss can be calculated.

$$L_{fs} = 32.45 + 20 \log 100 + 20 \log 10{,}000 = 152.4 \text{ dB}$$

Losses caused by atmospheric absorption can be calculated using Table 4 and Fig 5. The absorption caused by oxygen from Eq 8 is

$$L_o = 0.007 \times 100 = 0.7 \text{ dB}$$

The water-vapor-absorption is given by Eq 9.

$$L_w = 10 \times 0.50 \times 0.0004 \times 100 = 0.2 \text{ dB}$$

The total path loss is therefore

$$152.4 + 0.7 + 0.2 = 153.3 \text{ dB}$$

The transmitter effective radiated power by Eq 14 is:

$$P_{erp} = 10 \log 0.010 + 17 - 0 = -3 \text{ dBW}$$

And the receiver system noise power is determined by Eq 21.

$$P_n = 10 + 0 + 30 - 17 - 184 = -159 \text{ dBW}$$

The total system performance from Eq 12 is

$$P_s = -3 - (-159) = 156 \text{ dBW}$$

Finally, the expected signal-to-noise ratio can be calculated using Eq 13

$$S = 156 - 153.3 = 2.7 \text{ dB}$$

A signal-to-noise ratio of 2.7 dB is not sufficient to maintain solid FM communication, but a contact still may be possible under actual conditions. Ever-changing atmospheric conditions along the path often provide brief periods of slightly enhanced propagation conditions that could raise the signal-to-noise ratio slightly. Only a few decibels of enhancement would be required to raise the signal clearly above the noise.

Total system performance gain figures for typical stations at various frequencies are given in Table 7. These figures assume that identical stations exist at the receive and transmit ends of each path. This is rarely the case. Receiver and transmitter station performances normally must be calculated separately for each direction.

TROPOSPHERIC REFRACTION

Tropospheric refraction is the most common and most widely used mode of long-distance propagation in the amateur UHF and microwave bands.[5] Under standard atmospheric conditions, UHF and microwave signals are refracted (bent) slightly as they travel through the weather-producing, lowest 10 kilometers of the atmosphere called the troposphere. Just as light is refracted as it passes between different media—from air to water in one of the most familiar examples of refraction—a radio signal is refracted as it passes through the troposphere. Refraction occurs because the troposphere is not a homogeneous medium. Temperature, pressure, and moisture content normally decrease with altitude at such a rate to refract radio signals slightly toward the Earth, thus propagating signals beyond the optical horizon. Under favorable tropospheric conditions, signals may be refracted at greater than normal angles, further extending the effective radio horizon. *Superrefraction*, or *ducting* as it is often called, occurs when the angle of refraction is equivalent to, or greater than, the curvature of the Earth.

Index of Refraction

The refractive properties of air may be calculated from temperature, moisture, and atmospheric pressure. The index of refraction of air, at a very wide range of radio frequencies, is given in Eq 23.[6]

$$N = \frac{77.6\,p}{T} + \frac{3.73 \times 10^5 e}{T^2} \qquad \text{(Eq 23)}$$

where

N = index of refraction, N units
p = atmospheric pressure, millibars (mb)
e = partial pressure of water vapor, millibars
T = temperature, kelvins

The refraction of radio signals is a function of the change in the index of refraction with altitude. N varies between 290 and 400 at the Earth's surface and normally diminishes with altitude at the rate of 40 N units per kilometer, within the first few kilometers. This lapse rate is more conveniently noted as a change in N per meter altitude, or dN/m.

The effective Earth radius factor (k), introduced in the section Line of Sight, can be calculated directly from index of refraction data.

$$k = \frac{0.157}{0.157 - (dN/m)} \qquad \text{(Eq 24)}$$

where

k = effective Earth radius factor
dN/m = change in N units per meter (within 2 km of the Earth's surface)

Under standard atmospheric conditions, dN/m = 0.040 and k = 1.33. Radio waves are refracted slightly in the

Table 7

Total System Performance for Selected Station Characteristics

($P_s = P_{erp} - P_n$)

| ---Transmitter--- | | ---Antenna--- | | ---Receiver--- | | | | | |
Power Output (W)	Feed-line Loss (dB)	Type	Gain (dBi)	Noise Figure (dB)	Feed-line Loss (dB)	Band-width	Transmitter ERP (P_{erp}) (dBW)	Receiver System Noise Power (P_n) (dBW)	Total System Performance (P_s) (dBW)
432 MHz									
1500	1.0	8 × 19 el	26	0.5	0.5	100 Hz	56.8	−209.0	265.8
500	1.5	4 × 19 el	23	0.5	0.5	500 Hz	48.5	−199.0	247.5
100	1.5	1 × 19 el	17	2.5	1.5	2.3 kHz	35.5	−183.4	218.9
1296 MHz									
500	1.0	4-m dish	31	1	0.5	100 Hz	57.0	−213.5	270.5
100	2.5	4 × 27 el	26	1	0.5	500 Hz	43.5	−201.5	245.0
2	2.5	1 × 27 el	20	3	0.5	2.3 kHz	20.5	−186.9	207.4
3.3 GHz									
500	3.0	2-m dish	35	2	0.5	100 Hz	59.0	−216.5	275.5
10	0.5	1.5-m dish	31	2	0.5	500 Hz	40.5	−205.5	246.0
2	0	0.75-m dish	25	2	0	2.3 kHz	28.0	−193.4	221.4
10 GHz									
10	0	1-m dish	35	5	0	500 Hz	45.0	−207.0	252.0
0.01	0	horn	17	10	0	100 kHz	−3.0	−159.0	156.0
24 GHz									
0.01	0	0.5-m dish	40	12	0	500 kHz	20.0	−175.0	195.0

atmosphere, making it appear as if the radio horizon were 1.15 times further away than the visual horizon. With greater refraction, the value of k increases with dN/m. When dN/m exceeds 0.157, superrefraction (ducting) takes place, and radio waves are refracted enough to bring them back to the surface of the Earth. The value of k is infinite under such circumstances, suggesting an infinitely distant horizon. In actual practice, the radio horizon is limited to the geographic extent that atmospheric conditions yield dN/m greater than 0.157. Ducting conditions often cover a wide area and have allowed amateurs to cover UHF paths in excess of 4000 km.

Temperature is the major determinant of N. The left-hand portion of Eq 23, or the dry term, can be considered to vary only with changes in temperature, because atmospheric pressure decreases at a known constant rate that is nearly independent of weather conditions. As temperature rises, the value of the dry term in N units declines. Under most tropospheric conditions, the dry term contributes between 75 and 90% of the total value of N. The right-hand portion of the equation, or the wet term, is a function both of moisture and temperature. As water vapor content is reduced, the wet term's value in N units also declines. Although moisture usually plays only a supporting role in creating high refractivity lapse rates (large values for dN/m), dN/m may exceed the minimum 0.157 needed for ducting caused only by sharp decreases in the water vapor content of air. Generally, the greatest changes in dN/m occur when temperature rises and moisture declines simultaneously with increasing altitude.

Temperature Inversions and Ducts

A temperature *inversion exists* in the troposphere when temperature rises with altitude. This is called an inversion, because it is contrary to the usual temperature lapse for the lowest part of the atmosphere. Normally, temperature falls by 6.5°C per km. Moisture, measured in terms of dew point, also falls at the rate of 5.5°C per km.[7] These normal atmospheric profiles for temperature and dew point are shown in Fig 11, along with a hypothetical inversion. The inversion has a vertical dimension, or depth, corresponding to the distance through which temperature rises. In many natural inversions, water vapor content also declines sharply within the inversion layer. Most inversions that are useful to UHF and microwave refraction can be visualized as a layer of warm, dry air lying above cooler and more humid air.

Even though superrefractive conditions may exist, that is dN/m is greater than 0.157, all radio frequencies are not refracted to the same degree. The inversion depth determines the lowest frequency that is superrefracted. This phenomenon is often linked to a waveguide and its cutoff frequency. Shallow inversions create ducts with relatively high cut-off frequencies and deeper inversions allow lower minimum ducting frequencies. The relationship among dN/m, inversion depth, and frequency is shown graphically in Fig 12.[8] One important implication of these relation-

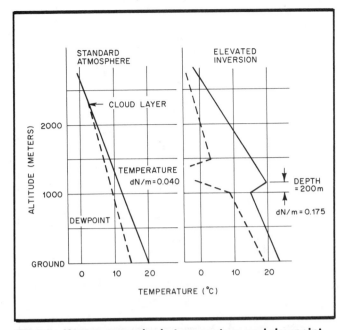

Fig 11—Upper atmospheric temperature and dewpoint profiles for the standard atmosphere and for an elevated temperature inversion with a base at 1000 meters altitude. Dewpoint is a measure of moisture content. Note that moisture also decreases rapidly within the inversion. This inversion is sufficient to create ducting as low as 432 MHz.

ships is that ducting requirements at higher microwave frequencies are less demanding than at UHF. During the formation of a temperature inversion, microwave ducting may actually be evident well before it is possible in the UHF range. Some ducts may never grow deep enough to support superrefraction in the UHF range.

A superrefracting inversion is more accurately envisioned as only the upper boundary of a very leaky duct or waveguide, and certain conditions further limit the direct application of the waveguide model to natural inversions. The inversion must meet the requirements of minimum refractivity and depth over a very wide geographic area. Radio signals are trapped, that is continuously refracted toward Earth, only so long as the duct covers the entire radio path. Any discontinuity ruins the path. Contrary to the waveguide model, inversion depth cannot be equated with a waveguide dimension. Inversion depth is merely one factor that determines whether or not an inversion layer can act as an upper refracting boundary at a certain frequency. The lower boundary of the duct is not clearly defined. Often it is simply the surface of the Earth. Thus stations need not be within the narrow confines of the inversion layer itself to make use of the ducting phenomenon. Radio signals must approach the inversion layer at very shallow angles, generally much less than 1°, to be refracted earthward. Signals at higher angles simply pass through the inversion, refracted insufficiently to bring them back toward the Earth's surface.

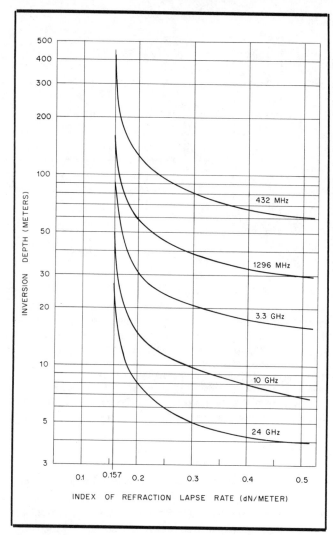

Fig 12—Minimum inversion depth and index of refraction lapse rate needed to create ducting at various frequencies.

Inversions that create strong ducting conditions are generally found between 500 and 1500 meters, although some inversions are much lower than this. They are rarely uniform in depth, refractivity, or altitude. Inversions usually have quite well defined propagation boundaries, but typically they gradually weaken, become more shallow, and become more elevated at their extreme edges. UHF and microwave signals may be propagated for thousands of kilometers within these natural ducts with low rates of attenuation, but path losses are difficult to calculate with any degree of assurance. Free-space path losses cannot be applied, because signals trapped by a superrefracting inversion are no longer propagated in free space. Losses caused by atmospheric absorption do apply and are likely to be substantial, because water vapor content is often high just below an inversion. At microwave frequencies, atmospheric losses may be the limiting factor in ducting propagation.

Calculations of the index of refraction of air in the upper atmosphere, necessary to evaluate inversion conditions, are not usually practical either. The required upper-air data are difficult to acquire, and the number of calculations necessary to derive a meaningful picture of upper-air conditions over a wide geographical region are time consuming, even with the aid of a personal computer. Even so, such calculations can be made. The National Oceanic and Atmospheric Administration (NOAA) sends up weather balloons twice daily from several dozen launching stations in the United States to collect temperature, moisture, pressure, and wind data. NOAA distributes the raw data via teletype and other means to airport weather offices and meteorological offices around the country. Amateurs wishing to make analyses of current upper-air conditions might find a weather office willing to share its current data. Even the N-profile of a single location can often prove helpful in assessing conditions. Several published works provide more detail on techniques for upper-air analysis.[9] NOAA also distributes current synoptic maps of upper-air conditions at standard altitudes that might be helpful in evaluating atmospheric conditions, although the data included are not sufficiently detailed to make meaningful calculations. Old data may be purchased on computer tape or in hard copy directly from NOAA as well.[10]

In spite of the difficulty of acquiring quantitative upper-air data, it is possible to predict general inversion conditions and their geographical limits from a close study of surface weather maps. Several well known physical processes create most temperature inversions that are useful for radio propagation. These natural atmospheric processes are closely related to a variety of distinctive weather conditions that can be observed directly or from weather maps published in daily newspapers or shown with television weather news. Close observation of surface weather features is often enough to make quite useful predictions of likely tropospheric radio propagation conditions.

Tropospheric inversions can be classified according to how they are created. *Radiation inversions* emerge from the rapid cooling of the Earth's surface after sunset. *Subsidence inversions* result from the compression, heating, and drying of air that is being forced downward through the troposphere. Lateral movements of large masses of air, such as occurs when a warm, dry mass of air flows over a stationary mass of cooler moister air, creates *advective inversions*. Finally, *evaporation inversions* exist over many warm bodies of water as the result of the high moisture content of air near the water's surface. Each of these four mechanisms and their associated weather are discussed in turn.

Radiation Inversions

Radiation inversions are probably the most common and widespread of the several inversion types. They form over land in the evening as the result of progressive cooling of air near the Earth's surface. As the sun goes down, the land cools by radiating heat into space. In turn, the air just above the Earth's surface is also cooled. Higher in the atmosphere, the air remains relatively warmer. The cooling process continues throughout the evening and predawn hours. The inversion deepens with time and may reach an altitude of 500 meters in extreme cases. Fig 13 shows the temperature profile of a deep radiation inversion. Note that the moisture content of the air is unaffected by radiation cooling. If the air near the ground cools to the dew point, water vapor may precipitate in the form of fog or dew.

Radiation inversions occur in all seasons, but they are most common during the summer when the ground is well warmed by daytime heating. Radiation inversions are most pronounced in dry climates, in areas with sparse vegetation, and in valleys, where cooled air sinks down the slopes and collects on the valley floor. The radiation process does not work well over water or in very wet areas, such as swamps, because water releases its heat very slowly. High humidity slows radiation as well. Cloud cover inhibits radiation formation by reflecting and trapping heat radiated by the Earth. Radiation inversions are also disrupted by wind, which mixes the cool and warm layers of air. It also must be emphasized that inversions do not form by the sun heating air aloft in the early morning hours. Air is not heated directly by the relatively short wavelengths of solar radiation. Rather the sun heats the Earth's surface, which in turn reradiates energy at longer wavelengths that can be more readily absorbed by the air.

Radiation inversions are local phenomena that are sensitive to topography, vegetation, and wind conditions. Local features, such as lakes, mountains, dense forests, and rivers may inhibit radiation or cause discontinuities in inversion formation. Continuous radiation inversions rarely cover a wide geographic area. In addition, the index-of-refraction lapse rate usually does not exceed the minimum necessary for ducting (dN/m greater than 0.157) because moisture makes almost no contribution to the change in N within a radiation inversion. Radiation inversions thus have limited potential for long-distance ducting.

In spite of these limitations, radiation inversions can be quite useful for UHF and microwave propagation. Enhanced propagation conditions are more likely to exist in the early morning hours because of the formation of radiation inversions during the night. Because they readily and commonly form in dry air, atmospheric losses caused by water vapor absorption are likely to be small at the same time a strong radiation inversion would provide some path enhancement. Radiation inversions can be useful in extending the range not only of line-of-sight paths to 300 km or greater, but they may also enhance tropospheric scattering, airplane reflections, and other propagation modes.

High-Pressure System Inversions

Strong inversions are a common feature of large, sluggish anticyclones, or high-pressure systems. The air within a high-pressure system expands outward and downward. Subsiding air is compressed as it is forced earthward, and as air is compressed, its temperature rises. Subsiding air is also likely to be exceedingly dry because of its origins as much cooler air higher in the atmosphere. Cool air can hold very little water even under saturated conditions, and subsiding air has no additional source of moisture. Two, three, or more distinct inversion layers may form, one above the other up to 3000 meters in altitude within a well-developed high-pressure system. Fig 14 shows the temperature and dew-point profile of a typical high-pressure system. The lowest inversion is usually the most significant for UHF and microwave propagation because it yields the highest values of dN/m. This lowest inversion often stabilizes between 500 and 1500 meters in altitude, although it may be forced all the way to the Earth's surface during the hours of darkness.

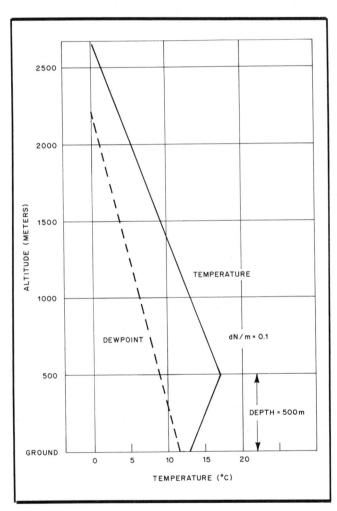

Fig 13—Typical deep radiation inversion found in a dry climate. There is almost no deviation of the moisture lapse rate from the normal profile, hence moisture makes a small contribution to the total value. This inversion is insufficient for ducting at any frequency. Only enhanced propagation would be observed at UHF and microwave frequencies.

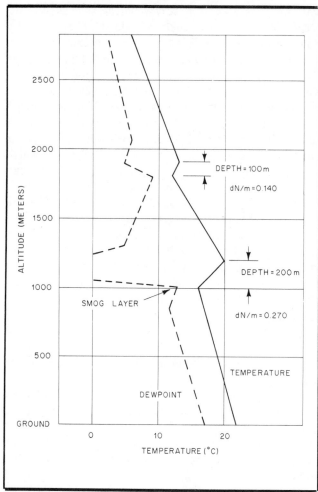

Fig 14—Typical upper atmospheric profile of subsidence inversion within a warm-core high pressure system. Stacking of two, three, and even more inversions is common. The upper inversion is not strong enough to create superrefraction at any frequency. The lower inversion exceeds the minimum dN/m and depth requirements to support ducting down to 432 MHz. Just below the lower inversion level, smoke, dust, and other particles accumulate, often creating a distinct visible layer of smog.

Two types of high-pressure systems are useful for UHF and microwave propagation. Sprawling, sluggish systems that appear most often in late summer over continental areas are common to the United States, western Europe, Australia, and other large land masses. In addition, vast high-pressure regions that exist more or less permanently over the oceans at about 30° north and south latitudes are important for propagation. Inversion-producing mechanisms are nearly identical in both types of highs, although there are some differences that are significant for radio propagation.

The most spectacular high-pressure systems over the continental United States and Canada appear in the late summer and early autumn.[11] They generally originate in the cool air of northwestern Canada and gradually move

south and east at about 750 kilometers per day, although they may slow down considerably with time and even stagnate over the eastern part of the United States. They begin as shallow cold-core systems and gradually grow into deep, sluggish, warm-core highs as they move over the warmer ground to the south.

The weather under high pressure is generally clear and calm, although smoke, dust, pollutants, and water vapor may be trapped under the lowest inversion layer, creating smog or haze. Often a distinct colored layer of air can be seen on the horizon where suspended particles have accumulated—an almost certain indication of inversion. During the daytime hours, the normally strong subsidence is countered by rising air heated by the Earth's surface. Low, puffy cumulus clouds are often formed by this daytime heating. As the sun goes down, the ground loses its heat rapidly and the air stops rising. Subsidence takes over, further compressing and warming the air aloft as it is forced downward. The warm, dry air usually completely evaporates the clouds before sunset. Through the evening, the subsidence inversion may continue to strengthen. Since clear skies and calm air generally prevail under high-pressure conditions, it is also common for radiation inversions to form as well. By morning, radiation and subsidence inversions may exist simultaneously.

Fig 15 shows a typical late-summer, high-pressure system and the extent of useful inversion (ducting) conditions. In North America, inversions usually appear to the south and west of the surface position of the center of high pressure. The reason for this is evident from the vertical profile of a typical warm-core high. As altitude increases, the center of high pressure is gradually displaced toward the source of nearby warm air. In the United States, warm-core highs appear to "lean" toward the southwestern deserts when viewed in profile. Strong inversions typically appear around the center of highest pressure between 1 and 2 kilometers. At this altitude, the center of the system is somewhat to the southwest of its position at the surface. The area of the inversion, as viewed from the ground, thus appears to be skewed somewhat to the south and west. Actual profiles of subsidence inversions show that they are generally stronger, deeper, and lower in altitude toward the centers than at the margins. Stations on the very edges of a ducting region may find some advantage in being located at higher elevations. Ducting conditions are generally more pronounced during the evening and early morning hours, but especially strong inversions may be useful into daylight. A stagnating high-pressure system may persist for several days, especially over the eastern third of the country during August and September. Stagnating highs are very rare in the mountainous West.

Although the sluggish warm-core highs of late summer have produced some of the most spectacular UHF and microwave propagation conditions over the continent, high-pressure systems in other seasons may also produce ducting or enhanced propagation conditions. There is a higher probability that larger, slower moving, and warmer

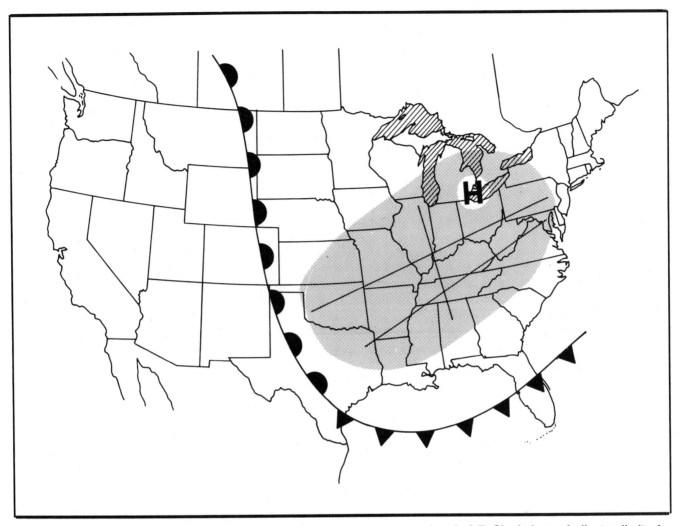

Fig 15—Typical high-pressure inversion common during late summer and early fall. Shaded area indicates limit of the useful inversion. Note UHF paths (straight lines) to the south and southwest of the high-pressure center. Based on weather data of September 9, 1979.

highs will produce strong stable inversions than cool, shallow, and fast-moving systems more typical of winter. Highs can be observed over a period of time to assess their characteristics and movements.

Some of the most spectacular and record-breaking UHF and microwave paths have been completed under vast regions of high pressure that are semipermanent climatic features between 20° and 40° north and south of the equator. High-pressure conditions are created within these two broad bands by the continuous subsidence of warm dry air associated with global air circulation patterns.[12] The effects of this subsidence are widespread. Most of the world's deserts, for example, lie within these latitudes and the calm clear air of the "horse latitudes" (so called because the lack of wind often forced becalmed sailing ships to throw cargos of dying horses overboard) are also consequences of permanent high pressure. These high-pressure regions also support large and essentially permanent inversions just north of the equator in the

Caribbean and across the Pacific, and just south of the equator between South America and Africa. Other regions of the world are similarly affected.

The huge eastern Pacific high-pressure system, which sprawls between the southwestern coast of the United States and the coast of Mexico across the Pacific, is especially noteworthy. It is most useful for transpacific UHF and microwave paths during the summer months because the whole system has a seasonal drift. In the winter, it moves south by several degrees latitude and away from the California coast. The system shifts northward during the spring and summer. When the California coast is on the edge of the Pacific high, occasionally inversion conditions will extend inland far enough for paths to open to the Hawaiian Islands. The Sierras, which rise to over 6000 meters, probably limit the eastward extent of inversion conditions. It is likely that paths much in excess of 4000 km could be worked if island stations west of Hawaii were active on UHF and microwave bands.

The "Bermuda high" is a similar high-pressure system that migrates off the southeastern coast of the United States south of Bermuda and into the Caribbean. It too is generally at its northern extreme in summer, often covering a large portion of the southeastern states. It moves further south in winter. Inversions associated with the Bermuda high have supported VHF and UHF paths from Bermuda to the mainland, paths nearly 3000 km long from the islands of Puerto Rico and Montserrat in the Caribbean to Florida, Georgia, and South Carolina, and 2000-km paths across the Gulf of Mexico (Fig 16). The potential for the Bermuda high is even greater than these examples indicate. Its extent suggests that ducting conditions could be sustained from the southern United States as far south as the northern coast of South America, west to Texas and Mexico, and at least as far east as Bermuda and Trinidad.

Semipermanent inversions associated with high-pressure regions exist in other parts of the world. Inversions between 500 and 2000 meters in altitude are a nearly permanent feature in the mid-Atlantic between Africa and South America just north and south of the equator. Extensions of these well known inversions may even intrude into the Caribbean. Similar conditions exist across the Indian Ocean and in the western Pacific. These inversions have yet to be exploited by amateurs because of the lack of activity on the VHF and higher bands in the affected areas.

Foehn Winds

Strong inversions may be created by a combination of subsidence and advection, a characteristic of *foehn wind* conditions. Foehn winds are created in conjunction with

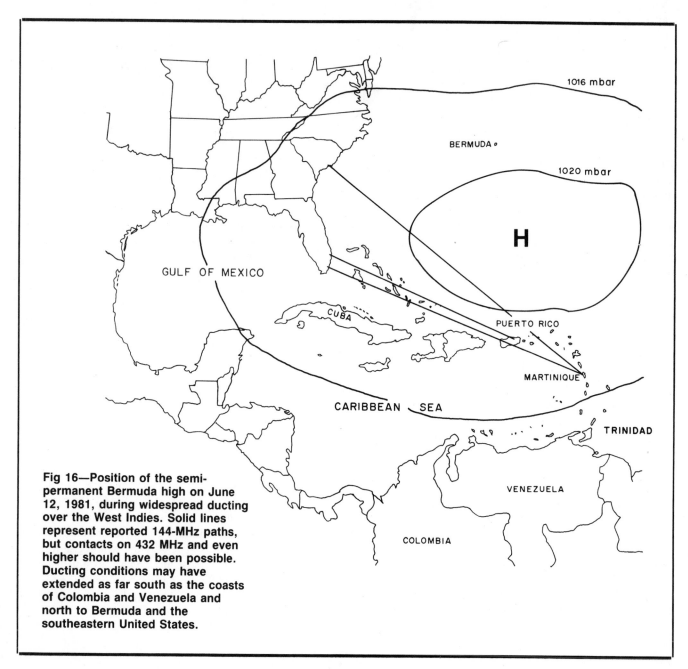

Fig 16—Position of the semi-permanent Bermuda high on June 12, 1981, during widespread ducting over the West Indies. Solid lines represent reported 144-MHz paths, but contacts on 432 MHz and even higher should have been possible. Ducting conditions may have extended as far south as the coasts of Colombia and Venezuela and north to Bermuda and the southeastern United States.

mountain ranges. An air mass forced up and over a mountain by prevailing winds is cooled as it ascends. If the air is moist, it is forced to yield its load of water vapor through precipitation on the windward side of the mountain. As the dried air descends the lee side of the mountain, it is warmed by compression at a faster rate than it was cooled. Air that spreads over the lowlands below is quite warm and dry. If the ground is cool and moist, very strong inversions may be created.

Foehn winds occur commonly in the Alps, where the term for this wind was named, the Caucasus, the Rocky Mountains, and elsewhere. In the American Rockies, the wind is known as the Chinook, or "snow eater" to the Indians of the Northwest who noticed how quickly the warm air evaporated snow. Chinook winds are most common in the spring, when snow may cover the Great Plains, creating ideal inversion-producing conditions. Inversions useful for UHF and microwave propagation may extend east of the Rockies as far north as Alberta and Saskatchewan, south to Texas, and perhaps east to the Mississippi River.

Sirocco Winds

Other types of local winds also create unusually strong inversions. The *sirocco wind* of the Mediterranean Sea is probably responsible for the inversion conditions that have allowed record-breaking 1600-km paths on 10 GHz. The sirocco is a very hot and dry wind that originates in the Sahara Desert. It blows northward across the Mediterranean, especially in the spring and autumn, in advance of east-wardly moving low-pressure centers. Inversion conditions are created when the hot, dry sirocco wind flows over a relatively cooler but much more humid layer of air above the Mediterranean Sea. The sirocco effect has been observed as far west as the Madeira Islands in the Atlantic Ocean and east into Lebanon and Israel.

Land Breeze

Land breezes are a local wind common in temperate coastal regions during the summer. They may create inversions of no more than 50 to 100 km wide but extending for up to several hundred kilometers along a coast. Land breezes develop after sunset on clear summer evenings. The land cools more quickly than the adjacent ocean. Air cooled over the land flows near the surface of the Earth toward the adjacent ocean to displace relatively warmer air that is rising over the water. The warm ocean air, in turn, travels inland at 200 to 300 meters in altitude to replace the cool surface air. Land-sea circulation of cool air near the ground and warm air aloft creates a mild inversion that may last for several hours. Land-breeze inversions are used regularly along the coast of the United States and may be observed in many other coastal regions of the world.

Wave Cyclone

An often overlooked but reliable producer of stable inversions is the *wave cyclone*. Unlike the more familiar stagnating high-pressure system, wave cyclones exist only for a few days from birth to complete collapse, and their usefulness for UHF and microwave propagation is often much shorter than that.

Wave cyclones appear along the global boundary between polar and temperate air regions called the polar front. This extremely long polar front is unstable, and waves appear along it as low-pressure centers when the jet stream (winds of 150 km/hr and greater at altitudes above 3000 meters) cross it from the southwest. Counterclockwise winds created by the cyclonic action of the wave pull cool air around from the northwest, creating a cold front that trails southwesterly from the center of low pressure. Breezes associated with a distant region of high pressure bring mild Gulf air northward when the wave cyclone is positioned over the eastern part of the United States, creating a warm front to the east of the low. The area to the south of the warm front is known as the warm sector. Fig 17 shows a typical wave cyclone with a well developed warm sector two to three days after its birth over Colorado.

As the wave continues to develop, the cold front is pushed eastward and eventually catches up with the slower moving warm front. In the last stages of the wave, the two fronts meet, the warm sector is cut off, and the wave ceases to exist. As the wave cyclone goes through its three- to five-day cycle, it also moves along a generally northeasterly tract. A wave that begins over Colorado or New Mexico may finally collapse over New England. Wave cyclones often form family groups as one wave after another appear along the same polar front. The polar front, with its family of waves, may stretch across North America, the Atlantic, and Europe.

The inversion associated with a wave cyclone is created almost entirely by strong wind patterns within the well developed warm sector. Mild, moist air flows steadily northward near the surface of the Earth from the Gulf of Mexico to the Great Lakes. Above the surface flow at 1500 meters and higher, very fast moving warm, dry air associated with the jet stream crosses the warm sector from the southwest. The intersection of these two winds, mild and moist below, very warm and dry above, creates a relatively flat inversion at about 1000 meters in altitude. Inversion conditions usually improve just after sunset when ground heating and local winds decrease. The most common UHF paths are north-south in the western part of the warm sector, no closer than about 100 km to the often violent cold front. Paths as long as 2000 km have been completed within the warm sector of a wave cyclone. Ideal conditions may last only a few hours because the wave cyclone is such a dynamic weather system.

Wave cyclones appear in any season, but they are

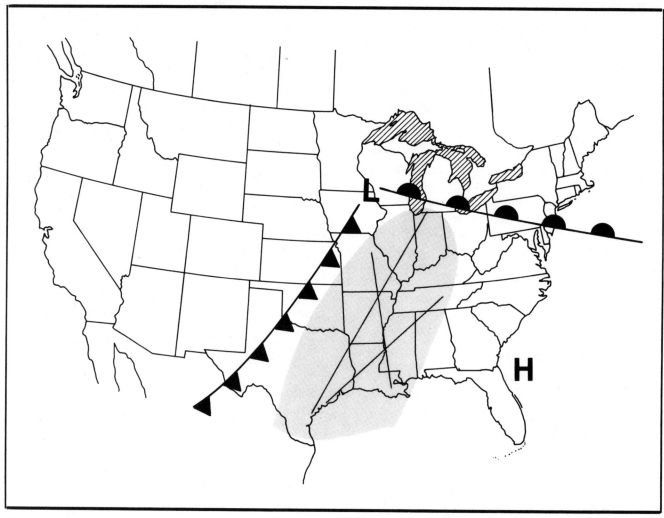

Fig 17—Wave cyclone inversion over the eastern part of the United States in early summer. Typical long paths at UHF are north-south within the warm sector, directly east of the cold front. Based on the wave cyclone of May 7, 1979.

more common over the continental United States during springtime, when the polar front makes its annual migration northward. The central part of the country, south of the Great Lakes and east of the Appalachians, is most affected. Productive wave cyclones have occasionally been oriented to create long paths right along the east coast of the United States as well, but never west of the Rocky Mountains.

Warm Fronts

The unsettled weather conditions that accompany frontal systems are usually associated with a deterioration of UHF and microwave propagation conditions. This is not always the case. Warm fronts and cold fronts have the potential to create inversions because fronts mark the boundaries between warm and cool air masses. Usually the confrontation between the two masses of air is unstable and even violent, but occasionally frontal conditions may give rise to stable superrefracting inversions.

A warm front marks the boundary between a mass of warm air that is advancing toward a relatively stationary and cooler mass of air. The less dense warm air overrides the cooler air in a long wedge that may create inversions up to 800 km ahead of the frontal boundary. Inversions are more likely to form when the warm front is slow and stable over a wide area. Fig 18 shows an unusual warm front that created a widespread superrefracting inversion in winter by flooding warm Gulf air over the cold and partially snow-covered Midwest. Slow moving warm fronts in other seasons may also create widespread inversions ahead of the front.

Cold Fronts

A cold front marks the surface boundary between cool air that is advancing toward more stationary warmer air. The cool air wedges under the warm air and forces it aloft in a very steep gradient. An inversion may appear in a very narrow band no more than 125 km behind the advancing

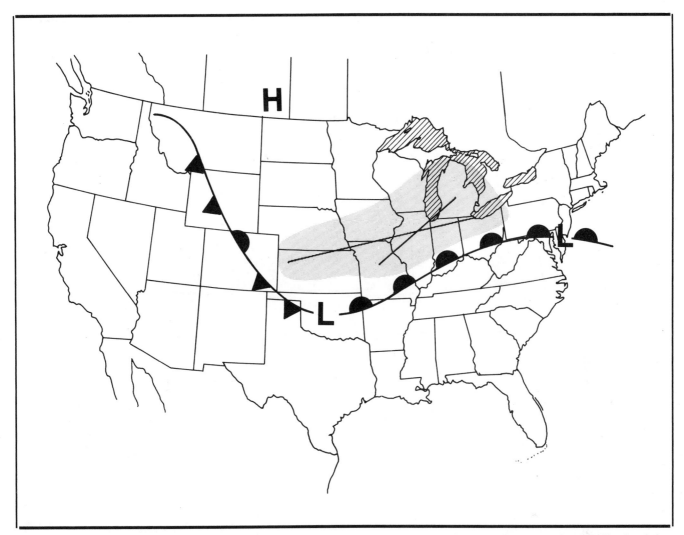

Fig 18—Broad inversion area created ahead of a winter warm front that was moving slowly northward. Much of the ground in the north was snow covered, and dense fog blanketed the region. UHF paths remained open all day. Based on reports of February 15, 1979.

cold front. The often sharp differences in temperature and moisture between the cool and warm air masses in a typical cold front suggest that the inversion might be strong, but this is usually not the case. Cold fronts are quite unstable. They almost always produce precipitation, and in warmer months when the contrasts between the two air masses is likely to be great, high winds, thunderstorms, and tornadoes are common. The stability required to sustain useful inversions is destroyed by the front itself.

In spite of the unstable nature of cold fronts, the passage of a cold front sometimes brings a very brief period of enhanced conditions. On rare occasions, inversions may be stable enough to sustain a few hours of ducting. Fig 19 shows such a case. The springtime cold front moved quickly south, spawning violent thunderstorms and high winds. Immediately after its early morning passage through the Midwest, VHF and UHF radio paths in the 1000-km range opened for about three hours in a narrow corridor behind the front.

Evaporation Inversions

All of the tropospheric inversions considered so far have depended primarily on temperature to create the large dN/m necessary for superrefraction. Moisture played a secondary, though sometimes crucial, contribution to the change in the refractive index. Superrefraction caused by *evaporation inversions* are sustained almost totally by changes in moisture content with altitude. Evaporation inversions form best over bodies of water with surface temperatures of at least 30 °C. The air within a few meters of the water's surface is saturated because of rapid evaporation, while the air above holds considerably less water. Evaporation inversions reach altitudes of only 3 meters under calm conditions, but with winds of 35 km/hr, inversions may reach altitudes as high as 12 to 20 meters. Inversions sustained almost totally by a rapid decrease in moisture with altitude can create a dN/m greater than 0.157. The shallowness of the resulting inversion also means that evaporation inversions usually have a cut-off

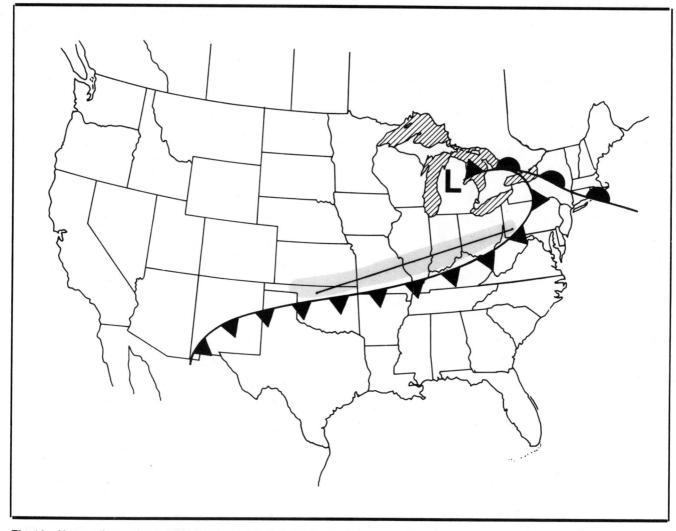

Fig 19—Narrow inversion created behind an early summer cold front. The front moved rapidly southward. UHF paths were open just behind the front for about three hours.

frequency higher than 3.3 GHz.

Evaporation inversions may be an almost constant daytime feature of warm water areas, such as the Mediterranean Sea, the Gulf of Mexico, the Caribbean, and other tropical oceans during the summer. Stations hoping to use evaporation ducts must locate themselves at sea level right on the beach. Water-vapor absorption will probably be the limiting factor in evaporation duct propagation at 24 GHz and higher, making 5.6 GHz and 10 GHz the most useful for this mode.

TROPOSPHERIC SCATTERING

A large portion of beyond-the-horizon UHF and microwave contacts are made via scattering within the troposphere, though many casual operators may not be aware they frequently use a scattering mode. Troposcatter takes place within the turbulent lower 10 km of the atmosphere, which contains three-fourths of the total atmospheric mass. It relies on the refractions from small variations in the index of refraction of air, clouds, dust, and other naturally occurring particles. There are also other types of atmospheric scattering. UHF and microwave signals can be scattered by rain, hail, and snow. Lightning can also be used as the basis of scatter paths. Even emphemeral phenomena, such as volcanoes that spew tons of material into the troposphere, may support unusual UHF and microwave paths. Each of these propagation phenomena are discussed in turn.

Troposcatter

Troposcatter is an important factor when stations are separated by beyond-the-horizon distances. If their antennas are pointed along the great circle (direct) path between them at a low angle, their beams will intersect a common volume of air that lies near the center of the path. Fig 20 shows the general geometry of a typical troposcatter path. A small portion of the signal passing through the troposphere at any point along the way is scattered, but only that part scattered within the atmospheric volume common to both stations is useful for communications.

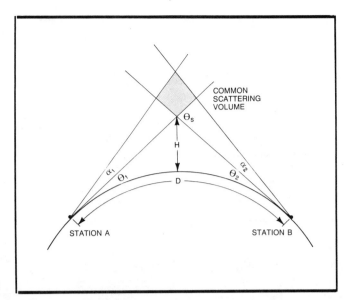

Fig 20—Troposcatter path geometry shows the elevation angles of stations A and B (θ_1, θ_2) and the half-power beam widths of the antennas used by both stations (α_1, α_2).

Assuming that the maximum altitude of the troposphere useful for scattering lies at about 10 km, a simple application of the distance to horizon equation, Eq 2, will show that the maximum distance that could be covered by tropospheric scattering is about 800 km. In practice, the maximum path distance is often considerably less than 800 km because of losses involved in the scattering process itself.

The path loss involved with tropo-scattered signals is the sum of free-space, atmospheric, and scattering losses. The scattering loss can be approximated with the following calculation.

$$L_s = 21 + 10\theta_s + 10 \log f + L_c \qquad \text{(Eq 25)}$$

where

L_s = scattering loss, dB
θ_s = scattering angle, degrees
f = frequency, MHz
L_c = aperture-to-medium coupling loss, dB

This formula assumes that antennas on both ends of the scatter path have clear views of a distant horizon.[13]

Several of the terms require further calculation. The scattering angle can be derived from the distance between the stations and the angle of elevation above the horizon of the two stations' antennas.

$$\theta_s = 0.005d + (\theta_1 + \theta_2) \qquad \text{(Eq 26)}$$

where

d = distance between the stations, kilometers
θ_1 = antenna elevation of first station, degrees
θ_2 = antenna elevation of second station, degrees

The aperture-to-medium coupling term accounts for the beamwidths of the two antennas and losses involved in the differences between them. It is calculated by

$$L_c = 2 + \frac{2\theta_s}{\sqrt{\alpha_1 \alpha_2}} \qquad \text{(Eq 27)}$$

where

α_1 = half-power beamwidth of one antenna, degrees
α_2 = half-power beamwidth of the second antenna, degrees

The half-power beamwidth can be derived from antenna gain, if horizontal and vertical beamwidth planes are assumed approximately equal. The required equation is

$$\alpha = \sqrt{\frac{1}{\text{antilog} \dfrac{G_a}{10}}} \qquad \text{(Eq 28)}$$

where

α = half-power beamwidth, degrees
G_a = antenna gain, dBi

Alternately, half-power beamwidths can be taken directly from Fig 21.

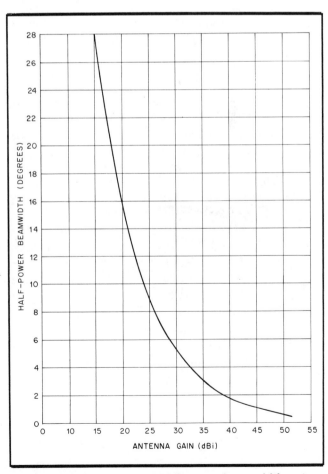

Fig 21—Antenna gain and half-power beamwidth.

Now that the basic formula for scattering loss has been defined in readily accessible terms, it can be rearranged and combined with the free-space path loss Eq 5 to derive a single expression that considers the two major components of loss for any troposcatter path. The combined losses can be calculated by

$$L_{sf} = 55.5 + 20 \log d + 30 \log f + 0.05d$$
$$+ 10 (\theta_1 + \theta_2) + \sqrt{\frac{2\theta_s}{\alpha_1 \alpha_2}} \qquad \text{(Eq 29)}$$

where L_{sf} = combined free-space and scatter loss in dB.

An inspection of this equation shows that for small antenna elevations, the bulk of the scattering path loss depends only on distance and frequency. The next-to-last term in the equation adjusts for antenna elevation and reveals a simple relationship. For each degree either antenna is raised above the horizon, the total path loss increases by 10 dB.

The last term, which consists of the residuals from the aperture-to-medium coupling loss term, also reveals some interesting characteristics of scatter loss. Further losses are incurred when the scattering angle increases, equivalent to raising antenna elevations, but it also appears that as antenna beamwidths increase, scattering losses should drop. This is a misleading conclusion, because there is a concurrent loss in total system performance with reduced antenna gain. Decreasing the beamwidth, that is increasing antenna gain, increases total system performance at a faster rate than is lost through the scattering mechanism. This relationship holds true until antenna beamwidth is approximately equal to the scattering angle. For antennas at effective 1° elevations above the horizon, the scattering angle is between 2.5 and 6° for distances of 100 to 800 km. In this quite typical case for amateur communications, there is little to be gained from using antennas with beamwidths smaller than 3°.

A Troposcatter Example

What would be the expected losses from a troposcatter path of 400 km at 3.3 GHz, using two small dish antennas with 30 dBi gain and a clear horizon at 1° elevation? The two auxiliary terms, antenna beamwidth and scattering angle need be determined first. From Eq 28, the antenna beamwidth is

$$\alpha = 164 \sqrt{\frac{1}{\text{antilog}\left(\frac{30}{10}\right)}} = 5.2°$$

The scattering angle from Eq 26 is

$$\theta_s = 0.005 \times 400 + (1 + 1) = 4°$$

Substituting all the variables into Eq 29 results in

$$L_{sf} = 55.5 + 20 \log 400 + 30 \log 3300 +$$
$$(0.05 \times 400) + 10 (1 + 1) + \frac{2 \times 4}{\sqrt{5.2 \times 5.2}}$$
$$= 254.6 \text{ dB}$$

Since atmospheric absorption is negligible at 3.3 GHz, the total loss expected is about 255 dB. Scatter problems can also be solved graphically using Fig 22 for average conditions.

At 10 GHz and higher, atmospheric absorption must be added to the total free space and scattering loss figure to derive an accurate total path loss. The method used for calculating atmospheric absorption in the previous section assumed that the total path lay within 1 km of the Earth's surface. For paths of 250 km and shorter, the scattering

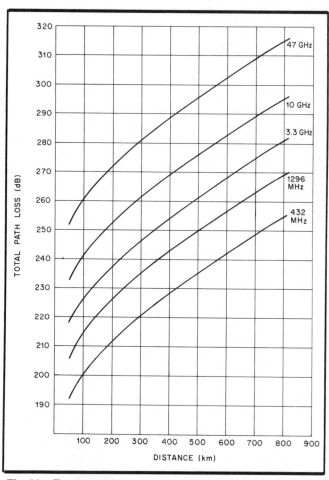

Fig 22—Troposcatter path losses include free-space losses but not attenuation caused by water vapor and oxygen absorption. Calculations assume antenna beamwidths of 5° (equivalent to antenna gains of 30 dBi) and antenna elevations of 1° above clear horizons.

volume does lie within 1 km altitude, so the atmospheric absorption calculated in this manner will be reasonably accurate. Part of the path lies above 1 km in longer troposcatter paths. The air at higher altitudes is less dense and normally drier than closer to the Earth, thus attenuation of microwave signals will be slightly less than the calculated figure.

Rain Scatter

Rain also makes an effective scattering medium over a limited range of microwave frequencies. Amateurs in Great Britain have used rain scatter over short, non-optical paths on 5.7 and 10 GHz, but relatively little precise information is known about forward scattering from rain.[14] Experiences from radar backscattering studies of various forms of precipitation are useful for suggesting some quantitative limits.

The practical frequency limits for rain scatter are probably between 1000 MHz and 10 GHz. At the lower frequency, the wavelength is appreciably greater than the dimensions of raindrops, and rain becomes an exceedingly inefficient scattering medium. At 10 GHz and higher, losses caused by absorption by rain and water vapor are excessive. Maximum theoretical distance for rain scatter is on the order of 700 km, derived simply as a function of the highest altitude rain is usually encountered, about 8 km. This is no doubt a highly optimistic estimate, but it probably marks extreme practical limits.

Expected path loss caused by rain scatter can only be approximated. Rain scatter losses are in addition to free-space attenuation, which must be considered separately. Rain scattering losses in Fig 23 are derived from figures used to estimate backscattering intensities from an area of rain 1 km in extent. At the upper frequency limit of rain scattering, forward scatter losses are somewhat less than the figures given in Fig 23. At the lower frequencies,

forward scatter losses are apt to be greater. The graphs should thus be used as a guide rather than as a precise calculation of expected losses. Rain intensities and the extent of rain will probably be estimates in any practical application.

As rainfall intensifies, scatter losses decrease. This is primarily because the average size of raindrops increase with the rate of rainfall, and the total mass of water in the atmosphere is greater. Both factors increase scattering efficiency. Most areas of rain will be greater than the 1 km assumed in the graphs. Thunderstorm cells average 8 to 10 km in diameter and rain is often distributed over a wider extent than this. It could be expected that path losses will decrease as the extent of rain increases, but this hypothesis needs testing.

Rain scatter is probably most useful over short obstructed paths and may extend the distances of beyond-the-horizon paths. General techniques and considerations that applied for troposcatter would work nearly as well for forward rain scatter. Useful rain-scatter paths may not necessarily be limited to where rain lies directly along the great-circle path, because backscattering is also an important component of rain scatter. Oblique rain-scatter paths might be possible by pointing antennas toward an area of rain within sight of both stations, but not necessarily along the direct path between them.

Snow, Hail, and Particle Scatter

Less is known about the scattering properties of snow and hail. Ice crystals make a much less efficient scattering medium than water drops. Scattering by snow and hail is therefore appreciably less than rain of the same intensity. Wet snow and partially melted hail, in contrast, may be nearly as good scattering media as rain.

Under unusual circumstances, other particles may be found in the atmosphere of sufficient size and density to make a good scattering medium. Smoke and dust particles are too small to scatter even the shortest wavelengths on their own, but material spewed up by a volcano might provide an interesting and novel opportunity for UHF and microwave scattering.

Lightning Scatter

Reports of lightning scatter have been rare in the frequencies above 432 MHz and little is known about its characteristics. The apparent scattering medium is the narrow cylinder of ionized air created by the high potential of the lightning strokes. Lightning scatter may support short-duration contacts up to 1000 km on 432 MHz and possibly higher in frequency. Lightning-scatter contacts on 144 and 432 MHz have been made over distances up to 725 km for 25 seconds at a time. Doppler shift was evident. The most useful lightning would appear to be cloud-to-cloud types high in thunderstorms.

IONOSPHERIC MODES

Familiar ionospheric F- and E-layer reflections, including sporadic-E, are unknown in the UHF and micro-

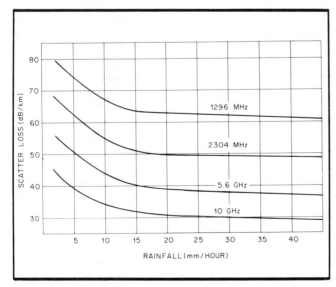

Fig 23—Scattering losses created by rain.

wave spectrum. The highest observed maximum usable frequency for F-layer reflections is about 70 MHz. Sporadic-E has been observed at 220 MHz on rare occasions, but no higher. Even so, the ionosphere plays a limited role in propagation in the lower reaches of the UHF spectrum. Aurora, meteor scatter, and trans-equatorial spread-F have all been observed at 432 MHz. Propagation via field-aligned irregularities may also be possible at 432 MHz, although it has not yet been observed.

Aurora

Scattering from the aurora borealis, or northern lights (aurora australis in the southern hemisphere) has been widely used in the VHF bands for several decades. By pointing directional antennas toward the center of aurora activity, contacts over 2000 km have been made (measured in terms of direct path distance) on 144 MHz and up to 1900 km on 432 MHz. Although there are no reported auroral contacts on 1296 MHz, it is well within the reach of well-equipped stations. Much has been written about aurora and VHF propagation that are useful for aurora propagation at 432 MHz and higher.[15] Station requirements will be greater in the UHF range, signal strength will be considerably weaker than on 144 MHz, and Doppler shift will be more evident.

The appearance of aurora is closely linked to solar activity. During massive solar storms, high-energy streams of electrons and protons spew out from the sun. The Earth's magnetic field traps these highly energized ions in the northern and southern magnetic polar regions. In turn, these particles ionize atmospheric gases as high as several hundred kilometers altitude. Aurora are usually visible because ionized gas molecules reradiate energy in the light spectrum as they recombine. Green, blue, white, and red curtains, streamers, and patches may be seen as far south as the Gulf Coast once every few years. In addition to providing colorful displays, auroral electrons descending from high in the atmosphere dramatically raise the ion density of the E-layer, where they are prevented from making any further descent. This E-layer ionization is often sufficient to scatter UHF radio signals.

Because radio aurora is a phenomenon restricted to the E-layer, UHF stations hoping to make aurora scatter contacts must be no further than 1000 km south of auroral activity, otherwise the aurora will be below the stations' radio horizon. Stations generally point their antennas north (in the northern hemisphere) when aurora is suspected and probe for the strongest signals. Offsets to the east and west may be considerable when the aurora is close to either station. Signals are scattered back toward the transmitter over a very wide angle, allowing contacts with stations up to 2000 km east or west, although 1000 km is probably more typical at 432 MHz. Signals will appear to be very wide and mushy, evidence of multiple Doppler shifting. CW is generally the only mode that can be used successfully.

Signal strength will be much reduced from levels heard on 144 MHz, given comparable equipment and conditions.

Scattered power from aurora varies as the seventh power of wavelength. For comparable stations, 432 MHz signals will be approximately 33 dB weaker than at 144 MHz. This is still within the reach of moderately equipped stations. Indeed, 432-MHz stations with as little as 10 W output have made aurora contacts. At 1296 MHz and higher, signal levels will be at least 67 dB below that heard on 144 MHz. Probably only 1296-MHz stations of EME capabilities will be able to work all but the most intense aurora.

Aurora activity can be anticipated. It occurs most often around the spring and fall equinoxes, that is during March-April and September-October, but spectacular aurora have appeared in all months of the year. Auroral radio activity generally peaks between 1600 and 2000 local time and then again between 0000 and 0300. Stations as far south as a line extending roughly from Virginia through Kentucky, Missouri, Colorado, and Oregon can expect to work aurora several times a year. Stations further north can make use of aurora more often.

Reports of solar geomagnetic activity issued hourly by WWV provide early warning of aurora. At 18 minutes after each hour, a recorded voice reports on past and present conditions and makes a prediction for the following 24-hour period. Aurora often accompany geomagnetic storms. The hourly WWV reports take note of existing and expected storms and evaluate geomagnetic conditions in terms of two indexes. The K index is a measure of geomagnetic activity for the previous three hours and varies between 0 and 9. The A index is an average value for the preceding eight K values, but calculated on a different scale that varies between 0 and 400. A K index of 4 and an A index of 30 are indications that a geomagnetic storm is in progress. The likelihood of aurora increases as the two index numbers rise. The Space Environmental Services Center also makes predictions of solar geomagnetic activity for a month in advance.[16] These predictions are published weekly and are often abstracted in amateur journals and newsletters. Solar storms often recur on a 27- to 28-day cycle, matching the sun's rotation. This phenomenon can also be used to anticipate the recurrence of auroral conditions.

Meteor Scatter

Contacts via reflections from the ionized trails left as meteors speed through the ionosphere are common at 50 and 144 MHz, but they are rare as high as 432 MHz. Contacts up to 2000 km are theoretically possible on 432 MHz, although the usual distances for those completing contacts are considerably shorter. Meteor scatter is unlikely using amateur equipment at 1296 MHz and higher.

Meteor scatter is made possible when very small particles, ranging in size from grains of sand to pea-sized, enter the Earth's upper atmosphere at high velocity. Their kinetic energy is sufficient to ionize a long column of air in the E-layer before they are completely evaporated. Meteor trails commonly last for only a few seconds at most, but large meteors may create trails that last for a minute and extend more than 20 km in length.

Radio signals in the 30- to 100-MHz range are reflected best by these briefly ionized columns, but the effect extends into the UHF range. Reflected power varies as the third power of wavelength in the VHF range and as the sixth power of wavelength in the UHF range. Duration varies as the square of wavelength. A 432-MHz meteor-scatter signal will thus be weaker by at least 27 dB and last only about one-eighth as long as a comparable 144-MHz signal. A typical good meteor burst might last 5 to 10 seconds and peak 40 dB out of the noise on 144 MHz. A 432-MHz signal reflected from that same meteor trail might last just 1 second and peak 13 dB above the noise at best.

Hundreds of thousands of meteors enter the Earth's atmosphere randomly every day, but only a few have the required orientation to the Earth, velocity, size, and position to be useful for UHF communication. Techniques similar to those used on 144 MHz have met with some success in making use of meteors on 432 MHz.[17] Given the marginal conditions for 432-MHz scatter, the best opportunities to complete UHF meteor scatter contacts are during one of the great annual meteor showers. Meteor showers occur when the Earth crosses one of the relatively stable streams of meteors that orbits the sun. The most productive meteor showers are the Perseids (August 12-13), Geminids (December 12-13), and the Quadrantids (January 3). Meteors are up to 10 times more numerous during these three showers than at non-shower periods. Prearranged schedules during one of the peak periods will significantly increase the chances of success.

Transequatorial Spread-F

Discovered in 1947, transequatorial spread-F (TE) makes possible contacts up to 8000 km across the equator in the VHF and UHF range, at least up to 432 MHz. Stations engaged in TE propagation must be roughly equidistant from the geomagnetic equator. Many contacts have been made on 144 MHz between southern Europe and South Africa, Japan and Australia, and Venezuela and the Caribbean with Argentina and Paraguay. Similar paths have been covered on 220 MHz and heard on 432 MHz, although no confirmed, two-way 432-MHz contacts have been made yet.

Unfortunately for most continental United States stations, the magnetic equator dips far to the south in the western hemisphere (Fig 24). Only the most southerly part of the United States lies within the maximum 4000 km of the magnetic equator. Contacts on 432 MHz from the southeastern part of the country may be possible with Argentina and southern Chile.

The physical mechanisms of TE are not well understood. The most popular hypothesis suggests that during the years of peak sunspot activity, the F layer within 15° north and south of the magnetic equator bulges and intensifies slightly. The maximum usable frequency (MUF) late in the day may increase to 1.5 times the daytime level. Coupled with the slight tilting of the ionosphere, VHF and

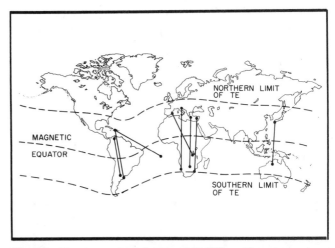

Fig 24—Transequatorial spread-F (TE) paths on 144 MHz. Note the symmetrical distribution of stations north and south of the magnetic equator. The path between Puerto Rico and Ascension Island across the mid-Atlantic suggests that a Florida to South Africa path might be possible, even on 432 MHz.

UHF signals may be refracted twice over the equator at smaller than critical angles, but creating a path nearly twice as long as the one-hop, F-layer contact common at high frequencies. Fig 25 depicts the presumed geometry of such an explanation.

Experience with TE indicates that it peaks during high sunspot years between 1700 and 2200 local time.[18] Signals have a rough aurora-like note. High power and large antennas are not required to work TE on 144 MHz, and it is likely that 432-MHz stations will make TE contacts with as little as 100 W and four Yagis.

Field-Aligned Irregularities

Propagation via field-aligned irregularities (FAI) have been observed on 50 and 144 MHz only since 1978.[19] FAI may be possible on 432 MHz as well, but none has been reported. FAI appears during, and up to an hour or two following, intense episodes of sporadic-E on 50 MHz. Intense patches of ionization associated with FAI lie in the E layer and is thought to be closely associated with sporadic-E clouds. Stations attempting to use FAI point their antennas toward a common scattering area corresponding to a known sporadic-E reflecting center. This is often off the great circle path. Fig 26 shows a typical FAI path geometry on 144 MHz that may duplicate a possible 432-MHz path as well.

Signals are weak and fluttery, although levels vary over a wide range. On some 144 MHz-paths, operators have observed Doppler-like shifts of 3 kHz on received signals. Stations running 100 W and single Yagis have worked FAI on 144 MHz. Maximum distances appear to be the same as for other types of E-layer propagation, about 2000 km.

The upper frequency limit of FAI is unknown, but it has been observed as low as 19 MHz and as high as

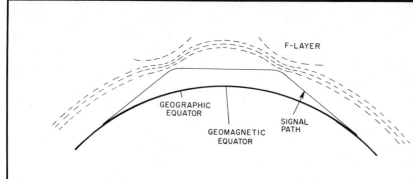

Fig 25—Cross-section of a transequatorial spread-F signal path, showing the effects of ionospheric tilting and the double reflection.

Fig 26—Typical field-aligned irregularities (FAI) scatter path geometry on 144 MHz. Similar paths may be possible on 432 MHz when sporadic-E is especially intense.

200 MHz. The best probability for 432-MHz FAI will come from cooperating pairs of well-equipped stations. Antennas should be pointed toward known centers of intense sporadic-E activity for an hour or so following E-skip on 50 MHz. Coordination could be maintained, perhaps using 50- or 144-MHz FAI.

REFLECTIONS

Metal objects, such as buildings, water towers, and airplanes are large enough to make effective reflectors of UHF and microwaves. British amateurs have made systematic use of gas storage tanks and industrial complexes to complete short microwave paths in crowded urban environments. Occasional reports of contacts made via airplane reflections indicate that paths in the 300- to 700-km range are also practical.[20] The general technique is simple. Two stations simply point their antennas toward a common reflector, whether stationary or moving. The reflecting object must be line-of-sight to both stations and be large enough to serve as an efficient reflector at UHF and microwave frequencies. The classic radar equation provides a theoretical basis for evaluating both stationary and moving reflectors.

The Radar Equation

The radar equation may be applied to a communications path completed by a reflection to calculate total path loss.

$$P_r = \frac{P_t G_t}{4\pi R_t^2} + \frac{G_r \lambda^2 S}{(4\pi)^2 R_r^2} \qquad \text{(Eq 30)}$$

where

P_t = transmitted power, watts
P_r = received power, watts
G_t = transmitter antenna gain, as a ratio
G_r = receiver antenna gain, as a ratio
R_t = range from transmitter to reflector, meters
R_r = range from reflector to receiver, meters
λ = wavelength, meters
S = radar cross section of reflector, square meters (m²)

The equation can be simplified by reducing the power and gain terms to unity and rewriting for dB path loss.

$$L_r = 10 \log \left(\frac{\lambda^2 S}{R_t^2 \, R_r^2} \right) - 153 \qquad \text{(Eq 31)}$$

where

L_r = total loss of a reflected path, dB
d_1 = distance of first station to reflector, kilometers
d_2 = distance of second station to reflector, kilometers

This modified equation for one-reflection path loss takes into account free-space losses.

The radar cross section of reflectors is often difficult to determine accurately. The easiest cases are simple geometric objects with dimensions that are large in relation to wavelength, assuming that reflections are perpendicular to the object's surface. The radar cross section of a flat plane given these assumptions is

$$S_p = \frac{4\pi a}{\lambda^2} \qquad \text{(Eq 32)}$$

where

S_p = radar cross section of a flat plane in m^2
a = geometric area of the plane in m^2

For a cylinder, the equation is

$$S_c = \frac{2\pi r \ell^2}{\lambda} \qquad \text{(Eq 33)}$$

where

S_c = radar cross section of a cylinder, m^2
r = radius of the cylinder, meters
ℓ = length of the cylinder, meters

And for a sphere the equation is

$$S_s = \pi r^2 \qquad \text{(Eq 34)}$$

where

S_s = radar cross section of a sphere, m^2
r = radius of the sphere, meters

These idealized radar cross sections of simple objects have limited practical use. In most cases, the radar cross section of an object is much smaller than the values these equations yield. When the object is large relative to wavelength, the radar cross section is essentially independent of frequency and orientation to the incident signal. Average practical radar cross sections can be approximated as half the geometric surface area if no better figure can be found.

Airplane Reflections

Radar cross sections of various aircraft types are given in Table 8. These figures can be used directly with Eq 30 for estimating total path loss. The total path loss at 1296 MHz for a single reflection from a Boeing 747 midway along a 500-km path is

$$L_r = 10 \log\left(\frac{0.23^2 \times 63}{250^2 \times 250^2}\right) - 153 = 243.7 \text{ dB}$$

Losses vary directly with the radar cross section of the airplane. If the radar cross section is increased or decreased by a factor of 10, the path losses also vary by 10 dB. Expected path loss for an average-sized commercial aircraft 10 m^2, located midway between stations separated by 100 to 800 km, for various frequencies, can be obtained directly from Fig 27. These graphs provide the worst-case placement for the aircraft. If the airplane is significantly closer to one station or the other, path loss is considerably less, but so is maximum total path distance for a given aircraft altitude.

Total path loss may be a limiting factor on the higher microwave bands, especially above 10 GHz where atmospheric losses must be added in as well. The maximum altitude that aircraft fly is probably a more important consideration in the UHF range. Few aircraft fly at altitudes higher than 12,000 meters. At that height, the radio horizon is 455 km distant, suggesting that the extreme limit of

Table 8
Radar Cross Sections of Selected Aircraft

Aircraft	Radar Cross Section (square meters, m^2)
Lear Jet	2
Douglas DC-9	8
Boeing 707	16
Boeing 747	63

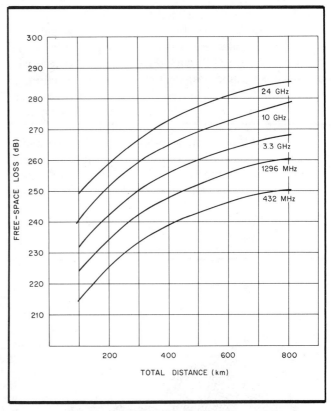

Fig 27—Maximum free-space path loss for a reflection from a single airplane at midpath with a radar cross section of 10 square meters.

single-reflection aircraft propagation is no more than about 900 km. Even this extreme distance may not be attainable. Attenuation is highest when the reflector is at midpath, and the airplane would be above the mutual horizon of both stations for only a few seconds at best. Under actual conditions, perhaps 600 to 800 km would be a more realistic maximum path distance. Doppler shift can be expected. Rockets and satellites might seem to hold promise of much greater range because of their extreme altitudes, but an application of the radar equation will show that losses are unacceptably high for relatively small objects at great distances.

Stationary Reflectors

Much larger and more efficient reflectors can be found in the man-made landscape or be erected specifically for the purpose. If reflectors on hilltops and mountains are used, distances worked via stationary object reflections can be 200 km and more. Water towers, for example, might be ideal reflector targets because they are usually very large in terms of wavelength, made of metal, and almost always mounted on high terrain. In general, the best stationary reflectors are large metal objects with simple geometries, such as planes and spheres, at elevated locations.

The radar equation can also be used for estimating path loss for ground-based reflectors. Radar cross sections of targets would have to be estimated. For large angles of reflection, the radar cross sections may approach the values obtained from Eq 31 through Eq 33. For small objects with complicated geometries, shallow angles of reflection, or targets at extended distances, the airplane model that approximates radar cross section as half the surface area of the reflector may provide a more realistic assessment.

Great advantage can be realized by placing one station as close as possible to the reflector and using large angles of reflection. A station nestled in the bottom of a valley, for example, may be able to use reflections from a water tower located on a nearby ridge to complete paths that were otherwise impossible. Specially designed reflectors could be erected in strategic locations just for this purpose. A large curved screen could serve several microwave bands over a large geographic area if a location was chosen carefully. Clusters of specially designed corner reflectors, a most efficient arrangement for radio reflection, might also be a worthy project. Reflecting screen design, sites, expected path losses, and other factors would have to be thoroughly tested before a permanent installation was made.

OBSTACLE LOSSES

Simple geometric analysis of radio paths might lead to the conclusion that a large obstacle, such as a mountain, would be an insurmountable barrier to a microwave path. It might further be assumed that any object not in the direct signal path between two stations would have little or no effect on communications. Both statements are not necessarily true. Microwave signals can be diffracted around mountains and other geographical features, and large objects that do not actually obstruct the line-of-sight path can reduce received power by 20 dB or more.

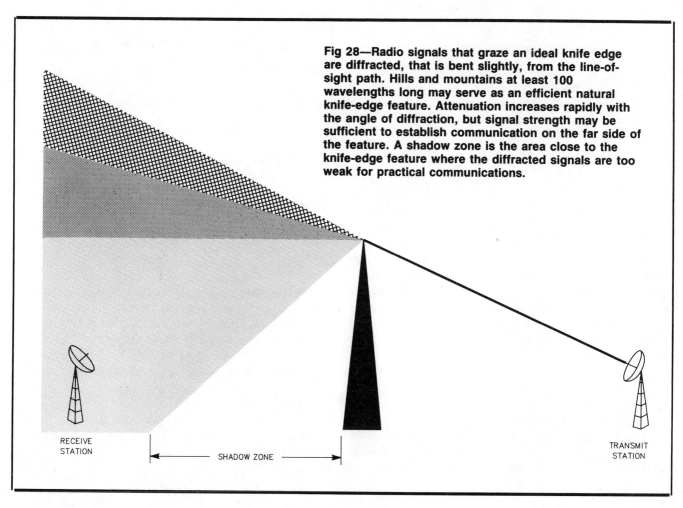

Fig 28—Radio signals that graze an ideal knife edge are diffracted, that is bent slightly, from the line-of-sight path. Hills and mountains at least 100 wavelengths long may serve as an efficient natural knife-edge feature. Attenuation increases rapidly with the angle of diffraction, but signal strength may be sufficient to establish communication on the far side of the feature. A shadow zone is the area close to the knife-edge feature where the diffracted signals are too weak for practical communications.

RECEIVE STATION

SHADOW ZONE

TRANSMIT STATION

Knife-Edge Diffraction

Radio signals can be diffracted over and around the peaks of well-defined ridges and mountains. High losses accompany diffraction paths, but even with the 20 to 50 dB additional attenuation, a path may be completed that otherwise would be impossible.

Knife-edge diffraction, as this phenomenon is called, is common to radio, light, and other electromagnetic radiation. Consider a radio-wave front approaching a thin plate many wavelengths long perpendicular to the signal path (Fig 28). Some of the radio energy is diffracted in all directions as it grazes the knife-edge plane. Signal levels decrease rapidly as the angle of diffraction increases. Even so, the tiny amount of signal that is diffracted behind the barrier can be useful in knife-edge diffraction propagation.

A clearly defined ridge, mountain, or hill a few hundred wavelengths long is a close enough approximation of a knife-edge plane at UHF and microwave frequencies. The ridge need not have a sharp peak, as rounded hills have served well in actual cases, but the knife-edge feature should have a sharp profile that is free of trees and other objects absorbent in microwave frequencies.

The losses involved in knife-edge propagation are a function of wavelength, distance between the stations and the knife-edge feature, and the height of the knife edge above the average elevation of the two stations. Fig 29 shows these relationships. The calculations of losses caused by diffraction assume that distance d_1 is at least 10 times the height of the knife-edge feature. The ridge or mountain should be at least 100 wavelengths high to serve as a effective knife edge.

Attenuation over a knife-edge diffraction feature varies as

$$\sqrt{\frac{2h^2}{\lambda}\left(\frac{1}{d_1} + \frac{1}{d_2}\right)}$$

where

    h = knife-edge height
    d_1 = distance of station closer to the knife edge
    d_2 = distance of station farther from the knife edge

In practical cases, d_2 is often much larger than d_1. As a result, $\frac{1}{d_2}$ is usually very small and can be ignored without significantly impairing accuracy. An equation that calculates knife-edge diffraction losses using this attenuation relationship can be written in terms of dB loss and adjusted for convenient measurements is

$$L_k = 20 \log\left(h\sqrt{\frac{f}{d_1}}\right) - 38.8 \qquad \text{(Eq 35)}$$

    L_k = knife-edge diffraction loss, dB
    h = elevation of the knife edge relative to the two stations, meters
    f = frequency, MHz
    d_1 = distance from the near station to the knife edge, km

Calculation of a diffraction loss for a 3.3-GHz path over

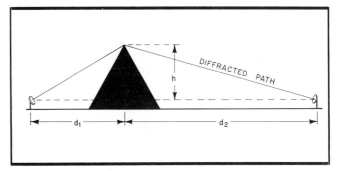

Fig 29—Knife-edge propagation path.

a 500-meter ridge, 25 km distant from the near station, is straightforward.

$$L_k = 20 \log\left(500 \sqrt{\frac{3300}{25}}\right) - 38.8 = 36.4 \text{ dB}$$

Losses in propagating a signal over the ridge will be 36.4 dB, in addition to free-space and atmospheric losses.

The computed figures are apt to be optimistic. Natural features are not ideal knife edges, although they often work surprisingly well. The computed figure will hold up over a wide range of distances on the far side of the knife-edge feature, that is as distance d_2 varies. Diffraction losses increase slightly as d_2 shortens and reaches a maximum of an additional 3 dB over the computed value when d_1 equals d_2. Knife-edge problems at 10 GHz can also be solved graphically using Fig 30. For frequencies other than

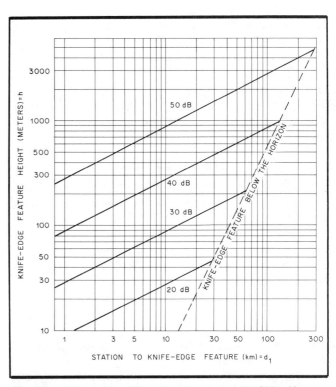

Fig 30—Knife-edge diffraction losses at 10 GHz. Use the correction factors in Table 9 for other frequencies.

Table 9

Correction Factors for Calculating Knife-Edge Diffraction Losses

Frequency	Correction Factor (dB)
432 MHz	−14
1296 MHz	−9
2304 MHz	−6
3.3 GHz	−5
5.6 GHz	−3
10 GHz	0
24 GHz	+4
47 GHz	+7
76 GHz	+9

Note: Use these correction factors in conjunction with Fig 30 to estimate knife-edge diffraction losses on frequencies other than 10 GHz.

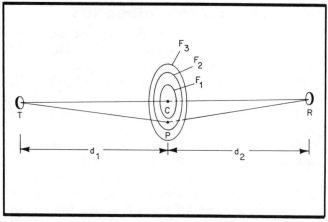

Fig 31—Fresnel zones along signal path T-R. F_1, F_2, and F_3 are the outer boundaries of the first three Fresnel zones. These concentric zones extend all along path T-R, forming an elipsoid, as depicted in Fig 32.

10 GHz, the correction factors provided in Table 9 must be added or subtracted from the values obtained from the graph.

Sometimes knife-edge diffraction is discussed in terms of total path gain.[21] It must be reasserted that diffraction aways involves significant attenuation, but in some situations obstacle gain may have relevance. For example, apparent gain may be realized when a beyond-the-horizon path obstructed by a mountain is first evaluated simply as a tropospheric path without consideration of the obstruction. When the path is reevaluated as a diffraction problem, calculated path losses may appear considerably less. Some authors treat this as net obstacle gain.

Diffraction losses diminish as the elevation of the knife edge is reduced. When the knife edge just grazes the signal path (h = 0), attenuation is still 6 dB. There is appreciable diffraction around the knife edge even when it is well below the line-of-sight path. Diffraction losses are reduced to zero only when the knife edge is well below the direct path. Understanding why this should be the case and its practical implications involves the concept of Fresnel zones.

Fresnel Zones

Consider a radio path between some transmitter T and receiver R, as shown in Fig 31, along with a diffracting knife edge at point P, some small distance in relation to wavelength from the direct path between T and R. Signals leaving T arrive at R by two separate paths. Part of the signal arrives by the direct path TCR, but a portion arrives via the diffracted path TPR. Because TPR is slightly longer than the direct path TCR, signals arriving at R by the longer route lag behind those from the direct path. The phase difference between the two signals can create destructive interference that accounts for up to 6 dB loss in signal strength at the receiver.

The phase of the signal arriving via the diffracted path TPR lags the direct signal increasingly as the distance be-

tween C and P grows. The distances between C and P that create lags of exactly one-half wavelength (180°) at the receiver form concentric rings around the direct signal path. The first three of these distances are indicated as F_1, F_2, and F_3 in Fig 31. The areas they enclose are known as Fresnel zones. The first Fresnel zone is the area in which a diffracting point causes a phase lag of up to half a wavelength at the receiver. A diffracting point within the second Fresnel zone creates a phase lag of between half a wavelength and a full wavelength, and so on indefinitely.

The dimensions of any Fresnel zone can be calculated using the following equation. For any Nth Fresnel zone,

$$F_N = 17.31 \sqrt{\frac{N(d_1 d_2)}{fd}} \qquad \text{(Eq 36)}$$

where

F_N = any Nth Fresnel zone outer boundary from the direct signal path, meters

N = any positive number

f = frequency, MHz

d_1 = distance from one station to some point along the signal path, meters

d_2 = distance from the second station to the same point along the signal path, meters

d = total path distance, meters

The first Fresnel zone boundary, or Fresnel clearance, for a 10-GHz path of 50 km, 15 km from one of the stations, is

$$F_1 = 17.31 \sqrt{\frac{1\,(15,000 \times 35,000)}{10,000 \times 50,000}} = 17.7 \text{ meters}$$

For a potential diffracting object to clear the first Fresnel zone 15 km from one of the stations, it must be at least 17.7 meters from the direct signal path. When a series of these calculations are made along a signal path, the Fresnel zone takes the shape of an elipsoid with its major axis the direct signal path. The maximum clearance distance for any zone is at midpath. This is shown in Fig 32.

Fresnel zones are useful in determining how close to a line-of-sight path a potential diffracting object may lie without causing unacceptable losses from phase interference. Fig 33 shows the loss (or sometimes gain) of a received signal, caused by phase interference, as a function of the relative distance of the diffracting object from the direct signal path. Losses are more than 25 dB when a diffracting edge is more than three Fresnel zones above the direct signal path. As the edge is lowered and approaches the zero mark (just grazing the direct path), the loss decreases to 6 dB. As the edge is moved below the signal path, losses are gradually reduced to nil at about 0.6 Fresnel zone. There is a slight gain of up to 1.2 dB with continued lowering, and then gains and losses oscillate by less than ±1 dB for all the following Fresnel zones.

The greatest Fresnel-zone losses generally occur when a diffracting object lies within the first 0.6 Fresnel zone. The losses and gains for all other Fresnel zones are small enough (1 dB or less) to be ignored. Fresnel-zone losses of up to 6 dB can be avoided by ensuring that there are no objects large enough to act as diffracting edges within the first 0.6 Fresnel zone. Topographic features and metal objects as small as several wavelengths wide can serve as troublesome diffractors. In general, the closer the object is to either station, the smaller it can be and still act as a diffractor. At a distance of a few tens of wavelengths, any metallic object of wavelength size within the first 0.6 Fresnel zone could adversely affect signal levels. Objects that do not approximate knife-edge refractors may be even more troublesome. If the object is rounded and large in relation to wavelength, losses may exceed 20 dB through several Fresnel zones.

The 0.6 Fresnel clearance for various distances along 10-GHz signal paths are graphed in Fig 34. These figures may be used directly for 10 GHz. Fig 35 provides 0.6 Fresnel clearances at midpath for several UHF and microwave bands. These worst-case curves overestimate the clearance near the ends of the paths, but they are convenient to use. It should be emphasized that Fresnel-zone clearances are important only along line-of-sight paths. In beyond-the-horizon propagation, phase relation-

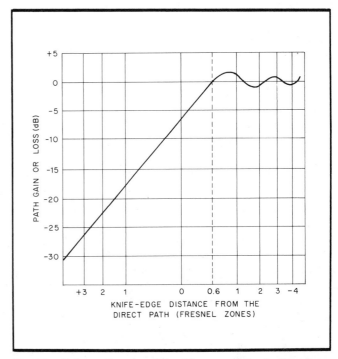

Fig 33—Gain or loss by diffraction around a knife-edge, at various distances from the signal path, measured in terms of Fresnel zones. The knife-edge obscures the direct path to the left of the zero mark, is just tangent at zero, and lies below the direct path to the right of zero.

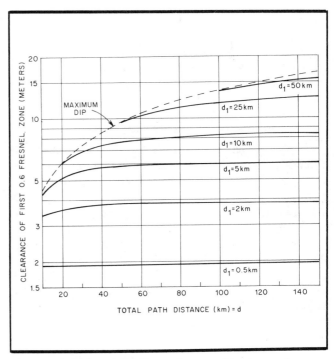

Fig 34—Calculated 0.6 Fresnel-zone clearance, at various distances and path lengths, at 10 GHz. The superimposed curve for the maximum dip (dashed line) corresponds to the 10-GHz curve in Fig 35. Total path length = d. Distance from one station to some point along the path = d_1.

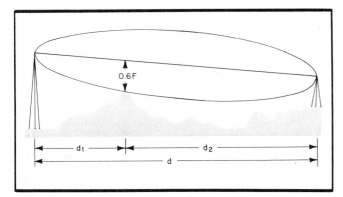

Fig 32—Clearance for 0.6 Fresnel zone.

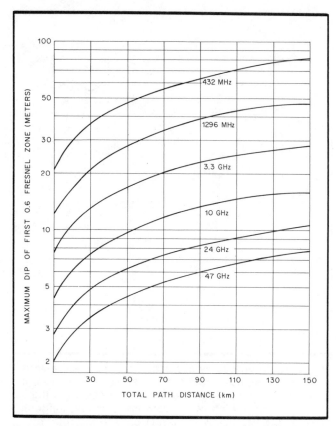

Fig 35—Maximum 0.6 Fresnel-zone clearance at various frequencies and path distances.

Table 10
Absorption by Trees

Frequency	Approximate Absorption (dB/meter)
432 MHz	0.1-0.3
1296 MHz	0.15-0.4
2304 MHz	0.25-0.5
3.3 GHz	0.4-0.6
5.6 GHz	0.5-1.5
10 GHz	1-2

Notes

[1]See the section "Tropospheric Refraction," for calculations of the k factor. For another discussion of the k factor and a computer program that calculates distance to the horizon, see Jack Priedigkeit, "A Simple Computer Model for VHF/UHF Propagation," *QST*, July 1983, pp 32-33. Standard atmospheric conditions are defined in terms of observed long-term average conditions. The temperature in a standard atmosphere declines at the rate of 6.5°C per km altitude (up to 5 km) and humidity, measured in terms of dewpoint, declines at 5.5°C per km. R. G. Barry and R. J. Chorley, *Atmosphere, Weather, and Climate*, 3rd edition (London: Methuen, 1976), pp 76-78.

[2]This is a tiny amount of power, but it can be detected in a very sensitive receiver. The received power can be used to determine the induced voltage of a signal at the input terminals of a receiver, although this is rarely done in UHF and microwave path-loss applications. The power equation (P = IE) and Ohm's Law (E = IR) can be used to determine the signal voltage. Substituting for the unknown value of current, signal voltage can be calculated from

$$E = \sqrt{PR}$$

where
   E = potential, volts
   P = power, watts
   R = resistance, ohms

For a received power of 6.3×10^{-16} W at the input of a receiver with a nominal resistance of 50 Ω, the induced voltage is 0.18 μV. In a practical situation, the transmitter power, antenna gains, and feed-line losses would have to be considered prior to calculating actual received power. For more information, see the section, Path Loss and Total System Performance.

[3]For more on the measurement and calculation of antenna gain, see Edward P. Tilton, Ed., *The Radio Amateur's VHF Manual* (Newington, CT: ARRL, 1972), pp 153-156 (out of print); and Gerald L. Hall, Ed., *The ARRL Antenna Book*, 15th edition (Newington: ARRL, 1988), Chapter 2.

[4]Further discussions of receiver system capabilities can be found in Chapter 2 of *The ARRL Handbook*; Bob Atkins, "Estimating Microwave System Performance," in Chapter 7 of this book; J. N. Gannaway, "Tropospheric Scatter Propagation," *QST*, Nov 1983, pp 46-47; D. W. Bray, "A Method for Determining V.H.F. Station Capabilities," *QST*, Nov 1961, pp 36-41, 162.

[5]More detailed discussions of tropospheric refraction are found in: G. R. Jessop, ed, *VHF/UHF Manual*, 4th edition (Potters Bar, England: RSGB, 1983), pp 2.2-2.18; Bradford R. Bean and E. J. Dutton, *Radio Meteorology* (Washington: Government Printing Office, 1966); James S. Collier, "Upper-Air Conditions for Two-Meter DX," *QST*, Sep 1955, pp 16-18; Emil Pocock, "The Weather that Brings VHF DX," *QST*, May 1985, pp 11-16.

[6]The degree to which a radio wave is refracted as it passes through the boundary between two media, such as contrasting layers of air, is dependent on the differences between their refractive indexes. A simple relationship exists among the two indexes and the angles of incidence and refraction of the radio wave relative to the boundary.

ships are influenced by many uncontrollable factors that cannot be predicted. For those with access to a computer, the PATHLOSS program (see the Appendix) automatically determines Fresnel-zone clearance and loss for UHF and microwave paths.

Near-Field Absorption

Objects that are not likely to act as knife-edge diffraction points may still cause high attenuation if they obstruct or partially obstruct the signal path. Trees, frame and brick buildings, and other objects that are nearly transparent at high frequencies are very absorbent at 432 MHz and higher. Absorption increases rapidly with frequency, but precise attenuation is difficult to calculate. The absorbent qualities of trees and buildings vary over a wide range of conditions. The losses through a brick wall at 3.3 GHz, for example, vary between 10 and 40 dB, depending on materials, thickness, and moisture. A wet brick wall is ten times more lossy at UHF and microwave frequencies than a dry one. Trees with leaves on them are more opaque than bare trees. Some indication of the magnitude of tree absorption can be gained from Table 10, but these figures cannot be considered accurate. It may be safe to assume that if light cannot penetrate a stand of trees, microwave losses will be unacceptable.

$$\frac{N_r}{N_i} = \frac{\sin(i)}{\sin(r)}$$

where

N_i = index of refraction of medium of the incident wave
N_r = index of refraction of the medium of the refracted wave
$\sin(i)$ = sine of the incident wave, normal to the boundary between the two media
$\sin(r)$ = sine of the refracted wave, normal to the boundary between the two media

The index of refraction of a medium is often stated in absolute terms by comparing the medium to a vacuum. The index of refraction of a vacuum is defined as unity. Therefore, the relationship given above can be reduced simply to

$$N = \frac{\sin(i)}{\sin(r)}$$

where

n = index of refraction of a medium
$\sin(i)$ = sine of incident wave, normal to a hypothetical boundary between a vacuum and the media
$\sin(r)$ = sine of the reflected wave, normal to the same boundary

The index of refraction of air near the earth's surface for a wide range of radio frequencies varies only between 1.0002 and 1.0004. Consequently, a radio wave is refracted considerably less than 1°. Because the radio index of refraction of air is so small, it is more convenient to express it in modified form as N units, where an N unit is defined as

$$N = (n - 1) \times 10^6$$

[7]Dewpoint, relative humidity, absolute humidity, and partial pressure of water vapor are all measurements of the amount of water vapor in the atmosphere. Dewpoint is the temperature to which a body of air must be reduced before saturation occurs, that is the point at which water just begins to precipitate as dew, rain, and so forth. The various units may be converted from one to the other. See Jessop, Ed., *VHF/UHF Manual*, pp 2.2-2.4.

[8]The cut-off frequency of inversions may be calculated from the depth of the inversion and the change in the index of refraction over that depth.

$$\lambda = 2.514 \times 10^{-3} \sqrt{\frac{dN}{m} - 0.157} \, (\sqrt{d})^3$$

where

d = inversion depth, meters
dN/m = change in N units per meter over the entire depth
λ = cutoff wavelength, meters

[9]Jessop, ed, *VHF/UHF Manual*, pp 2.2-2.28, is geared toward amateurs. Bean and Dutton, *Radio Meteorology*, is more technical.

[10]Upper-air data inquiries should be addressed to the National Oceanic and Atmospheric Administration, Environmental Data Service, National Climatic Center, Federal Building, Asheville, NC 28801.

[11]Descriptions of spectacular tropospheric openings appear regularly in The World Above 50 MHz column in *QST*, Microwaves and 4-2-70 in *Radio Communication* (the journal of the Radio Society of Great Britain), and many other amateur journals. For a description of a high-pressure opening in the United States, see James G. Botts, "A Night to Remember—and a Morning after, Too," *QST*, Jan 1970, pp 88-89. For a report of a similar event in Europe, see R. G. Flavell, "Studies of an Extensive Anticyclone Propagation Event and Some Short-Term Enhancements Observed at VHF and UHF," *DUBUS VHF/UHF/SHF Technik II* (Berlin, 1984), pp 8-17.

[12]Standard weather texts provide more discussions of global winds and climate patterns that have interesting implications for UHF and microwave propagation. For example, see Albert Miller and Jack C. Thompson, *Elements of Meteorology*, 3rd edition (Columbus, OH: Charles E. Merrill, 1979), pp 121-135; Barry and Chorley, *Atmosphere, Weather, and Climate*, pp 283-289.

[13]More extensive discussions of troposcatter are found in Gannaway, "Tropospheric Scatter."

[14]Reports of rain scatter experiments are Charles Suckling, "Rain Scatter Tests on 10 GHz," *Radio Communication*, Nov 1981,

p 1042; and Charles Suckling, "Rain Scatter on 5.7 GHz," *Radio Communication*, Oct 1982, p 434.

[15]A more complete review of aurora for Amateur Radio propagation is Richard Miller, "Radio Aurora," *QST*, Jan 1985, pp 14-18. See also Emil Pocock, "Practical Radio Aurora," *QST*, Mar 1990, pp 20-25. The K and A indexes are discussed more thoroughly in Chapter 22 of *The ARRL Handbook* and in Chapter 23 of *The ARRL Antenna Book*.

[16]"Preliminary Report and Forecast of Solar Geophysical Data" is a weekly publication of NOAA and the Space Environmental Services Center. Most university libraries and some large public libraries subscribe.

[17]Excellent works on meteor scatter are Walter F. Bain, "VHF Propagation by Meteor-Trail Ionization," *QST*, May 1974, pp 41-47, 176; Joe Reisert, "Improving Meteor Scatter Communications," *Ham Radio*, June 1984, pp 82-92; Clarke Greene, "Meteor-Scatter Communications," *QST*, Jan 1986, pp 14-17; and Michael R. Owen, "VHF Meteor Scatter—An Astronomical Perspective," *QST*, Jun 1986, pp 14-20.

[18]There are several good introductions to TE. See R. G. Cracknell, "Transequatorial Propagation of V.H.F. Signals," *QST*, Dec 1959, pp 11-17; Joseph H. Reisert and Gene Pfeffer, "A Newly Discovered Mode of VHF Propagation," *QST*, Oct 1978, pp 11-14; Ray Cracknell, et al, "The Euro-Asia to Africa VHF Transequatorial Circuit during Solar Cycle 21," *QST*, Nov 1981, pp 31-36, Dec 1981, pp 23-27.

[19]For more on FAI, see Thomas F. Kneisel, "Ionospheric Scatter by Field-Aligned Irregularities at 144 MHz," *QST*, Jan 1982, pp 30-32.

[20]Results of tests with stationary reflectors can be found in Charles Suckling, "Using Passive Reflectors to Work Obstructed Paths," *Radio Communication*, Jan 1981, p 47; and "10 GHz Tests Using Reflections from Obstacles," *DUBUS VHF/UHF/SHF Technik II*, pp 33-34. Experiments with aircraft reflections are discussed in Doug McArthur, "Aircraft Enhancement of VHF/UHF Signals," *Amateur Radio* (Australia), Jul 1985, pp 4-6; and Charles Suckling, "Aircraft Scatter Propagation," *Radio Communication*, May 1983, p 434.

[21]Julian H. Craig, "Obstacle Gain Techniques for 50 MHz and Higher," *QST*, Mar 1958, pp 18-21.

GENERAL REFERENCES

Attwood, Stephen, ed., *Radio Wave Propagation* (New York: Academic Press, 1949).

Bean, Bradford R. and E. J. Dutton, *Radio Meteorology* (Washington: Government Printing Office, 1966).

Boithias, Lucien, *Radio Wave Propagation* (New York: McGraw-Hill, 1987).

David, P. and J. Voge, *Propagation of Radio Waves* (Oxford: Pergamon, 1969).

Davies, Kenneth, *Ionospheric Radio Propagation* (Washington: US Government Printing Office, 1966).

Engineering Considerations for Microwave Communications (San Carlos, CA: GTE Lenkurt, 1975).

Harvey, A. F., *Microwave Engineering* (London: Academic Press, 1963).

Jessop, G. R., ed., *VHF/UHF Manual* (Potters Bar, England: RSGB, 1983).

Kerr, Donald C., ed., *Propagation of Short Radio Waves* (New York: McGraw-Hill, 1951).

Livingston, Donald C., *The Physics of Microwave Propagation* (Englewood Cliffs, NJ: Prentice-Hall, 1970).

Reference Data for Engineers: Radio, Electronics, Computer and Communications, 7th edition (Indianapolis: Howard Sams, 1985).

Skolnik, Merrill, ed., *Introduction to Radar Systems* (New York: McGraw-Hill, 1980).

Practical Line-of-Sight Path Evaluation

By Dennis L. Haarsager, N7DH
1171 Border Ln
Moscow, ID 83843

Repeater communications, amateur television, high-speed data links, and remote control of distant stations are among many applications of reliable point-to-point amateur microwave communications. This section provides a practical step-by-step procedure for evaluating the reliability of line-of-sight UHF and microwave paths. It includes analysis of path profiles created from topographical maps, calculation of the radio index of refraction, application of the effective Earth radius factor, Fresnel-zone interference, path attenuation, and precise calculations of distance and azimuth. Consideration of each of these areas is necessary to evaluate properly line-of-sight paths.

Path Profile

The terrain along a proposed radio path, such as between two hill tops, may be analyzed by using topographical maps published by the United States Geological Survey.[1] In the United States, topographical maps are generally available covering 7.5′ per side ("7.5-minute topographical maps"), 15′ per side, and 1 × 2 degrees in size. The first two types are useful for terrain analysis because of their large scales (2000 feet per inch and 1 mile per inch, respectively) and elevation contours every 10, 20, 40, or 80 feet, depending on local topography. The 1 × 2-degree maps are not recommended for specific path studies, because the scale is just 4 miles per inch and elevation contours are drawn every 200 feet. These maps correspond precisely to the popular Maidenhead locator grids used in VHF, UHF, and microwave communications, contests and awards, however, and may be useful for broad planning work.

Topographical maps show in wonderful detail land forms, streams, rivers and other natural features; political boundaries; and roads, bridges, buildings, quarries, electric power transmission lines and many other man-made additions to the landscape. Users unfamiliar with standard topographical maps may find helpful the US Geological Survey booklet "Topographical Maps," which outlines map symbols and provides other hints on map reading.[2] The small section of a 7.5-minute map shown in Fig 1 does not reproduce the vast amount of detail available, much of which is in color.

The first step in analyzing a proposed microwave line-of-sight path is to draw a *profile of the path terrain*. This can be done easily from a topographical map, or from a series of maps if the path is more than a few miles long.[3] Simply draw a line, corresponding to the proposed radio path, across the maps. Rule off a convenient scale of distance, perhaps every half mile, along the line. Then transfer the elevations from the map to a linear profile, as shown in Fig 2. Additional or intermediate points may be necessary

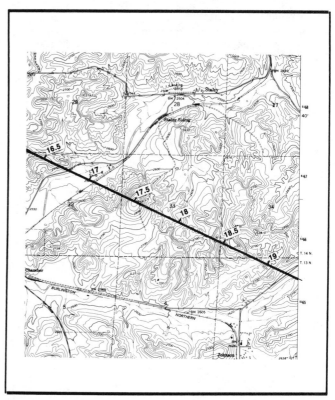

Fig 1—A portion of a 7.5-minute US Geological Survey topographical map, with a section of a radio path marked.

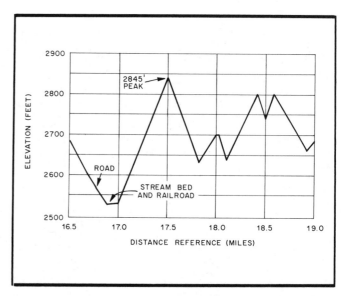

Fig 2—Land elevation profile based on the path drawn on Fig 1.

if a high elevation or other unusual feature lies between half-mile points.

Some problems of interpreting the maps may arise. Not infrequently, the communications path will go over the top of a hill whose peak elevation is not given, and instead of being able to interpolate the elevation between two contours, you are left without a higher contour for reference. The rule of thumb in such cases is to assume that the hilltop is half the normal contour above the highest contour given. Trees and buildings should be treated as if they were solid granite at microwave frequencies, but the height of buildings and trees (green shaded areas) are not given on topographical maps. The height of these features may be estimated, or better yet, checked in the field.

Fig 3 shows the results of plotting a much longer 47.36-mile path using the same method. In both cases, the completed profiles were plotted as if the Earth were flat. Compensation must be made for the *effective Earth radius* for radio paths, discussed previously in the section Tropospheric Refraction. Drawing path profiles on special curved 4/3rd graph paper is convenient, but it restricts the plot to the standard effective Earth radius factor for temperate climates, k = 1.33. Under typical conditions, k varies from at 1.2 to 1.6 depending on location, weather, seasons, and time of day. Table 1 shows some representative values.

The choice of which value of k to use depends on the application. For casual work, an average value might suffice. If long-term reliability over a set path is sought, extreme values of k ought to be plotted and the results analyzed. More precise values of k may also be calculated from readily available measures of temperature, humidity, and atmospheric pressure.

Table 1
Typical Values of Effective Earth Radius, K

	Summer	Winter
Dry mountain above 1500 m	1.20	1.20
Mountains to 1500 m	1.25	1.25
Midwest and Northeast	1.50	1.30
South and West Coast	1.55	1.35
Southern Coast	1.60	1.50

Calculation of the Radio Index of Refraction

The radio index of refraction (N) must be determined before the effective Earth radius factor can be derived. The calculation of N (provided previously as Eq 23) may be applied directly to this problem:

$$N = \frac{77.6\,p}{T} + \frac{3.73 \times 10^5\,e}{T^2} \qquad \text{(Eq 1)}$$

where
  N = index of refraction, N units
  p = atmospheric pressure, millibars (mb)
  e = partial pressure of water vapor, mb
  T = temperature, kelvins (K)

The actual measurements at a given location should be used, but the units commonly available may be different than those required. The following conversions may be helpful for temperature:

$$K = 273.15 + C \qquad \text{(Eq 2)}$$

$$C = 5/9 \, (F - 32) \qquad \text{(Eq 3)}$$

where
  K = kelvins
  C = degrees, Celsius
  F = degrees, Fahrenheit

And for atmospheric pressure:

$$p = 33.86 p_{in} \qquad \text{(Eq 4)}$$

where
  p = atmospheric pressure, mb
  p_{in} = atmospheric pressure, inches of mercury

It should be noted that barometric pressure is most often reported at sea level, or barometric pressure "reduced to sea level," regardless of the elevation of a particular reporting station. Atmospheric pressure decreases by a rate that is generally independent of weather. Care must be taken

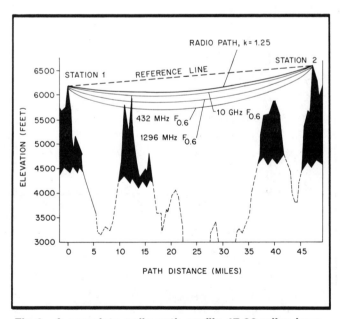

Fig 3—A complete radio path profile 47.36 miles long. The radio path has been calculated at an effective earth radius k = 1.25. The 10 GHz 0.6 Fresnel zone clears the peak to the left, but the peak penetrates the 1296 MHz $F_{0.6}$ zone. Two peaks lay within the 432 MHz $F_{0.6}$ zone.

to use actual barometric pressure or to adjust pressure reduced to sea level to the actual location. Fig 4 provides approximate adjustment factors for the elevations below 10,000 feet.

The conversion of common measures of humidity to the *partial pressure of water vapor* (e) is a bit more complicated. The partial pressure of water vapor is that portion of the total atmospheric pressure that is attributable to water vapor in the air. The *saturation vapor pressure* (e_s) is the pressure contributed by water vapor when the air is saturated, that is at 100 percent relative humidity. The calculation of saturation vapor pressure is difficult, but as it is dependent only on temperature, it may be more conveniently estimated from Fig 5.[4] The actual vapor pressure is simply the saturation vapor pressure times the relative humidity, taken as a decimal. Thus when air temperature and relative humidity are known:

$$e = He_s \qquad \text{(Eq 5)}$$

where

  e = partial pressure of water vapor, mb
  H = relative humidity, as a decimal
  e_s = saturation vapor pressure, mb

The temperature at saturation is also known as the *dewpoint*, because any further drop in temperature would result in a portion of the water vapor precipitating as dew, mist, or rain. Thus the dewpoint can be used interchangeably with the temperature at saturation in Fig 5. The *dewpoint depression* is the number of degrees to which a given parcel of air must be cooled in order to reach the dewpoint. Thus air temperature less dewpoint depression yields dewpoint.

What would be the radio index of refraction of air over Pullman, Washington, elevation 2600 feet above sea level, on a warm summer day? The local news reports the following conditions: temperature 82° Fahrenheit, relative humidity 45 percent, and barometric pressure 30.10 inches. First, all the units must be converted to those needed by the index-of-refraction equation. Using Eq 2 and Eq 3, temperature is calculated at 27.8°C or 300.9 K. The atmospheric pressure at sea level converts to 1019.2 mb, using Eq 4. According to Fig 4, the atmospheric pressure at 2600 feet is 91.2 mb less than at sea level, making the actual pressure at Pullman 928 mb. At 27.8°C, the saturation vapor pressure from Fig 5 is approximately 37 mb. Given a relative humidity of 45 percent, Eq 5 yields a partial vapor pressure of 16.65. All of these values can now be substituted into Eq 1:

$$N = \frac{77.6\ (928)}{300.9} + \frac{3.73 \times 10^5 (16.65)}{(300.9)^2} = 307.9$$

The radio index of refraction at Pullman on that day is thus 307.9. This value will change with the weather. On

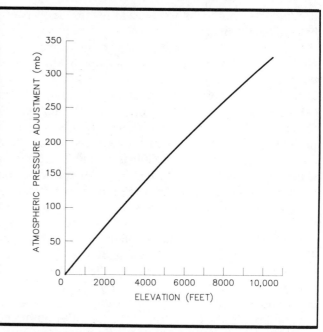

Fig 4—Decrease in atmospheric pressure as a function of elevation under normal conditions.

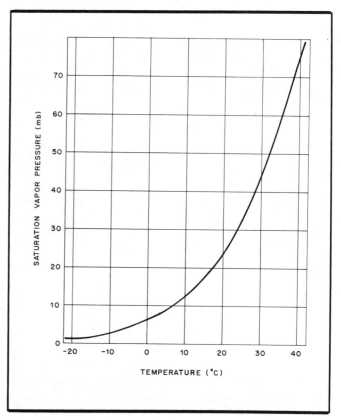

Fig 5—Saturation vapor pressure as a function of temperature.

more humid days, the value of N will be greater; on cooler days it will be considerably less.

Effective Earth Radius

The *effective Earth radius factor* can be calculated as a function of the index of refraction,[5] and this has been conveniently plotted in Fig 6. From the example above, the value of N at Pullman is 307.9 and thus k is approximately 1.36, just above standard conditions of 1.33. Once the effective Earth radius is known, the curvature of the Earth along any point along a radio path may be calculated:

$$C = \frac{d_1 d_2}{1.5k} \qquad \text{(Eq 6)}$$

where

C = curvature depression, feet
d = total path distance, miles
d_1 = a point some distance from station 1, miles
$d_2 = d - d_1$
k = effective Earth radius factor

Values calculated for the effective Earth radius may be transferred to a flat-Earth profile to compensate for the curved radio path. First, draw a straight line from station 1 to station 2. This reference line is nearly parallel to the surface of the Earth but has no particular significance for radio paths. Its altitude at any point may be easily calculated as:

$$A = \frac{d_1(E_1 - E_2)}{d} \qquad \text{(Eq 7)}$$

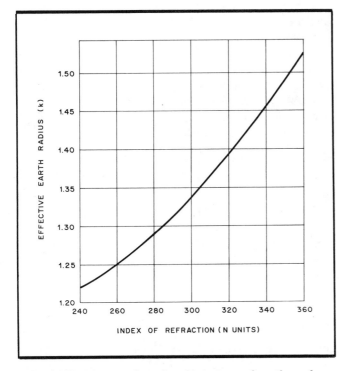

Fig 6—Effective earth radius factor as a function of radio index of refraction.

where

A = altitude at any point distance d_1
E_1 = elevation of station 1 (the higher location)
E_2 = elevation of station 2

Then at various distances (d_1) reduce the elevation perpendicular to the reference line by corresponding values of C. The resulting curved line represents the radio path for a designated effective Earth radius. This has been done in Fig 3 for k = 1.25, a value typical for mountainous areas. From this plot, it appears as if there is a clear radio-line-of-sight path between the two stations, but is this necessarily so? One further factor must be considered before this conclusion can be reached: the Fresnel clearance zones.

Fresnel Zone Clearance

Objects near the direct radio line of sight may act as diffraction points and introduce as much as 6 dB additional attenuation. If the object is large and rounded on top, attenuation can be 20 dB and greater. In order to avoid diffraction losses, **all** objects (peaks of hills and mountains, as well as trees, power lines, buildings and the like) must lie outside the first 0.6 Fresnel ($F_{0.6}$) clearance zone. An application of Eq 36 can be used to calculate the dimensions of the $F_{0.6}$ zone:

$$F_{0.6} = 43.24 \sqrt{\frac{d_1 d_2}{fd}} \qquad \text{(Eq 8)}$$

where

$F_{0.6}$ = 0.6 Fresnel zone clearance, feet
d = total path distance, miles
d_1 = distance from station 1, miles
$d_2 = d - d_1$
f = frequency, GHz

The *0.6 Fresnel clearance zone* may then be plotted on the path profile by subtracting the various calculated values of $F_{0.6}$ at their corresponding distances d_1 along the radio path. The $F_{0.6}$ zones at 432 MHz, 1296 MHz, and 10 GHz have also been included on Fig 3. For paths up to 93 miles (150 km) and frequencies between 432 MHz and 48 GHz, the approximate $F_{0.6}$ clearance distances can be read from Fig 35, provided in the earlier Fresnel Zone section.

Even if an object appears within the $F_{0.6}$ zone, it may be that up to 20 dB additional path loss could be tolerated in certain situations. There may be more than enough total station gain to overcome all path attenuation plus the additional Fresnel diffraction losses. Calculations of the extreme range of N likely to be encountered in a given location, and thus the effective Earth radius factor k, may indicate that only in rare instances would some ground feature or object penetrate the 0.6 Fresnel zone. This too may be acceptable. It is not inconceivable that the path may even be blocked all or part of the time (again depending on the index of refraction at any moment), but the considerably greater knife-edge diffraction losses could also be overcome by the total system performance. (Review the Fresnel Zone section for calculating knife-edge diffraction losses.)

Path Budget

There is one additional consideration that must be analyzed before it can be concluded that a given UHF or microwave line-of-sight path is possible and reliable. The total path loss must be calculated and compared with the total system performance of the proposed stations. The equations, tables, and examples provided in the previous section, Free Space and Atmospheric Losses, and in the Path Loss and Total System Performance section are sufficient for making these analyses.

Distance and Azimuth

Closely related to path analysis is the accurate determination of distance and azimuth from one station to another, especially those using very high-gain narrow beamwidth antennas. Distance and azimuths between station sites are relatively easy to determine from geographical coordinates. The accuracy of both depends on the accuracy of the original site coordinates, so it is important to use the best map possible. On a 7.5-minute map, it should be possible to locate a site within 1 second of a degree. The easiest way to determine geographical coordinates is to use a simple proportional method.

Mark the site on a large-scale map that indicates longitude and latitude. Note the distance in decimal degrees between the longitude and latitude reference marks either side of the site and record as X_w and Y_w respectively. (A formula to convert from degrees, minutes, and seconds to decimal degrees is given below.) On a 7.5-minute map, the reference latitudes and longitudes are $2'30''$ (0.041667 degrees) apart. Record the reference longitude east of the site (X_{ref}) and the reference latitude south of the site (Y_{ref}) in decimal degrees. Then measure carefully with a decimal-scale rule (a metric rule is very convenient for this purpose) the width between the two longitude and latitude reference marks (W_x and W_y respectively); the distance from the site to the eastern reference longitude (d_x); and distance from the site to the southern reference latitude (d_y).

Then use the following formulas to determine site longitude and latitude in decimal degrees:

$$X_{site} = X_{ref} + X_w \frac{W_x}{d_x} \qquad \text{(Eq 9)}$$

where

X_{site} = site longitude, decimal degrees
X_{ref} = eastern reference longitude, decimal degrees
X_w = width of longitude reference interval, decimal degrees
W_x = width of longitude reference interval, mm (or other convenient decimal scale)
d_x = distance between site and eastern reference longitude, mm (or other convenient decimal scale)

$$Y_{site} = Y_{ref} + Y_w \frac{W_y}{d_y} \qquad \text{(Eq 10)}$$

where

Y_{site} = site latitude, decimal degrees
Y_{ref} = southern reference latitude, decimal degrees
Y_w = width of latitude reference interval, decimal degrees
W_y = width of latitude reference interval, mm (or other convenient decimal scale)
d_y = distance between site and southern reference latitude, mm (or other convenient decimal scale)

To convert degrees, minutes, and seconds to decimal degrees, the following algorithm may be used if you do not have a calculator with the appropriate function keys:

$$Z = D + \frac{m}{60} + \frac{S}{3600} \qquad \text{(Eq 11)}$$

where

Z = coordinate in decimal degrees
D = degree portion of coordinate
M = minute portion of coordinate
S = second portion of coordinate

Using Eq 11, $45°07'24''$ converts to: $45 + 7/60 + 24/3600 = 45 + 0.11667 + 0.00673 = 45.1234°$. The conversion from decimal degrees back to degrees, minutes and seconds takes three steps:

(1) D = integer portion of decimal coordinate
(2) M = integer part of (60 × decimal residual of step 1)
(3) S = 60 × decimal residual of step 2

Converting 45.1234 degrees back to degrees, minutes and seconds is straightforward:

(1) D = 45
(3) 60 × 0.1234 = 7.404, thus M = 7
(4) S = 60 × 0.404 = 24.24

And the result is $45°07'24.24''$.

The *distance* between two sites can be determined in several ways. For many purposes, a careful measurement made directly from large-scale topographical maps may be sufficient. The standard trigonometric solution assumes the Earth is a perfect sphere, and although it introduces some inaccuracies, it is simple to use and is often close enough for short distances (less than 10 km):

$$\cos(d) = \sin Y_1 \sin Y_2 + \cos Y_1 \cos Y_2 \cos(X_1 - X_2) \qquad \text{(Eq 12)}$$

where

d = arccosine(d) = path distance, degrees of arc
d_{mile} = 69.041d = path distance, miles
X_1 = longitude of first site, decimal degrees
X_2 = longitude of second site, decimal degrees
Y_1 = latitude of first site, decimal degrees
Y_2 = latitude of second site, decimal degrees

When making these calculations with a pocket calculator or personal computer, define and retain variables with as great a precision as possible. Calculating trigonometric functions for small angles are particularly troublesome for some programs. ArccosineX is simply the angle whose cosine is X and can be thought of as the inverse of cosine. It is often entered as "inverse cos" on many pocket calculators.

Azimuth, or the angular distance from one site to another, can be accurately determined using spherical Earth trigonometry as well:

$$\cos(B) = \frac{\sin Y_2 - \sin Y_1 \cos(d)}{\cos Y_1 \sin(d)} \qquad \text{(Eq 13)}$$

where variables are defined as in Eq 11 and

B = arccosine(B), bearing from north
Az = true bearing from north determined as follows:
   $Az = B$, if $X_1 > X_2$
   $Az = 360 - B$, if $X_1 < X_2$

Consider Krell Hill (47°34′34″ N, 117°17′58″ W) and Kamiak Butte (46°51′43″ N, 117°10′26″ W). What is the distance and azimuth from Krell Hill to Kamiak Butte? The coordinates are first converted to decimals and labeled:

$X_1 = 117.299$ $X_2 = 117.173$
$Y_1 = 47.576$ $Y_2 = 46.862$

The distance between the two peaks is calculated by substituting these values into Eq 12:

$\cos(d) = \sin(46.862)\sin(47.576) + \cos(47.576)\cos(46.862)$
   $\times \cos(117.299 - 117.173)$
$\cos(d) = (0.729709 \times 0.7381728) +$
   $(0.6746117 \times 0.6837579 \times 0.9999976) = 0.9999213$

$\text{arccosine}(0.9999213) = 0.71896° = d$

$d_{mile} = 69.041 \times 0.71896 = 49.64$ miles

Azimuth can be found by using these same values in Eq 13:

$$\cos(B) = \frac{\sin(46.862) - \sin(47.576)\cos(0.71896)}{\cos(47.576)\sin(0.71896)}$$

$$= \frac{0.729709 - (0.7381728 \times 0.9999213)}{0.674617 \times 0.0125479} = 0.99300$$

$\text{arccosine}(0.99300) = 173.21° = B = Az$

The Earth is not a perfect sphere, and distance can be calculated with greater accuracy if an algorithm that takes into consideration the Earth's slightly oblate shape is used. For the short distances involved in typical microwave paths, the following method agrees closely enough with more complicated geodetic algorithms that have been proposed to compensate for the Earth's non-spherical shape:

$h = (X_1 - X_2)[68.962 + 0.04525(Y_m) - 0.01274(Y_m)^2$
   $+ 0.00004117(Y_m)^3] \qquad \text{(Eq 14)}$

$v = (Y_1 - Y_2)[68.712 - 0.001184(Y_m) + 0.0002928(Y_m)^2$
   $- 0.000002162(Y_m)^3] \qquad \text{(Eq 15)}$

$d = \sqrt{h^2 + v^2} \qquad \text{(Eq 16)}$

where variables are defined as in Eq 12 and
   h = horizontal distance, miles
   v = vertical distance, miles

$$Y_m = \frac{Y_1 + Y_2}{2}$$

d_{mile} = path distance, miles

Substituting into these equations the same values used in the above examples:

$h = (117.299 - 117.173) [68.962 + 0.04525 (47.219)$
   $- 0.01274(47.219)^2 + 0.00004117(47.219)^3]$
   $= 5.9254679$

$v = (47.576 - 46.862)[68.712 - 0.001184(47.219) +$
   $0.00002928(42.219)^2 - 0.000002162(47.219)^3]$
   $= 49.324055$

$d = \sqrt{(5.925)^2 + (49.324)^2} = 49.678$

The result, 49.68 miles compares closely with the 49.64 miles obtained with the spherical Earth model.

Notes

[1]US Geological Survey Maps may be ordered directly from Distribution Branch, US Geological Survey, Box 25268, Federal Center, Denver CO 80225. Indexes are available from the same source. Maps are also sold by regional US Geological Survey Sales Counters; by many state geological survey departments, outdoor outfitters, and survey suppliers; and some university and other bookstores.

[2]"Topographical Maps" is available from National Cartographic Information Center, US Geological Survey, 507 National Center, Reston VA 22092.

[3]Feet and miles are used in this section to measure distances primarily because most US topographical maps use the US Customary system. 1 mile = 1.609 km

[4]There is no easy way to calculate saturation vapor pressure, but it may be approximated by the following:

$e_s = \exp(1.805 + 0.0738T - 0.000298T^2)$

where
   e_s = saturation vapor pressure, mb
   T = temperature, °C
   $\exp(x) = e_x$, or antilog$_e x$

Fig 5 was constructed using values calculated from this equation.

[5]The effective Earth radius may be calculated when the index of refraction is known:

$$k = \frac{1}{1 - 0.04665\exp(0.005577N)}$$

where
   k = effective Earth radius factor
   N = index of refraction, N units

In this application, calculation of k as a function of N at one location assumes that the k is constant over the whole radio path; that no unusual weather conditions have stratified the air, creating inversions or negative refractive conditions; and that the two radio sites are at about the same elevation. These assumptions hold true only for short paths under average or "normal" atmospheric conditions and may not apply at all times. A more accurate determination of the refractive properties over a radio path require data from several points along the path at many different altitudes, analyzed using the more comprehensive effective Earth radius factor Eq 24, discussed in the previous Index of Refraction section. As this is rarely practical, the method discussed in the text is suggested as providing a fair guideline.

BIBLIOGRAPHY

Bean, B. R. et al, *A World Atlas of Atmospheric Radio Refractivity* (Boulder, CO: Environmental Science Services Administration, 1966).

Bomford, G., *Geodesy* (Oxford, England: Clarendon Press, 1971).

Bullington, K., "Radio Propagation Fundamentals," *Bell System Technical Journal*, May 1957, pp 593-626.

Corbell, I. T., "Microwave Engineering for the Broadcaster," *NAB Engineering Handbook* (Washington, DC: National Association of Broadcasters, 1957).

Hall, Gerald L., Ed., *The ARRL Antenna Book*, 15th edition (Newington: American Radio Relay League, 1988).

Stephansen, E. T., "Clear-Air Propagation on Line-of-Sight Radio Paths: A Review," *Radio Science*, Sep-Oct 1981, p 610.

Vigants, A., "Microwave Radio Obstruction Fading," *Bell System Technical Journal*, Jul-Aug 1981, pp 785-801.

White, R. F., *Engineering Considerations for Microwave Communications Systems* (San Carlos, CA: GTE Lenkurt, 1970).

Chapter 4

Microwave Devices

By Richard P. Banghart
517 Farmstead Ln
Lansing, MI 48917

SPECIAL CONSIDERATIONS OF THE MICROWAVE REGION

The microwave region of the electromagnetic spectrum imposes new limitations and offers new possibilities for electronic components. The biggest challenge to microwave designers is the extremely small wavelengths involved. In lower-frequency circuits, components (or at least their active portions) are small compared to the wavelength of the signal they are handling. At microwave frequencies, the size of a component is often larger than the wavelength of the signal. The size of a component relative to its design frequency has a great deal to do with circuit operation. Fig 1 shows the relative size of some microwave transistors and silicon MMICs (monolithic microwave integrated circuits). Components that physically approach even 10% of their circuit's frequency can affect performance. The microwave devices discussed in this chapter confront this problem in one of two ways. One way is simply to make the device smaller. The other way is to employ new design concepts, unique to microwave components.

It is helpful to remember that all descriptions of electronic behavior are models that approximate what is actually happening. Even the complex mathematical formulas used by electrical engineers are approximations. The model we use to describe any electronic phenomenon is useful only as long as it recognizes important factors and ignores unimportant ones. For example, at lower frequencies, lead inductance and interelectrode capacitance play an insignificant role in circuit behavior, so they are ignored in the circuit analysis. As frequency increases, these factors take on greater importance and must be considered. In the microwave region of the electromagnetic spectrum (above about 400 MHz), many of the assumptions made at lower frequencies can no longer be made.

When we first learned how electronic components operate, many of us were taught to think of current as the flow of electrons, voltage as the "pressure" causing the flow and resistance as the narrowing of the "pipes" carrying the flow. Those mechanistic models of electronics have the advantage of being consistent with the way we

Fig 1—Some transistors and silicon MMICs used for VHF through microwaves (clockwise from top): 70-mil hermetic package with gold-plated leads; "85" molded plastic package; "micro-X" 85-mil metal-ceramic package with tinned leads. *(photo courtesy Avantek)*

normally experience the world around us. For dc electronics and lower-frequency ac electronics, those models provide predictable results. When we move to RF electronics, a different set of models comes into play. The models that help us understand RF electronics have less to do with the way we normally experience the world. In fact, we often have to ignore "common sense" in favor of a mathematical model to get predictable results. For microwave circuits we use yet another set of models to understand and predict circuit behavior.

CATEGORIES OF MICROWAVE DEVICES

Devices used at microwave frequencies can be broken down into two broad categories. One category consists of devices that operate in essentially the same way as their

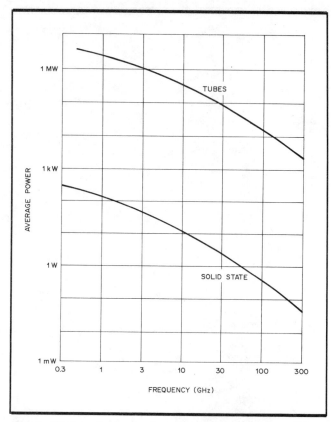

Fig 2—Comparison of microwave tubes versus solid-state device power-handling capability.

increases, these physical features effectively become larger, that is, they take on more importance in our analysis of the circuit. With this in mind, it is clear that for a triode to operate at higher frequencies it must be designed with short leads and close electrode spacing.

The planar triode (shown in Figs 3 and 4) is an example of employing special construction techniques for operation at higher frequencies. The planar triode (or lighthouse tube) is capable of operation near 1 GHz. Instead of the usual arrangement of cathode, grid and plate as concentric cylindrical sections, they are arranged as layered, flat surfaces. This allows for close electrode spacing, reducing transit-time effects. With no electrode leads, as such, connections to the elements of the tube are easily made.

At lower frequencies, we are accustomed to thinking

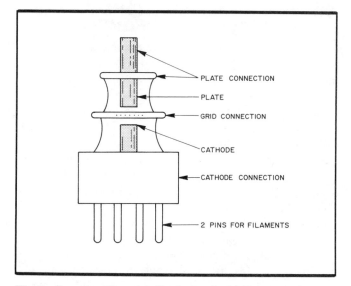

Fig 3—Construction detail of a typical "lighthouse" tube (planar triode).

lower-frequency counterparts, but have been designed and constructed to allow operation at higher frequencies. The second category consists of devices that depend on characteristics of the microwave region for their operation. This second group is incapable of (or quite inefficient when) operating at lower frequencies.

Fig 2 shows the power-handling capabilities of solid-state and tube devices versus frequency. With the current state of the art, tubes out-power solid-state devices by a factor of about 1000. Because of cost, power supply and weight considerations, however, if a particular application falls under the solid-state curve, solid-state components should be used.

EXTENDING FUNCTION TO THE MICROWAVE REGION

Tubes

The conventional triode can be made to operate satisfactorily at up to several hundred MHz if we take into account certain facts of life at these high frequencies. The triode depends on movement of electrons for its operation. As long as the physical features of the tube remain a small fraction of the wavelength of the energy involved, we can expect the tube to operate consistently. The physical features include the size and length of leads, and the spacing and size of the electrodes. As the operating frequency

Fig 4—Varian glass/metal planar triode vacuum tube. (photo courtesy Varian Associates, Inc)

of circuit components as separate parts connected to the rest of the circuit by leads. At microwave frequencies, the component interacts intimately with the circuit surrounding it, often depending entirely on the proximity of other circuit elements for its operation. The lighthouse tube is made for easy coupling to waveguide or an RF cavity. Planar triodes used in amateur service include the 2C39, 2C43, 5675 and 5893.

Solid-State Devices

Familiar solid-state devices are capable of operating much further into the microwave region than conventional tube devices. By employing special manufacturing techniques (and taking advantage of their inherent size advantages) to reduce the distance from emitter to collector, bipolar transistors can be made to operate at frequencies between 2 and 3 GHz. Popular microwave-capable bipolar transistors include the MRF901, BRF91, BOU98 and MRF559. For power applications, the NEL130681 and the NEL132081 are commonly used.

FETs can operate up to nearly 10 GHz. Aside from careful manufacturing techniques and circuit layout, these devices operate according to the same principles as their lower-frequency counterparts. Even though FETs designed to operate at higher frequencies are more expensive, one should avoid thinking the extra expense will translate into improved lower-frequency operation. Many high-frequency FETs suffer from increased instability if operated below their rated frequency of operation.

There is an alphabet soup surrounding FETs. The three types of FETs include the P-N junction gate, the MES gate (metal-semiconductor or Schottky-barrier gate) and the MIS gate (metal-insulator-semiconductor). The basic structure of the FET may require a moment's review. An FET differs from a bipolar transistor in that current conduction occurs only by majority carriers (electrons or holes depending on whether N- or P-type semiconductor material is used). The type of gate connection is the main determinant of the characteristics of the device. Most of the initials associated with FETs describe the gate connections.

GaAsFETs (gallium-arsenide field-effect transistors) possess special properties that make them especially suitable for microwave applications. See Fig 5. Since GaAs is a compound (silicon and germanium are elements), it exhibits greater electron mobility (see Table 1) and a correspondingly higher maximum operating frequency. GaAsFETs are available for a wide range of power and low-noise applications. Commonly used GaAsFETs are manufactured by Hewlett-Packard (HFET-2201 and HSC H001), Plessey (GAT5 and GAT6) and Nippon Electric Company (NEC). Other popular devices are the MRF966/967, 3SK97, MGF1100, MGF1402 and the NE41137. Although bipolar transistors can be manufactured to provide acceptable high-frequency performance, the FET is preferred for most microwave work.

There are many other solid-state devices that will operate from MF through the microwave bands, such as varac-

Fig 5—A typical MMIC amplifier package. *(photo courtesy Avantek.)*

Table 1

Approximate Electron and Hole Mobility of Several Semiconductors at Room Temperature

Material	Electron mobility	Hole mobility
silicon (Si)	1500	600
germanium (Ge)	3900	2000
gallium arsenide (GaAs)	8500	400
gallium antimonide (GaSb)	4000	1400
indium phosphide (InP)	4600	150
indium arsenide (InAs)	33,000	460
indium antimonide (InSb)	78,000	750

tor diodes, tunnel diodes, point-contact diodes, hot-carrier diodes and others. For organizational purposes, these devices are discussed later in the chapter.

PASSIVE COMPONENTS

Capacitors

At microwave frequencies, just as at HF, capacitors are used in coupling, matching, tuning and bypass applications. Because of the small wavelengths involved in microwave work, capacitors have evolved over the years and are now available in a wide variety of sizes and compositions. Even at microwave frequencies we use electrolytics to bypass low-frequency parasitics. Other capacitor formulations include: metallized film, various ceramic types for medium-frequency bypassing, ceramic and mica types for coupling and bypassing to UHF, and ceramic chip capacitors for VHF and UHF applications. Of course, chip capacitors are used extensively in the microwave bands. Table 2 shows approximate frequencies of use for various capacitor types.

A detailed discussion of capacitor design parameters is beyond the scope of this chapter. There are, however, several basic circuit-design considerations that need to be mentioned. As operating frequencies increase, it becomes necessary to make the capacitor physically smaller—while maintaining the required Q and power-handling capability. Other factors come into the equation as well: temperature,

voltage, environmental conditions, mounting methods and dielectric material.

Construction details of a typical chip capacitor are shown in Fig 6. The gold-plated internal electrodes are hermetically sealed within a cube of nonporous porcelain. The outer edges of the end electrodes are used as solder points to connect the capacitor to the circuit board. The nonporous exterior protects the capacitor from being contaminated during the soldering process or from other chemicals present in the operating environment.

Pellet-sized chip capacitors range from 0.055 inch square, to approximately 0.12×0.11 inch square. See Fig 7.

Table 2
Capacitors Typically Used in RF Circuits

Fixed Capacitors

Type	Frequency Range
Electrolytic, aluminum or tantalum	ac-audio
Metallized film	audio-5 MHz
Disc ceramic	1-500 MHz
Uncased mica, large	5-500 MHz
Uncased mica, small	100-1000 MHz
100-mil chip	50-4000 MHz
50-mil chip	0.5-10 GHz

Variable Capacitors

Mica compression trimmer	2-500 MHz
Rotary film	100-1500 MHz
Rotary ceramic	50-1300 MHz
Glass tubular piston	400-2000 MHz
Ceramic tubular piston	400-3000 MHz
Sapphire piston	1-10 GHz

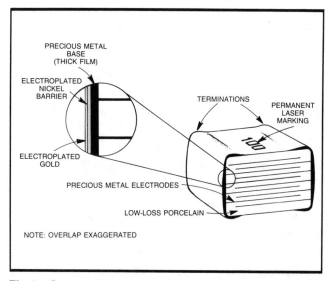

PRECIOUS METAL BASE (THICK FILM)

ELECTROPLATED NICKEL BARRIER

ELECTROPLATED GOLD

TERMINATIONS

PERMANENT LASER MARKING

PRECIOUS METAL ELECTRODES

LOW-LOSS PORCELAIN

NOTE: OVERLAP EXAGGERATED

Fig 6—Construction detail of a typical chip capacitor.

Resistors

Although resistors are normally used in dc networks, there are several RF circuit applications, such as attenuator pads or RF loads. Resistors are also used as lossy RF chokes, and are often placed between a transistor's base and emitter leads to stabilize the circuit. As with capacitors, physical size and lead lengths must be reduced to minimize unwanted inductances.

The older-style carbon composition resistors work best at RF because they have lower inductances than metal or carbon-film types—the latter are usually quite reactive and lossy, and are not recommended.

At frequencies above 500 MHz, chip resistors are probably the best performers. They are constructed much like chip capacitors, and are commonly available in a range of 10 ohms to 1 MΩ. See Fig 8 for construction details.

Switches and Relays

Switching microwave energy—especially at high power levels—requires a different approach than switching dc or lower-frequency RF energy. Whether you're switching antenna connections, amplifier lines, internal IF paths, or an in-line preamplifier, there are several important considerations. These are isolation, power-handling capability, SWR, switching time, impedance, connectors and coil voltage.

Isolation. No RF relay is perfect—some power is always going to be present at the port(s) that are not selected. For example, in an SPDT antenna relay, some (hopefully small) amount of RF will be present on the receive port when the relay is in the transmit position (and the transmitter is emitting a signal). If the RF at the receive port is too great, the front end of your receiver may be destroyed. If a relay with 30 dB of isolation is used to switch an antenna between a 1-kW transmitter and a receiver, a 1-W (30 dB less than 1 kW) signal will be present at the receive port. Look for a switch or relay that has at least 50 to 60 dB of isolation for high-power applications.

CASE SIZE AND TYPE	OUTLINES	BODY DIMENSIONS		
		LENGTH (L)	WIDTH (W)	THICKNESS (T)
A CHIP	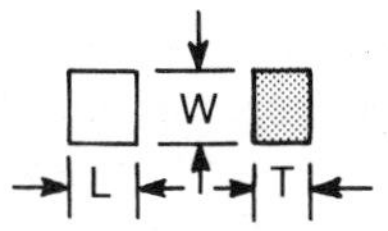 W/T IS A TERMINATION SURFACE	.055 ± .010 (1.4 ± .25)		.055 (1.4) MAX.
B CHIP		.110 ± .015 (2.79 ± .38)		.100 (2.54) MAX.
A PELLET / B PELLET	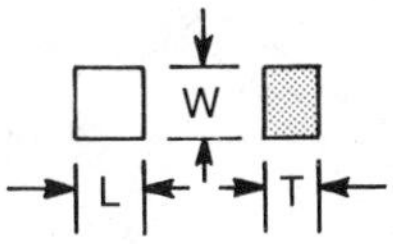 W/T IS A TERMINATION SURFACE	SAME AS CHIP PLUS TWICE SOLDER BUILD-UP: SOLDER BUILD-UP FOR SIZE A IS: .003 (.076) TYP. SOLDER BUILD-UP FOR SIZE B IS: .005 (.127) TYP.		
B MICROSTRIP	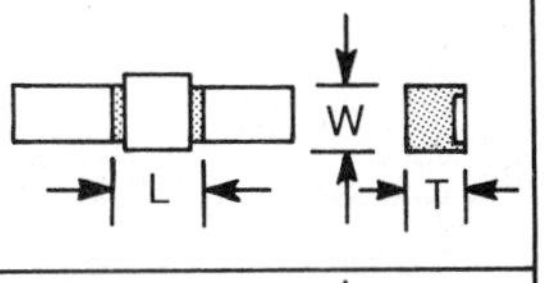	.120 (3.05) MIN. .150 (3.81) MAX.	.110 ± .015 (2.79 ± .38)	.100 (2.54) MAX.
B AXIAL RIBBON	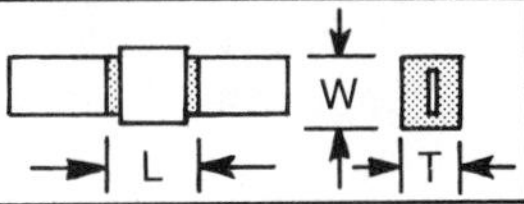			
B RADIAL RIBBON	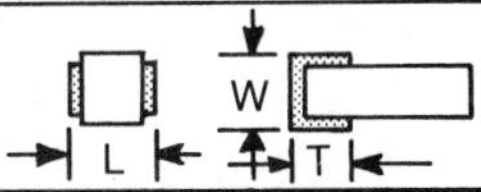			
B NARROW AXIAL RIBBON	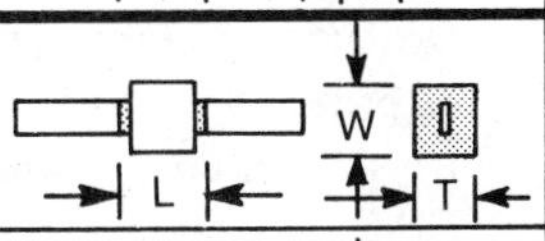	.120 (3.05) MIN. .155 (3.94) MAX.	.110 ± .015 (2.79 ± .38)	.100 (2.54) MAX
B NARROW MICROSTRIP	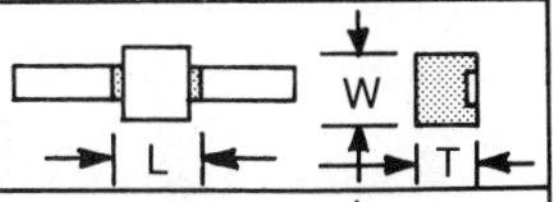			
B VERTICAL NARROW MS	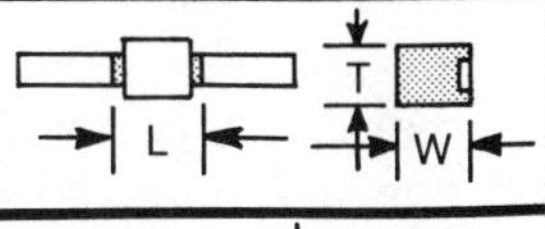			
B RADIAL WIRE	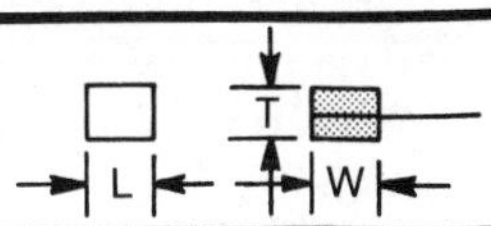	.120 (3.05) MIN .165 (4.19) MAX.	.110 ± .015 (2.79 ± .38)	.100 (2.54) MAX
B AXIAL WIRE	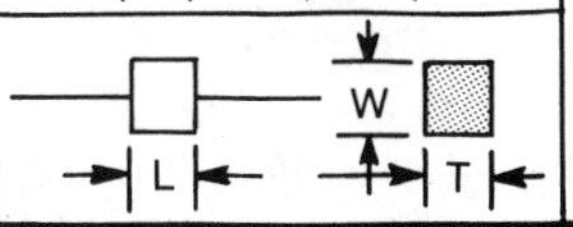			

Fig 7—Mechanical specifications for a typical series of chip capacitors.

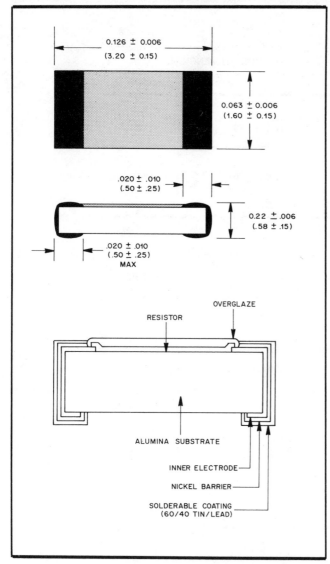

Fig 8—Construction detail of a typical chip resistor.

Reduced isolation is acceptable for low-power applications.

Power rating. Manufacturers usually specify a maximum average power at a range of frequencies. As with coaxial cable, losses increase with frequency, thereby reducing the power-handling capability. Power ratings are usually specified at a unity SWR. A poorly matched antenna will reduce the power rating of a relay or switch because of the mismatch loss.

SWR. This specification refers to the mismatch introduced by the switch or relay when the unit is terminated with a 50-ohm load. The SWR varies with the frequency—the closer to 1:1 the better.

Switching time. This is the time it takes for a relay to go from one position to another—usually 10 to 100 ms. Switching time is important when designing a TR sequencing scheme so that RF is not applied at the wrong time to the wrong place.

Impedance. Coaxial relays are usually designed for a nominal 50-ohm impedance. Other impedances may be okay, but watch the SWR specifications.

Connectors. The connectors should have adequate SWR and power ratings for the frequency in use. UHF connectors are okay below 148 MHz. Type N connectors are a better choice; these are usable through 10 GHz. SMA connectors are convenient for 2304 MHz and above because of their small size and low SWR.

Coil voltage. Relays with 12-V coils are handy for use with modern equipment, but 24- and 28-V relays abound on the surplus market. Some relays have 120-V coils; these are suitable for indoor use, if treated with caution.

There are hundreds of different relays on the market. Table 3 is a sampling of what's available.

Solid-State Switching

The PIN diode is widely used as an RF switch at microwave frequencies. Its characteristics are ideal for that purpose: very low impedance in the on state, and very high impedance in the off state. PIN diodes are physically small and nearly instantaneous in operation. They can be used in high-power, high-frequency applications (if you're willing to spend a lot of money!). Their main disadvantage is their relatively low isolation (and higher losses) compared to quality RF relays.

PIN diode switches often show up in low-level applications where their reduced isolation isn't a problem. With careful design and construction, a PIN diode TR switch can exhibit 30 dB of isolation and losses of only a couple tenths of a decibel. Fig 9 shows two PIN diode TR switches. (A) is a simple SPDT arrangement. When going from transmit to receive, the appropriate diode is energized at point A or point B to allow RF to pass. R1 is chosen for proper current through the diodes. (B) is a series/shunt PIN diode switch. R1 is optimized to allow 100 mA to flow through D1 and D2 on transmit.

EXCLUSIVELY MICROWAVE DEVICES

In the vacuum tubes discussed so far, and the solid-state devices commonly used at lower frequencies, the basic principle of operation concerns the space charge. That is, all amplification or oscillation occurs because of the interaction of charge differentials across some distance. In the case of a vacuum tube, the charge at the plate attracts electrons from the cathode, and a varying charge on the grid modulates the electron current. The transistor uses a base (analogous to the tube's grid) to control the amount of current flowing from emitter to collector. In both cases, a flow of charge carriers is modulated by some intervening element. The usual way of assuring oscillation is to couple some of the energy in the output back to the input. With the necessary physical spacing involved in a tube or transistor there is an inherent limitation on the circuit's ability to couple output energy to the input in a way that will sustain oscillation. One limitation is the inability

Table 3
RF Relay Specifications

Manufacturer	Part No.	Frequency (MHz)	Isolation (dB)	Power (W)	Insertion Loss (dB)	SWR	Connector Type	Notes
Amphenol	317	2304	60	120	0.3	1.2:1	BNC	
Dow Key	DK-60	50	60	1000	*	1.1:1	UHF, N	ISOL > 100 dB with G option
		144	50	1000	*	1.3:1		
		432	40	500	*	1.5:1		
	DK-77	432	45	400	*	1.1:1	BNC	
		1296	25	150	*	1.5:1		
EME Electronics	HF400	144	>60	1500	0.1	1.1:1	N	
		432	>60	1500	0.1	1.1:1		
		1295	45	700	0.2	1.2:1		
		2304	35	500	0.2	1.2:1		
	RK500	144	>60	1000	0.2	1.2:1		
		432	>60	500	0.2	1.2:1		
		1296	50	100	*	*		
		2304	35	50	*	*		
Omron	G4Y	900	65	15	0.25	*	None	PC-mount coaxial
		1296	40	10	0.5	*		
Transco	D	144	90	800	0.1	1.1:1	N	
		432	90	450	0.1	1.1:1		
		1296	70	300	0.1	1.2:1		
		2304	60	220	0.2	1.2:1		
		10000	60	100	0.3	1.2:1		
	DO	1296	90	150	0.1	1.1:1	SMA	
		3456	90	80	0.2	1.1:1		
		10000	90	50	0.3	1.3:1		
	Y	144	70	1600	0.1	1.1:1		
		432	60	800	0.1	1.1:1		
		1296	50	500	0.1	1.2:1		
		2304	40	300	0.2	1.2:1		
		10000	25	100	0.4	1.3:1		

*Not rated.

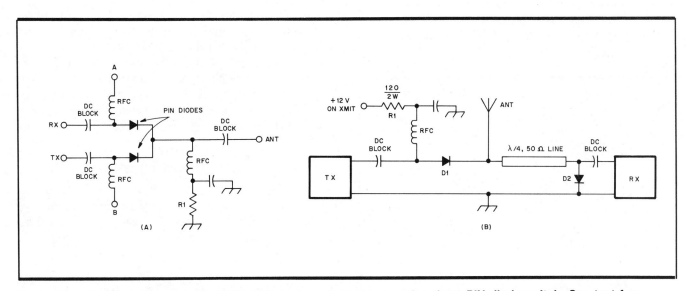

Fig 9—The circuit at A is a simple SPDT PIN diode switch. B is a series-shunt PIN diode switch. See text for details.

to exercise any control over the charge carriers. As the frequency increases, the transit time of the charge carriers becomes significant when compared to the period of the RF energy. Imagine a traffic light going through a complete cycle in less time than it takes one car to cross the intersection. Control of the flow is lost. Another limitation lies in the increasing role of capacitive reactance as the frequency increases. A small amount of interelectrode capacitance can become a major concern as the frequency increases, until eventually it "shorts out" the high-frequency signal.

Microwave Tubes

Tubes that are used to provide performance well into the microwave region rely on essentially different operating properties than do conventional tubes. The reflex klystron and beam klystron are examples of turning a physical liability into an asset. As mentioned before, in a conventional vacuum tube, a stream of electrons is controlled by a grid placed between an emitting cathode and a receiving plate. The time the electrons take to travel from cathode to grid is referred to as transit time. At lower frequencies, transit time can be disregarded because it represents a small fraction of the rate at which the electron stream is modulated. But at higher frequencies, the modulating grid can swing through several cycles during the transit time. This causes the electron stream to become confused, resulting in reduced efficiency and, eventually, a complete failure to amplify. In a klystron, shown in Fig 10, the transit time of a high-velocity beam of electrons is exploited by applying velocity modulation.

The job of any amplifier or oscillator is to transfer energy produced in the power supply to the output of the circuit, with appropriate modulation or oscillation. The reflex klystron, beam klystron, magnetron and traveling-wave tube all permit the transfer of energy from the power supply to the output by appropriately *slowing* electrons. The faster an electron is traveling, the more energy it has.

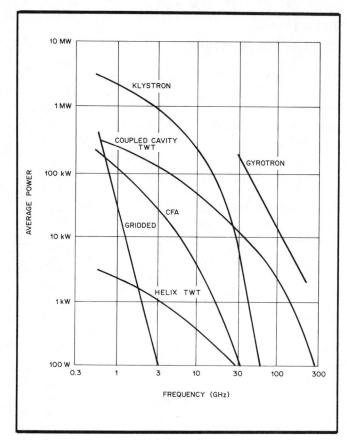

Fig 11—Comparison of average power capabilities of several microwave amplifier tubes.

In slowing down, electrons give up some of their energy. The reflex klystron creates a situation where energized electrons can give up their energy to a resonant circuit.

Fig 11 compares the average power output of several types of microwave amplifier tubes versus frequency. Note that conventional grid tubes provide plenty of power, but only at the low end of the microwave spectrum. The remaining tubes will operate at higher frequencies, but they are more frequency dependent and generally require more complicated power supplies and resonant circuits. Table 4 examines the operating parameters of the amplifier tubes of Fig 11.

REFLEX KLYSTRON

The reflex klystron, shown in Figs 12 and 13, uses a heated cathode to supply the energized electrons that are accelerated into the resonator because of its positive dc potential. The electrons travel at a uniform velocity until they reach the resonator. At the resonator, the speed of the electrons is either increased or decreased depending on the phase of the RF at the resonator. Those electrons that gain speed are sent closer to the repeller, and take longer to return to the resonator. Electrons that lose energy to the resonator (slow down) are able to return to the resonator sooner. Over the period of one cycle, the electrons

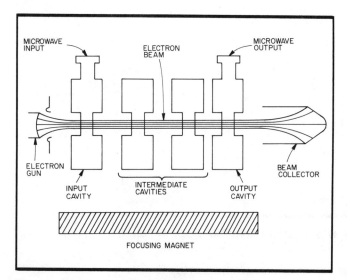

Fig 10—Block diagram of a typical klystron.

Table 4

Comparison of Microwave Tubes

Type	Bandwidth (%)	Efficiency (%)	Gain (dB)	Relative Spurious Signal Level*	Relative Operating Voltage	Relative Complexity of Operation*
Gridded tube	1-10	20-50	6-15	4	low	2
Klystron	1-5	30-70	40-60	2	high	4
Helix TWT	30-120	20-40	30-50	6	high	6
Coupled-cavity TWT	5-40	20-40	30-50	6	high	6
CFA	5-40	40-80	10-15	10	low	8
Gyrotron	1	20-40	30-40	8	high	10

*1 = best, 10 = poorest

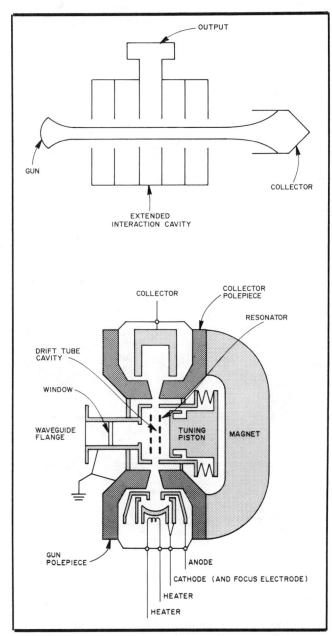

Fig 12—Internal cross-section of a typical reflex klystron.

Fig 13—Reflex klystrons. (photo courtesy Varian Associates, Inc)

that are sent closer to the repeller are caused to arrive back at the resonator at nearly the same time as the following electrons that lost energy while passing through the first time. The result is bunches of electrons passing through the resonator at regular intervals. By selecting appropriate operating voltages and, thereby, the right speed for the electrons, the resonator can be made to spend most of its time slowing electrons down. Remember, slowing electrons down is the only way to get energy from them. Since the energy is coming in periodic packets, and the resonant circuit is absorbing energy from the electrons, the conditions are right for sustaining oscillation.

Klystrons offer very high peak and average power, high gain and reasonable efficiency, but suffer from a very narrow bandwidth (only a few percent).

BEAM KLYSTRON

The beam klystron, shown in Fig 14, uses transit effects and the bunching of velocity-modulated electrons to provide either oscillation or amplification. The beam of electrons is formed by a focusing electrode and accelerat-

Fig 14—Beam klystron. *(photo courtesy of Varian Associates, Inc)*

ed by a modulating anode. The electrons travel past the modulating anode in a tight beam, and are prevented from striking the positively charged body by a protective magnetic field generated by externally mounted coils.

Upon leaving the electron gun portion of the klystron, the beam enters the input cavity in the body of the tube. The input cavity is resonant at a frequency near that of the input signal. It is here that velocity modulation is applied to the beam. The input signal is applied to a simple loop within the cavity, setting up a circulating RF field. The dc beam encounters this oscillating field upon entering the input cavity. As the charge across the RF gap alternates, electrons are alternately accelerated and decelerated across the gap of the cavity. This is velocity modulation.

The electrons then pass through an RF-neutral drift tube. This is where the effects of transit time are used to cause amplification of the RF signal. Electrons that were accelerated will tend to catch up with those ahead, forming bunches of negatively charged electrons. As the velocity-modulated beam enters the first tuned intermediate cavity it sets up a circulating RF field that reinforces the bunching action begun in the input cavity. This process is repeated as the beam passes through the remaining intermediate cavities. The electrons then enter the output cavity as a series of negatively charged ''bullets.'' These packets of electrons excite the cavity, generating a strong circulating field that is coupled to the outside world by another simple loop inside the output cavity.

RF output power is dependent on dc beam power and RF input power. Output power will increase in proportion to the input power until a saturation point is reached. After saturation, an increase in input power will actually result in a decrease in output power. Output power will also vary with slight changes in beam power, necessitating careful regulation of the beam supply.

Much less than half of the beam power is converted to RF power, leaving the remaining power to be dissipated as heat at the collector. In smaller klystrons this presents

no problem, but some klystrons are capable of delivering more than 50 kW of output power. For these larger klystrons, elaborate water-vapor cooling systems are necessary. Further, in the higher-power tubes, disruption of the magnetic field created by the magnet coils can allow the beam to strike the body of the klystron, destroying the tube almost instantly. For that reason, body current is metered continuously and beam power is removed if the body current exceeds certain limits. Additional protective circuits are used to prevent damage caused by arcing or excessive reflected power. Klystrons that show up in amateur service include the 723A/B, 2K25 and KS9-20.

MAGNETRON

The magnetron is currently produced in greater numbers than any other microwave tube—mostly due to the proliferation of microwave ovens! Although noisier than other microwave tubes, magnetrons are very efficient (up to 80 percent efficiency), inexpensive and can be used in high-power applications. Fig 15 shows a typical industrial magnetron.

The operating theory behind the magnetron shares several principles with that of the klystron. The main idea is to transfer energy from a dc electron beam to a resonant cavity. In the klystron, the electron beam travels in a straight line. In the magnetron, the electron beam is curved by a magnetic field. The physical structure can be seen in Fig 16(A), and the electron motion in Fig 16(B). The emitting cathode is in the center of the structure. As electrons are emitted, they are attracted to the positively charged

Fig 15—Industrial-grade magnetron. Notice the precision tuning mechanism on the top of the unit. *(photo courtesy of Varian Associates, Inc)*

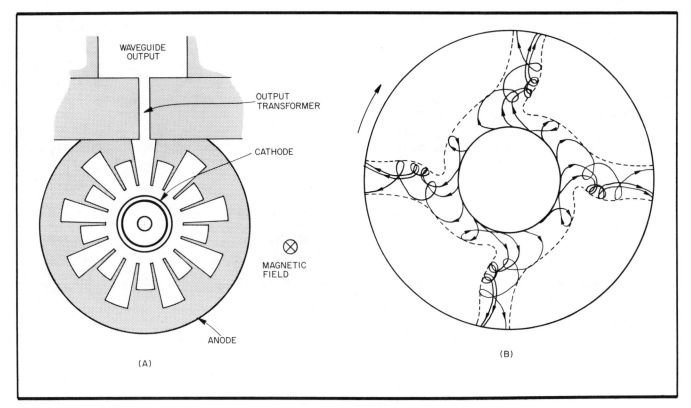

Fig 16—Drawing (A) and electron motion (B) of typical magnetron.

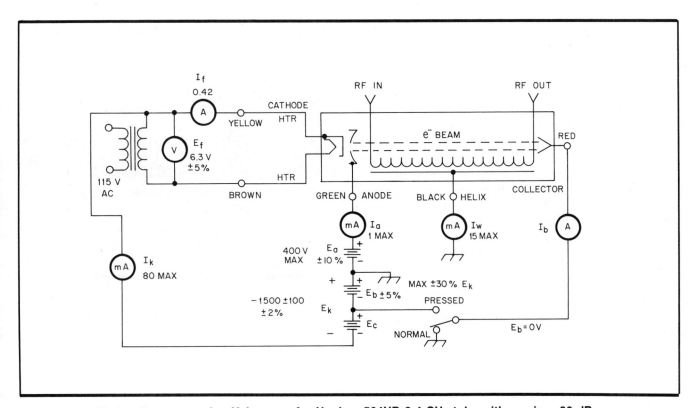

Fig 17—A 10-W traveling-wave tube. Values are for Hughes 564HD 2-4 GHz tube with a gain >30 dB.

outer ring. Instead of taking a straight-line course to the anode, electrons are deflected by a transverse magnetic field (causing them to take a curved path). Again, we find a resonant cavity that adds its charge to that of the magnetic field. At what point in the RF cycle an electron is emitted will determine the curvature of its path. An electron emitted when the charge causes it to take a less-curved path, will travel directly to the anode—the resonant cavity adds to the speed of the electrons. When the resonant cavity slows an electron down, the slower electron curves away from the anode and gives up some of its energy to the resonant cavity. This is called a working electron. Because working electrons stay in the interaction space for a longer period of time, the net result is that the RF cavities receive more energy than they give up. This, again, is the formula for oscillation.

TRAVELING-WAVE TUBE (TWT)

The traveling-wave tube (TWT), shown in Figs 17 and 18, is a close relative of the beam klystron. TWTs are used extensively to generate RF power above 2.3 GHz. Gain figures of 30 to 60 dB are common, but TWTs often need exotic multivoltage power supplies to function correctly. The price of a new TWT can easily reach $1000; the price of used or surplus TWTs varies. Because of the stringent power-supply requirements, commercially packaged TWTs with built-in power supplies, called traveling-wave tube amplifiers (TWTAs), are a sought-after item. Unfortunately, TWTAs are even more difficult to obtain than TWTs.

The beam generating portion of the TWT is identical to the klystron, but the beam modulation is applied in a fundamentally different manner. The input RF energy is applied to a radiating element that is positioned parallel to the path of the electron beam. The element is referred to as a slow-wave structure and is constructed in a way that "slows" the field propagation along the length of the element to near that of the speed of the electron beam. Individual electrons traveling beside the slow-wave structure "see" the same input phase the entire length of their travel. As in the case of the klystron, electrons that are accelerated "clump together" with electrons ahead of them that are slowed down. The interaction between the radiating element and the beam is such that the beam becomes velocity modulated. The output power is extracted from a resonant cavity at the end of the electron beam's travel, just as in a klystron.

BACKWARD-WAVE OSCILLATOR

The backward-wave oscillator is a special type of magnetron or traveling-wave tube. Fig 19 shows a typical BWO. In the backward-wave oscillator, the interaction between emitted electrons and a series of resonant cavities results in the build-up of RF energy in a "backward" direction, that is, the strongest RF field is closest to the emitting portion of the anode. See Fig 20. With only minor modifications, the backward-wave oscillator can become a forward-wave oscillator. The operation is identical; only the direction of wave propagation is different.

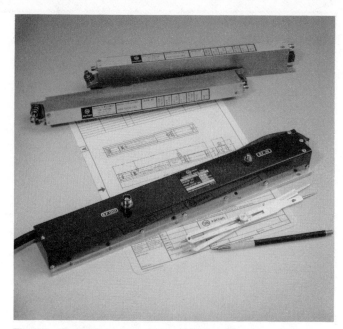

Fig 18—Traveling-wave tubes. Note size references. (photo courtesy Varian Associates, Inc)

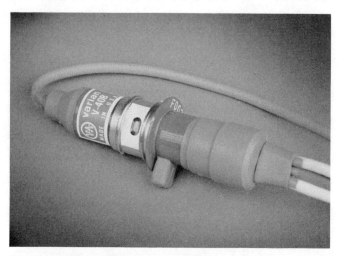

Fig 19—Varian V-40B backward-wave oscillator. (photo courtesy Varian Associates, Inc)

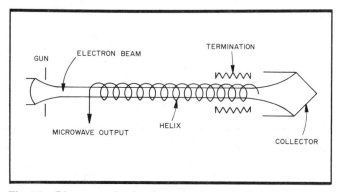

Fig 20—Diagram of a backward-wave oscillator.

Solid-State Devices

Until the development of solid-state devices, the only method of generating and amplifying microwave energy was to density modulate a flow of electrons. With solid-state devices, novel techniques of generating microwave energy have emerged. Three-terminal solid-state devices include bipolar transistors, FETs, HEMTs and a relative newcomer to the microwave field, the MMIC (monolithic microwave integrated circuit). Two-terminal devices for generation and amplification of microwave energy include the Gunn diode, TRAPATT and IMPATT diodes, step-recovery diodes (SRDs), varactor diodes and tunnel diodes. Other microwave diodes, primarily used as detectors, include the point-contact diode and the hot-carrier diode. These devices employ mechanisms fundamentally different from those of most tubes and three-terminal solid-state devices.

We'll briefly discuss two other solid-state type devices: the DRO (dielectric resonator oscillator) and the magnetic resonator oscillator, commonly called a YIG (which stands for yttrium iron garnet, a crystalline growth similar to silicon).

GUNN DIODE

A popular device for generating microwave energy, the Gunn diode is named after its developer, J. B. Gunn, and is typically made from a compound semiconductor such as GaAs. Because of its operating characteristics, the Gunn diode can oscillate without an external resonant cavity. Fig 21 shows the equivalent circuit of a Gunn diode.

Negative differential resistance is a concept used in understanding the operation of any amplifying or oscillating device, but it's particularly suited to a description of the Gunn diode. The Gunn diode is a "transferred electron device" (TED) that exhibits "negative differential resistance" (NDR). Normally, as we increase voltage across a device, we expect the current to increase as well. That is, we expect the resistance to remain constant. In a Gunn diode, there is a range of voltages where this is not true. As the voltage across the Gunn diode is increased, current increases to a certain point—but as the voltage goes beyond a certain threshold, instead of increasing current, the added energy goes to transferring electrons to higher mass. Thus, an increase in voltage corresponds to a decrease in current. This can be interpreted as a lowering of the diode's resistance as the voltage increases, or a negative differential resistance. Fig 22 shows the Gunn diode's electron velocity versus the applied electric field. The negative resistance region is clearly visible.

Consider the physics behind negative differential resistance. A brief review of the nature of conduction will be helpful. When we cause conduction in a material, we are applying voltage to move electrons through it. In a conductor, electrons already have sufficient energy to move freely through the material, so we need apply only a small voltage to create cause conduction. An insulator is a material in which the valence electrons need much more

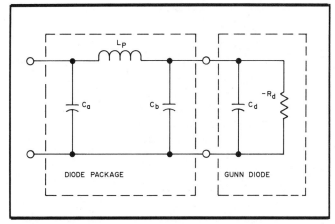

Fig 21—Equivalent circuit of a Gunn diode. The parasitic reactances of the diode package are included.

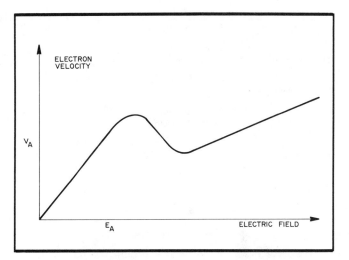

Fig 22—The Gunn diode's electron velocity versus applied electric field. The negative resistance region is clearly visible.

encouragement (in the form of higher voltage) to provide conduction. A semiconductor is an in-between material where valence electrons have only slightly less energy than is needed for conduction. With the application of sufficient voltage, conduction can be produced.

Electrons available for conduction in the semiconductor material used in a Gunn oscillator can conduct in one of two energy states. The energy state a particular electron conducts in is a matter of chance, with the odds determined by the applied charge (voltage). As the charge is increased, so is the likelihood of an electron occupying the higher energy state. The electrons occupying the higher-energy band actually have a greater mass, and move more slowly than the low-energy electrons under the same charge. (The higher-energy electrons are said to have a lower mobility.) Since we measure current as the number of electrons crossing a point during a fixed period of time, slower moving electrons result in less current.

There is a range of applied voltage where the electrons migrate from the lower energy state to the higher energy state. During this range of voltage, negative differential resistance occurs. By carefully controlling the application of the voltage across the device, we can create a situation where the NDR region is reached at the cathode end. This can result in higher-energy electrons moving more slowly through the semiconductor material than neighboring lower-energy electrons. As the electrons pass through the solid-state device, the slower electrons bunch up against the faster, lower-energy electrons. At the point where the electron energy differential becomes significant (the NDR region), instead of normal electron flow we see a region where electrons are scarce, followed by a region where electrons are plentiful. This creates a charge dipole that drifts through the solid-state material until it emerges at the anode end as a powerful pulse. When this charge dipole forms, the charge outside the dipole region drops below the threshold NDR region. Not until the mature dipole passes through to the anode will the charge at the cathode end return to the NDR threshold, causing another pulse to form and drift through the diode. The frequency is dependent only on the length of the drift and the velocity of the electrons through the material.

A key feature of the Gunn diode is its ability to oscillate without any resonant cavities. Although no resonant cavities are required to cause the diode to oscillate, an external resonant circuit is required to extract the microwave power. It is the negative differential resistance that accounts for the behavior that occurs within the semiconductor material.

IMPATT DIODE

IMPATT stands for IMPact ionization Avalanche Transit-Time operation. The IMPATT diode differs from the Gunn diode in several respects. The Gunn diode consists of a simple bulk semiconductor. The IMPATT diode is a more complex structure consisting of several layers of semiconducting material of different majority charge carrier and levels of doping. See Fig 23. The IMPATT diode operates with a negative bias close to the avalanche breakdown point. When proper circuit conditions are present, the IMPATT diode delivers current pulses that lag the applied input voltage by nearly 180°. The lag is caused by a combination of the time required to create the current pulse and the time necessary for the pulse to drift through the diode. If the diode is placed in a resonant cavity with a period near that of the time for the current pulse to form and drift through the device, the result is a negative differential resistance. That is, the output current pulse occurs during the negative excursion of the input RF signal. Fig 24 shows an IMPATT oscillator with a resonant cavity.

Because of the low efficiency of the single-drift IMPATT (12 to 15 percent), an alternate structure has been devised offering 20 to 30% efficiency. The modified structure simply allows the use of both hole and electron charge

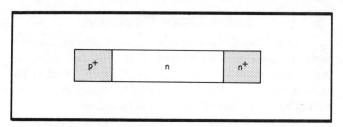

Fig 23—Construction detail of an IMPATT diode.

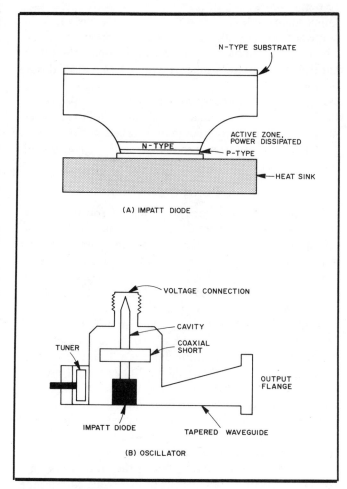

Fig 24—An IMPATT oscillator and associated waveguide cavity.

carriers, allowing each to drift through the device and contribute to the current pulse. This is referred to as a double-drift device.

IMPATTs are used at frequencies ranging from 3 to 100 GHz. Because the avalanche breakdown is noisy, use of IMPATT devices as receiver LOs is unusual. Despite the fact that IMPATTs are natural oscillators, most IMPATTs are used as amplifiers. Use of an IMPATT as an amplifier requires an RF circulator to isolate the input from the output, and to allow coupling to the device.

TRAPATT DIODES

TRAPATTs (TRApped Plasma Avalanche Triggered Transit), curiously, were developed in large part to operate at frequencies lower than IMPATTs are capable of. TRAPATT construction and operation is similar to the IMPATT. In fact, many TRAPATT devices will operate in either IMPATT or TRAPATT mode. Trapped plasma is a high-density region of charge carriers (both holes and electrons) in a low-level electric field. The plasma is said to be trapped because it moves slowly in comparison to the saturation velocity of the charge carriers. When a pulse is applied to the TRAPATT diode that is biased near avalanche breakdown, an "avalanche shock front" travels through the device at a rate faster than the saturation velocity of the carriers. This shock front creates the plasma condition within the semiconductor material. The high density of positive and negative charge carriers has dielectric properties, and is effectively shielded from the external electric charge. This results in the relatively slow sweeping of the charge carriers from the region.

The shock front passing through the semiconductor material causes the terminal voltage to rapidly fall to a low value. The fast change in voltage makes the device appear to be a fast, low-impedance electronic switch. If the device is placed in a circuit, this switch action will result in a current pulse being delivered to the transmission line. The action of the low-pass filter is responsible for providing the necessary current pulses to maintain the oscillation. The filter will accept energy at the fundamental TRAPATT frequency, but will reflect energy at higher frequencies. Since the current pulse has a fast rise-time, the signal will be rich in harmonics, providing ample reflected energy to sustain oscillations.

TUNNEL DIODES

The tunnel diode is another "negative resistance" semiconductor, consisting of an alloy junction in which the impurity level is several thousand times that of a conventional diode. The high impurity level permits fast electron transit times, but the diode junction must be kept small to minimize junction capacitance, which is higher than in most other diodes. Fig 25 shows current and voltage curves for a tunnel diode and a conventional diode. The negative resistance region, so common among microwave diodes, permits the tunnel diode to be used as an oscillator. The extreme simplicity of the device makes it ideal for use in stripline waveguides (see Fig 26).

VARACTOR DIODES

The varactor diode consists of a PN junction whose capacitance varies with the amount of applied reverse voltage. See Figs 27(A) and 27(B). The electrons in the N-type material are attracted to the positive battery terminal, and the electrons in the P-type material are attracted to the negative terminal. This creates a "depletion zone" at the center of the diode. See Fig 27(B). This depletion zone acts as a dielectric between the two "plates" (the P- and N-

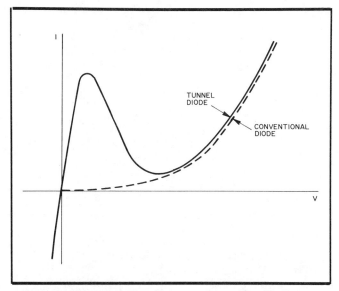

Fig 25—Tunnel diode characteristics compared to those of a conventional diode.

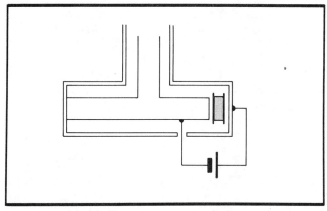

Fig 26—A tunnel diode mounted in a coaxial resonator.

type material); as the reverse voltage increases, the "plates" move farther apart, decreasing the capacitance of the junction. A representative varactor circuit is shown in Fig 28.

Varactor capacitance values range from a few picofarads to more than 100 pF (MV2101 through MV2115, or 1N5441A through 1N5476A). Varactors function well into the microwave spectrum; they're excellent frequency multipliers and can be used as voltage-controlled oscillators. Fig 29 shows the capacitance versus reverse-voltage curves for three Motorola™ varactors.

STEP-RECOVERY DIODES

The step-recovery diode, sometimes called a "snap" diode, is used extensively in microwave frequency multipliers and comb generators. The SRD is characterized by its extremely low capacitance and short storage time. Switch-

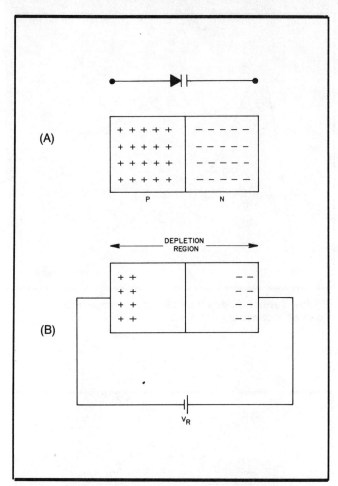

Fig 27—A varactor diode is a heavily doped PN diode (A). The capacitance of the diode is controlled by the reverse-bias voltage (B). See text for details.

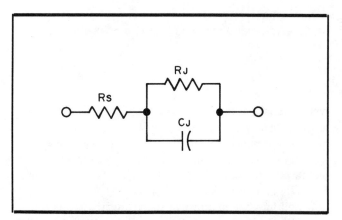

Fig 28—Representative circuit of a varactor diode showing case resistance, junction resistance and junction capacitance.

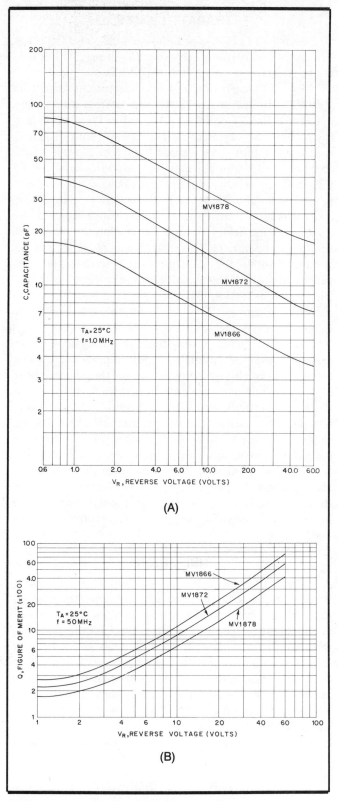

Fig 29—Electrical characteristics of three popular Motorola® varactor diodes.

ing the device in and out of conduction is the multiplication mechanism; its power efficiency is inversely proportional to the frequency multiple.

A single harmonic of the excitation frequency can be selected by an interdigital filter. A 1-W, 220-MHz exciter can drive an SRD multiplier ($\times 46$) to produce a 10-mW, 10-GHz signal (see Fig 30).

HEMTs

Another state-of-the-art microwave device that is catching the interest of microwave designers is the HEMT (High-Electron-Mobility Transistor), a GaAsFET derivative. HEMTs have a cutoff frequency roughly twice that of comparable GaAsFETs—with a much better noise figure. HEMTs, shown in Fig 31, are still in the developmental stage, so the HEMTs that are available over the counter cost about $150 (at the time of this writing). As the devices become commercially available the prices will drop—much the same way GaAsFETs did in the late '70s. Fig 32 compares the noise figures of several types of microwave transistors.

MONOLITHIC MICROWAVE INTEGRATED CIRCUITS (MMICs)

MMICs are high-performance, self-contained RF amplifiers that function well into the microwave spectrum. Fig 33 shows the external geometry of a typical MMIC. These four-terminal (signal in, signal out and two ground connections) devices are inexpensive, have 50-ohm input and output impedances, and are easily cascadable—thus simplifying many microwave circuits. Fig 34 shows typical gain figures for several popular MMIC series. Fig 35 shows typical output power levels for the same devices. MMICs are generally used from HF through 6 GHz, with 1-GHz noise figures of 3 to 7 dB. A representative MMIC circuit is shown in Fig 36.

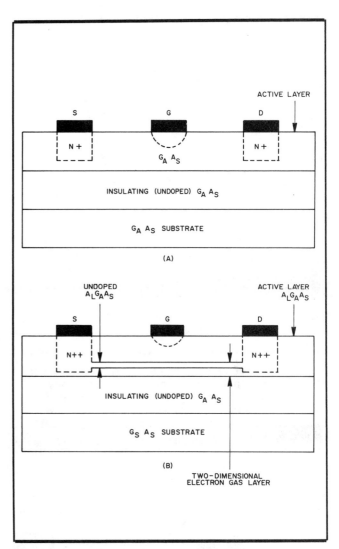

Fig 31—Physical structure of a GaAsFET (A), and a recent variation, the HEMT (B). Diagrams are not shown to scale.

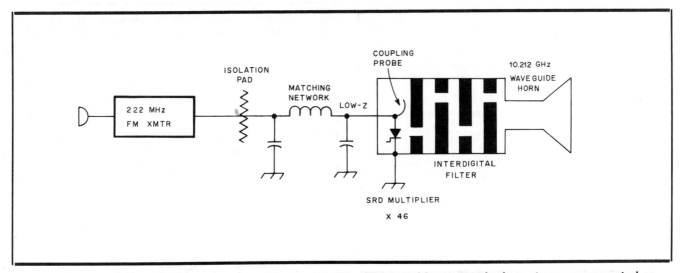

Fig 30—Step-recovery-diode frequency multiplier for 10 GHz. The matching network elements are represented as lumped components but would take the form of a microstripline in an actual design.

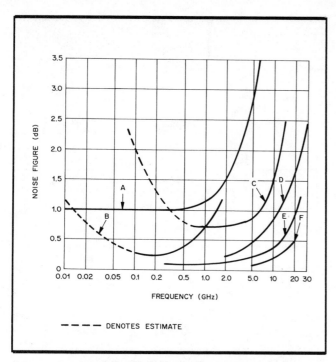

Fig 32—Late 1980s-era state-of-the-art noise figures: (A) uncooled bipolar transistor; (B) low-frequency GaAsFET at room temperature; (C) high-frequency GaAsFET at room temperature; (D) HEMT at room temperature; (E) GaAsFET cooled to 10 K; (F) HEMT cooled to 10 K.

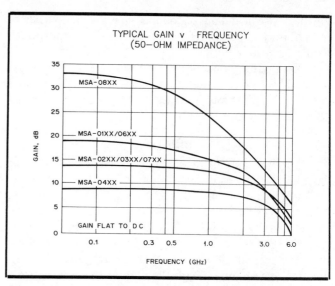

Fig 34—Gain versus frequency charts for several popular MMICs. *(diagram courtesy of Avantek)*

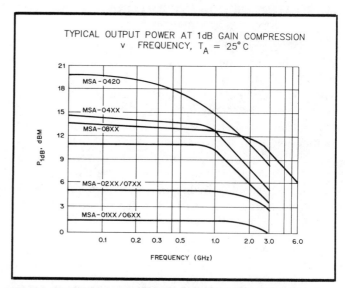

Fig 35—Power output versus frequency for several popular MMICs. *(diagram courtesy of Avantek)*

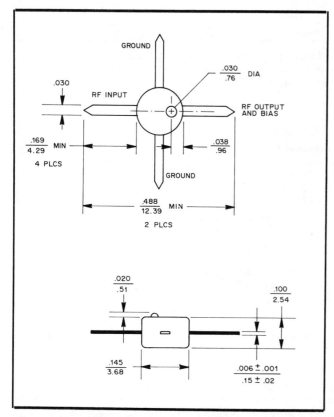

Fig 33—External detail of a typical MMIC. *(diagram courtesy of Avantek)*

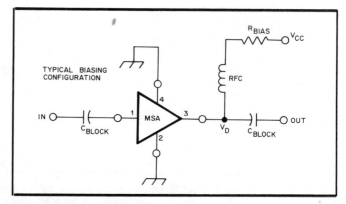

Fig 36—A typical MMIC amplifier circuit.

DIELECTRIC RESONANT OSCILLATOR (DRO)

Another interesting microwave device is the dielectric resonator oscillator (DRO). See Fig 37. The DRO is purchased as a complete module, requiring only the application of power to operate at its designed frequency. The key component in a DRO is the dielectric resonator itself. Instead of relying on a resonant cavity or transit-time effects to stabilize its frequency, the DRO relies on the coupling of a resonant field induced in a cylindrical section of dielectric material. The dielectric resonator is in close proximity to a microstrip transmission line. The resonant frequency of the dielectric encourages oscillations at the desired frequency and damps oscillations at other frequencies, exactly as a resonant cavity does. See Fig 38. The ceramic material used to construct DROs is barium tetratitanate, which has a dielectric constant of about 38. The cylindrical resonator is usually located between two grounded plates, as shown in Fig 38(A). The magnetic and electric fields are shown in Figs 38(C) and 38(B). The resonant frequency is determined by the shape of the ceramic material, the spacing of the grounded plates and the amount of coupling to the oscillator circuit. In addition to its stable frequency output, the DRO is an economical alternative for microwave generation. Advantages of the DRO include ease of use, temperature stability and low cost. The disadvantages include a susceptibility to FM noise and a relatively narrow tuning range. DROs operate from approximately 4 to 16 GHz, with power outputs ranging between a few milliwatts to 40 mW.

YIGs (MAGNETIC RESONATOR OSCILLATORS)

A typical YIG consists of a small, polished sphere of yttrium iron garnet, a coupling loop and a fixed magnetic field (see Fig 39). The YIG sphere is magnetized, and if permitted, would align itself within the fixed magnetic field, much like the needle of a compass. To stop this rotation, the sphere is attached to the end of a support rod with just enough "tension" to allow a small amount of lateral force to be exerted on the YIG. When an RF signal is passed through the coupling loop, it magnetically interacts with the sphere, especially if the signal in the loop is close to the natural resonant frequency of the sphere. The resonant frequency of the YIG can be adjusted by changing the intensity of its surrounding magnetic field (with an external electromagnet).

Fig 40 shows a typical YIG-tuned oscillator. Nearly the whole package represents the structure of the electromagnet. Table 5 compares the performance characteristics of several microwave oscillators.

(A)

(B)

Fig 37—At A, a dielectric resonator oscillator (DRO). At B, a DRO microwave oscillator circuit built using thin-film circuitry on a ceramic substrate. *(photos courtesy of Avantek)*

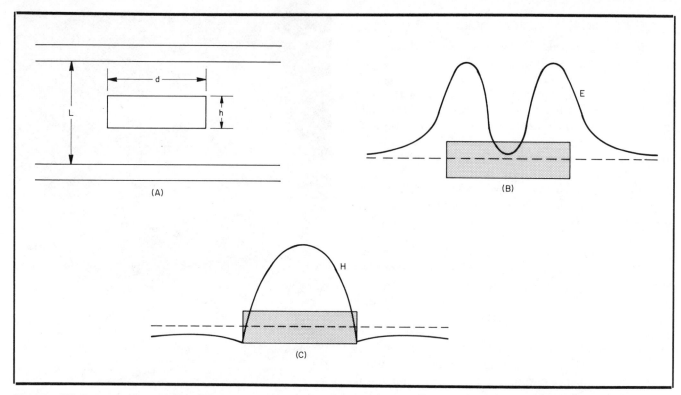

Fig 38—(A) Construction of the dielectric resonator oscillator. (B) and (C) show the distribution of electric and magnetic fields within the resonator.

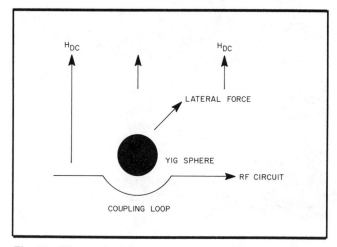

Fig 39—Theoretical construction of a YIG resonator.

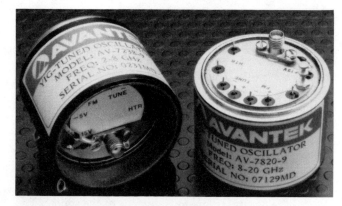

Fig 40—Although the actual electronic circuitry in a YIG-tuned oscillator may weigh only a few grams, the complete oscillator can weigh more than a pound. *(photo courtesy of Avantek)*

Table 5

Oscillator Performance Characteristics

Oscillator Type	Frequency Range (GHz)	Bandwidth	RF Power (W)	Phase Noise*
VCO	0.01 to 20	2:1 or less	10 mW	3
YIG	0.5 to 26.5	4:1	10 mW	2
TED(Gunn)	10 to 80	1.5:1	10 mW	1
IMPATT	10 to 250	1.2:1	1 W	4

*phase noise: 1(low), 4(high)

Detectors

The metal-semiconductor diode is the device most commonly used as a microwave detector. "Metal-semiconductor" is a generic term referring to a type of diode construction where the rectifying junction is metal to semiconductor rather than, say, semiconductor to semiconductor. This technique was first used in the germanium point-contact diode where a tungsten wire is formed to press in a point on to a semiconductor slab (see Fig 41).

The principle of operation involves majority carriers only and is especially suited to high-frequency operation because of the low resultant junction capacitance. Recombination time is largely responsible for the effective capacitance of a diode junction. In a forward-biased PN junction, majority carriers cross the junction and become minority carriers. It takes some time for these minority carriers to recombine, and if the bias reverses before recombination occurs, the carriers will return across the junction as a current pulse. This effect is very much like that of a capacitor's stored charge and is called the junction's storage capacitance. Because the point-contact diode uses only majority carriers, recombination times are extremely short.

The principle of operation behind the point-contact diode is difficult to explain without resorting to complex concepts. The theory, developed by Schottky in 1938, proposed that a potential barrier could arise in a semiconductor without the presence of a chemical layer. Hence, a contact between metal and semiconductor would result in an energy difference (potential barrier) between electrons in the metal and semiconductor such that bias in one direction would lower the barrier height, allowing electrons to cross the junction, and bias in the other direction would add to the barrier height, preventing current flow. Diodes of that type are referred to as Schottky-barrier diodes.

Another more recent advance in MES or Schottky-barrier diodes is the hot-carrier diode (HCD), shown in Fig 42. The HCD uses layers of N-type semiconductor appropriately doped to allow a current of higher mobility ("hotter") electrons. The HCD improves on virtually all characteristics of a microwave diode.

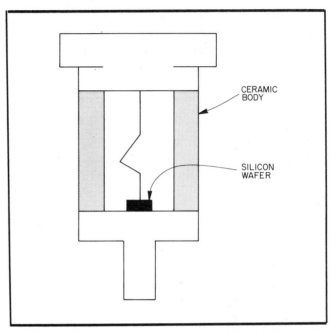

Fig 41—Point-contact diode in a coaxial mount.

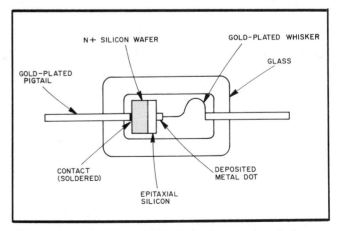

Fig 42—Construction detail of the hot-carrier diode.

Bibliography

Brodribb, P. B., G3ONL, "Microwave diodes." *Radio Communication,* August 1971.

Cheung and Levien, Eds, *Microwaves Made Simple: Principles and Applications.* Dedham, MA: Artech House, Inc, 1985.

Coleman, *Microwave Devices.* Reston, Virginia: Reston Publishing, 1982.

Griffiths, H., G4CNV, "Traveling-wave tube amplifiers." *Radio Communication,* September 1980.

Harvey, *Microwave Engineering.* New York: Academic Press, 1963.

Liao, *Microwave Solid-State Devices.* Englewood Cliffs, New Jersey: Prentice-Hall, Inc, 1985.

Pehl, E., *Microwave Technology.* Dedham, MA: Artech House, 1985.

Reich, H., *Microwave Principles.* Princeton, NJ: Van Nostrand, 1957.

Rizzi, P., *Microwave Engineering (Passive Circuits).* Englewood Cliffs, NJ: Prentice Hall, 1988.

Sze, *Physics of Semiconductor Devices.* New York: Wiley-Interscience, 1969.

Van Der Heijden, B. J., "Dielectric-resonator oscillators—a new microwave signal source." *Electronic Components and applications*, Vol 4 No. 4, August 1982 (Philips Tech pub 081).

Walworth, J. H., "Theory of Operation of the DRO." *RF Design,* January 1985.

Chapter 5

Transmission Media

By Dr H. Paul Shuch, N6TX
Professor of Electronics
Pennsylvania College of Technology
1 College Ave
Williamsport, PA 17701

5.1 INTRODUCTION

One way of differentiating between microwaves and the rest of the electromagnetic spectrum is through the distinction of lumped versus distributed constants. In the microwave region, we frequently replace inductors, capacitors and resistors with transmission lines that exhibit the properties of inductance, capacitance and resistance. In this chapter, we will analyze different types of transmission lines to determine their electrical properties at microwave frequencies. We will then review a number of different practical transmission media in terms of physical implementation, electrical limitations and interconnect requirements. The underlying theme of this chapter is that a transmission line, as used by microwave experimenters, is far more than a convenient way of connecting a transceiver to an antenna!

Before we begin our study of the transmission of electromagnetic waves through various media, it is important to standardize on a common set of concepts and terminology. The importance of such standardization is vastly underrated by radio amateurs, and is best emphasized by means of a personal example.

Although a schoolteacher by trade, I frequently find myself engaged as a consulting engineer in the field of microwave communications. I recently wheeled into a prospective client's parking lot, eager to tackle a new technical challenge, and was met by my employer. Inquiring about the significance of my personalized license plates, he was told that they displayed my Amateur Radio call letters. "You are an *amateur* radio operator?" he mused in disbelief. "I thought I was hiring a professional."

There was a time, not long ago, when radio amateurs were much in demand as consultants or employees, when the major breakthroughs of the communications art came not from the halls of academia or the well-equipped laboratories of industry, but from the basements, garages and tool sheds of our self-trained brethren who were willing to accomplish any task, not knowing the meaning of the word "impossible." If we have fallen into disfavor in the world of professional electronics, it is because we may have failed to mature with the industry. This is most evident in our inability, as a group, to communicate advanced technical concepts with clarity. We tend (and I realize all generalizations are untrue, including this one) to shun rigid standardization of terms and concepts, in favor of a loose, informal jargon, so that we fail to communicate effectively with our more structured, professional colleagues. And communications is what Amateur Radio is supposed to be all about!

To avoid any miscommunication in these pages, I would like to devote a few paragraphs to the standardization of terminology, before we address the subject of transmission lines in earnest. And since transmission lines carry energy from point A to point B, we should really start with energy fundamentals.

5.2 FUNDAMENTAL ENERGY CONCEPTS

If we had to define technology in its most basic terms, we might describe it as man's efforts to harness and convert energy. Energy, the capacity for performing work, occurs in nature in many different forms (including, but not limited to, chemical, mechanical, thermal, nuclear, and of course electrical). What we call technological progress is merely our ever-increasing ability to alter the environment by converting energy from one form to another—at will and under complete control. It is this modification of the environment that we call work. Of course, no energy conversion is one hundred percent efficient, and the Laws of Thermodynamics tell us that, in any energy conversion, we are going to "spill" some along the way—usually in the form of heat.

Just as matter can exist in various states (solid, liquid, gaseous), so energy, of whatever form, can occupy two possible states: potential and kinetic. We generally define potential energy as energy of position or location, and kinetic energy as that of a mass in motion. Since potential and kinetic energy are duals, any manipulation we perform on one has its dual, or equivalent manipulation, for the other. It is this duality that interrelates the various reciprocal electronics parameters with which we are familiar.

Electrical potential energy per unit charge (V or E) we recognize as electromotive force (EMF) or potential difference, measured in volts.[1] Since electrical current (I), measured in amperes, specifies the rate of motion of charged particles (that exhibit mass), current is a manifestation of electrical kinetic energy per unit flux. Just how much mass do charged particles exhibit? Precious little. A single electron, for example, weighs about a billionth of a billionth of a billionth of a gram! Yet any mass in motion, no matter how minute, exhibits kinetic energy. And current is normally measured in coulombs per second (amperes), a coulomb being about six billion billion electrons' worth of charge. Hence the kinetic energy represented by each ampere of current is hardly insignificant.

Our harnessing of electrical energy involves the ability to convert it from the potential to the kinetic state, and back again, at will. Resistance (R) represents the conversion of electrical potential to kinetic energy. Its value, measured in ohms, is merely an expression of the ratio of potential energy per unit charge (EMF) applied, to the resulting kinetic energy per unit flux (current). We call the mathematical expression of this ratio Ohm's Law, and it merely quantifies the conversion of potential to kinetic energy.

I know, you've probably been taught that resistance is the opposition to current flow, and as far as that statement goes, it's correct. But opposition defines one of the things resistance *does*, not what resistance *is*.

The dual of resistance, conductance (G), represents the conversion of electrical kinetic to potential energy. Its value, measured in mhos or siemens (after Werner von Siemens, the inventor of coaxial cable), is an expression of the ratio of kinetic energy (in amperes) applied, to the resulting potential energy (in volts) appearing across the circuit.

The ability of a capacitor to store potential energy (in the form of electrostatic lines of force) should be familiar to you. Capacitance (C) is defined as the ratio of potential energy (EMF) to stored charge. Similarly, an inductor (which is the dual of a capacitor) stores kinetic energy in the form of a magnetic field. Thus inductance (L) can be defined as the ratio of kinetic energy (current) to stored flux.

As you will recall, both inductors and capacitors exhibit a reactance (X), measured in ohms, that involves both stored energy and angular velocity. Thus we can consider reactance as involving energy stored per unit time. The dual of reactance is susceptance, measured in mhos or siemens, which we can relate to energy *released* from storage over time.

We define impedance (Z) as the combination of resistance and reactance occurring in a series circuit. It is important to note that the term impedance is properly applied to series circuits *only*, and if any other circuit configuration exists, it must be converted to its series equivalent before impedance can be specified. Mathematically, impedance is the vector sum of resistance (the conversion of potential to kinetic energy) and reactance (energy stored over time).

The dual of impedance is admittance (Y), measured in mhos or siemens. This we define as the combination of conductance and susceptance found in a parallel circuit. It is important to note that the term admittance is properly applied to parallel circuits *only*, and if any other circuit configuration exists, it must be converted to its parallel equivalent before admittance can be specified. Mathematically, admittance is the vector sum of conductance (the conversion of kinetic to potential energy) and susceptance (energy released from storage over time).

The mathematical purist will deem the above definitions simplistic, and rightly so. They do, however, provide us with a framework within which to quantify the behavior of microwave transmission lines, and thus all circuits and systems that operate on the principle of distributed constants.

5.3 TRANSMISSION LINE CONCEPTS

Let us now consider the transfer of power (P), a function of both potential energy (V) and kinetic energy (I).[2] An electromagnetic wave consists of orthogonal electrostatic and magnetic fields. Since the electrostatic field is a manifestation of potential energy and the magnetic field is a manifestation of kinetic energy, it should be obvious that an electromagnetic wave can transfer power through space—or any other transmission medium. The physical orientation of the electrostatic and magnetic fields, with respect to each other and to the direction of wave propagation, defines the propagation mode of the electromagnetic wave.

Propagation of Electromagnetic Waves

The simplest model for wave propagation involves electromagnetic induction. Consider that a wave may be coupled into its transmission medium through the application of an electrostatic (E) field, which expands and collapses over time at a rate established by the frequency of the wave.

This expanding and collapsing electrostatic field will induce, ahead of it in the transmission medium, a corresponding expanding and collapsing magnetic (H) field, that will in turn induce in front of it yet another electrostatic field, and so forth. This repeated conversion of energy from its potential state to its kinetic state, and back again, repeats unabated until the wave encounters an impedance discontinuity in its transmission medium. And the physical space between successive recurrences of the electrostatic (or magnetic) fields represents wavelength. This, of course, is related to the frequency of the wave by the velocity at which the wave propagates through its medium.

CHARACTERISTIC IMPEDANCE

One way to quantify the energy conversions that apply within any medium through which electromagnetic radiation propagates is to define the ratio of total potential to kinetic energy as the wave travels infinitely through the medium. From this theoretical (though somewhat impractical) measure comes one of the fundamental parameters of a transmission medium, its characteristic impedance.

Communications textbooks traditionally define characteristic impedance as the impedance (potential to kinetic energy ratio) seen by an electromagnetic wave propagating through an infinitely long section of the medium.[3] Another expression for characteristic impedance is surge impedance, and both are abbreviated Z_0.

Since financial constraints alone (not to mention physical limitations) impact the ready availability of infinitely long transmission lines, an alternate definition is desirable. The one presented in the textbooks represents the kind of circuitous logic worthy of the best of government agencies: Characteristic impedance is the impedance seen by an electromagnetic wave propagating through a finite section of a given transmission medium, the far end of which is terminated in its characteristic impedance!

Measuring characteristic impedance is not really as hopeless as it may seem, thanks to a phenomenon known as wave reflection. We will discuss reflections in greater detail in a later section, but for now suffice it to say that any time an electromagnetic wave propagating through a transmission medium encounters an impedance discontinuity, a portion of the wave turns around and travels in the opposite direction. Since numerous laboratory techniques exist for measuring the magnitude of such reflections, we can find the characteristic impedance of a finite line by terminating it in a variable impedance and adjusting the termination impedance until reflections disappear. Having done so, the load is measured, and its impedance is of course equal to the transmission line's Z_0.

An alternative measurement technique involves successively terminating a finite transmission line section in an open and a short circuit, and measuring the input impedance for each case, at a given frequency. Characteristic impedance at that frequency[4] is then found from

$$Z_0 = \sqrt{Z_{oc} \times Z_{sc}} \qquad \text{(Eq 1)}$$

where

    Z_{oc} = the measured input impedance with the line terminated in an open circuit

    Z_{sc} = measured input impedances with the line terminated in a short circuit

One limitation of the above technique is that it may be impossible to terminate the physical line in a true open circuit. This problem will be explored in Section 5.4.

An analytical approach to the definition of surge impedance involves quantifying the total resistance, conductance, inductance and capacitance in a finite section of the transmission medium. At a given frequency, characteristic impedance is then found algebraically

$$Z_0 = \sqrt{\frac{R + j\omega L}{G + j\omega C}} \qquad \text{(Eq 2)}$$

where

    R = the series resistance of the line

    G = the shunt conductance of the line

    L = the distributed inductance of the finite line section

    C = the distributed capacitance of the finite line section

    ω = the angular velocity, in radians per second, found from

$$\omega = 2\pi f \qquad \text{(Eq 3)}$$

    where f is the frequency in Hz.

Unfortunately, as the presence of the imaginary operator (the factor $+j$ in Eq 2) indicates, this fundamental expression of characteristic impedance involves the use of complex algebra. For those who are easily intimidated by mathematics (and that includes your author!) let me assure you that "complex" in this case does not necessarily mean "difficult." Complex numbers are simply those containing both real and imaginary numbers, with an imaginary number being one that contains the square root of a negative number. The imaginary operator, j, represents the square root of negative one, or more properly, that number whose square equals negative one. You say that's impossible? That's why it's called an imaginary number!

While on the subject of complex numbers, it is important to note that their manipulation is a mainstay of *analog* circuit analysis. It is therefore ironic that the development of what was arguably the world's first *digital* computer resulted from a need to solve for the complex impedance of transmission lines. Model One was constructed by Dr George Stibitz at Bell Laboratories between 1937 and 1939, at a cost of $20,000. Its two eight-foot high relay racks housed 32 bytes (yes, that's bytes, *not* kilobytes!) of binary memory. Although Model One's relay banks were perhaps 500 times slower than the vacuum tube computers that were to follow, this machine succeeded in reducing the computation time for transmission line analysis by two thirds. And where else but the phone company would you expect to find mechanical switching relays solving for the imaginary operator?

For those who employ only ideal, lossless transmission lines in their ham stations (and doesn't that include all of us?) a simplification of Eq 2 is possible that eliminates the need for complex arithmetic. Consider that a perfect transmission line (or a short length of imperfect transmission line) may have so low a series resistance and shunt conductance that the two can be considered negligible. That being the case, the characteristic impedance equation becomes

$$Z_0 = \sqrt{L/C} \qquad \text{(Eq 4)}$$

Notice that the imaginary operators and angular velocities cancel, leaving surge impedance equal to simply the square root of the ratio of distributed inductance to capacitance. You will also note that the characteristic impedance of an ideal transmission medium appears to be independent of frequency! We shall make use of this discovery shortly. Although there are specific transmission lines (particularly waveguide) for which these simplifying assumptions do not hold, Eq 4 is a convenient tool for transmission line analysis—one that we will use extensively throughout this chapter.

CHARACTERISTIC ADMITTANCE

The dual of impedance being admittance, the reciprocal of a transmission medium's Z_0, in ohms, is simply characteristic admittance, Y_0, measured in siemens. As our earlier discussions in Section 5.2 imply, Z_0 would be used when the transmission line is modeled as a series equivalent circuit, and Y_0 when a parallel circuit model is employed.

ATTENUATION AND INSERTION LOSS

It should be evident by now that at its operating frequency, any transmission medium can be represented by a series combination of resistance, inductive reactance and capacitive reactance, these values defining its characteristic impedance Z_0. Alternately, we can model the same transmission medium as a parallel combination of conductance, inductive susceptance and capacitive susceptance, these values together defining the medium's characteristic admittance Y_0. If we apply a signal of known power to one end of a finite section of the transmission medium, a signal of some lesser power is available at its output end. The amplitude difference between the input and output signals is called insertion loss. Insertion loss is abbreviated α (the Greek letter alpha) and is generally measured in decibels (see Chapter 7).

Two separate factors contribute to the insertion loss in a transmission medium: reflection and dissipation. Each is related to a different portion of the transmission line model employed. Let us first consider the dissipative losses, which are also known as attenuation.

A transmission line's attenuation refers to the power loss it introduces into the system because of heat. That is, as a transmission line carries power between a source and a load, some of that power will be dissipated. You may recall that, in any circuit, power dissipation is the product of potential, current, and the so-called Power Factor (which is equal to the cosine of the phase angle between the EMF and current waveforms).

A transmission line is a combination of resistance, conductance, capacitance and inductance, but only the resistive and conductive parts can dissipate power. That is because it is only in R and G that the potential and current waveforms are in phase. Capacitors and inductors each exhibit a 90-degree phase difference between the EMF across them and the current waveform through them, and the cosine of 90 degrees is zero. Zero power factor means zero dissipated power—which means that attenuation is related to the resistive and conductive losses in a transmission line alone, not its reactive elements.

Does this mean that the inductance and capacitance in a transmission line cannot contribute to losses through it? No! I have only said that they do not contribute to *attenuation*. Another form of loss, mismatch or reflective loss, occurs when the source and load impedances are not perfectly matched to the transmission line connecting them. You can see from Eq 4 that if the inductance and capacitance per unit length of a transmission line are not as planned, the transmission line's characteristic impedance will change. This will generate an impedance mismatch in the system, that will in turn cause some of the signal to be reflected from the load back into the cable, or from the cable back into the source. This reflected energy is lost to the system (reflection loss), even if the cable is "lossless" from a standpoint of its dissipative attenuation.

In summary, a transmission medium exhibits insertion loss that is the algebraic sum of its dissipative (attenuative) and reflective (mismatch) losses. Attenuation is a function primarily of a transmission line's design and materials, while mismatch losses are as much a function of its application.

Quantifying Reflections

The various parameters for expressing impedance mismatch and the attendant reflective losses in a transmission line system include *standing wave ratio* (SWR, which can be expressed either as an EMF ratio or in dB); *reflection coefficient*; *return loss*; and *mismatch loss*. Since these various parameters all describe the same phenomenon, they are all mathematically interrelated. Here we will define the mathematical conversions between reflection parameters.

You are probably familiar with the term *voltage standing wave ratio (VSWR)*, but if you've read note 1, you will understand why I prefer to call it simply *standing wave ratio*, or *SWR*. Whenever two sinusoidal waves propagate in opposite directions along the same transmission line, as occurs in any system exhibiting reflections, an EMF interference pattern is formed along the line, as illustrated in Fig 1. It is this standing wave of potential that is measured along the transmission medium by a slotted line or lecher wires. The pattern consists of EMF maxima, or nodes, and EMF minima, or nulls, with successive nodes (or nulls) separated by one-half the guide wavelength of the applied signal.[5] In fact, guide wavelength is generally measured by shorting a transmission line (to create an impedance mismatch and the resulting standing wave pattern), and then measuring the physical distance between successive nulls.[6]

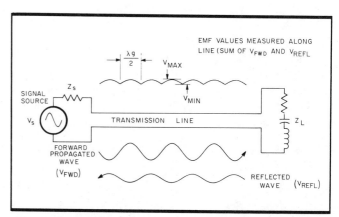

Fig 1—Derivation of standing wave ratio and reflection coefficient (see text).

For the purposes of quantifying reflection magnitude, however, we are interested in the amplitude of the potential nodes and nulls. Standing wave ratio is defined as the ratio of the EMF maximum to the EMF minimum along a transmission line, as follows

$$SWR = \frac{V_{max}}{V_{min}} \qquad \text{(Eq 5)}$$

Note that the potential maximum must always be greater than the minimum, thus SWR is always greater than or equal to one. Furthermore, if no reflections exist, no standing wave pattern exists along the line, and the EMF values measured at all points along the transmission line are equal. In this case impedance match is perfect, the numerator and denominator are equal, and SWR equals unity.

Since the EMF measured anywhere in a transmission system varies directly with the impedance across which it is measured, it is reasonable to expect SWR (a potential ratio) to vary with the ratio of source to load impedance. The relationship is

$$SWR = \frac{Z_{source}}{Z_{load}} \qquad \text{(Eq 6)}$$

or,

$$SWR = \frac{Z_{load}}{Z_{source}} \qquad \text{(Eq 7)}$$

whichever yields a value greater than unity.

In the system illustrated in Fig 1, we find a transmission line between a source and a load impedance, and we must not neglect the line itself when applying the above equations. There are actually two points of reflection in the system illustrated—the interface between the source and the transmission line, and that between the transmission line and the load. In the first case, Z_{source} is the generator impedance, and Z_{load} the characteristic impedance of the transmission line. In the second, Z_{source} is actually the cable's Z_0, and Z_{load} is the impedance of the termination. Note that if the transmission line is matched neither to its source nor to its load, two different points of reflection—and two different SWRs—may exist in the system.

The above relationships are convenient when both source and load impedances are nonreactive (that is, purely resistive). When the impedances involved contain both real and imaginary numbers, however, the required division involves complex algebra. The simplest technique involves rationalizing the denominator by multiplying both the numerator and the denominator by the denominator's conjugate. This doesn't lend itself well to calculator solution, unless your calculator happens to have a "j" key. Mine doesn't! But don't despair, Chapter 6 will introduce a graphical technique for solving for standing wave ratio in complex circuits.

Let us now return to Fig 1. The interference pattern that allowed us to determine SWR was in fact comprised of two separate sinusoidal waves, one forward propagated, the other reflected. Techniques exist (primarily through the use of directional couplers) for measuring the EMF amplitudes of the forward and reflected waves independently. Doing so will allow us to quantify another reflection term, *reflection coefficient*.

$$\rho = \frac{V_{refl}}{V_{fwd}} \qquad \text{(Eq 8)}$$

where ρ, the Greek letter lower-case rho, is the symbol for reflection coefficient (sometimes called voltage reflection coefficient, but see again note 1). Another symbol sometimes encountered for reflection coefficient is Γ, the Greek letter capital Gamma.

You will note that the value of the reflected EMF cannot exceed that of the forward propagated EMF waveform. Thus the numerator of the above equation will always be less than the denominator, and the magnitude of reflection coefficient will always fall between 0 and 1.

Unlike SWR, which is a scalar quantity, ρ is actually a vector, consisting of both a magnitude and a phase angle. Eq 8 actually expresses only the magnitude of ρ. Its phase angle is simply the phase difference, in degrees or radians, between the incident and reflected waveforms. Don't confuse the phase angle of reflection coefficient, however, with the phase angle of a complex impedance, expressed in polar form. The latter is the phase difference between the EMF waveform across an impedance, and the current waveform through it. Confusing the two phase angles is a common enough mistake, one that I made in print several years ago, only to be corrected by Walt Maxwell, W2DU.[7,8]

If a given SWR is known, the magnitude of reflection coefficient can be readily calculated, as follows

$$\rho(\text{magn}) = \frac{SWR - 1}{SWR + 1} \qquad \text{(Eq 9)}$$

and conversely,

$$SWR = \frac{1 + \rho}{1 - \rho} \qquad \text{(Eq 10)}$$

Remember, however, that we are dealing here with the *magnitude* of the reflection coefficient vector. There is no way to determine its phase angle from SWR (a scalar quantity) alone.

Since both SWR and reflection coefficient magnitude are potential ratios, they can each be readily converted to dB. If impedance in the measurement system is constant, an EMF ratio is converted to dB by taking ten times the common logarithm of its square. Thus

$$S\ (dB) = 10 \log (SWR^2) \qquad \text{(Eq 11)}$$

and

$$\rho\ (dB) = 10 \log (\rho^2) \qquad \text{(Eq 12)}$$

I know of no particular useful application of S (dB) to amateur microwave, although here it is if you ever need it. ρ (dB), on the other hand, becomes an extremely useful quantity. Since reflection coefficient magnitude is always less than unity, Eq 12 will always yield a negative number. But by simply changing its sign, we have an expression for return loss, the parameter measured directly by most microwave reflectometer systems. Thus

Return Loss (dB) $= -10 \log (\rho^2)$ (Eq 13)

Finally, from reflection coefficient magnitude, we can find mismatch loss, that energy loss in a transmission line system which stems from reflections. You will recall that insertion loss is the dB sum of attenuation and mismatch loss. Mismatch loss is found from

Mismatch Loss (dB) $= -10 \log (1 - \rho^2)$ (Eq 14)

If you find all of the above algebraic relationships somewhat intimidating, you will be pleased to learn that such microwave transmission line manipulations lend themselves readily to both computer and graphical solutions, which will be presented in later chapters of this book.

5.4 FREE SPACE AS A TRANSMISSION MEDIUM

Even though we use free space for the transmission of electromagnetic radiation as a matter of course, we seldom think of it in transmission line terms. This is probably because of the great difficulty encountered in trimming a length of it to desired dimensions and installing the required connectors. Such mechanical constraints notwithstanding, it is convenient to use free space as a reference medium for developing a number of our basic transmission line concepts. It is important to note, however, that typical laboratory experiments in electromagnetic propagation actually involve not free space, but rather wave propagation through the mixture of nitrogen, oxygen and trace gasses that make up the Earth's atmosphere.

Fortunately, the electromagnetic properties of air are virtually the same as those of a pure vacuum, so that, at least below the millimeter-wave bands, air presents a fairly good first-order approximation to free space.[9] Thus whatever we say here about free-space propagation will also apply to signals traveling through air.

Characteristic Impedance

Since ideal free space represents the least lossy of all transmission media, it is safe to neglect the dissipative elements (series resistance and shunt conductance) included in Eq 2, and the lossless simplification of Eq 4 will apply. But to what, exactly, are the distributed inductance and capacitance of free space equal? You can't simply cut off a short section of free space and measure its L and C on an impedance bridge!

If you recall that capacitance is the ability to store charge in electrostatic lines of force, then permittivity, the ability to support an electrostatic field, is related to capacitance. Permittivity is also known as dielectric constant, and is sometimes abbreviated K. The charac-

teristic permittivity of free space, ϵ_0, is a known and measurable physical constant

$$\epsilon_0 = \left(\frac{1}{36\pi}\right) \times 10^{-9} \text{ F/m} \qquad \text{(Eq 15)}$$

which relates to the capacitive nature of free space.

Similarly, inductance represents the ability to store flux in magnetic lines of force. Permeability, the ability to support a magnetic field, is thus related to inductance. The characteristic permeability of free space, μ_0, is also a known and measurable physical constant

$$\mu_0 = 4\pi \times 10^{-7} \text{ H/m} \qquad \text{(Eq 16)}$$

which relates to the inductive nature of free space.

Notice that the unit of measure for permittivity is farads per meter (F/m) and the unit of measure for permeability is henrys per meter (H/m). If you divide permeability by permittivity, the "per meters" cancel, leaving a ratio of inductance to capacitance. Thus, if the permittivity and permeability of a transmission medium are known, we can restate Eq 4

$$Z_0 = \sqrt{L/C}$$

to read

$$Z_0 = \sqrt{\mu/\epsilon} \qquad \text{(Eq 17)}$$

Inserting the appropriate physical properties of free space,

$$Z_0 = \sqrt{\frac{\mu_0}{\epsilon_0}} = \sqrt{\frac{4\pi \times 10^{-7}}{\left(\frac{1}{36\pi}\right) \times 10^{-9}}} \; \Omega \qquad \text{(Eq 18)}$$

$$= \sqrt{(4\pi \times 10^{-7}) \times (36\pi \times 10^{9})} \; \Omega$$

$$= \sqrt{4 \times 36 \times \pi^2 \times 10^2} \; \Omega = \sqrt{2^2 \times 6^2 \times \pi^2 \times 10^2} \; \Omega$$

$$= (2 \times 6 \times \pi \times 10) \; \Omega = (120\,\pi) \; \Omega = 377 \; \Omega$$

The characteristic impedance of free space is a fundamental constant, independent of frequency, and will be used in determining the characteristic impedance of other transmission media in later sections of this chapter.

Incidentally, you can see from the above value for free-space Z_0 why a transmission line with nothing connected to its far end is not necessarily terminated in an open circuit. There's a significant difference between 377 ohms and infinity! This leads to some interesting results when trying to determine the characteristic impedance of, say, a waveguide, using the method represented by Eq 1. This dilemma will be resolved in our waveguide discussion in Section 5.6.

Propagation Velocity

The velocity at which an electromagnetic wave propagates through a transmission medium is determined by the same properties that establish the medium's characteristic impedance—its inductance and capacitance per unit length. Now we all know that electromagnetic radiation propagates through free space at the speed of light, 3×10^8 meters per second. But wouldn't it be reassuring to prove that?

Consider the behavior of a discrete delay line, consisting of numerous cascaded sections of series inductance and shunt capacitance. The time, in seconds, required for a sine wave to propagate through each section of the delay line is

$$t = \sqrt{LC}$$

where L and C are inductance, in henrys, and capacitance, in farads, per section of the lumped constant delay line. Now if we consider our delay line to be fabricated from a transmission line, the L and C per section become the transmission line's inductance and capacitance per unit length, or distributed L and C.

Next we must standardize units. For a standard unit length of one meter, the above relationship allows us to determine the time required for a signal to propagate through a transmission line one meter long. And since velocity equals the reciprocal of propagation time, we can now determine the velocity of wave propagation in our transmission line

$$v = \frac{1}{\sqrt{LC}} \qquad \text{(Eq 19)}$$

where

v = propagation velocity in meters per second
L = distributed inductance in henrys per meter
C = distributed capacitance in farads per meter

You may recall from the previous section that permittivity, ϵ, just happens to be measured in farads per meter, and permeability, μ, in henrys per meter! This allows us to restate Eq 19

$$v = \frac{1}{\sqrt{\mu\epsilon}} \qquad \text{(Eq 20)}$$

and for free space,

$$v_0 = \frac{1}{(4\pi \times 10^{-7})\left(\frac{1}{36\pi} \times 10^{-9}\right)} = \frac{1}{\sqrt{\frac{4\pi \times 10^{-7}}{36\pi \times 10^9}}}$$

$$= \sqrt{\frac{36\pi \times 10^9}{4\pi \times 10^{-7}}} = \sqrt{\frac{36}{4} \times 10^{16}}$$

$$= \sqrt{\frac{6^2}{2^2} \times 10^{16}} = \frac{6}{2} \times 10^8 = 3 \times 10^8 \text{ m/s}$$

$$v_0 \approx 3 \times 10^8 \text{ m/s} \qquad \text{(Eq 21)}$$

The above derivation not only confirms the speed of light for free space, but illustrates why, and how, velocity will vary for waves propagating through media with different permittivity or permeability.

TEM Propagation in Free Space

Signals traveling through free space propagate in a true transverse electromagnetic (TEM) mode. That is, their electrostatic field, magnetic field and direction of wave propagation are all mutually orthogonal (at right angles to each other) in three dimensional space. TEM propagation is illustrated in Fig 2.

The polarization of a TEM wave is described in terms of the physical orientation of the electrostatic (E) field. If the wave's E field is oriented perpendicular to the surface of the earth, we say the wave is vertically polarized. For wire radiating elements (such as vertical whip, ground plane, or dipole antennas, as well as more complex arrays driven by radiating wire elements), the electrostatic field aligns itself with the physical orientation of the radiating element. That is, the wave emanating from a horizontally oriented dipole or Yagi will have its E field oriented horizontally, thus will exhibit horizontal polarization. A vertically oriented quarter-wave whip or ground plane will radiate a vertically oriented E field, hence a vertically polarized TEM wave.

Slot antennas radiate a TEM signal with the magnetic field oriented with the wide dimension of the slot. Thus a vertically oriented slot will radiate a vertically oriented H field, a horizontally oriented E field, and hence a horizontally polarized TEM wave.

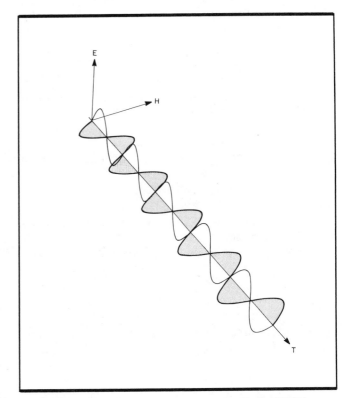

Fig 2—Model for transverse electromagnetic (TEM) propagation in free space. Because the electrostatic (E) field is oriented in the vertical plane, the wave is said to be vertically polarized.

The polarization of waves radiated by loop elements, be they rectangular, circular, or triangular (delta) loops, depends on the orientation of the feed point. The electrostatic field orients perpendicular to the point at which the loop is excited or fed. Thus, a loop fed at the top or bottom will radiate a horizontally polarized TEM wave, while one fed at the side will be vertically polarized. The same holds for arrays of loops, such as loop Yagis, Quagis, and quads. These antennas will be discussed more fully in Chapter 9.

It is important to note that the plane of polarization of a TEM wave may not necessarily remain constant throughout the transmission path. A number of factors, including reflection, refraction, diffraction, and Faraday rotation, may conspire to vary the physical orientation of the E and H fields. The two fields will, however, always be oriented at right angles to each other, and at right angles to the direction of wave propagation, as the wave propagates through free space.

We often speak about the importance of proper antenna orientation in electromagnetic communications systems, and of course the receive antenna must be properly polarized to most efficiently recover the radiated wave. As the above discussion should suggest, however, it is the polarization of the incoming signal, and not that of the transmit antenna, which determines the proper orientation of the receive antenna. Remember that the wave as received may not necessarily be polarized the same as the wave leaving the transmit antenna.

One solution to the wave polarization dilemma is to design and construct antennas that are physically rotatable along their axis of radiation, thus are rotatable in polarization. Another is to employ a mode of TEM radiation known as circular polarization. A circularly polarized wave still exhibits TEM properties; that is, its E field, H field and propagation direction are all mutually orthogonal. As the wave propagates, however, the physical orientation of the E and H fields rotates, completing a 360 degree change in orientation for each wavelength of forward wave propagation. If the wave rotates in a clockwise direction along its axis of propagation, its polarization is said to be right-hand circular. Counter-clockwise rotation results in left-hand circular polarization. The direction of rotation of a circularly polarized TEM wave is also referred to as its circularity sense.

TEM waves propagating between two circularly polarized antennas of like sense will efficiently couple from one to the other, regardless of how the propagation path may further rotate the orientation of their fields. However, communication between circularly polarized antennas of opposite sense suffers the same losses as that between linear antennas of opposite polarization. Finally, it should be noted that the reflection of circularly polarized TEM waves reverses their sense, so that if circular polarization is employed and a reflective path (such as EME) is anticipated, some means must be provided for switching the circularity sense of the receive antenna.

Free Space Path Loss

Before quantifying the insertion loss experienced by a signal propagating through free space, it is important to note that it will differ significantly from the insertion loss observed in any bounded transmission line. This is because, in free space, there are neither series resistance and shunt conductance to cause signal dissipation, as discussed previously, nor impedance discontinuities to cause reflective losses. Rather, the loss mechanism associated with free space derives from its unbounded nature. That is, unlike signals traveling in cable or waveguide, those propagating in free space spread out as they distance themselves from their source. The angle at which the signal spreads is a function of the gain and beamwidth of the transmit antenna, but some degree of spreading is inevitable. This means that, for a receive antenna of given capture area, less of the transmitted signal will be recovered as distance between transmitter and receiver increases. How much less? Read on!

Even before Congress passed the Inverse Square Law, it was well known that S-meter readings vary inversely with the distance to the DX station. To understand the relationship between distance and attenuation, we need to consider two points (A and B) of a communications path, separated by distance D and communicating via electromagnetic waves of wavelength λ. And to remove from the analysis the effects of antenna gain, beamwidth, radiation pattern or capture area, we will assume that both the transmitter (at Point A) and the receiver (at Point B) are connected to perfectly matched, ideal, lossless isotropic antennas.

As long as the distance D is great relative to antenna size, it can be shown that the EMF recovered by the receive antenna is a fraction of the EMF applied to the transmit antenna, which varies with the ratio λ over D. The equality is

$$Av = \frac{\lambda}{4\pi D} \qquad \text{(Eq 22)}$$

where Av is the voltage ratio (V received)/(V transmitted), and the constant 4π comes to us from spherical trigonometry, representing the number of steradians in a sphere. Of course, since Av is a unitless ratio (volts over volts cancels), it is important that λ and D be expressed in the same units.

Since we defined our antennas as being ideal, they are perfectly matched to free space. Thus the potentials transmitted and received are measured across the same impedance, and power ratio becomes the square of potential ratio. We can therefore say

$$Ap = Av^2 = \left(\frac{\lambda}{4\pi D}\right)^2$$

and we know how to convert power ratios to dB

$$dB = 10 \log Ap$$

$$= 10 \log \left(\frac{\lambda}{4\pi D}\right)^2 \qquad \text{(Eq 23)}$$

The above yields a *negative* number, since path gain is less than unity.

Changing the sign, it follows that free-space path *loss* (α, the Greek letter lower-case alpha) would be

$$\alpha = -10 \log \left(\frac{\lambda}{4\pi D}\right)^2$$

and since $-10 \log (x) = 10 \log (1/x)$,

$$\alpha = 10 \log \left(\frac{4\pi D}{\lambda}\right)^2 \qquad \text{(Eq 24)}$$

This relationship allows us to predict free-space path loss at any frequency, over any line-of-sight distance, as long as we measure distance and wavelength in the same units. It is certainly easier to employ than the various nomographs provided for that purpose in the literature, and is far easier to remember than those published equations that contain fudge-factors to compensate for distance expressed in, say, miles, and wavelength in inches. Furthermore, if you understand the meaning of the decibel, the above equation should allow you to visualize the relationship in a physical sense.

It is important to note that free-space path loss α, as calculated in Eq 24, assumes a completely free and open path between the transmit and receive antennas, and neglects the effects of absorption, reflection, refraction, or obstruction. Not all microwave communications paths are so blessed, and in fact the more exotic DX modes (ducting, troposcatter, sporadic E, meteor scatter, moonbounce, trans-equatorial, and so on) are decidedly *not* line of sight. As was indicated in Chapter 3, it is not always possible to predict the existence of such propagation modes, much less determine the degree of signal enhancement that they might provide. However, when propagation enhancement exists, experience over a given path may well provide some insight as to the *degree* of enhancement to expect, in dB over the free-space path. Thus, even when non-line-of-sight communications modes are being employed, the calculation of free-space path loss may prove beneficial in anticipating the actual path loss for a given propagation mode.

Matching to Free Space

The previous sections have helped us to derive a number for the characteristic impedance of free space and have shown us how impedance discontinuities add losses to a communications system. We can now begin to appreciate that a vital function of antennas is to provide an impedance transformation between the characteristic impedance of transmission lines and that of free space.

Consider the case of a transmitter matched to a familiar 50-ohm coaxial cable, which in turn drives a simple quarter-wave vertical antenna. You can consider the antenna to be a simple quarter-wave matching transformer, designed to exhibit an input impedance closely matched to 50 ohms, and an output impedance closely matched to 377 ohms.

The adequacy of the impedance match seen by our transmitter, and the efficiency with which energy is coupled into free space, depend on how effectively the quarter-wave vertical performs its impedance transformation. Obviously, its performance is going to be frequency dependent. Less obvious is the effect of ground on the antenna's impedance matching abilities. An imperfect ground will alter the impedance of the radiating element, which will result, of course, in reflective losses. In the chapters that follow, you will encounter countless other examples of quarter-wavelength transmission line segments serving as impedance transformers.

I would be remiss in my discussion of impedance matching, however, if I did not share with you one important caveat. As before, I shall present it in terms of a personal example.

Early in my engineering career, I was assigned by my employer (a large aerospace company) the task of designing a broadband microwave antenna for an airborne military system. The specs were challenging: 2 to 12 GHz operation at a standing wave ratio of less than 2. After weeks of effort, I had produced a workable prototype, and hastened to present it to the project engineer. "Look at this," I effused, "1.8 SWR from 2 to 12 GHz!"

My supervisor was unimpressed. "I have in my desk drawer," he told me, "an antenna that exhibits a 1.2 or lower SWR from dc to 18 GHz. And I don't imagine it radiates any better than yours." He then opened his desk, and showed me a coaxial dummy load.

Perhaps because impedance match is so readily measured, we hams tend to overestimate its importance in the scheme of things. Let us never forget that the primary function of an antenna is to radiate (or recover) energy over a specified pattern, with particular beamwidth, sidelobes, capture area, gain and efficiency. Certainly impedance matching to free space contributes to an antenna's effectiveness, but it should never be considered the ultimate objective.

5.5 COAXIAL CABLES AND CONNECTORS

Coaxial Cable as a Transmission Medium

From the time of its invention more than a hundred years ago, coaxial cable (originally known as "concentric line") could well be described as a solution in search of a problem. Other transmission lines (chiefly twin-lead) were simpler, less costly, and easier to construct and interconnect. What possible advantages could coaxial cable offer to justify its complexity?

The answer didn't become apparent until the development of video transmission systems in the late 1920s and early 1930s. A television system is inherently broadband, with its information content dependent upon maintaining uniform amplitude and phase information of signal components widely separated in frequency. Coaxial cable is blessed with a uniform amplitude response over a wide range of frequencies, as well as uniform group delay characteristics (the ability to maintain the phase integrity of wideband signals propagating through it). Additionally, it has the ability to completely contain electrostatic and magnetic lines of force, thus preventing losses caused by transmission-line radiation.

One early experiment in video transmission was conducted by Bell Labs in 1932. It involved stringing a concentric line between the Murray Hill Exchange in New York City and the Bourch Building in downtown Philadelphia. Interestingly, the video signals transmitted over this early coaxial cable were generated by a 36-segment scanning disk. Later all-electronic scanning techniques owed their success, in part, to the availability of coaxial transmission lines. Those of us who today take coaxial cable for granted may find it interesting to note that it is now being "rediscovered" by the computer industry, where the very properties that made it desirable for video transmission also enable it to efficiently handle high-speed digital signals.

Coaxial cable is a transverse electromagnetic (TEM) transmission medium. Unlike free space, however, its propagation polarization is neither linear nor circular. A model for TEM propagation in coaxial cable is illustrated in Fig 3. Consider that a cross-sectioned coaxial cable consists of a center wire and an outer shield (both conductors), separated by an insulating medium (a dielectric). Thus the cable exhibits capacitive properties. (Any two conductors separated by a dielectric comprise a capacitor.)

In any charged capacitor, an electrostatic field exists through the dielectric, between the two conductors. Coaxial cable is no exception. As a signal propagates along the cable, an expanding and collapsing E field extends radially between the center and outer conductors.

The center conductor of a coaxial cable carries a current, and any current-carrying conductor is surrounded by a magnetic field. As the ac in the center conductor varies, the magnetic flux lines around it expand and collapse, forming a concentric H field.

You can see from Fig 3 that the H field surrounding the center conductor crosses all electrostatic lines of force in the dielectric region at a right angle. Both the E and the H fields exist perpendicular to the longitudinal axis of the cable (which in turn represents the axis of wave propagation). Thus coaxial cable, with its radial-spoke E field and circular-concentric H field, is indeed a TEM transmission medium.

A common lumped constant model for coaxial cable is shown in Fig 4. The series R represents dissipative losses in the conductors themselves. The shunt G shown represents primarily leakage losses in the dielectric. The shunt C represents the capacitance per unit length existing between the conductors, and the magnetic field surrounding the current-carrying center conductor accounts for the series L shown in the model. For finite lengths of coaxial transmission line, the series resistance and shunt conductance may be considered negligible, and the simplified model of Fig 5 results.

Note the striking resemblance between Fig 5 and the traditional model for an LC low-pass filter. You might imagine that coaxial transmission lines would thus be a low-pass medium, and you would be correct. This is one reason why the losses in coaxial cable increase with frequency. More on this later.

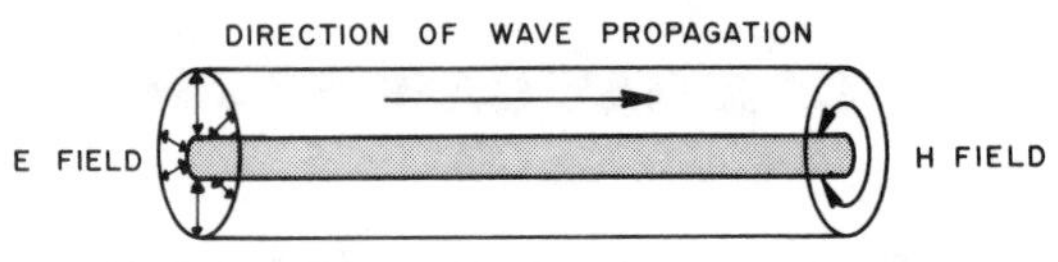

Fig 3—Coaxial cable as a transverse electromagnetic (TEM) wave medium.

Fig 5—Simplified model for a lossless coaxial cable. Three of an infinite number of sections are shown.

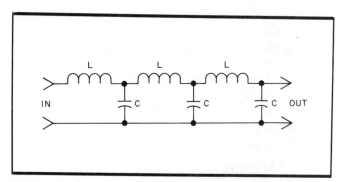

Fig 4—Lumped-constant model for coaxial cable. Two of an infinite number of sections are shown.

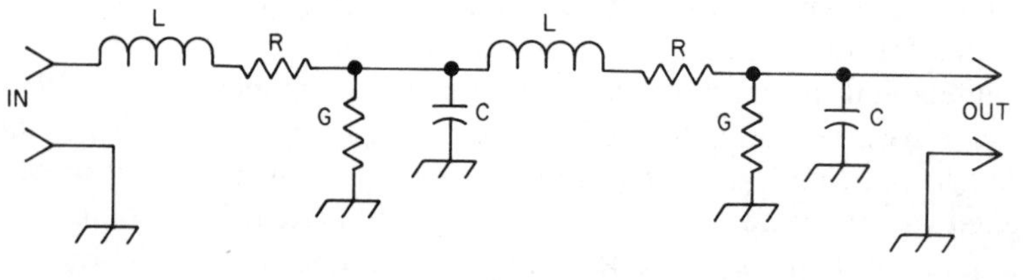

Physical Realization of Coaxial Cables

In this section we will discuss the significance of physical materials and fabrication techniques to the performance of coaxial cables. The examples used here are common coaxial cable types found in many amateur installations. The electrical properties of any coaxial cable are chiefly a function of the physical dimensions and surface conductivity of the inner and outer conductors, and of the dielectric material that separates these conductors. We will examine these characteristics in detail.

CONDUCTORS

Because of the phenomenon of skin effect, electro-magnetic waves tend to propagate along the surface of, rather than inside, conductors. Thus it is surface conductivity, rather than internal wire conductivity, that interests us for RF analysis. Coaxial cable performance depends upon the *outer* surface of the inside conductor and the *inner* surface of the shield or outer conductor. To minimize losses, it is these surfaces that need to be highly conductive.

If the surface of a wire determines its losses, its internal structure serves merely to establish its surface dimensions. In fact, if the center conductor of a coaxial cable were hollow, its electrical performance at RF would not be affected; only its mechanical properties would change. It is common practice to fabricate coaxial cable from copper wire (a relatively inexpensive material with fair surface conductivity), and then plate the copper wire with a thin layer of tin, silver, or even gold to achieve optimum conductivity. Examples of coaxial cables employing silver-plated center and outer conductors include types RG-9, RG-55B, RG-141, and RG-142.

The center conductor of a coaxial cable can be fabricated from either a single wire of the desired outer diameter, or from a twisted bundle of smaller strands. Solid center conductors provide the greatest uniformity of outer diameter dimension, which contributes to stable electrical characteristics. However, the use of stranded center conductors improves cable flexibility. Cables such as RG-8, RG-9, RG-11 and RG-58A all employ stranded center conductors, while such types as RG-55, RG-58, RG-58B, RG-141, and RG-142 use solid wire for the center conductor. See Fig 6.

A cable's outer conductor can be fabricated from a solid conductive pipe or from a braided shield composed of wire strands. A solid pipe provides the most uniform physical dimensions—and thus the most uniform electrical specifications. Solid outer conductors, however, are not flexible. The so-called semi-rigid cables, such as type UT-141 from Uniform Tubes Inc, use copper tubing for their outer conductors.[10] See Fig 7. I prefer to call them "semi-flexible." They can be bent, but usually only once. Any attempt to straighten out a bent piece of "semirigid" cable generally results in a cracked outer conductor. Some types of semi-rigid cable are made specifically for repeated bending, but they are more expensive and more difficult to find.

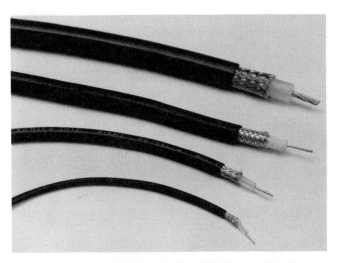

Fig 6—Coaxial cables come in a variety of sizes. Center conductors may be stranded or solid.

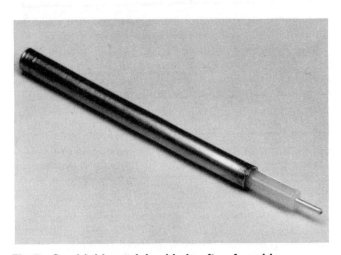

Fig 7—Semirigid coaxial cable is often found in amateur microwave installations. The UT-141 cable shown here has a solid copper outer conductor, TFE dielectric and a silver-plated center conductor.

Hardline, often used in the cable TV industry, contains an outer conductor consisting of solid aluminum pipe. See Fig 8. The flexibility and bend radius of such cables can be improved by varying the diameter of the otherwise rigid outer conductor. What results are the corrugated Hardlines, produced by such companies as Andrew Corp and Cablewave Systems. All are popular in amateur applications where high power handling capability and low loss are significant considerations.

Braided shields will never be as effective electrically as solid outer conductors because gaps in the woven outer conductor permit some signal leakage or radiation from the cable. Nearly all of the popular flexible coaxial cables, including types RG-8, 9, 11, 58, 59, 141 and 213, employ braided shields. Where flexibility requirements dictate a woven outer conductor, but radiation through the shield

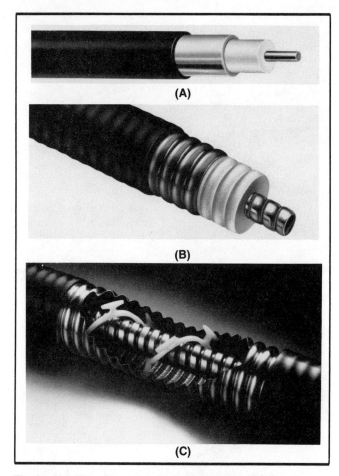

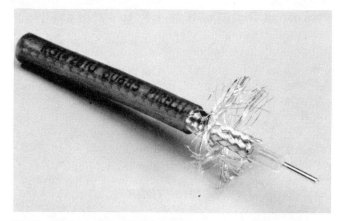

Fig 9—High-quality coaxial cable such as RG-142 has a double-shielded outer conductor, TFE dielectric and silver-plated conductors.

Fig 8—Hardline for antenna feed lines comes in a variety of styles and sizes. CATV Hardline with foam dielectric and a solid aluminum outer conductor is shown at A. A more flexible Hardline with a corrugated copper outer conductor is shown at B and C. Flexible Hardline is available in a variety of sizes from several manufacturers. It can have foam (B) or air (C) dielectric material. *(photos courtesy Cablewave Systems)*

is a concern, it is sometimes possible to weave two layers of shield, with the strands of each layer positioned to overlap the gaps in the other. See Fig 9. Examples of such double-shielded coaxial cable include types RG-5, 55, 142 and 214. Double-shielded cables exhibit improved isolation and reduced radiation losses as compared to single-shielded cable, along with a penalty of somewhat degraded mechanical flexibility.

DIELECTRIC MATERIALS

The dielectric material that separates the outer conductor of a coaxial cable from its center conductor performs two critical functions. (1) It determines the intensity of the electrostatic field that can exist between the conductors (thus establishing distributed capacitance, which influences the cable's electrical parameters). (2) It provides for the physical centering of the inner conductor within the shield. The two requirements of the dielectric are somewhat mutually exclusive.

Common dielectric materials for coaxial cable include polyethylene, polystyrene, butyl rubber and tetrafluoroethylene (TFE, which you may know by the DuPont

trademark Teflon®). Any of these materials can contribute to cable losses through dielectric leakage, as none is really a perfect insulator. Most of the popular flexible coaxial cables, including types RG-8, 9, 11, 55, 58 and 59, use a solid polyethylene dielectric. Losses in polyethylene are low, though not necessarily negligible, and it is an inexpensive material to produce and process. Polyethylene can be characterized as a cost-effective compromise for all but the most demanding applications.

The chief drawback of polyethylene dielectrics is the very feature that keeps their manufacturing costs low: It melts at moderate temperatures. For systems that must operate at significantly elevated ambient temperatures, TFE dielectrics are superior. Their greater thermal tolerance, however, is offset by a significant increase in processing costs. Typical TFE dielectric cables include the popular UT-141 semi-rigid, single-shielded RG-141, and double-shielded RG-142. RG-142 is among the lowest loss flexible microwave cables, usable well into the millimeter wave bands, with electrical characteristics paralleling semi-rigid types. A drawback is that its cost in small quantities exceeds $2 per foot.

The least lossy dielectric material imaginable is free space, or pure vacuum, but its use as a cable dielectric would require overcoming some interesting mechanical difficulties. For example, even neglecting the problem of maintaining the position of the center conductor within the shield, it is costly to develop and maintain even a reasonable facsimile of a pure vacuum within a cable. Any leaks that do occur will draw in, among other things, moisture from the surrounding environment. Moisture and other contaminants can promote corrosion of the cable's conductive surfaces, increasing losses.

For these reasons, any technique that requires maintaining a negative pressure differential between the cable and the outside world is to be avoided. On the contrary, a positive pressure within the cable is desirable to drive out, rather than draw in, contaminants should a leak occur. You will recall from our earlier discussions that the electromagnetic properties of air closely parallel those of free space, so it might seem desirable to pressurize a coaxial cable with air. This is done in the so-called "air dielectric" low loss cables, such as Andrew Corp Heliax™. It is necessary, however, to dry the air, usually by passing it through a desiccant, to remove any moisture that might later promote corrosion within the cable. A better choice is to pressurize such cables with nitrogen, which after all constitutes 70 percent of the earth's atmosphere and can be readily kept free of moisture. A small flask of liquid nitrogen, purchased from a chemical supply house, can vent enough dry gaseous nitrogen to pressurize a typical length of Heliax transmission line. A pressure differential on the order of five pounds per square inch is sufficient to keep the inside of the cable dry.

Of course, even "air dielectric" cables contain insulating spacers in the dielectric region to maintain separation between and centering of the conductors. These spacers may be disks, or they may be solid ribbons of insulating material spiral-wound around the center conductor. See Fig 10. One cable especially popular in amateur installations, Belden type 9913, uses a widely spaced polyethylene filament that is spiral-wound around the center conductor. The center conductor and filament assembly is then surrounded by a polyethylene tube. The outside of the tube is wrapped with aluminum foil, which is then surrounded by a braided shield. This arrangement provides for a dielectric that is mostly air, so it exhibits considerably lower losses than similar cables with solid dielectrics.

A compromise technique that has proved quite popular among cable manufacturers and radio amateurs alike is to mix low-cost polyethylene with low-loss nitrogen. This is accomplished by bubbling nitrogen gas through molten polyethylene dielectric material before the polyethylene solidifies. The result is a dielectric material composed of polyethylene—providing complete physical support of the center conductor—but uniformly filled with minute air bubbles. The material is variously known as cellular polyethylene dielectric, foam dielectric, or poly-foam. It offers half the dielectric losses of solid polyethylene at a modest increase in cost.

Fig 10—A popular feed line among amateurs is Belden 9913. This cable has a partial air dielectric, and uses a foil shield as well as a braid shield. Loss is lower than with conventional RG-8 size cables.

Electrical Characteristics

The relative permittivities of various dielectric materials are shown in Table 1. It is the permittivity of a cable's dielectric that determines, in large part, its electrical characteristics, as discussed in the following sections.

Table 1

Relative Permittivities of Various Common Coaxial Cable Dielectrics

Material	Relative Permittivity
Vacuum	1.0
Dry air	1.00068
Cellular polyethylene	1.5
Tetrafluoroethylene	2.1
Solid polyethylene	2.3
Butyl rubber	3.0

CHARACTERISTIC IMPEDANCE

The characteristic impedance of an ideal, lossless coaxial transmission line is related to its inductance and capacitance per unit length. Eq 5 applies to the model shown in Fig 5, as well as to free space. Consider, for example, the characteristic impedance of the familiar type RG-58 cable, which exhibits a distributed capacitance of about 100 pF per meter, and a distributed inductance on the order of 250 nH per meter of length.[11] From Eq 5

$$Z_0 = \sqrt{\frac{250 \times 10^{-9} \text{ H/m}}{100 \times 10^{-12} \text{ F/m}}}$$

$$= 50 \; \Omega$$

This agrees perfectly with the characteristic impedance listed for RG-58 in coaxial cable catalogs.

Now consider the physical coaxial cable, depicted in cross section in Fig 11. It should be possible to derive an expression for characteristic impedance that is related to the physical dimensions and electrical properties portrayed in the model, assuming we can relate each to either the distributed capacitance or the distributed inductance of the cable.

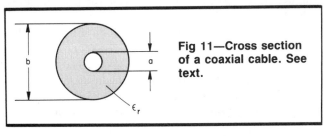

Fig 11—Cross section of a coaxial cable. See text.

Obviously, the distributed inductance varies inversely with the inner conductor diameter A, as inductance of any conductor always varies inversely with its diameter. Similarly, capacitance varies inversely with the outer conductor diameter B, because the greater the diameter of the outer conductor, the greater the distance between the "plates" of our "capacitor." And distributed capacitance should vary directly with the square root of the permittivity of the dielectric, just as the capacitance of any capacitor increases by a factor of four if the dielectric constant is doubled.

The above generalizations will combine with Eq 5 to express the characteristic impedance of any coaxial cable. Z_0 will vary directly with B, inversely with A, and inversely with the square root of ϵ. The equality is

$$Z_0 = \frac{120\pi}{e\sqrt{\epsilon}} \times \log\left(\frac{B}{A}\right) \qquad \text{(Eq 25)}$$

where

120π = the characteristic impedance, in ohms, of free space (derived in Eq 18)

e = the base of the natural, or Napierian, logarithm system

ϵ = the relative permittivity of the dielectric material

B/A = the ratio of the inside diameter of the shield to the diameter of the inner conductor, with both expressed in the same units

If we combine the numeric coefficients in the above expression, we can derive the coaxial cable characteristic impedance equation most often found in microwave textbooks:

$$\frac{230\pi}{e} = 138$$

thus,

$$Z_0 = \frac{138}{\sqrt{\epsilon}} \times \log(B/A) \qquad \text{(Eq 26)}$$

or, if you don't mind dealing in natural logarithms, a still simpler expression is possible:

$$Z_0 = \frac{60}{\sqrt{\epsilon}} \times \ln(B/A) \qquad \text{(Eq 27)}$$

where ln represents the natural logarithm, or log to the base e. This expression is most useful when evaluating coaxial cable impedance by computer, in languages such as BASIC that perform logarithmic operations in the base e, rather than the base ten.[12]

Let's test the above relationships on a known cable type. Again we can employ RG-58. The inner conductor is made of either solid or stranded AWG 20 copper wire, which has a diameter of 0.81 mm. The inside diameter of the braided shield outer conductor is 2.95 mm. And the cable employs polyethylene dielectric, with a relative

permittivity of 2.3. We can use Eq 26 to determine the resulting characteristic impedance.

$$Z_0 = \frac{138}{\sqrt{2.3}} \times \log\left(\frac{2.95 \text{ mm}}{0.81 \text{ mm}}\right)$$

$$= 51 \ \Omega$$

which correlates well with the characteristic impedance found from the ratio of distributed inductance to capacitance. As you would expect, Eq 27 yields the same results.

The above relationships suggest that it should be possible to fabricate coaxial cables of any desired characteristic impedance simply by varying the conductor diameters and dielectric material. This is true, up to a point. Reducing the diameter of the inner conductor increases L and decreases C, thus raising Z_0. If carried to extremes, however, this results in inner conductor diameters so small that manufacturing variations become significant, and a constant Z_0 cannot be maintained. Similarly, if the inner conductor diameter is increased, L goes down, C goes up, and Z_0 decreases. But if carried to extremes, the separation between the inner and outer conductors becomes minute, and the cable will break down or arc over, regardless of the dielectric material employed. Thus physical limitations intervene below characteristic impedances of about 25 Ω, or above about 100 Ω.

The most commonly encountered characteristic impedances for commercial coaxial cables are 50 Ω, 70 Ω, and 93 Ω. Specialized cables do exist with characteristic impedances of 25, 35, 125, 150, 185, and even 950 ohms! But which is the *best* coaxial cable impedance to use in amateur microwave systems? Consider that both power handling capability and cable losses vary with Z_0. It has been shown that cable losses are minimum at a characteristic impedance on the order of 75 Ω, while power handling capability is maximum at a Z_0 of about 30 Ω.[13]

In the cable TV industry, where signals distributed are of a low amplitude, the major consideration is attenuation, and a 75-Ω impedance standard has emerged. The result is that the surplus market has been flooded with quantities of CATV 75-Ω Hardline, which many radio amateurs have been using successfully in our microwave bands. As long as an impedance match at both ends of the transmission line is assured, and the cable's power limits are not exceeded, CATV cable makes an entirely acceptable transmission line. In fact, minimum-loss 75-Ω coaxial cable would appear to be the optimum transmission line standard for amateur weak-signal reception.

In transmit applications, on the other hand, cable loss and power handling capabilities may be equally significant considerations. Here a reasonable trade-off between the two objectives can be accomplished by standardizing on a cable characteristic impedance that is the geometric mean (square root of the product) of the two target impedances mentioned above. The favored system impedance is thus 50-Ω, which has emerged as a coaxial-cable transmission line standard throughout the microwave industry. Chances are your amateur microwave endeavors will revolve around the use of 50-Ω coaxial cable. This is the impedance for which most transmitters, receivers, antennas, connectors, and test equipment are designed.

VELOCITY OF PROPAGATION

Microwave experimenters frequently need to know the phase length, in degrees, radians, or fractions of a wavelength, of a transmission-line section at a given operating frequency. This parameter is readily calculated if the velocity at which waves propagate in the transmission medium is known. Velocity of propagation is variously expressed in conventional velocity units (meters per second), or as velocity factor, a percentage of the "speed of light" in free space, which we derived in Eq 21.

You will recall that we can determine the velocity of wave propagation in any transmission medium, as a function of distributed inductance and capacitance, from Eq 19. Thus for coaxial cables of known L and C per unit length (or of known inner conductor diameter, outer conductor diameter, and dielectric constant, since these parameters determine L and C), Eq 19 applies.

Let us consider, for example, the RG-58 coaxial cable for which we calculated characteristic impedance in the previous section. Since its inductance per meter and capacitance per meter are known, we can apply Eq 19.

$$v = \frac{1}{\sqrt{(250 \times 10^{-9} \text{ H/m}) \times (100 \times 10^{-12} \text{ F/m})}}$$

$$= 2.0 \times 10^8 \text{ meters per second.}$$

To determine relative velocity factor v_{rel}, simply divide the actual velocity of propagation by that in free space

$$v_{rel} = \frac{V}{V_0} \qquad \text{(Eq 28)}$$

$$= \frac{2.0 \times 10^8 \text{ m/s}}{3.0 \times 10^8 \text{ m/s}}$$

$$= 0.67$$

We could also say the velocity factor for this cable is 67%.

Applying Eq 19 does accurately determine propagation velocity if you happen to know a coaxial cable's distributed inductance and capacitance. But there's a much easier way. Without belaboring the mathematics, it turns out that propagation velocity and permittivity are inversely proportional. If you know the relative permittivity of a cable's dielectric, you can readily determine its relative velocity, or velocity factor relative to free space. The relationship is

$$v_{rel} = \frac{1}{\sqrt{\epsilon_{rel}}} \qquad \text{(Eq 29)}$$

Since we know that the polyethylene dielectric used in RG-58 cable has a relative permittivity of 2.3, we can determine the velocity factor as

$$v_{rel} = \frac{1}{\sqrt{2.3}}$$

$$= 0.66$$

which correlates well with the previous method discussed. Now to find propagation velocity, simply multiply velocity factor by the speed of light.

INSERTION LOSS OF COAXIAL CABLES

Section 5.3 has indicated that the insertion loss of any transmission medium is a function of both reflective and dissipative components. The former are a function of impedance match, which is application dependent. Thus only the dissipative losses in the cable, which we call attenuation, are a function of the design and fabrication of the cable itself. The terms insertion loss and attenuation tend to be used interchangeably in coaxial cable literature, even though it should be clear that they are equal only when reflective losses are negligible.

Here we shall consider dissipative losses, or attenuation, of coaxial cables. To avoid confusion, remember that when the characteristic impedance of a transmission line is perfectly matched to both its source and load impedances, reflective losses become negligible. Insertion loss then becomes solely a function of the cable's dissipative losses, or attenuation.

The two possible sources of dissipative loss in coaxial cable are (1) the series ohmic resistance of the conductors; and (2) the leakage, or shunt conductance, of the insulator separating the conductors. The former is often referred to in the literature as conductor loss α_{cond}, and the latter as dielectric loss, α_{diel}. If the two are expressed in logarithmic units, such as dB per meter or nepers per meter, then total attenuation constant or attenuation factor α is the sum of conductor and dielectric losses.

Conductor loss is related primarily to the diameter of the center conductor and the material from which it is constructed. (We tend to neglect the outer shield, as it generally exhibits a significantly greater cross-sectional area than the center conductor; thus the resistance of the center conductor dominates series losses). Because of skin effect (the tendency for RF currents to concentrate themselves near the surface of a conductor), the series cable losses also vary with frequency. One expression for conductor loss, in nepers per meter,[14] is

$$\alpha_{cond} = Y_0 \sqrt{\frac{f\mu_0}{16\pi}} \times \left(\frac{1}{a\sigma_a} + \frac{1}{b\sigma_b}\right) \qquad \text{(Eq 30)}$$

The shunt losses in the dielectric vary with the thickness of the dielectric (that is, the distance between the conductors), as well as the relative permittivity and power factor (or loss constant) of the insulating material. Reference 13 gives us an expression for dielectric loss as well, also in nepers per meter of cable length.

$$\alpha_{diel} = \pi \ V_{TEM} \ (diel) \ f \ \tan \delta \qquad (Eq \ 31)$$

[Author's note: I know this is going to disappoint all the mathematicians out there, but I'm not even going to define the literals in the above two equations, because frankly, you're not going to want to use them. It's far more practical to determine cable losses from data tables and manufacturer's spec sheets, than to try to compute them from physical properties. Eqs 30 and 31 are presented merely to illustrate that coaxial cable attenuation, like anything else in the realm of microwave communications, can be determined analytically should the need arise.]

As a generalization, cable losses vary inversely with the diameter of the cable. Thus, if you desire to reduce cable losses in a particular application, use a larger cable. The major exception to this rule occurs at the higher microwave frequencies. If the physical dimensions of the cable approach a significant fraction of the operating wavelength, the propagation mode in the cable will transition to a waveguide mode, and TEM losses will soar. The shortest practical wavelength for efficient TEM propagation through a coaxial cable is related to the arithmetic mean of the conductor diameters, and may be found from

$$\lambda_c = \pi\sqrt{\epsilon} \times \frac{A + B}{2} \qquad (Eq \ 32)$$

where

λ_c = cutoff wavelength for transition to waveguide propagation

A and B = the cable inner and outer conductor diameters

ϵ = the dielectric constant, or relative permittivity of the dielectric

A, B and λ_c are expressed in the same units. Once you have calculated cutoff wavelength, the determination of cutoff frequency follows by simply dividing into the speed of light.

Eq 32 suggests, for example, that if we neglect dissipative losses, RG-58 will support TEM propagation as high as 32 GHz, while RG-9 is a TEM transmission line only up to about 13.5 GHz.

My personal experience has been that published attenuation figures for commonly encountered coaxial cables correlate quite well with laboratory measurements, so long as the test cables are properly terminated in high quality connectors. For your convenience, Table 2 presents mechanical and electrical characteristics for a number of popular coaxial cable types.

In an excellent article on transmission lines, Joe Reisert, W1JR, has indicated that the overall insertion loss of coaxial cables varies logarithmically with frequency.[15] Thus if the loss (in dB per foot, nepers per meter, dB per 100 meters, etc) of a given cable at any one frequency is

Table 2

Electrical Properties of Common 50-Ω Coaxial Cables at 1 GHz

Cable Type	Insertion Loss (dB/100 m)	Maximum Power (W)	Velocity Factor
Semi-rigid miniature cable:			
UT-141	38	600	0.75
Flexible miniature cable:			
RG-58C	66	44	0.66
RG-142B	46	500	0.70
Flexible standard cable:			
RG-8A	30	190	0.66
Belden 8214	23	215	0.78
Belden 9913	15	520	0.84
Andrew foam-dielectric Heliax® :			
FHJ1-50	20	300	0.79
LDF2-50 (1/4 ")	12	350	0.88
LDF4-50A (1/2 ")	8	650	0.88
LDF5-50A (3/8 ")	4	1750	0.89
LDF6-50A (1-1/4 ")	3.2	2750	0.89
LDF7-50A (1-5/8 ")	2.3	3750	0.88
Andrew air-dielectric Heliax® :			
HJ4-50 (1/2 ")	9	1000	0.91
HJ5-50 (7/8 ")	4.2	3000	0.92
HJ7-50A (1-5/8")	2.3	6500	0.92

known, it can be approximated at other frequencies

$$\frac{\alpha_H}{\alpha_L} = \sqrt{\frac{f_H}{f_L}} \qquad (Eq \ 33)$$

where

α_H = the insertion loss, in dB or nepers per unit length, at the higher of the two frequencies

α_L = the insertion loss at the lower of the two frequencies, measured in the same units as α_H

f_H and f_L = the higher and lower of the two frequencies (that at which insertion loss is known, and that at which we wish to determine loss), respectively

A similar relationship exists for the maximum power-handling capability of coaxial cables, which Reference 15 indicates varies *inversely* with the square root of frequency. Thus

$$\frac{P_H}{P_L} = \sqrt{\frac{f_L}{f_H}} \qquad (Eq \ 34)$$

where P_H and P_L represent the maximum power, in watts, that the cable can handle at the higher and lower of two frequencies, respectively, and f_H and f_L are as defined for Eq 33.

These equations allows us to estimate the cable losses and power limits for coaxial cables at any frequency below that corresponding to the cutoff limit established by Eq 32. All we need to know are the cable specifications at a single frequency, as found in Table 2.

Practical Coaxial Cables

In the United States, various government agencies have for years comprised the primary market for RF and microwave products and services. In fact, it was only in the 1980s that microwave expenditures in the private sector exceeded those of government and military users. It is not surprising that the only standardization of hardware characteristics in the microwave industry is that imposed by government procurement agencies.

As far as coaxial cables are concerned, the governing document in the United States is a Military Specification (MilSpec), MIL-C-17. This is the document that has established the familiar "RG" nomenclature for coaxial cable types, to which we have made reference throughout this chapter. Although MIL-C-17 standardizes only those cable types sold to government agencies, or used in government projects, the private sector has tended to adopt it as a *de facto* standard to ensure a degree of uniformity between coaxial cables from various manufacturers.

Consider RG-58. The letter R indicates this is a Radio Frequency (RF) cable, and the G specifies that it is built to General specification. The number 58 is a sequential number assigned in the MilSpec to uniquely identify this particular cable type. Modifications to the basic cable type are indicated by revision letters, such as RG-58A, RG-58B, RG-58C, and so on.

To receive government approval as a supplier of MilSpec cables, a manufacturer must submit both its product and its manufacturing process to considerable government scrutiny. The cost of reliability and quality assurance testing can be a significant factor in the market price of the resulting cable. It is often not cost effective to submit to such rigorous standardization cables that will be marketed to the private sector. (Few radio amateurs really need the quality and reliability that MilSpec cables provide, and fewer still can afford it!) Yet it is the military procurement document that standardizes cable parameters, and the RG number that specifies the type of cable being sold.

Many cable manufacturers produce a commercial-grade product that meets the intent, if not the requirements, of their government-certified counterpart. These products are identified through use of the word "type." For example, you can purchase "RG-58A type" coaxial cable for perhaps half the price of true RG-58A. Its performance in amateur systems will, for all practical purposes, equal that of the high-priced spread. Of course, the time honored method of acquiring hardware for a ham station is through surplus outlets, and it is on the surplus market that many of us obtain used but serviceable MIL-C-17 cables at pennies per pound.

One final point is that many products destined for military markets first appear as commercial-grade items, awaiting government approval. Thus outstanding cables may become available, with manufacturers' house numbers, months or even years before they are assigned RG numbers. A case in point are the very fine 9913 and 9914 cables from Belden. Although these cables have not yet been assigned an RG number or approved in the MilSpec, they have nevertheless emerged as a favorite feed line among UHF and microwave amateurs. We can only speculate, but it is not unreasonable to expect that once government approval is obtained, the price of these outstanding products may increase significantly.

Coaxial Interconnect

Considering the emphasis that we have placed on the characteristic impedance of coaxial cables, it should come as no surprise to you that the characteristic impedance of the connectors that we use to interconnect coaxial cables and devices is an equally significant parameter. Low-frequency applications often require merely that any connectors used afford continuity between the respective center and outer conductors, along with perhaps a modicum of shielding. However, at the shorter wavelengths that are the domain of the microwave experimenter, the physical dimensions of a connector can attain a significant fraction of a wavelength. Thus the impedance discontinuities associated with improperly matched connectors can degrade system performance significantly.

A case in point are the so-called "type UHF" connectors popular on HF equipment and antennas. Developed in the 1930s (when "UHF" might properly have been applied to any wavelength shorter than a few tens of meters), these connectors are best known by their military designations, SO-239 and PL-259. Their name notwithstanding, these connectors are highly undesirable at frequencies above VHF, primarily because their design makes no attempt to maintain a constant characteristic impedance throughout the length of the interconnect. In short, "type UHF" is a misnomer.

The factors that affect coaxial-cable connector characteristic impedance are the same as those determining the Z_0 of the cable itself—conductor diameter ratio and dielectric constant. As you might expect, Eqs 26 and 27 apply to coaxial connectors as well as to the cables that they join. The significance of this relationship to connector design was recognized perhaps 40 years ago by two engineers at Bell Labs who were searching for a constant-impedance coaxial connector. Paul Neill and Carl Concelman went on to design six of the most widely used connector types in the microwave realm. Their connector designs remain industry standards to this day.

Best known of their designs is the type BNC (for Bayonet Neill-Concelman) connector, a quick-disconnect, 50-Ω interface device commonly found on oscilloscope probes, meter test leads, and of course in RF equipment. See Fig 12. Although the internal dimensions and dielectric materials are chosen to maintain a constant impedance throughout the connector, type BNC is not, strictly speaking, a microwave connector. This is because grounding of the outer conductor is accomplished chiefly through the bayonet tabs of the female connector and spring fingers of the male half.

After repeated use, the connector's shielding can become erratic, and leakage at microwave frequencies can

Fig 12—BNC connectors are popular for low-power VHF applications.

Fig 14—Type N connectors are the most popular high-power VHF/UHF connectors for amateur use.

Fig 13—The TNC connector is similar to type BNC, except it has a threaded interface. TNC connectors are usable well into the microwave region.

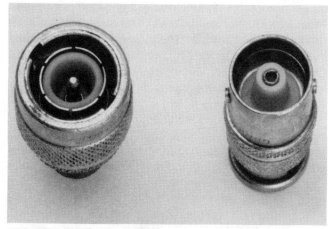

Fig 15—Type C connectors are quick-disconnect bayonet connectors similar in size to N connectors.

become significant. Although some BNC connectors are specified by their manufacturers for operation well into the microwave spectrum, most serious experimenters agree that their use should be restricted to frequencies below 1 GHz. Consider the BNC connector an excellent general-purpose instrumentation interface, and use it only through VHF.

An improvement on the BNC connector, as far as integrity of the shield is concerned, is the TNC, or Threaded Neill-Concelman connector. See Fig 13. Identical in all critical interface dimensions to type BNC, its threaded interface affords excellent outer conductor continuity well into the microwave region. TNC connectors are routinely and reliably applied through 12 GHz and beyond.

Perhaps the coaxial connector best known to microwave experimenters, type N (for Neill) is a physically larger, more rugged version of the TNC connector. See Fig 14. This is the connector most frequently found on UHF transceivers, amplifiers and antennas. By virtue of its size it can handle the legal amateur power limit. Although some

versions of type N connector exhibit self-resonances above about 10 GHz, they are widely used through the amateur 3-cm band.

Not to be outdone, Concelman developed the type C connector, a rugged, quick-disconnect, bayonet connector similar in size to the type N, but with a larger diameter, blunt center pin. Type C is widely used in military avionics applications, but is seldom encountered in amateur microwave systems. See Fig 15.

The last of the Neill-Concelman connectors we will discuss are types HN and SC. SC (for Screw C) is a threaded version of the C connector, and like its bayonet counterpart, is seldom encountered in amateur microwave systems. See Fig 16. HN is a scaled up version of the N connector. See Fig 17. Its physically larger separation between center and outer conductors increases the potential differences which it can sustain without breaking down or arcing over; hence the "H" in its name, for High voltage. HN makes an excellent connector for high-power pulsed microwave applications. It is found on the legendary

Fig 16—The SC connector is similar to type C, but has a threaded interface.

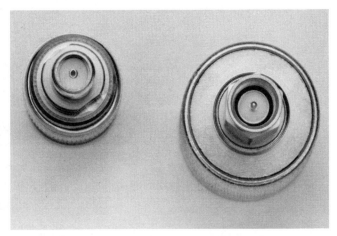

Fig 18—SMA connectors are the most popular UHF/microwave connectors in use today.

Fig 17—The HN connector is a high-voltage version of the N connector.

APX-6 airborne radar transponder, with which many radio amateurs made their first microwave contacts in the 23-cm band.

SMALL IS BEAUTIFUL

Perhaps you can recall a time when the microwave spectrum was widely regarded as an electromagnetic wasteland, of no practical value, fit for habitation only by that strange and hardy breed known as radio amateurs. When I joined the ranks of the fraternity, around 1960, amateur privileges included all frequencies "above 10 kilomegacycles." Today, of course, the centimeter-waves are a widely populated region—in part through the efforts of one company, Omni-Spectra, and their miniature coaxial connector.

Dubbed type OSM (for Omni-Spectra Miniature), the first Ku-band coaxial connector to gain wide acceptance is similar to the familiar type TNC, only about half the size. See Fig 18. Early versions of the OSM connector proved reliable through 18 GHz, with its more recent descendants operating beyond 26 GHz. The commercial success of the OSM connector was enhanced by the decision of its designers to license its production to other connector manufacturers on a royalty basis.

Though it assured the ready availability of high quality microwave connectors from a variety of sources, this licensing of the OSM design also contributed to considerable confusion within the microwave community. If Ford Motor Company, for example, were to produce an automotive design under license from Chevrolet, do you think they'd market it under the Chevy logo? Of course not! And neither would the dozen or so companies manufacturing OSM-compatible connectors identify them by Omni-Spectra's trade name. The result was an alphabet-soup of OSM clones, and chaos in the microwave industry's purchasing departments.

In a triumph for free enterprise, the United States Government (still the microwave industry's primary customer at the time) stepped in with a revision to MIL-C-39012, the military procurement document that standardizes coaxial connector dimensions and specifications. The OSM connector was renamed Type SMA, for Sub-Miniature, type A. (There are also types SMB and SMC, as shown in Fig 19). SMA became an industry standard, today outselling all of the Neill-Concelman connector types combined! And all manufacturers of OSM-compatible connectors quickly adopted the new nomenclature. All, that is, except for Omni-Spectra Corp, which markets their connectors under the OSM label to this day.

Incidentally, an examination of the accompanying photographs indicates an interesting difference between the SMA connector and all of the Neill-Concelman designs. Note that the Neill-Concelman types all have knurled surfaces where they are grasped for installation or removal, while the SMA plug has smooth, flat hexagonal surfaces. This is significant, in that the presence of a knurl communicates the appropriate tool to use for tightening and loosening connectors: *fingers only*! The SMA

Fig 19—Two variations on the SMA connector are the SMB connector (shown at A) and the SMC connector (shown at B).

(B)

connector, on the other hand (pun intended), is really meant to be installed and removed with a small open-end wrench, and in fact has a torque specification of 6 to 8 inch-pounds. Too little torque results in an erratic connection, while excessive torque bends the center pin. If you don't happen to have a torque wrench available while installing SMA connectors, a workable procedure seems to be "finger tight and a little bit more."

MALE AND FEMALE, CREATED HE EACH

Have you ever noticed that whenever you have a need to interface two coaxial devices, their connectors are more often than not of the same gender? It is for this very interface challenge that the ubiquitous barrel adapter, with its identical connectors at opposite ends, was invented. However, the use of barrels is not without its own difficulties. In critical measurement applications, any adapter between the measurement instrumentation and the device under test will introduce losses and degrade impedance matching. In phase-critical applications such as antenna stacking, adapters can introduce devastating propagation delays. At best, barrel adapters are an inconvenience. At worst, they can provide an insurmountable electromagnetic hindrance.

To manufacturers and users of precision microwave test instrumentation, the solution of choice is the development of sexless microwave connectors, designed so that all connectors in the system are identical, and any one can interface to any other, without the use of adapters. One such connector type was developed by General Radio (now

GenRad) Corporation, and is designated type GR-874. See Fig 20. Among radio amateurs, the 874 is often known simply as the GR connector. It is frequently found on surplus slotted lines, directional couplers, and signal generators, and it operates reliably through about 4 GHz.

Fig 20—The GR-874 is a sexless connector.

Fig 21—The N6TX Universal GR Barrel Adapter is a must for the UHF experimenter's tool kit.

A few years ago, I designed and brought to market an important new device, the Universal GR Barrel Adapter (see Fig 21). My adapter is able to interface any two GR connectors, regardless of their gender, simply by rotating its ends in 90 degree increments until a fit is achieved. Although sales to date have been somewhat underwhelming, I remain hopeful that publication of this book will renew public interest in my invention. Score one more for ham radio innovation.

Less common in ham circles than the GR adapter, and significantly more costly, is the APC-7 connector. The designation stands for Amphenol Precision Connector, 7 millimeter (the inside diameter of the outer conductor at the connector interface). See Fig 22. The APC-7 is quickly becoming an instrumentation standard. Truly a high-precision sexless connector, the APC-7 is found in top-of-the-line microwave network analyzers, reflectometer bridges, directional couplers, attenuators, and related test accessories. It provides nearly lossless, reflection-free interface through 18 GHz and beyond. Someday these items are bound to find their way into the ham shack of the serious microwave experimenter.

The importance of proper interface hardware for microwave transmission lines cannot be overemphasized. Many an amateur has invested in the ultimate coaxial cable to connect the finest available antenna system to the most powerful possible transmitter, only to see the whole system fall apart through use of the wrong coaxial connector. After learning the specifications, capabilities, and limitations of the various connector types discussed here, you should now be in a position to avoid sacrificing station performance to inferior connectors.

Fig 22—Another sexless connector, the APC-7, provides nearly lossless interconnection through 18 GHz and beyond.

5.6 WAVEGUIDE TRANSMISSION MEDIA

The ability of hollow metallic pipes to conduct electromagnetic waves was first demonstrated in London in 1894. Ironically, this was the year of Heinrich Hertz's premature death at the age of 37. One can only speculate as to the uses that Hertz might have found for waveguide transmission lines, had he enjoyed a greater span of years. He might well have been among the first experimenters to observe that signals propagate through waveguide with significantly less path loss than they suffer traveling through free space.

At Karlsruhe Technische Hochschule (now the University of Karlsruhe), Hertz had observed "that the action of an electric oscillation spreads out as a wave in space."[16] The signal captured at the receive end of a communications path thus represents but a fraction of the transmitted energy. A properly matched and terminated waveguide, on the other hand, contains and directs the wave from its source to load, with no spreading of the wave, hence minimal signal attenuation. In fact, waveguide is among the lowest loss transmission media known, which is why it is of considerable interest to the microwave experimenter.

Derivation and Propagation

The simplest model for waveguide behavior is the combination of twin-lead transmission line and quarter wavelength "metallic insulators." Consider an electro-

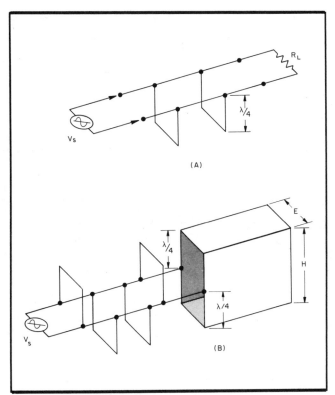

Fig 23—Quarter-wavelength metallic insulators installed on a twin-lead transmission line (A). An infinite number of quarter-wavelength insulator sections form a waveguide (B).

magnetic wave traveling down the twin-lead, as illustrated in Fig 23A. Since any transmission line of exactly one-quarter wavelength at the operating frequency serves as an impedance inverter, a quarter-wave shorted line section shunting the signal path appears to the twin-lead as an open. Thus any number of such shorted sections can be appended to the twin-lead, as shown in Fig 23B. An infinite number of these "metallic insulators" on two sides of the twin-lead form a rectangular pipe of width "h," completely containing the electromagnetic wave. Note that since the waveguide is composed of quarter wavelength insulators both above and below the original twin-lead, the critical dimension "h" is exactly one-half the operating wavelength ($\lambda/2$).

Although the above analogy would seem to imply that waveguide can support but a single operating frequency, in fact a waveguide can propagate a fairly wide band of frequencies. If you imagine that waveguide, like coaxial cable, functions as a distributed-constant filter, you are entirely correct. And to determine the pertinent filter characteristic, you need only perform a simple experiment. A high-frequency signal generator (the sun) is "connected" to one end of a hollow metallic waveguide, and a high frequency detector (a human eye) is "connected" to the other, as illustrated in Fig 24A. Can you see that the waveguide supports propagation of the applied signal? Good!

Next, repeat the experiment for a low-frequency generator (a battery) and a low-frequency detector (a dc voltmeter), as shown in Fig 24B. Obviously the waveguide does not support low-frequency propagation. Now if you agree that sunlight represents a high-frequency electromagnetic wave, and dc a low one, then it is evident that the waveguide exhibits a high-pass response. It can thus be modeled as a combination of series capacitance and shunt inductance, as shown in Fig 24C.

If waveguide is in fact a high-pass filter, it must exhibit a lower cutoff frequency, and it stands to reason this cutoff frequency should be in some way related to the physical dimensions of the guide. It turns out the critical dimension is the *widest* interior dimension of the waveguide, which was referred to as "h" in Fig 23B, and cutoff occurs at the frequency for which the h dimension represents one-half wavelength ($\lambda/2$). For a rectangular waveguide of given dimensions, cutoff wavelength λ_c is found by doubling the widest inside dimension.

$$\lambda_c = 2h \qquad \text{(Eq 35)}$$

Cutoff frequency, in GHz, is found in the usual way, by dividing cutoff wavelength, in centimeters, into the numeric constant 30

$$f_c \text{ (GHz)} = \frac{30}{2h \text{ (cm)}} \qquad \text{(Eq 36)}$$

Since the insertion loss of any filter at cutoff is not insignificant, it is desirable to operate any waveguide at frequencies reasonably removed from cutoff if minimum attenuation is desired. A practical limit is to restrict waveguide use to frequencies at least 20 percent above cutoff. Thus

$$f_{min} = 1.20 \ f_c \qquad \text{(Eq 37)}$$

Since waveguide is a high-pass medium, in theory it can support propagation of any frequency above the minimum identified by Eq 37. Differences in propagation modes, however, create an effective upper frequency limit for waveguide as well. This limit will be discussed in the sections that follow.

The lumped constant waveguide model shown in Fig 24C, though convenient for explaining waveguide behavior through analogy, is also misleading. This is because, unlike the lumped constant model for coaxial cable introduced earlier, the distributed inductance and capacitance of waveguide transmission line are neither tangible, measurable, nor constant. Rather they vary with frequency and propagation mode.

Fig 25 shows that an electromagnetic wave propagates not straight down a waveguide, but rather obliquely, bouncing repeatedly off the inner conductive walls. This oblique propagation mode suggests that waveguide transmission lines do not support transverse electromagnetic (TEM) waves. In fact, components of either the magnetic (h) or electrostatic (e) fields will exist *parallel* to the plane of wave propagation. The two possible propagation modes for electromagnetic waves in waveguide are: (1) Transverse

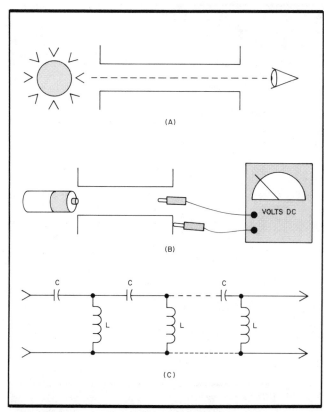

Fig 24—Waveguide passes high frequencies (A) but not low frequencies (B). The equivalent circuit of a waveguide is shown at C.

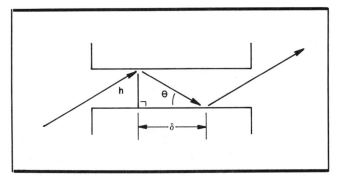

Fig 25—Reflection of an electromagnetic wave off the walls of a waveguide.

Electric (TE), in which the electrostatic field is perpendicular to the direction of propagation, with a component of the magnetic field parallel; and (2) Transverse Magnetic (TM), which describes magnetic flux lines orthogonal to the direction of wave propagation, with an electrostatic field component parallel. Propagation modes are further delineated by two subscripts (for example, TM_{01} or TE_{11}) which define the number of half wave repetitions of the e- and h-fields, respectively, across the cross-sectioned width and height of the waveguide. For any given waveguide at a specified frequency, there is one dominant propagation mode resulting in minimum wave attenuation, and it is the dominant mode that the balance of this chapter will address.

The distance δ between successive reflections shown in Fig 25 is related to wavelength, but the interior waveguide dimension h is fixed. Thus the angle θ is related to frequency. And it is this angle that determines the distributed reactances within the waveguide. Therefore, such transmission-line operating parameters as propagation velocity and characteristic impedance, which have been previously shown to be related to distributed inductance and capacitance, will for waveguide also vary with frequency.

Fortunately, the waveguide interior dimension h, the wavelength related dimension δ, and the reflection angle θ collectively describe a right triangle, the hypotenuse of which is defined by the Pythagorean Theorem. Thus, it is possible to employ elementary trigonometry to correlate the various waveguide operating parameters to signal wavelength. This will be done in the following section.

Rectangular Waveguide

Waveguide can be designed in any imaginable shape and form factor, depending on the intended application. Common examples include square, ridged rectangular, circular and elliptical cross sections. By far the most common configuration encountered is rectangular waveguide with an interior aspect ratio slightly greater than 2:1. The guide must of course be conductive to RF and may be constructed from aluminum, tin-plate or brass. It is not unusual for the inner, conducting surfaces of a waveguide to be silver plated to minimize dissipative losses.

Fig 26 shows a typical rectangular waveguide in cross section. The narrow and wide inside dimensions are designated e and h respectively, for their ability to support electrostatic and magnetic fields in the primary propagation mode. Recall that the h-field inside dimension represents one-half wavelength at the guide's lower cutoff frequency. The outside dimensions E and H are abbreviated in capitals to distinguish them from the inner conductive surfaces, and differ from their interior counterparts by twice the wall thickness t.

Fig 27 is presented as a memory aid in distinguishing between the e- and h-fields of a rectangular waveguide. Imagine the difficulty one might encounter in producing a right angle bend in rigid rectangular guide. While it might be *easy* to bend the guide in the narrow (e-field) direction, it would be *hard* to do so in the wide (h-field) plane. Not surprisingly, the components illustrated in Fig 27 are referred to as e-field and h-field bends.

Rectangular waveguides manufactured in the United States under MIL-W-85, the applicable government standard for military and aerospace procurement, have an outside H dimension exactly twice the E dimension, for

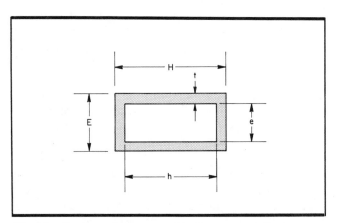

Fig 26—Rectangular waveguide in cross section.

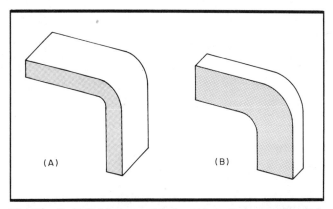

Fig 27—An E-field waveguide bend is in the *easy* direction (A), while an H-field bend is in the *hard* direction (B).

an exterior aspect ratio of 2:1. Since the wall thickness t is uniform, the resulting interior aspect ratio must be greater than 2:1, as mentioned previously. The military specification assigns a unique designator to each standardized waveguide size, consisting of the letters WR (for Waveguide, Rectangular) followed by two or three digits representing the inside h-field dimension, in hundredths of an inch.[17] Thus WR-90 is rectangular waveguide with an inside h-field dimension of 0.90 inch, or 2.286 cm. Since this dimension sets the lower cutoff frequency of the guide, the MIL-W-85 designation provides useful information as to the guide's operating frequency range.

The WR designations for waveguide, like the RG designations for coaxial cable described previously, have emerged as a *de facto* standard for the microwave industry. They are used to describe a given transmission line type, regardless of whether it was produced for government consumption.

The standard outside aspect ratio of WR type waveguides allows one to determine all pertinent dimensions from the military designation, along with just one additional physical dimension. Consider, for example, a WR-90 waveguide with a uniform 0.05 inch wall thickness. Since the h-field inside dimension, h, is 0.9 inch, the outside H dimension equals (h + 2t), or 1.0 inch. The E outside dimension must be H/2, or 0.5 inch. And the internal e-field dimension is then (E − 2t), or 0.4 inch.

Once found, these dimensions can be converted to the more useful metric units for analysis of the waveguide's electrical operating characteristics, as shown in Fig 28. As indicated by Eq 35, lower cutoff occurs when the inside dimension h is half a wavelength. Cutoff wavelength therefore equals 1.8 inches, or 4.572 cm. From Eq 36, the corresponding cutoff frequency is 6.56 GHz, and Eq 37 then yields a minimum operating frequency of roughly 8 GHz. Thus WR-90 is clearly X-band waveguide.

But what of the upper operating frequency limit alluded to earlier? If WR-90 is usable above 8 GHz, can it not support Ku band propagation, millimeter wave propagation, infrared and visible light as well? It can indeed, but *not in the desired propagation mode*.

The dominant propagation mode for rectangular waveguide, that which results in minimal signal attenuation over the "normal" operating frequency range, is TM_{01}. This mode represents Transverse Magnetic propagation, with a single half-wave repetition of the wave pattern along the h-field dimension, and none along the e-field. At frequencies slightly above cutoff, this is the *only* mode of propagation that the guide can support. As operating frequency is increased, wavelength decreases. If the frequency of the signal applied to the waveguide is high enough for the dimension e to represent one-half wavelength or less, then the propagation mode changes to TE_{11}, with the wave's magnetic, or h, field now aligned with the guide's e plane. The result is a cross polarized wave, as far as the intended propagation mode is concerned, which suffers the same losses as a signal from a vertically polarized antenna transmitting across free space to a horizontally polarized antenna.

Note that this transition occurs at the frequency for which the waveguide's inside e-field dimension represents one-half wave. The mode transition wavelength λ_m thus equals

$$\lambda_m = 2\,e \qquad\qquad (Eq\ 38)$$

with the corresponding mode transition frequency found from

$$f_m = \frac{30}{2e} \qquad\qquad (Eq\ 39)$$

where f_m is expressed in GHz and e is the inside dimension of the waveguide, expressed in cm.

To minimize orthogonal polarization losses, it is desirable to operate a rectangular waveguide at least 15 percent below the frequency at which a change in propagation mode would occur. This establishes a maximum usable frequency for single mode propagation

$$f_{max} = 0.85\,f_m \qquad\qquad (Eq\ 40)$$

Consider again the WR-90 waveguide used in the previous example. With an inside e-field dimension of 0.4 inch or 1.016 cm, Eq 38 indicates a mode transition wavelength of 2.032 cm for a corresponding frequency (from Eq 39) of roughly 14.8 GHz. Finally, Eq 40 indicates a practical upper frequency limit of 12.5 GHz for WR-90. Thus WR-90 waveguide covers the entire frequency range designated as X-band in a single propagation mode.

Table 3 shows the physical dimensions, WR designations and operating frequency limits of other common MIL-W-85 type waveguides.

VELOCITY OF PROPAGATION

Field and wave theory suggests that an electromagnetic wave ought to propagate through a waveguide at the speed of light. The reflective nature of wave propagation

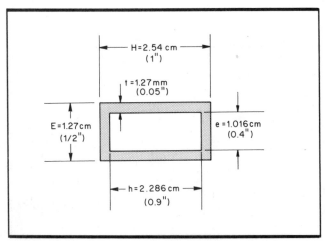

Fig 28—Critical dimensions for WR-90 waveguide, converted to metric measurements.

Table 3

Rectangular Waveguides for Amateur Radio Use

Band	WR No.	Frequency Range (GHz)	Waveguide Dimensions (in.)				
			E	H	e	h	t
23 cm	650	1.12 - 1.7	3.410	6.660	3.250	6.500	0.080
13 cm	430	1.7 - 2.6	2.310	4.460	2.150	4.300	0.080
	340	2.2 - 3.3	1.860	3.560	1.700	3.400	0.080
9 cm	284	2.6 - 3.95	1.500	3.000	1.340	2.840	0.080
	229	3.3 - 4.9	1.273	2.418	1.145	2.290	0.064
5 cm	187	3.95 - 5.85	1.000	2.000	0.872	1.872	0.064
	159	4.9 - 7.05	0.923	1.718	0.759	1.590	0.064
	137	5.85 - 8.2	0.750	1.500	0.622	1.372	0.064
3 cm	102	7 - 11	0.610	1.120	0.510	1.020	0.050
	90	8.2 - 12.4	0.500	1.000	0.400	0.900	0.050
	75	10 - 15	0.475	0.850	0.375	0.750	0.050
1.2 cm	42	18 - 26.5	0.250	0.500	0.170	0.420	0.040
	34	22 - 33	0.250	0.420	0.170	0.340	0.040
6 mm	22	33 - 50	0.192	0.304	0.112	0.224	0.040
	19	40 - 60	0.174	0.268	0.094	0.188	0.040
4 mm	12	60 - 90	0.141	0.202	0.061	0.122	0.040
	10	75 - 110	0.130	0.180	0.050	0.100	0.040
2.5 mm	8	90 - 140	0.120	0.160	0.040	0.080	0.040
	7	110 - 170	0.098	0.130	0.033	0.065	0.033
2 mm	7	110 - 170	0.098	0.130	0.033	0.065	0.033
	5	140 - 220	0.091	0.116	0.026	0.051	0.033

Note: See text and Fig 10 for explanation of abbreviations.

within a rectangular guide, as illustrated in Fig 25, however, suggests that the actual forward velocity component of the wave might be something other than the speed of light, with the actual velocity dependent upon the angle θ. Since, in the words of the ancient proverb, an experiment is worth a thousand theories, it might be informative to actually *measure* the propagation velocity within a guide. This is most easily accomplished with a slotted line.

The apparatus shown in Fig 29 consists of a shorted section of waveguide transmission line, with a slot cut along its axis of radiation to allow the insertion of a movable probe. Connected to the probe is a diode detector, which drives a voltmeter or oscilloscope vertical deflection axis. Since the probe is coupled into the e-field of the waveguide, it samples the incident and reflected EMF at any given point along the length of the line. By moving the probe assembly and observing the voltmeter or scope indications, the voltage standing wave pattern along the line can be discerned.

A fully reflected wave produces nodes and nulls along its transmission line. At the nodes, the incident and reflected waves reinforce; at the nulls, they cancel. Successive nulls (or nodes) distribute themselves along the transmission line at half-wave intervals. If, however, the distance between successive EMF nulls is measured on the slotted line, it will be seen to considerably *exceed* a free-space half wavelength at the frequency used. Does this not imply that

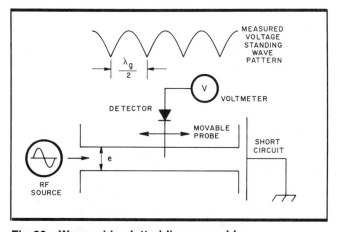

Fig 29—Waveguide slotted line assembly.

the wave within the guide is traveling *faster* than the speed of light?

No, the laws of Einsteinian physics are not being violated. What you are observing with the slotted line is the apparent velocity of the *wave front*, the point of intersection of the wave with the wall of the guide. And since this point of intersection is not itself matter (it has no mass), it is not bounded by the universal speed limit. In fact, the apparent wave front velocity will exceed the speed of light to the same extent, and by the same amount, that the hypotenuse in Fig 25 exceeds the forward propagation distance δ.

Though the forward propagated wave in a guide travels at 3×10^8 meters per second, it is the higher *apparent wave front velocity* that determines the physical dimension that constitutes a wavelength in a given guide. Wave front velocity in turn depends upon frequency.

Fig 30 shows that guide wavelength λ_g, free-space wavelength λ_o, and cutoff wavelength λ_c are all interrelated by a right triangle. Remember that cutoff wavelength is twice the inside h-field dimension of the guide, and free-space wavelength is found by dividing the operating frequency into the speed of light. Thus if a signal of unknown frequency is applied to a waveguide slotted line of known dimensions, and distance between successive nulls is measured, the free-space wavelength (and hence frequency) of the signal can be determined. The Pythagorean Theorem yields

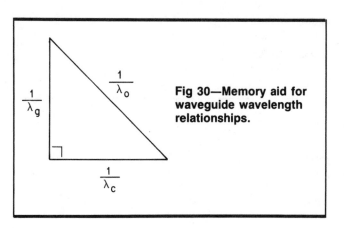

Fig 30—Memory aid for waveguide wavelength relationships.

$$\left(\frac{1}{\lambda_o}\right)^2 = \left(\frac{1}{\lambda_c}\right)^2 + \left(\frac{1}{\lambda_g}\right)^2 \qquad \text{(Eq 41)}$$

where guide wavelength λ_g is twice the distance between successive nulls (remember that nulls occur one-half wavelength apart), cutoff wavelength λ_c is twice the h-field inside dimension, and all three wavelengths are expressed in the same unit (typically centimeters).

Solving for free-space wavelength, Eq 41 becomes

$$\lambda_o = \frac{1}{\sqrt{\left(\frac{1}{\lambda_c}\right)^2 - \left(\frac{1}{\lambda_g}\right)^2}} \qquad \text{(Eq 42)}$$

and a little algebra allows us to determine guide wavelength for a known free-space wavelength (or frequency).

$$\lambda_g = \frac{1}{\sqrt{\left(\frac{1}{\lambda_o}\right)^2 - \left(\frac{1}{\lambda_c}\right)^2}} \qquad \text{(Eq 43)}$$

This relationship will be exploited in the following chapters, where guide wavelength will be used to design waveguide impedance-matching networks, antennas, and feed horns.

CHARACTERISTIC IMPEDANCE

You have seen in Section 5.5 that the characteristic impedance of coaxial cable and its velocity of propagation are each a function of the cable's distributed inductance and capacitance, both of which are independent of frequency. This is true of all TEM transmission lines. Waveguide is not a TEM medium, and it has just been shown that the velocity of propagation in waveguide varies with frequency. Therefore it stands to reason that the characteristic impedance of waveguide should be frequency dependent as well. Once again, a slotted line measurement can be made to experimentally verify the theory.

The test setup shown in Fig 31 resembles that of Fig 29, except that instead of being terminated in a short circuit, the waveguide is radiating into free space. *Caution: Great care should be taken to avoid directing the radiating end of the slotted line toward living beings, or into metallic surfaces or objects that can reflect radiation toward living beings.* As is mentioned in Chapter 2, the eyes are most susceptible to damage from microwave radiation. Please remember that looking down the open end of a waveguide to see if it's radiating is like looking down the barrel of a shotgun to see if it's loaded.

Since the characteristic impedance of waveguide differs from that of free space, an impedance mismatch exists in the test setup of Fig 31, and a voltage standing wave pattern results, as indicated in the diagram. Since the characteristic impedance of free space is known, from the measured VSWR one can calculate the waveguide characteristic impedance, with only a little ambiguity.

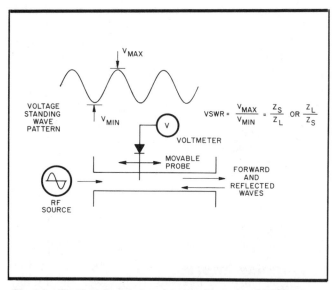

Fig 31—Slotted line setup to compare waveguide to free space characteristic impedance.

$$VSWR = \frac{Z_s}{Z_1} \qquad \text{(Eq 44)}$$

or

$$VSWR = \frac{Z_1}{Z_s} \qquad \text{(Eq 45)}$$

whichever yields a voltage ratio greater than unity. Here Z_1 represents the load impedance (that of free space, or 377 Ω), and Z_s is the characteristic impedance of the waveguide that you are trying to characterize. Clearly two possible solutions to Z_s present themselves, and null shift measurement indicates that the lesser of the two possibilities is the correct one.

Waveguide characteristic impedance can also be determined analytically. One approach is to start with the characteristic impedance of free space, and modify it for the physical boundaries imposed upon the wave by the walls of the guide, and for a factor related to the guide's velocity of propagation. For this latter correction factor, one can employ the ratio of guide wavelength to free-space wavelength. The equality is

$$Z_g = 377 \left(\frac{e}{h} \right) \left(\frac{\lambda_g}{\lambda_0} \right) \qquad \text{(Eq 46)}$$

where
  Z_g = the characteristic impedance of the waveguide, in ohms
  377 = the characteristic impedance of free space, in ohms
  e = the inside e-field dimension of the guide
  h = the inside h-field dimension of the guide
  λ_g = the guide wavelength (found from Eq 43)
  λ_0 = the free-space wavelength

It is important to note that the variable most useful in manipulating waveguide characteristic impedance is the e-field inside dimension of the guide. This is because the h-field dimension sets lower cutoff frequency and influences guide wavelength.

As an example, consider the characteristic impedance of a WR-90 X-band waveguide, operating at the weak signal calling frequency of 10.368 GHz. The associated free-space wavelength is 2.894 cm, and the e and h dimensions of WR-90 are 0.4 by 0.9 inch, or 1.016 by 2.286 cm. Cutoff wavelength is twice h, or 4.572 cm. From Eq 43, the guide wavelength at the operating frequency is 3.738 cm. Finally, Eq 46 yields a guide characteristic impedance of 216.4 Ω.

Radiating into free space, Eq 44 suggests a VSWR of 1.74, which is confirmed by actual slotted line measurements. Further, the above analysis indicates that a WR-90 waveguide flange radiating into free space serves as a slightly mismatched, but useful, antenna.

Waveguide Interconnect Considerations

Efficient propagation of electromagnetic radiation through rectangular guides requires that the electrostatic and magnetic lines of force align themselves with the waveguide's e and h fields, respectively. It is therefore important that the e and h fields not be transposed when waveguide sections or components are interfaced. Failure to maintain constant polarization would have the same effect on a waveguide-propagated signal as receiving a horizontally polarized wave at line-of-sight with a vertically polarized antenna.

Fortunately, the physical design of waveguide flanges generally precludes cross polarization, as Fig 32 indicates. Note that the spacing of the screw holes shown is not symmetrical. Thus, should two waveguide flanges be joined with their respective e and h fields misaligned, it would be impossible to install all of the necessary hardware. If any connecting screw will not pass easily through its associated flange hole, the guide sections or components are quite likely cross polarized. But, if the screw fits, wear it!

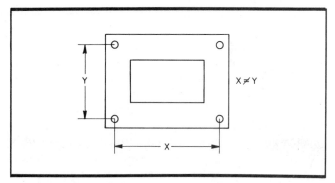

Fig 32—Attachment holes in waveguide flanges are *not* symmetrical.

One concern when employing waveguide as a transmission medium is that the wave be completely isolated from the outside environment, even where waveguide sections or components interconnect. Leakage, whether of the waveguide-propagated signal to its surroundings, or of external signals into the waveguide, will diminish system effectiveness. In hydraulic or pneumatic systems, gaskets are commonly used to assure a secure seal, preventing leakage of the fluid at the junction of transmission line sections. Waveguides are sealed in the same way, although the composition of a waveguide gasket differs somewhat from that of its fluid counterpart.

Fig 33 shows a typical waveguide EMI (Electromagnetic Interference) gasket. It is composed of a woven cloth of metallic and carbon fibers, with an opening consistent with the guide's internal e and h dimensions. The gasket is compressed between two flat waveguide flanges, and held in place with screws, nuts, and lock washers.

An alternative approach (see Fig 34) involves a length of braided shielding material composed of individual small conductive strands, similar to the braid commonly used

Fig 33—Waveguide EMI gasket. (*photo by WA5VJB*)

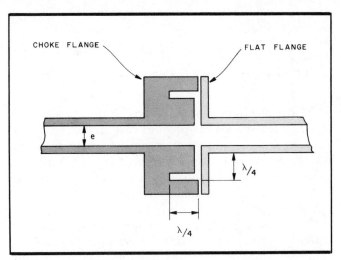

Fig 35—Waveguide choke flange mated against a flat flange (see text).

in coaxial cables. This "weather stripping" is inserted in a groove cut around the opening in a waveguide flange, but will only flatten and seal the interface if the grooved flange is butted against a flat flange, as shown.

In addition to the use of gaskets, isolation at the interface of two waveguide sections or components is often enhanced through the inclusion of resonant grooves within the waveguide flange. These grooves serve as RF chokes. As seen in Fig 35, a choke flange contains a groove one-quarter wavelength deep at the guide's mean operating frequency, located a quarter wavelength away from the e-field opening. Any signal escaping the guide is coupled

into the groove, where it circulates rather than radiates.

Note that if choke grooves and gasket grooves are both employed in the same waveguide flange, the choke groove is the deeper of the two, and is located within (that is, inside) the gasket groove. Also, a choke flange should be interfaced only to a flat flange. Interconnecting two choke flanges will produce a groove one-half wavelength deep, which will have just the opposite of the desired effect.

Although not widely employed by radio amateurs, waveguide in high-power systems is sometimes pressurized with dry nitrogen, much as is done in air dielectric coaxial cables. The objective is to keep out moisture, which might otherwise cause corrosion to the conductive inside surfaces

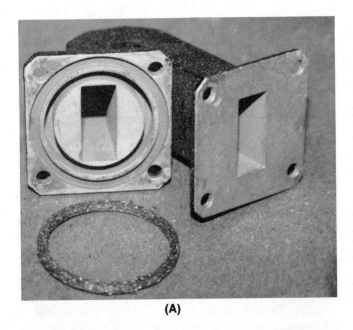

(A)

(B)

Fig 34—An alternative method of installing EMI shielding at waveguide flange connections involves braid inserted in a groove machined in the flange. (*photo by WA5VJB*)

of the guide. In pressurized systems, the outer groove of a choke flange is fitted not with an RFI gasket, but rather with a rubber or neoprene O-ring, used to maintain a slight positive pressure within the guide.

A need frequently arises to interface coaxial devices to waveguide systems, or vice versa, which necessitates the development of waveguide-to-coax adapters. The most common design employs a section of waveguide roughly one-half guide wavelength at the mean operating frequency, terminated at one end in a standard waveguide flange, and at the other in a short circuit. A quarter-wavelength monopole is connected to the center pin of a coaxial connector (typically type N, although other connector families have been used successfully), which is in turn inserted into the guide's e-field, one-quarter guide wavelength ahead of the short. One such adapter is illustrated in Fig 36, in both front and side views. An additional application for the coax-to-waveguide adapter comes to mind when one considers that the characteristic impedance of waveguide can be a reasonably close approximation to that of free space. Thus the adapter introduced here can serve as a reasonably efficient coaxially fed antenna, as is discussed in Chapter 9.

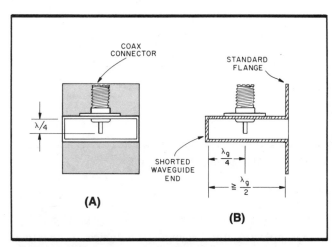

Fig 36—Waveguide-to-coax adapter shown from end (A) and side (B).

Circular Waveguides

Although less frequently encountered in commercial systems than rectangular guide, waveguides with circular cross section are popular among microwave experimenters because they can be readily fabricated from available materials such as copper water pipe and tin cans. The principles of electromagnetic wave propagation within a circular guide are really no different from those pertaining to rectangular guide, except that now the e and h inside dimensions are equal. This will affect the guide's cutoff wavelength, guide wavelength and characteristic impedance, as well as its dominant propagation mode and the wavelength at which it transitions to the next higher mode.

The dominant mode of propagation in circular waveguide is TE_{11}, which suggests that, unlike rectangular waveguide, a component of the magnetic field will exist in the plane of wave propagation. The guide will exhibit a cutoff wavelength equal to its diameter times a factor of not two, but rather 1.706. Since this factor is nearly equal to the square root of 3, we can approximate cutoff wavelength to within about one percent from

$$\lambda_c \approx \sqrt{3} \text{ diam}$$

Once cutoff wavelength has been determined, the Pythagorean Theorem can be invoked to determine guide wavelength for a given free-space wavelength, using Eq 43. To determine the corresponding characteristic impedance, Eq 46 applies, as it did for rectangular waveguide. In the case of circular guide, however, the physical dimensions of e and h are equal, so the factor (e/h) becomes unity. Eq 46 then simplifies to

$$Z_0 = 377 \left(\frac{\lambda_g}{\lambda_o} \right) \qquad \text{(Eq 47)}$$

Since guide wavelength will always exceed free-space wavelength, Eq 47 suggests that the characteristic impedance of circular cross section waveguide will always be slightly higher than that of free space. This is in marked contrast to the characteristic impedance of rectangular waveguide, which is generally less than free-space impedance.

The next highest propagation mode for circular waveguide is TM_{01}, which you will recall was the dominant mode for rectangular guide. Transition to TM_{01} in circular guide occurs at a wavelength related to the guide's diameter by the factor 1.3065. Therefore

$$\lambda_{min} = 1.3065 \text{ diam}$$

It can be seen that if operation over a single propagation mode is desired and operation near cutoff is to be avoided, the useful frequency range of circular waveguide is considerably narrower than that of rectangular guide.

Just as rectangular waveguides are standardized by WR designations, a system exists for describing standard circular waveguide parameters. The designations for circular waveguide begin with WC. Table 4 lists critical dimensions and TE_{11} mode frequency limitations of several WC waveguides used in amateur microwave bands.

It might appear that with its narrow operating bandwidth, circular waveguide is less desirable than its rectangular counterpart. The symmetry of circular guide, however, gives it a capability that rectangular waveguide lacks: the ability to support two different propagation polarizations simultaneously.

Since the aperture of a circular waveguide is constant at all angles and equal to the diameter of the guide, it should be obvious that the guide will support electromagnetic propagation of any polarization. That is, it is no

Table 4

Circular Waveguides for Amateur Radio Use

Band	WC No.	Frequency Range (GHz)	Inside Diameter (in.)
33 cm	992	0.8 - 1.1	9.915
23 cm	847	0.94 - 1.29	8.470
	724	1.1 - 1.51	7.235
13 cm	451	1.76 - 2.42	4.511
	385	2.07 - 2.83	3.853
9 cm	281	2.83 - 3.88	2.812
	240	3.31 - 4.54	2.403
5 cm	175	4.54 - 6.23	1.750
	150	5.30 - 7.27	1.500
3 cm	94	8.49 - 11.6	0.938
	80	9.97 - 13.7	0.797
1.2 cm	44	18.2 - 24.9	0.438
	38	21.2 - 29.1	0.375
6 mm	22	36.4 - 49.8	0.219
	19	42.4 - 58.1	0.188
	17	46.3 - 63.5	0.172
4 mm	13	63.5 - 87.2	0.125
	11	72.7 - 99.7	0.109

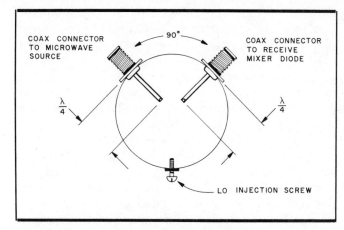

Fig 37—A polaplexer takes advantage of the fact that circular waveguide can support two waves of orthogonal polarization at the same time. See text. Note that both coax connectors are located $\lambda_g / 4$ in front of the shorted end of the circular waveguide (see Fig 36).

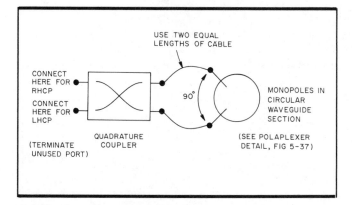

Fig 38—Circular polarization adapter.

longer necessary for the magnetic field of the wave to orient itself along the wide dimension of the guide, since the e and h dimensions are now equal. Thus, a monopole can be inserted into a circular guide section at any angle, inducing a wave polarized with its electrostatic field aligned with the monopole. By placing in a circular waveguide two monopoles at 90 degree angles to each other, two waves of orthogonal polarization can be supported at the same time.

This characteristic of circular waveguide led to the development of the Polaplexer (polarization duplexer) by the San Bernardino Microwave Society in the 1950s.[18] In a polaplexer, two orthogonal monopole probes are inserted into a circular waveguide (see Fig 37). One probe is attached to a transmit source (originally a reflex klystron; more recently a Gunn diode oscillator). The other monopole drives a receive mixer. The receive and transmit e-fields are thus at right angles to each other, and the only transmit energy coupled into the receive mixer is that slight amount resulting from discontinuities in the guide. These can be controlled to provide efficient injection of a portion of the transmit signal into the mixer diode as a local oscillator. Full duplex communication results from offsetting the transmit frequencies at both ends of a communications path by the frequency of the IF receiver.

Using an arrangement similar to the polaplexer, a circular waveguide can be used to generate or collect a circularly polarized wave. The two phase quadrature ports of a branch line hybrid coupler are connected through equal lengths of cable to the two orthogonal monopoles in a circular guide, as shown in Fig 38. The wave propagating within the guide will exhibit either right- or left-hand circular polarization, depending on which of the two remaining coupler ports is driven. By connecting the transmitter and receiver to opposite ports of the quadrature hybrid, it is possible to use the waveguide as a dual mode circular feed. This will allow transmission on one circular polarization, and reception on opposite circularity, as is required for moonbounce operation.

Waveguide and Coaxial Cable: A Comparison

It was pointed out previously that waveguides are among the lowest loss transmission lines known. That waveguide has not supplanted other microwave transmission media entirely is indicative of its various operating limitations. These include bandwidth, rigidity, size constraints, impedance and velocity considerations, as well as cost.

The operating frequency range of waveguide transmission lines is bounded by cutoff at one end and by transition to higher-order propagation modes at the other. The two limits are seldom separated by more than half an octave. Coaxial cables exhibit no lower cutoff frequency. Their upper usable frequency is limited by increasing insertion loss and by the transition to waveguide propagation modes, but these effects can be controlled through judicious selection of the outer conductor diameter. The useful frequency range of coaxial cable easily spans the entire microwave spectrum.

Techniques exist for extending the useful frequency range of waveguide, among them insertion of ridges within the guide's interior walls (see Fig 39). Such practices, however, increase the cost and complexity of the waveguide, and increase the difficulty of efficiently coupling energy into and out of the guide. Thus the use of waveguide is normally restricted to relatively narrowband applications.

The problems associated with the rigid nature of waveguide become evident when one tries to route a waveguide transmission line through a rack of equipment. Flexible waveguide sections (see Fig 40) are manufactured with corrugated walls, much like the corrugated outer conductors used to improve the flexibility of coaxial Hardline cables. A drawback is that the process results in fluctuations in the inside dimensions of the e and h planes along the length of the guide. Since cutoff frequency, propagation mode, guide wavelength and characteristic impedance are all interior dimension dependent, these fluctuations can severely degrade performance. In applications requiring transmission line flexibility, coaxial cables are clearly superior to even "flexible" waveguide sections.

To efficiently propagate energy, a waveguide's interior dimensions have to exceed a specified fraction of the operating wavelength. Thus it is evident that the physical size of any waveguide will be inversely proportional to the operating frequency. Although military systems have successfully applied waveguides at frequencies as low as the VHF spectrum, their size exceeds that of ventilation ducts used in the construction industry. It is generally regarded as impractical to employ waveguide much below L-band.

At the other end of their operating spectrum, waveguides become so small that they impose stringent constraints upon the precision with which their dimensions are maintained. Millimeter-wavelength guides can become so minute that they require precision micro-machining, specialized tooling for interconnection and handling, and magnifying equipment for inspection and troubleshooting. Of course, since coaxial cable diameters must be kept small relative to the operating wavelength to prevent waveguide moding, it can be seen that waveguide and coaxial transmission lines share similar high-frequency limitations.

One significant advantage of coaxial transmission lines is that their characteristic impedance and velocity of propagation are relatively independent of frequency. It has been shown above that, even within the confines of its relatively narrow operating bandwidth, a waveguide will exhibit significant, frequency-dependent variations in

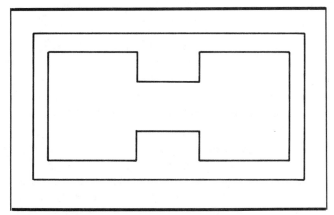

Fig 39—Double-ridged waveguide shown in cross section.

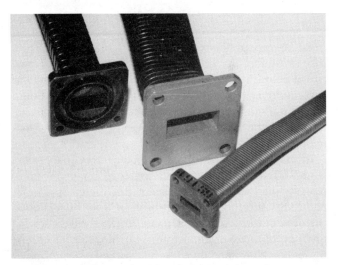

Fig 40—Flexible waveguide sections. (*photo by WA5VJB*)

characteristic impedance and wave front velocity. Thus those broadband systems requiring uniform phase relationships or group delay will likely require coaxial, rather than waveguide, implementation.

In military, aerospace, and biomedical systems, the relatively high cost of waveguide is readily justified by the critical nature of the application. Microwave experimenters can seldom afford to incorporate commercial waveguide devices into their systems, and often resort to homemade techniques or modified surplus hardware. Fortunately, in much of the microwave spectrum, and especially at X band, the surplus market affords a wealth of waveguide hardware at modest cost.

Despite the obvious limitations of waveguide when contrasted with coaxial cable, it should be remembered that waveguide transmission line affords its user with significantly lower insertion loss than its coaxial counterpart. Waveguide is able to handle higher power levels than coax, is mechanically sturdy, and if properly interfaced, exhibits the highest degree of electromagnetic isolation of any known transmission medium. Thus waveguide has earned a valued and respected position in the communications systems of countless microwave experimenters worldwide.

5.7 STRIP TRANSMISSION MEDIA

You have no doubt seen microwave circuit assemblies in which a significant number of components were implemented by transmission lines. Fig 41 depicts one such assembly; the project construction chapters of this book contain others. The ability to employ the distributed properties of transmission lines in place of lumped constant components is one of the features that differentiates microwave technology from low-frequency electronics. This section will explore the use of two popular strip transmission media: microstrip and stripline.

Microstrip

Microstrip is a transmission line, much like coaxial cable or waveguide, except that it is fabricated not from wire or tubing, but rather by etching traces on a printed circuit board. It's doubtful that the average radio amateur is going to run a long, thin strip of printed circuit board up a tower, so the actual application of microstrip transmission media is likely to be something other than feeding antennas.

In an ideal microstrip application, the traces on a printed circuit board that interconnect discrete ("lumped") components themselves form etched ("distributed") components. By selecting strip transmission lines of a desired characteristic impedance and phase length, the designer can produce capacitors, inductors, matching transformers, power combiners and dividers, baluns, and a host of other passive components. These can be employed in antenna systems, filters, amplifiers, mixers, oscillators, and detectors, or just about any other desired circuit for microwave communications or instrumentation.

Microstrip performance is closely related to that of a single wire positioned above a continuous ground plane (see Fig 42). The distributed inductance along such a line is a function primarily of the wire diameter d. The wire's diameter, its height above ground (h), and the relative permittivity or dielectric constant ϵ of the insulating medium jointly influence its distributed capacitance. If the wire diameter is small relative to its height above ground ($d < < h$), the medium will support transverse electromagnetic (TEM) wave propagation, as does coaxial cable.

You may recall the relationship developed to earlier quantify the characteristic impedance of coaxial cable (Eq 27).

$$Z_0 = \frac{60}{\sqrt{\epsilon}} \times \ln\left(\frac{B}{A}\right)$$

For the transmission line shown in Fig 42, the relationship is strikingly similar:

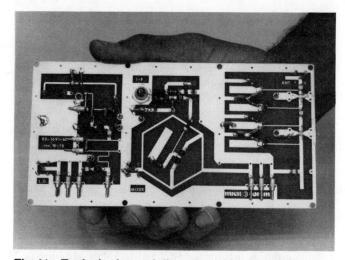

Fig 41—Typical microstripline assembly. This S-band downconverter board, designed by N6TX, includes a 2-stage low-noise preamp, 3-pole input bandpass filter, balanced mixer, local oscillator/multiplier chain with output filter, 2-stage IF amplifier and power supply decoupling circuitry. (Photo by WB6SFC)

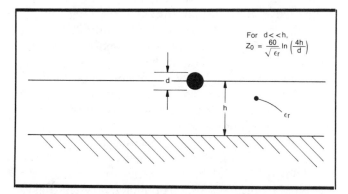

For $d < < h$,
$$Z_0 = \frac{60}{\sqrt{\epsilon_r}} \ln\left(\frac{4h}{d}\right)$$

Fig 42—TEM transmission line composed of a single wire against an infinite ground plane. If wire diameter d is small relative to its height above ground, the characteristic impedance is easily found from the equation shown.

$$Z_0 = \frac{60}{\sqrt{\epsilon}} \times \ln\left(\frac{4h}{d}\right) \qquad \text{(Eq 48)}$$

Unfortunately, when the wire is flattened out into a true microstrip, the derivation of its characteristic impedance becomes somewhat more complicated. The relationship between strip dimensions and electromagnetic properties is explored later.

A true microstrip implementation is depicted in Fig 43. Note that the strip transmission line is etched onto one side of a double-clad printed circuit board, the other side of which remains fully clad and serves as a ground plane. The strip and ground plane are thus two conductors sepa-

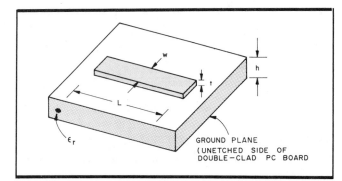

Fig 43—Several variables affect the performance of a microstripline etched on double-sided PC board material. W is the width of the line; h is the height of the line above ground; t is the thickness of the conductor that the strip is made from; l is the length of the strip; and ϵ_r is the dielectric constant of the substrate.

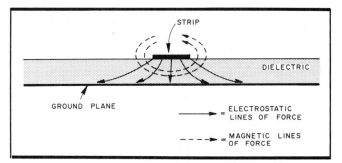

Fig 44—Cross section of a microstripline supporting TEM propagation.

rated by a dielectric. With respect to electromagnetic waves propagating along the microstrip, the assembly exhibits shunt capacitance. Additionally, propagation of a wave along the strip will result in an expanding and collapsing magnetic field surrounding the strip; thus, the assembly exhibits series inductance.

The electrostatic and magnetic fields associated with a wave propagating along a microstrip transmission line are shown in Fig 44. The propagation mode would appear to approach transverse electromagnetic (TEM). Thus the low-pass filter model developed for coaxial cable in Figs 4 and 5 should apply equally well to microstrip transmission lines.

When microstrip is used to support TEM wave propagation, the general expression for characteristic impedance presented in Eq 4 will apply. That is, the characteristic impedance of a microstripline will vary with the square root of the ratio of distributed inductance to distributed capacitance. Similarly, the relationship defining propagation velocity, introduced as Eq 19, will generally apply to strip transmission lines, to the extent that they support TEM propagation.

Quantifying the relationship between physical dimensions, characteristic impedance and propagation velocity is difficult, because those parameters that influence distributed inductance tend to influence distributed capacitance as well. The physical variables available for manipulation are the thickness t of the conductive traces, the height h of the strip above the ground plane, the width w of the strip, and the dielectric constant ϵ of the insulating medium. Though the effects of all of these parameters are interactive, as a rule any dimensional changes that increase distributed inductance tend to increase characteristic impedance and reduce propagation velocity in a given microstrip. Conversely, those changes resulting in increased distributed capacitance will have the effect of reducing both characteristic impedance and velocity of propagation.

From the above relationships, a number of interesting generalizations can be developed.[19] Consider first the effect of microstrip width on its electromagnetic performance. Since a microstrip transmission line is etched against a ground plane, it exhibits a capacitance to ground that varies with the width of the strip. Wide strips thus exhibit high capacitance, hence lower characteristic impedance than narrower strips. And since, because of skin effect, the distributed inductance of a conductor varies inversely with its surface area, wide strips similarly exhibit reduced inductance compared to narrower ones, which further reduces characteristic impedance.

Note that changing strip width causes capacitance and inductance to vary in opposite directions. In analyzing propagation velocity (which according to Eq 19 involves the LC product), one would expect the two effects to cancel, and in fact they partly do. But while the relationship between strip width and capacitance is linear, that between inductance and strip width is not. Thus, all other parameters being held constant, a decrease in microstrip width will slightly increase the velocity of wave propagation.

The thickness of the metal plating forming both the microstrip and ground-plane conductors will not significantly affect distributed capacitance, but it will influence inductance. However, if a strip conductor is very wide relative to its thickness (and this is usually the case), the cross-sectional surface area of the strip will remain relatively constant with changes in trace thickness. Thus microstrip characteristic impedance and propagation velocity both remain relatively independent of conductor thickness.

Substrate thickness, on the other hand, significantly influences both characteristic impedance and propagation velocity. Capacitance varies inversely with the spacing between a capacitor's plates, which causes strips on thin substrates to exhibit lower characteristic impedances than those with thicker dielectrics. However, reducing substrate thickness also concentrates the magnetic field around the strip, increasing inductance slightly. This interaction complicates attempts to model strip performance mathematically.

Similarly, an increase in the relative permittivity, or dielectric constant, of the substrate will increase the electrostatic field, hence the capacitance between the microstrip and the ground plane. Since the dielectric constant has no significant effect upon strip inductance, raising ϵ will tend to decrease both characteristic impedance and propagation velocity.

Finally, the velocity of propagation on microstrip is dominated by the permittivity of the substrate, which is relatively independent of the substrate's thickness. Thus, for strips of like characteristic impedance on substrates of similar material and different thickness, propagation velocity will remain nearly equal. The mathematical stripline models that appear in the following paragraphs bear out these generalizations.

During the 1950s and '60s, a number of studies emerged that explored the electromagnetic performance of microstrip transmission lines.[20-31] Because of the evolutionary nature of computer modeling techniques, most early attempts to quantify microstrip performance were empirical in nature, and the resulting relationships somewhat complex. Recent advances in computer analysis have given us simplified models to approximate microstrip performance as a function of physical quantities.[32]

For a first order approximation of microstrip characteristic impedance as a function of strip width, many microwave experimenters now use an analysis equation derived by Fisk:[33]

$$Z_0 \approx 120 \, \pi \times \frac{\sqrt{\epsilon_r}\sqrt{\epsilon_r}}{\left(\dfrac{W}{h}\right) + 1} \qquad \text{(Eq 49)}$$

while for circuit synthesis, this equation can be rearranged as:

$$W/h \approx \frac{120 \, \pi}{\left(Z_0 \sqrt{\epsilon_r + \sqrt{\epsilon_r}}\right) - 1} \qquad \text{(Eq 50)}$$

For a microstrip transmission line of given physical properties, the velocity of wave propagation (relative to that in free space) is approximated by:

$$\left(\frac{1}{V_r}\right)^2 \approx 1 + \left[(\epsilon_r - 1)\left(0.5 + \sqrt{\frac{0.5}{1 + \dfrac{10h}{W}}}\right)\right] \quad \text{(Eq 51)}$$

In Eqs 49 to 51, all dimensional literals are as defined in Fig 43.

Tables 5 through 10 provide microstrip dimensions over a range of characteristic impedances, for several of the more commonly encountered substrate types and thicknesses, calculated using Eqs 49 through 51. The Wavelength columns indicate the strip length corresponding to 1 λ at a frequency of 1 GHz. Since guide wavelength varies inversely with frequency, this dimension can be readily scaled for other frequencies.

Table 5

Microstripline Dimensions on 1/16-in. Thick Fiberglass-Epoxy PC Board

Substrate thickness: 0.059 in. (1.5 mm)
Dielectric constant: 4.8
Operating frequency: 1000 MHz

Z_0 (ohms)	Microstrip Width (in.)	(mm)	Velocity Factor	Wavelength (mm)	(in.)
5	1.624	41.2	0.47	141.0	5.551
10	0.782	19.9	0.48	144.1	5.673
15	0.502	12.7	0.49	146.6	5.771
20	0.362	9.2	0.50	148.7	5.854
25	0.278	7.0	0.50	150.5	5.924
30	0.221	5.6	0.51	152.1	5.986
35	0.181	4.6	0.51	153.5	6.042
40	0.151	3.8	0.52	154.7	6.092
45	0.128	3.2	0.52	155.9	6.139
50	0.109	2.8	0.52	157.0	6.181
55	0.094	2.4	0.53	158.0	6.221
60	0.081	2.1	0.53	159.0	6.259
65	0.070	1.8	0.53	159.9	6.295
70	0.061	1.6	0.54	160.8	6.329
75	0.053	1.4	0.54	161.6	6.362
80	0.046	1.2	0.54	162.4	6.394
85	0.040	1.0	0.54	163.2	6.426
90	0.034	0.9	0.55	164.0	6.457
95	0.030	0.8	0.55	164.8	6.487
100	0.025	0.6	0.55	165.5	6.518
105	0.021	0.5	0.55	166.3	6.548
110	0.017	0.4	0.56	167.1	6.580
115	0.014	0.4	0.56	167.9	6.612
120	0.011	0.3	0.56	168.8	6.646
125	0.008	0.2	0.57	169.7	6.683
130	0.006	0.1	0.57	170.8	6.723
135	0.003	0.1	0.57	172.0	6.772

Table 6

Microstripline Dimensions on 1/32-in. Thick Fiberglass-Epoxy PC Board

Substrate thickness: 0.028 in. (0.71 mm)
Dielectric constant: 4.8
Operating frequency: 1000 MHz

Z_0 (ohms)	Microstrip Width (in.)	(mm)	Velocity Factor	Wavelength (mm)	(in.)
5	0.770	19.6	0.47	141.0	5.551
10	0.371	9.4	0.48	144.1	5.673
15	0.238	6.0	0.49	146.6	5.771
20	0.172	4.4	0.50	148.7	5.854
25	0.132	3.3	0.50	150.5	5.924
30	0.105	2.7	0.51	152.1	5.986
35	0.086	2.2	0.51	153.5	6.042
40	0.072	1.8	0.52	154.7	6.092
45	0.061	1.5	0.52	155.9	6.139
50	0.052	1.3	0.52	157.0	6.181
55	0.045	1.1	0.53	158.0	6.221
60	0.039	1.0	0.53	159.0	6.259
65	0.033	0.8	0.53	159.9	6.295
70	0.029	0.7	0.54	160.8	6.329
75	0.025	0.6	0.54	161.6	6.362
80	0.022	0.6	0.54	162.4	6.394
85	0.019	0.5	0.54	163.2	6.426
90	0.016	0.4	0.55	164.0	6.457
95	0.014	0.4	0.55	164.8	6.487
100	0.012	0.3	0.55	165.5	6.518
105	0.010	0.3	0.55	166.3	6.548
110	0.008	0.2	0.56	167.1	6.580
115	0.007	0.2	0.56	167.9	6.612
120	0.005	0.1	0.56	168.8	6.646
125	0.004	0.1	0.57	169.7	6.683
130	0.003	0.1	0.57	170.8	6.723
135	0.002	0.0	0.57	172.0	6.772

Table 7

Microstripline Dimensions on 1/16-in. Thick Teflon-Fiberglass PC Board

Substrate thickness: 0.059 in. (1.5 mm)
Dielectric constant: 2.55
Operating frequency: 1000 MHz

Z_0 (ohms)	Microstrip Width (in.)	(mm)	Velocity Factor	Wavelength (mm)	(in.)
5	2.126	54.0	0.64	191.2	7.529
10	1.033	26.2	0.65	193.9	7.635
15	0.669	17.0	0.65	196.1	7.721
20	0.487	12.4	0.66	198.0	7.794
25	0.378	9.6	0.67	199.6	7.858
30	0.305	7.7	0.67	201.0	7.914
35	0.253	6.4	0.67	202.3	7.964
40	0.214	5.4	0.68	203.4	8.009
45	0.184	4.7	0.68	204.5	8.050
50	0.159	4.1	0.68	205.4	8.088
55	0.140	3.5	0.69	206.3	8.123
60	0.123	3.1	0.69	207.2	8.156
65	0.109	2.8	0.69	208.0	8.187
70	0.097	2.5	0.70	208.7	8.217
75	0.087	2.2	0.70	209.4	8.245
80	0.078	2.0	0.70	210.1	8.271
85	0.070	1.8	0.70	210.7	8.297
90	0.062	1.6	0.70	211.4	8.321
95	0.056	1.4	0.71	212.0	8.345
100	0.050	1.3	0.71	212.6	8.368
105	0.045	1.1	0.71	213.1	8.391
110	0.040	1.0	0.71	213.7	8.413
115	0.036	0.9	0.71	214.2	8.435
120	0.032	0.8	0.72	214.8	8.456
125	0.028	0.7	0.72	215.3	8.478
130	0.025	0.6	0.72	215.9	8.499
135	0.022	0.6	0.72	216.4	8.520

Table 8

Microstripline Dimensions on 1/32-in. Thick Teflon-Fiberglass PC Board

Substrate thickness: 0.028 in. (0.71 mm)
Dielectric constant: 2.55
Operating frequency: 1000 MHz

Z_0 (ohms)	Microstrip Width (in.)	(mm)	Velocity Factor	Wavelength (mm)	(in.)
5	1.009	25.6	0.64	191.2	7.529
10	0.490	12.5	0.65	193.9	7.635
15	0.318	8.1	0.65	196.1	7.721
20	0.231	5.9	0.66	198.0	7.794
25	0.179	4.6	0.67	199.6	7.858
30	0.145	3.7	0.67	201.0	7.914
35	0.120	3.1	0.67	202.3	7.964
40	0.102	2.6	0.68	203.4	8.009
45	0.087	2.2	0.68	204.5	8.050
50	0.076	1.9	0.68	205.4	8.088
55	0.066	1.7	0.69	206.3	8.123
60	0.058	1.5	0.69	207.2	8.156
65	0.052	1.3	0.69	208.0	8.187
70	0.046	1.2	0.70	208.7	8.217
75	0.041	1.0	0.70	209.4	8.245
80	0.037	0.9	0.70	210.1	8.271
85	0.033	0.8	0.70	210.7	8.297
90	0.030	0.8	0.70	211.4	8.321
95	0.027	0.7	0.71	212.0	8.345
100	0.024	0.6	0.71	212.6	8.368
105	0.021	0.5	0.71	213.1	8.391
110	0.019	0.5	0.71	213.7	8.413
115	0.017	0.4	0.71	214.2	8.435
120	0.015	0.4	0.72	214.8	8.456
125	0.013	0.3	0.72	215.3	8.478
130	0.012	0.3	0.72	215.9	8.499
135	0.010	0.3	0.72	216.4	8.520

Table 9

Microstripline Dimensions on 0.025-in. Thick Epsilam-10™ PC Board

Substrate thickness: 0.025 in. (0.64 mm)
Dielectric constant: 10.0
Operating frequency: 1000 MHz

Z_0 (ohms)	Microstrip Width (in.)	(mm)	Velocity Factor	Wavelength (mm)	(in.)
5	0.989	25.1	0.33	99.1	3.901
10	0.470	11.9	0.34	102.1	4.020
15	0.296	7.5	0.35	104.5	4.113
20	0.210	5.3	0.35	106.4	4.190
25	0.158	4.0	0.36	108.1	4.255
30	0.123	3.1	0.37	109.5	4.313
35	0.098	2.5	0.37	110.8	4.364
40	0.080	2.0	0.37	112.0	4.411
45	0.065	1.7	0.38	113.1	4.454
50	0.054	1.4	0.38	114.2	4.495
55	0.044	1.1	0.38	115.2	4.534
60	0.037	0.9	0.39	116.1	4.571
65	0.030	0.8	0.39	117.0	4.608
70	0.024	0.6	0.39	118.0	4.644
75	0.019	0.5	0.40	118.9	4.681
80	0.015	0.4	0.40	119.8	4.718
85	0.011	0.3	0.40	120.8	4.757
90	0.008	0.2	0.41	121.9	4.800
95	0.005	0.1	0.41	123.2	4.849
100	0.002	0.0	0.42	124.8	4.912

Table 10

Microstripline Dimensions on 0.05-in. Thick Epsilam-10™ PC Board

Substrate thickness: 0.05 in. (1.27 mm)
Dielectric constant: 10.0
Operating frequency: 1000 MHz

Z_0 (ohms)	Microstrip Width (in.)	(mm)	Velocity Factor	Wavelength (mm)	(in.)
5	0.989	25.1	0.33	99.1	3.901
10	0.470	11.9	0.34	102.1	4.020
15	0.296	7.5	0.35	104.5	4.113
20	0.210	5.3	0.35	106.4	4.190
25	0.158	4.0	0.36	108.1	4.255
30	0.123	3.1	0.37	109.5	4.313
35	0.098	2.5	0.37	110.8	4.364
40	0.080	2.0	0.37	112.0	4.411
45	0.065	1.7	0.38	113.1	4.454
50	0.054	1.4	0.38	114.2	4.495
55	0.044	1.1	0.38	115.2	4.534
60	0.037	0.9	0.39	116.1	4.571
65	0.030	0.8	0.39	117.0	4.608
70	0.024	0.6	0.39	118.0	4.644
75	0.019	0.5	0.40	118.9	4.681
80	0.015	0.4	0.40	119.8	4.718
85	0.011	0.3	0.40	120.8	4.757
90	0.008	0.2	0.41	121.9	4.800
95	0.005	0.1	0.41	123.2	4.849
100	0.002	0.0	0.42	124.8	4.912

Stripline

One of the chief disadvantages of microstrip transmission lines is that their performance is somewhat influenced by their surrounding environment. Specific limitations to microstrip performance include radiation losses, fringing capacitance and proximity effects.

Radiation losses occur in any transmission line supporting electromagnetic propagation, if the electrostatic and magnetic fields are not completely contained. Since the TEM microstrip is not completely enclosed (a ground plane being present on only one side of the strip), the transmission line is free to radiate to the outside world. The magnitude and mode of such radiation are a function of standing waves on the line (hence its impedance match), and can be controlled—permitting the fabrication of efficient microstrip antennas. Unfortunately, inadvertent radiation from strips not intended to serve as antennas can diminish system efficiency, generate electromagnetic interference, or make the microstrip assembly vulnerable to interference from external sources.

The etched strip of a propagating microstrip transmission line is completely surrounded by an expanding and collapsing magnetic field, and the resulting flux lines are always crossed at right angles by electrostatic lines of force. Thus an electrostatic field radiates away from the strip in all directions. Because the strip is not completely surrounded by the ground plane, however, not all e-field lines return to it. In addition, electrostatic lines emanating from the side of the strip not immersed in dielectric behave differently from those completely contained in the dielectric. The resulting fringing capacitance impacts performance, as well as complicating analysis.

You've experienced proximity effects any time you have attempted to align resonant circuits with a metallic screwdriver. Perfect alignment is achieved, only to degrade when the screwdriver is removed from the vicinity of the variable capacitor or inductor. With microstrip, you need not even place a conductive screwdriver on a trimmer to experience similar grief. The mere motion of a hand near the strip conductors can detune them, to the point that circuit alignment can be very touchy indeed.

Stripline transmission media attempt to overcome the effects of radiation losses, fringing capacitance and proximity effect by immersing the conductive strip in its dielectric medium, and surrounding the two completely by a continuous ground plane. The stripline configuration known as Tri-Plate (a registered trademark of Sanders Associates)[34] consists of a slab conductor in a dielectric medium, equidistant between two parallel ground planes. Its derivation from coaxial cable is depicted in Fig 45.

Tri-plate is most readily fabricated as a sandwich of two microstrip type circuit boards, although the physical dimensions of the strip for a desired performance differ. The relationships shown in Fig 45 as Eqs 56 and 57 were derived from the work of Cohn[35], and are fully explained in Howe's fine stripline textbook.[36] The other equations introduced in Fig 45 are found in References 37 through 39.

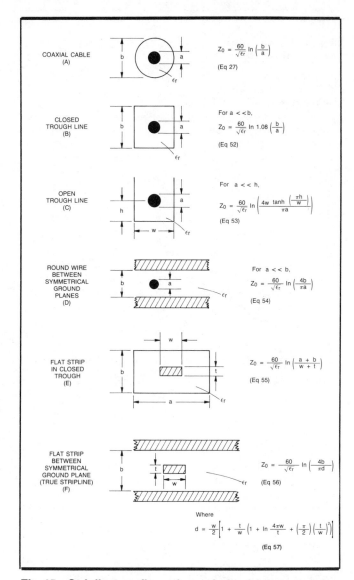

Fig 45—Stripline configurations, derived from coaxial transmission line.

Tables 11 through 16 provide dimensions for striplines comprised of two layers of printed circuit material, one supporting an etched strip trace. The calculated values are based upon Eqs 56 and 57 in Fig 45. A copper trace, plated at a thickness of one ounce of copper per square foot of laminate, is assumed.

In comparing Tables 11 through 16 to the microstrip dimensions in Tables 5 through 10, you will note that the stripline trace becomes extremely narrow, making precision fabrication quite difficult. This is one reason why enclosed striplines etched on printed circuit board material have not been popular among microwave amateurs. Another advantage of microstrip over stripline is that the microstrip structure, with one side exposed, makes it far easier to attach discrete components to the etched transmission lines.

Table 11
Stripline Dimensions for an Assembly Fabricated from Two Layers of 1/16-in. Thick Fiberglass-Epoxy PC Board, Clad with 1 oz Copper

Substrate height: 0.059 in. (1.5 mm)
Trace thickness: 0.00175 in. (0.044 mm)
Dielectric constant: 4.8

Stripline Width (mm)	(in.)	d	Z_0 (ohms)
0.050	0.002	0.005	91.79
0.100	0.004	0.006	88.02
0.150	0.006	0.007	83.10
0.200	0.008	0.008	78.95
0.250	0.010	0.010	75.42
0.300	0.012	0.011	72.36
0.350	0.014	0.012	69.66
0.400	0.016	0.013	67.23
0.450	0.018	0.014	65.02
0.500	0.020	0.015	62.99
0.550	0.022	0.016	61.12
0.600	0.024	0.017	59.38
0.650	0.026	0.018	57.75
0.700	0.028	0.019	56.22
0.750	0.030	0.020	54.78
0.800	0.031	0.021	53.41
0.850	0.033	0.022	52.11
0.900	0.035	0.023	50.88
0.950	0.037	0.024	49.70
1.000	0.039	0.026	48.57
1.100	0.043	0.028	46.45
1.200	0.047	0.030	44.49
1.300	0.051	0.032	42.67
1.400	0.055	0.034	40.96
1.500	0.059	0.036	39.36
1.600	0.063	0.038	37.85
1.700	0.067	0.040	36.42
1.800	0.071	0.042	35.06
1.900	0.075	0.044	33.77
2.000	0.079	0.046	32.54
2.200	0.087	0.050	30.23
2.400	0.094	0.054	28.11
2.600	0.102	0.058	26.15
2.800	0.110	0.062	24.31
3.000	0.118	0.066	22.60
3.500	0.138	0.076	18.73
4.000	0.157	0.086	15.35
4.500	0.177	0.096	12.35
5.000	0.197	0.106	9.64
5.500	0.217	0.116	7.18
6.000	0.236	0.125	4.93
6.500	0.256	0.135	2.85
7.000	0.276	0.145	0.91

Table 12
Stripline Dimensions for an Assembly Fabricated from Two Layers of 1/32-in. Thick Fiberglass-Epoxy PC Board, Clad with 1 oz Copper

Substrate height: 0.028 in. (0.71 mm)
Trace thickness: 0.00175 in. (0.044 mm)
Dielectric constant: 4.8

Stripline Width (mm)	(in.)	d	Z_0 (ohms)
0.050	0.002	0.005	71.37
0.100	0.004	0.006	67.61
0.150	0.006	0.007	62.69
0.200	0.008	0.008	58.54
0.250	0.010	0.010	55.01
0.300	0.012	0.011	51.95
0.350	0.014	0.012	49.25
0.400	0.016	0.013	46.82
0.450	0.018	0.014	44.61
0.500	0.020	0.015	42.58
0.550	0.022	0.016	40.71
0.600	0.024	0.017	38.97
0.650	0.026	0.018	37.34
0.700	0.028	0.019	35.81
0.750	0.030	0.020	34.36
0.800	0.031	0.021	33.00
0.850	0.033	0.022	31.70
0.900	0.035	0.023	30.46
0.950	0.037	0.024	29.29
1.000	0.039	0.026	28.16
1.100	0.043	0.028	26.04
1.200	0.047	0.030	24.08
1.300	0.051	0.032	22.25
1.400	0.055	0.034	20.55
1.500	0.059	0.036	18.95
1.600	0.063	0.038	17.44
1.700	0.067	0.040	16.01
1.800	0.071	0.042	14.65
1.900	0.075	0.044	13.36
2.000	0.079	0.046	12.13
2.200	0.087	0.050	9.82
2.400	0.094	0.054	7.70
2.600	0.102	0.058	5.73
2.800	0.110	0.062	3.90
3.000	0.118	0.066	2.19

Air dielectric striplines, fabricated from sheet metal plates supported on insulating standoffs, have gained wide acceptance as high Q resonators for vacuum tube power amplifier assemblies.[40-43] If the resulting strip resonator is fully enclosed in a chassis, the closed trough arrangement of Fig 45E results, and Eq 55 will apply.

Another variation on the stripline theme that is still widely used in amateur microwave equipment is the circular conductor in a rectangular trough, depicted in Figs 45B and 45C. Trough line resonators exhibit significantly higher Q and lower losses than either microstrip or dielectric-filled stripline circuits. Trough line resonators are useful in receiving equipment, such as the 23-cm receive converter presented in Reference 44.

The use of circular conductors between symmetrical ground planes, as shown in Fig 45D, enables low-loss interdigital and combline filters to be readily fabricated. This subject is treated in detail by Troetschel, K6UQH, in Chapter 6 of this book.

Thus far, we have failed to quantify the velocity of wave propagation along any of the strip transmission lines introduced in Fig 45. Note that any true stripline is completely immersed in its dielectric medium, much as is the center conductor of a coaxial cable. Hence, the velocity of propagation along the strip is a function of the permit-

Table 13

Stripline Dimensions for an Assembly Fabricated from Two Layers of 1/16-in. Thick Teflon-Fiberglass PC Board, Clad with 1 oz Copper

Substrate height: 0.059 in. (1.5 mm)
Trace thickness: 0.00175 in. (0.044 mm)
Dielectric constant: 2.55

Stripline Width (mm)	(in.)	d	Z_0 (ohms)
0.050	0.002	0.005	125.93
0.100	0.004	0.006	120.76
0.150	0.006	0.007	114.01
0.200	0.008	0.008	108.32
0.250	0.010	0.010	103.48
0.300	0.012	0.011	99.28
0.350	0.014	0.012	95.57
0.400	0.016	0.013	92.23
0.450	0.018	0.014	89.20
0.500	0.020	0.015	86.42
0.550	0.022	0.016	83.86
0.600	0.024	0.017	81.47
0.650	0.026	0.018	79.23
0.700	0.028	0.019	77.13
0.750	0.030	0.020	75.15
0.800	0.031	0.021	73.28
0.850	0.033	0.022	71.50
0.900	0.035	0.023	69.80
0.950	0.037	0.024	68.18
1.000	0.039	0.026	66.64
1.100	0.043	0.028	63.73
1.200	0.047	0.030	61.04
1.300	0.051	0.032	58.54
1.400	0.055	0.034	56.20
1.500	0.059	0.036	54.00
1.600	0.063	0.038	51.93
1.700	0.067	0.040	49.97
1.800	0.071	0.042	48.10
1.900	0.075	0.044	46.33
2.000	0.079	0.046	44.64
2.200	0.087	0.050	41.48
2.400	0.094	0.054	38.57
2.600	0.102	0.058	35.87
2.800	0.110	0.062	33.36
3.000	0.118	0.066	31.00
3.500	0.138	0.076	25.70
4.000	0.157	0.086	21.06
4.500	0.177	0.096	16.94
5.000	0.197	0.106	13.23
5.500	0.217	0.116	9.86
6.000	0.236	0.125	6.76
6.500	0.256	0.135	3.91
7.000	0.276	0.145	1.25

Table 14

Stripline Dimensions for an Assembly Fabricated from Two Layers of 1/32-in. Thick Teflon-Fiberglass PC Board, Clad with 1 oz Copper

Substrate height: 0.028 in. (0.71 mm)
Trace thickness: 0.00175 in. (0.044 mm)
Dielectric constant: 2.55

Stripline Width (mm)	(in.)	d	Z_0 (ohms)
0.050	0.002	0.005	97.92
0.100	0.004	0.006	92.76
0.150	0.006	0.007	86.01
0.200	0.008	0.008	80.31
0.250	0.010	0.010	75.48
0.300	0.012	0.011	71.28
0.350	0.014	0.012	67.56
0.400	0.016	0.013	64.23
0.450	0.018	0.014	61.20
0.500	0.020	0.015	58.42
0.550	0.022	0.016	55.85
0.600	0.024	0.017	53.46
0.650	0.026	0.018	51.23
0.700	0.028	0.019	49.13
0.750	0.030	0.020	47.15
0.800	0.031	0.021	45.27
0.850	0.033	0.022	43.49
0.900	0.035	0.023	41.80
0.950	0.037	0.024	40.18
1.000	0.039	0.026	38.63
1.100	0.043	0.028	35.72
1.200	0.047	0.030	33.04
1.300	0.051	0.032	30.53
1.400	0.055	0.034	28.19
1.500	0.059	0.036	25.99
1.600	0.063	0.038	23.92
1.700	0.067	0.040	21.96
1.800	0.071	0.042	20.10
1.900	0.075	0.044	18.33
2.000	0.079	0.046	16.64
2.200	0.087	0.050	13.48
2.400	0.094	0.054	10.57
2.600	0.102	0.058	7.87
2.800	0.110	0.062	5.35
3.000	0.118	0.066	3.00

Notes and References

[1]You will notice that I have steadfastly avoided the use of the expression "voltage." I do so to differentiate between parameters and units of measure. The *parameter* EMF (or electrical potential) is measured in the *unit* volts. If you step on a scale, you are measuring the parameter mass (or weight), in the unit kilograms (or pounds). You are *not* measuring "poundage" or "kilogrammage"; neither is the term "voltage" grammatically correct for electrical potential, although it's widely used.

[2]Let us not confuse transmitted power with dissipated power, the vector product of potential and kinetic energy in a circuit. Power dissipation varies with the cosine of the phase angle between the potential and current waveforms (the so-called Power Factor), and accounts for that inevitable energy loss that accompanies any energy transformation, as mentioned in Section 5.2.

[3]Miller, Gary W., *Modern Electronic Communication*, Second Edition (Englewood Cliffs, NJ: Prentice-Hall, 1983), p 385.

[4]We are accustomed to considering characteristic impedance of transmission lines frequency-independent, and it is, for coaxial

tivity of the dielectric alone, and Eq 29, introduced in the Coaxial Cable section of this Chapter, will apply:

$$v_{rel} = \frac{1}{\sqrt{\epsilon_{rel}}} \qquad \text{(Eq 29)}$$

The construction chapters that follow contain numerous circuits implemented in a variety of transmission-line techniques. The material just presented should help you to identify the transmission medium selected, and understand its capabilities, limitations, and associated design criteria.

Table 15

Stripline Dimensions for an Assembly Fabricated from Two Layers of 0.05-in. Thick Epsilam-10™ PC Board, Clad with 1 oz Copper

Substrate height: 0.05 in. (1.27 mm)
Trace thickness: 0.00175 in. (0.044 mm)
Dielectric constant: 10

Stripline Width (mm)	(in.)	d	Z_0 (ohms)
0.050	0.002	0.005	60.45
0.100	0.004	0.006	57.84
0.150	0.006	0.007	54.43
0.200	0.008	0.008	51.56
0.250	0.010	0.010	49.11
0.300	0.012	0.011	47.00
0.350	0.014	0.012	45.12
0.400	0.016	0.013	43.44
0.450	0.018	0.014	41.91
0.500	0.020	0.015	40.50
0.550	0.022	0.016	39.20
0.600	0.024	0.017	38.00
0.650	0.026	0.018	36.87
0.700	0.028	0.019	35.81
0.750	0.030	0.020	34.81
0.800	0.031	0.021	33.86
0.850	0.033	0.022	32.96
0.900	0.035	0.023	32.11
0.950	0.037	0.024	31.29
1.000	0.039	0.026	30.51
1.100	0.043	0.028	29.04
1.200	0.047	0.030	27.68
1.300	0.051	0.032	26.42
1.400	0.055	0.034	25.24
1.500	0.059	0.036	24.13
1.600	0.063	0.038	23.08
1.700	0.067	0.040	22.09
1.800	0.071	0.042	21.15
1.900	0.075	0.044	20.26
2.000	0.079	0.046	19.40
2.200	0.087	0.050	17.81
2.400	0.094	0.054	16.34
2.600	0.102	0.058	14.97
2.800	0.110	0.062	13.70
3.000	0.118	0.066	12.52
3.500	0.138	0.076	9.84
4.000	0.157	0.086	7.50
4.500	0.177	0.096	5.41
5.000	0.197	0.106	3.54
5.500	0.217	0.116	1.84
6.000	0.236	0.125	0.27

Table 16

Stripline Dimensions for an Assembly Fabricated from Two Layers of 0.025-in. Thick Epsilam-10™ PC Board, Clad with 1 oz Copper

Substrate height: 0.025 in. (0.63 mm)
Trace thickness: 0.00175 in. (0.044 mm)
Dielectric constant: 10

Stripline Width (mm)	(in.)	d	Z_0 (ohms)
0.050	0.002	0.005	47.30
0.100	0.004	0.006	44.69
0.150	0.006	0.007	41.28
0.200	0.008	0.008	38.40
0.250	0.010	0.010	35.96
0.300	0.012	0.011	33.84
0.350	0.014	0.012	31.97
0.400	0.016	0.013	30.28
0.450	0.018	0.014	28.75
0.500	0.020	0.015	27.35
0.550	0.022	0.016	26.05
0.600	0.024	0.017	24.85
0.650	0.026	0.018	23.72
0.700	0.028	0.019	22.66
0.750	0.030	0.020	21.66
0.800	0.031	0.021	20.71
0.850	0.033	0.022	19.81
0.900	0.035	0.023	18.96
0.950	0.037	0.024	18.14
1.000	0.039	0.026	17.36
1.100	0.043	0.028	15.89
1.200	0.047	0.030	14.53
1.300	0.051	0.032	13.27
1.400	0.055	0.034	12.09
1.500	0.059	0.036	10.98
1.600	0.063	0.038	9.93
1.700	0.067	0.040	8.94
1.800	0.071	0.042	8.00
1.900	0.075	0.044	7.10
2.000	0.079	0.046	6.25
2.200	0.087	0.050	4.66
2.400	0.094	0.054	3.18
2.600	0.102	0.058	1.82
2.800	0.110	0.062	0.55

cable. But not so for waveguide, microstrip, and other transmission media. In fact, if we go high enough in frequency, even coaxial cable begins to act like waveguide; thus, its Z_0 will vary with frequency.

[5]Remember that guide wavelength is not necessarily equal to free-space wavelength, because the wave may be traveling through the transmission line at a velocity other than the speed of light.

[6]Distance between nulls is used, rather than between nodes, because although the two values are theoretically equal, the nulls are much narrower than the nodes (see Fig 1), and are thus easier to measure with precision.

[7]Shuch, H. Paul, WA6UAM, "Microstripline Preamplifiers for 1296 MHz," *Ham Radio*, Apr 1975, p 12.

[8]Maxwell, Walter, W2DU, Correspondence, *Ham Radio*, Jan 1976, p 68.

[9]The actual difference in permittivity, for example, between free space and dry air at +25°C represents something less than seven hundredths of a percent.

[10]The designation of this particular cable type is not arbitrary. For Uniform Tubes products, the number indicates the inside diameter of the outer conductor, in hundredths of an inch. Thus type UT-141 has a 0.141-inch shield ID, UT-085 has a 0.085-inch shield, and UT-250 is a quarter-inch at the inside of its outer conductor.

[11]These values can be readily measured on an RCL bridge. For cable of known length, distributed capacitance is found by measuring capacitance between the center and outer conductors, with the far end of the cable open. Distributed inductance is measured from the center conductor to the shield, with the far end of the cable shorted.

[12]In computer analysis, if common logarithms are desired and only natural logs are available, a useful expression is $\log_{10}(X) = \ln(x) / \ln(10)$.

[13]Moreno, Theodore, *Microwave Transmission Design Data*, Dover Publications, 1948.

[14]Gray, David A., *Handbook of Coaxial Microwave Measurements* (West Concord, MA: General Radio Company, 1968), pp 17-20.

[15]Reisert, Joseph, W1JR, "VHF/UHF World," *Ham Radio*, Oct 1985, pp 83-94.

[16]Hertz, H. R., *Electric Waves*, English translation by D. E. Jones (London: MacMillen & Co, 1893).

[17]Note that in proper military syntax, it's "waveguide-comma-rectangular." You can pick up quantities of WR type waveguides at the market-comma-flea of any fest-comma-ham.

[18]Tillitson, George, K6MBL, "Polaplexer Design," *Ham Radio*, Mar 1977, p 40.

[19]Shuch, H. Paul, N6TX, "Microstrip—Magical PC Technique Explained." *73*, Oct 1978, p 80.

[20]Grieg, D. D. and Engleman, F. H., "Microstrip—A New Transmission Technique for the Kilomegacycle Range," *Proceedings of the IRE*, Dec 1952, p 1644.

[21]Cohn, S. B., "Characteristic Impedance of the Shielded-Strip Transmission Line," *IRE Transactions on Microwave Theory and Techniques*, Jul 1954, p 52.

[22]Cohn, S. B., "Shielded Coupled-Strip Transmission Line," *IRE Transactions on Microwave Theory and Techniques*, Oct 1955, p 29.

[23]Wu, T. T., "Theory of the Microstrip," *Journal of Applied Physics*, Mar 1957, p 299.

[24]Wheeler, H. A., "Transmission-Line Properties of Parallel Wide Strips by a Conformal-Mapping Approximation," *IEEE Transactions on Microwave Theory and Techniques*, May 1964, p 280.

[25]Wheeler, H. A., "Transmission-Line Properties of Parallel Strips Separated by a Dielectric Sheet," *IEEE Transactions on Microwave Theory and Techniques*, Mar 1965, p 172.

[26]Caulton, H., Hughes, J. J., and Sobol, H., "Measurements of the Properties of Microstrip Transmission Lines for Microwave Integrated Circuits," *RCA Review*, Sep 1966, p 377.

[27]Sobol, H., "Extending IC Technology to Microwave Equipment," *Electronics*, Mar 20, 1967, p 112.

[28]Silvester, P., "TEM Wave Properties of Microstrip Transmission Lines," *Proceedings of the IEE* (London), Jan 1968, p 43.

[29]Yamashita, E., and Mittra, R., "Variational Methods for the Analysis of Microstrip Lines," *IEEE Transactions on Microwave Theory and Techniques*, Apr 1968, p 251.

[30]Bryant, T. G., and Weiss, J. A., "Parameters of Microstrip Lines and of Coupled Pairs of Microstrip Lines," *IEEE Transactions on Microwave Theory and Techniques*, Dec 1968, p 1021.

[31]Schneider, M. V., "Microstrip Lines for Microwave Integrated Circuits," *Bell Systems Technical Journal*, Jun 1969, p 1421.

[32]Several papers in the *Proceedings of the European Microwave Conference*, 1975.

[33]Fisk, J. R., W1HR, "Simple Formula for Microstrip Impedance," *Ham Radio*, Dec 1977, p 72.

[34]*Tri-Plate Handbook* (Nashua, NH: Sanders Associates, Inc, 1957).

[35]Cohn, S. B., "Problems in Strip Transmission Lines," *RE Transactions on Microwave Theory and Techniques*, Mar 1955, p 119.

[36]Howe, H. Jr., *Stripline Circuit Design* (Dedham, MA: Artech House, 1974), 344 pp.

[37]Jordan, Edward C. (editor), *Reference Data for Engineers: Radio, Electronics, Computer, and Communications*, 7th edition (Indianapolis, IN: Howard W. Sams & Co, 1985), Chapter 29.

[38]Weiner, K., DJ9HO, *The UHF Compendium*, Verlag Rudolf Schmidt, Fed Rep of Germany, Section A.2.3.

[39]US Army Research and Development Laboratory, "Strip Transmission Lines and Components," *Final Report on U. S. Army Contract DA36-039 sc-63232*, Stanford Research Institute, Menlo Park CA, Feb 1957.

[40]Laakmann, Peter, WB6IOM, "Cavity Amplifier for 1296 Mc," *QST*, Jan 1968, p 17.

[41]Orr, W. I., W6SAI, and Chambers, J. T., W6NLZ, "Stripline Kilowatt for 432 MHz," *Ham Radio*, Sep 1968, p 6.

[42]Knadle, R., K2RIW, "Dual-Band Stripline Amplifier-Tripler for 144 and 432 MHz," *Ham Radio*, Feb 1970, p 6.

[43]Fisher, R. E., W2CQH, et al, "Power Amplifier for 1296 MHz," *Ham Radio*, Mar 1970, p 43.

[44]Troetschel, W., K6UQH, "1296 Revisited," *QST*, Jul 1973, p 40.

Chapter 6

Design Techniques

Printed-Circuit Boards and Microstrip Circuit Elements

By Bill Troetschel, K6UQH
16615 Bohlman Rd
Saratoga, CA 95070

PC board used in the construction of UHF and microwave amplifiers is invariably double sided, so that one copper side can serve as a ground plane while the other side is etched or otherwise cut away to form transmission lines and other conductive areas. Conventionally, the copper is specified as 1-ounce or 2-ounce weight, which corresponds to a copper thickness of 0.0014 and 0.0028 inch, respectively. In general, 1-ounce copper board is used for low-power amplifiers, and 2-ounce copper board is used for high-power amplifiers.

The two most commonly available dielectric materials for amateur use are epoxy fiberglass (G-10) and Teflon®. At the frequency of interest, the dielectric material must be a low-loss insulator with an isotropic dielectric constant. Teflon board meets this requirement at amateur microwave frequencies up to at least 10 GHz, while epoxy fiberglass is useful up to about 1.5 GHz before its nonisotropic characteristics and losses become excessive.

MICROSTRIP TRANSMISSION LINES

V_P, the velocity of propagation of electrical energy on a PC board, is a function of the dielectric constant (ϵ_r) of the dielectric used in the board, and is defined as

$$V_P = \frac{1}{\sqrt{\epsilon_r}}$$

Thus, the dielectric material affects the design of the circuits on a board in the same manner as the dielectric of a coaxial cable affects the electrical length of the cable, that is

$$\lambda = V_P \frac{11803}{f} \text{ (inches)}$$

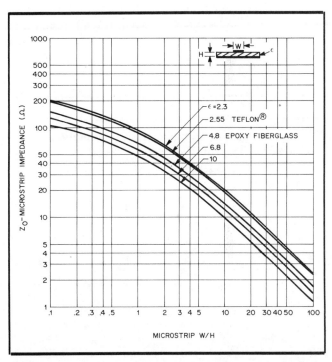

Fig 1—Characteristic impedance of microstrip, plotted as a function of the ratio of line width (W) to dielectric height (H).

or

$$\lambda = V_P \frac{29980}{f} \text{ (cm)}$$

where f = frequency in MHz.

Microstrip-transmission-line impedances are determined by the dielectric constant and by the ratio of the stripline width to the thickness or height of the dielectric material. Fig 1 shows the relationship between the microstrip impedance and the width/height ratio as a function of the dielectric constant. The narrower the line, the higher the impedance for a given dielectric material and thickness. Because the electric field is not absolutely confined to the dielectric, V_P will vary as a function of the line width, increasing in value as the line width decreases. Table 1 lists the characteristic impedance and velocity of propagation for microstrip on 1-ounce Teflon board; the equivalent information for 1-ounce epoxy-fiberglass board appears in Table 2.[1]

MICROSTRIP CIRCUIT ELEMENTS

To visualize the concept of using lengths of microstrip as discrete circuit elements—capacitors and inductors—refer to Fig 2 to review what happens in a parallel-resonant circuit at resonance and at frequencies below and above resonance. At resonance, X_L is equal to X_C. Therefore, line current I is at its minimum value and is in phase with circuit voltage E and the circuit looks like a very high impedance. At frequencies below the resonant frequency, X_L is less than X_C, so greater current flows through the

coil. Therefore, the line current is inductive and lags the circuit voltage. At frequencies above resonance, the line current is dominated by the capacitor, leads the circuit voltage, and is capacitive.

Fig 3 shows the characteristics of a shorted quarter-wave line. At the shorted end, voltage E_s and impedance Z_s must be zero, and current I_s must be at its maximum value. At the reference end, a quarter wavelength from the grounded end, E_s and Z_s are at their maximum values, and I_s is at a minimum. Thus, a quarter-wave line, shorted at the far end, has the properties of a parallel-resonant circuit. The line will therefore be inductive at frequencies below resonance (that frequency at which the line is exactly one-quarter wavelength long), and capacitive above resonance.

For shorted quarter-wavelength lines, the shape of the voltage distribution is a sine wave and the shape of the current distribution is a cosine wave. The basic equations are shown in Fig 3. (They are really hyperbolic trigonometric functions wherein line losses are accounted for.) See Note 5 for a detailed discussion. Assuming that short lines are

Table 1

Characteristic Impedance (Z_0) and Velocity of Propagation (V_P) for Microstrip Etched on Teflon® PC Board (ϵ_r = 2.55), Double-Clad with 1-Ounce Copper

		Microstrip Width 1/32" Board		Microstrip Width 1/16" Board		
Z_0	w/h	mils	mm	mils	mm	V_P
10	20.96	593	15.1	1246	31.6	0.646
15	13.27	375	9.5	789	20.0	0.654
20	9.47	267	6.8	563	14.3	0.661
25	7.21	203	5.2	429	10.9	0.667
30	5.72	161	4.1	340	8.6	0.672
35	4.66	131	3.3	277	7.0	0.676
40	3.88	109	2.8	231	5.9	0.681
45	3.28	92	2.3	195	5.0	0.685
50	2.80	78	2.0	166	4.2	0.688
55	2.42	67	1.7	143	3.6	0.691
60	2.10	58	1.5	124	3.1	0.694
65	1.84	51	1.3	107	2.7	0.697
70	1.61	44	1.1	95	2.4	0.700
75	1.42	39	1.0	83	2.1	0.702
80	1.26	34	0.86	73	1.8	0.705
85	1.12	30	0.79	64	1.6	0.707
90	0.991	26	0.66	57	1.4	0.709
95	0.882	23	0.60	51	1.3	0.711
100	0.785	20	0.51	45	1.1	0.713
105	0.700	18	0.45	39	1.00	0.714
110	0.625	16	0.40	35	0.89	0.716
115	0.558	14	0.35	31	0.78	0.717
120	0.498	12	0.31	27	0.69	0.718
125	0.445	11	0.27	24	0.61	0.720
130	0.398	9.2	0.23	21	0.54	0.721
135	0.356	8.0	0.20	19	0.48	0.772
140	0.318	7.0	0.18	17	0.42	0.723
145	0.285	6.0	0.15	15	0.37	0.724
150	0.254	5.1	0.13	13	0.32	0.725

Table 2

Characteristic Impedance (Z_0) and Velocity of Propagation (V_P) for Microstrip Etched on Epoxy Fiberglass PC Board (ϵ_r = 4.8), Double-Clad with 1-Ounce Copper

		Microstrip Width 1/32" Board		Microstrip Width 1/16" Board		
Z_0	w/h	mils	mm	mils	mm	V_P
10	14.93	422	10.7	887	22.5	0.481
15	9.35	264	6.7	556	14.1	0.490
20	6.59	186	4.7	392	10.0	0.498
25	4.96	139	3.5	295	7.5	0.505
30	3.89	109	2.8	230	5.8	0.510
35	3.13	87	2.2	185	4.7	0.516
40	2.56	71	1.8	152	3.9	0.520
45	2.13	59	1.5	126	3.2	0.524
50	1.79	49	1.2	105	2.7	0.528
55	1.52	41	1.04	89	2.3	0.532
60	1.30	35	0.88	75	1.9	0.535
65	1.11	30	0.76	64	1.6	0.538
70	0.955	25	0.64	54	1.4	0.541
75	0.823	21	0.53	46	1.2	0.544
80	0.711	18	0.46	40	1.02	0.546
85	0.614	15	0.38	34	0.86	0.548
90	0.532	13	0.33	29	0.74	0.550
95	0.460	11	0.28	25	0.61	0.552
100	0.399	9	0.23	21	0.54	0.553
105	0.346	7.6	0.20	18	0.46	0.555
110	0.299	6.4	0.16	15	0.39	0.556
115	0.260	5.2	0.13	13	0.33	0.557
120	0.225	4.3	0.11	11	0.28	0.559
125	0.195	3.4	0.09	9	0.23	0.560
130	0.169	2.8	0.069	7.6	0.20	0.561
135	0.147	—	—	6.5	0.17	0.562
140	0.127	—	—	5.4	0.14	0.563
145	0.111	—	—	4.5	0.11	0.564
150	0.096	—	—	3.7	0.09	0.565

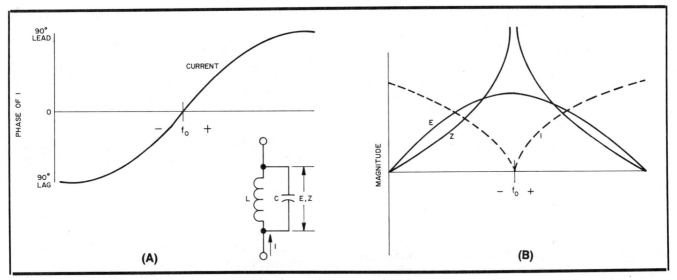

Fig 2—Characteristics of a lossless parallel-resonant circuit tuned to f_0.

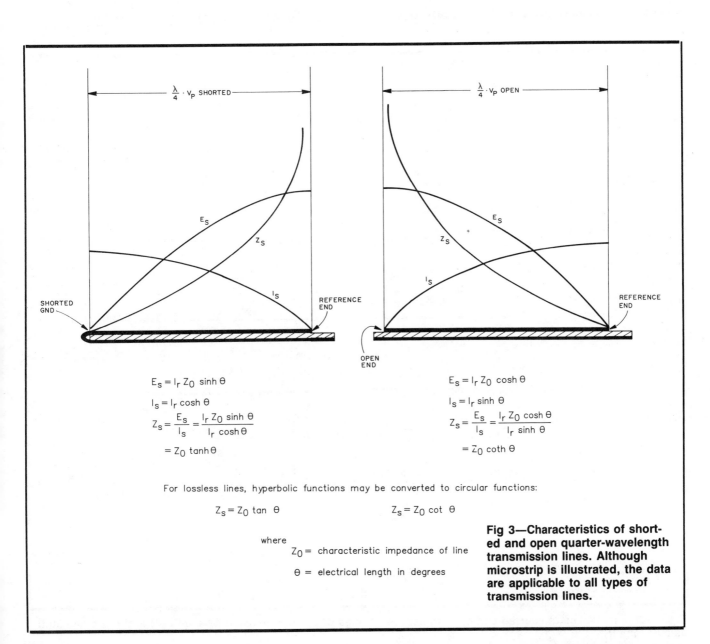

$$E_s = I_r Z_0 \sinh \theta$$

$$I_s = I_r \cosh \theta$$

$$Z_s = \frac{E_s}{I_s} = \frac{I_r Z_0 \sinh \theta}{I_r \cosh \theta}$$

$$= Z_0 \tanh \theta$$

$$E_s = I_r Z_0 \cosh \theta$$

$$I_s = I_r \sinh \theta$$

$$Z_s = \frac{E_s}{I_s} = \frac{I_r Z_0 \cosh \theta}{I_r \sinh \theta}$$

$$= Z_0 \coth \theta$$

For lossless lines, hyperbolic functions may be converted to circular functions:

$$Z_s = Z_0 \tan \theta \qquad\qquad Z_s = Z_0 \cot \theta$$

where

Z_0 = characteristic impedance of line

θ = electrical length in degrees

Fig 3—Characteristics of shorted and open quarter-wavelength transmission lines. Although microstrip is illustrated, the data are applicable to all types of transmission lines.

lossless, converting from hyperbolic to circular trigonometric functions allows the following:

$$Z_S = E_S / I_S = sine / cosine = tangent$$

The same method may be used for open quarter-wavelength lines with opposite conclusions. In this case, the shape of the voltage curve is a cosine function and the shape of the current curve is a sine function:

$$Z_S = E_S / I_S = cosine / sine = cotangent = 1 / tangent$$

These reactive tangent impedance curves provide a mathematical tool to use line stubs, typically less than a quarter wavelength long, to perform the functions of discrete components.

There are many uses for line stubs as reactive elements such as inductors or capacitors. High-quality tuning capacitors suitable for microwave frequencies are expensive. Replacing them with an open stub of the correct length represents a cost-effective solution. A good wire-wound RF choke at microwave frequencies is not easy to realize.

An RF and/or dc shorted quarter-wave stub, however, is an easy component solution.

Because reactive impedance along a length of line is either a tangent or cotangent function, line length can be expressed in terms of electrical degrees. That is, a quarter-wavelength line is expressed as 90° and an eight-wavelength line as 45°.

For a shorted line of less than a quarter wavelength, the line reactance in ohms (X_L) is equal to the line impedance (Z_0, in ohms) times the tangent of θ (line length in degrees). As an equation:

$$X_L = Z_0(TAN\theta)$$
or
$$\theta = ARCTAN(X_L / Z_0)$$

For an open line of less than a quarter wavelength, the equations are:

$$X_C = Z_0(1 / TAN\theta)$$
or
$$\theta = ARCTAN(Z_0 / X_C)$$

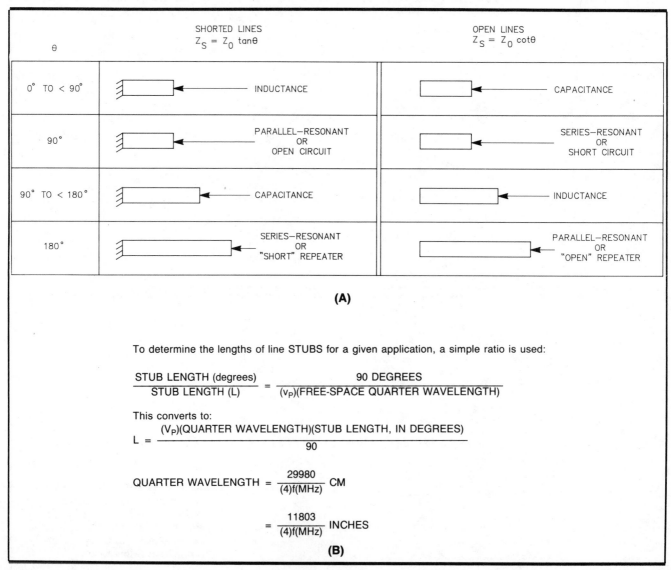

(A)

To determine the lengths of line STUBS for a given application, a simple ratio is used:

$$\frac{STUB\ LENGTH\ (degrees)}{STUB\ LENGTH\ (L)} = \frac{90\ DEGREES}{(v_P)(FREE\text{-}SPACE\ QUARTER\ WAVELENGTH)}$$

This converts to:

$$L = \frac{(V_P)(QUARTER\ WAVELENGTH)(STUB\ LENGTH,\ IN\ DEGREES)}{90}$$

$$QUARTER\ WAVELENGTH = \frac{29980}{(4)f(MHz)}\ CM$$

$$= \frac{11803}{(4)f(MHz)}\ INCHES$$

(B)

Fig 4—Characteristics of shorted and open transmission lines of up to one-half wavelength (A) and basic line-stub calculations (B).

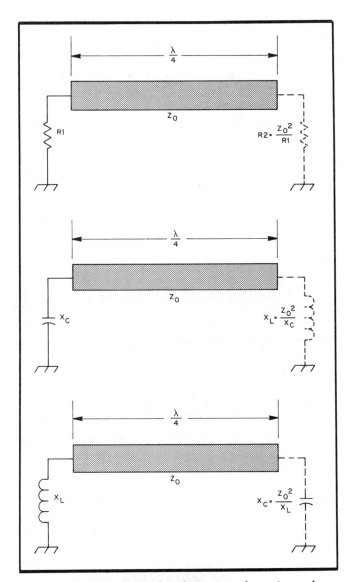

Fig 5—Transformation of resistance and reactance by quarter-wave transmission lines. The dashed components at the right represent the transformed components at the left.

A special case exists when the line length is exactly 1/8 wavelength. An eighth-wavelength line = 45° and the tangent or the cotangent = 1. The magnitude of X_C or X_L = Z_0, which means that the reactance value is equal to the line impedance in ohms—either capacitive or inductive—depending on whether the line is open or shorted.

For any type of line solution you must remember that the line impedance and the related velocity of propagation (for the circuit board dielectric) must be considered, as they will affect the required line length for your application.

Fig 4A shows the general characteristics of shorted and open lines and Fig 4B shows the basic line-stub equations.

A quarter-wave transmission line section can be used to match two resistive elements. The line impedance required to effect the match is determined from the equation

$$Z_0 = \sqrt{R1 \times R2}$$

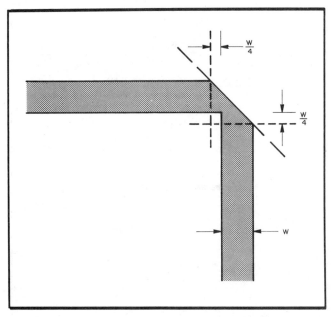

Fig 6—Method of forming a right-angle bend in microstrip.

The quarter-wave section can also be used to transform and invert terminating reactances, as shown in Fig 5. The transformation factor is always (Z_0^2) divided by the terminating impedance.[2] If the terminating impedance is a pure reactance, however, both its value and algebraic sign are transformed, so a capacitive reactance is transformed into an inductive reactance, and vice versa.

MICROSTRIP CONSTRUCTION TECHNIQUES

Board space can be conserved and, in many cases, board layout improved, by forming bends in microstrip lines. Fig 6 shows the method of forming a right-angle bend which minimizes the impedance discontinuity in the line. Achieving an effective RF ground on the circuit side of a PC board at microwave frequencies requires specialized techniques. RF ground areas at the edges of the circuit side of the board must be bonded to the ground-plane side of the board by forming thin copper or shim stock around the edges of the board and soldering it to both sides of the board.

For RF ground areas on the circuit side of the board, but not at the edge, drilling through the board and soldering through-the-board ground wires or straps to both sides of the board will generally work at VHF. A length of wire equal to the board thickness, however, can form an inductance as great as 1 nH. Multiple ground straps and/or the use of thinner board material can reduce this inductance, but still may create problems at microwave frequencies.

Consider a typical grounded-emitter amplifier. A few nanohenrys of inductance in the emitter circuit can provide considerable degeneration, and severely effect the gain of the amplifier. In a class-C grounded-base transistor, base inductance may cause regeneration which can cause the amplifier to oscillate, or have an undesirable turn-on characteristic which can create CW key clicks.

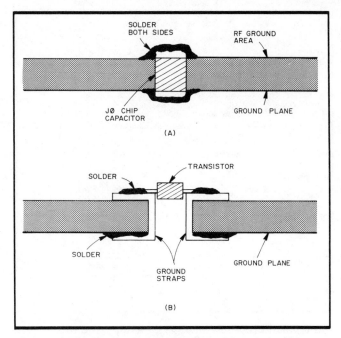

Fig 7—Methods of effective RF grounding using (A) a J0 chip bypass capacitor and (B) through-the-board grounding straps. See the text for a discussion of J0 capacitors.

Fig 7 illustrates the method of grounding the base or emitter leads of a transistor by means of through-the-board ground straps. It also shows the use of a J0, or zero-reactance, capacitor to connect the RF ground area on the circuit side of a PC board to the ground plane on the opposite side.

A J0 capacitor is one whose capacitance value has been chosen to series-resonate the parasitic inductance of the capacitor leads and/or housing. Typically, a 100-mil (0.1-inch) ceramic chip capacitor has an approximate inductance of 0.5 nH, while that of a 50-mil (0.05-inch) chip capacitor is 0.25 nH. Therefore, the inductive reac-

tance of the capacitor can be estimated at the frequency of interest. This should be resonated by selecting a value of capacitance which provides an equivalent capacitive reactance at the same frequency. The result will be a capacitor that is series resonant and has the lowest possible series impedance.

For example, to find the optimum 50-mil chip capacitor for use as a bypass or dc block at 2304 MHz, calculate the inductive reactance of 0.25 nH at that frequency:

$$X = 2 \pi f L = 3.6 \text{ ohms}$$

Then, determine the capacitance required for a reactance of 3.6 ohms at the same frequency:

$$C = \frac{1}{2 \pi f X} = 19.1 \text{ pF}$$

The closest standard value is 20 pF, which will provide a nearly ideal J0 capacitor.

Fig 8 shows simplified layouts of two amplifiers—one for VHF, the other for use at microwave frequencies. They demonstrate some of the techniques that have been discussed.

CHARACTERIZATION OF BIPOLAR TRANSISTORS

Power level, thermal control, gain, stability, biasing conditions and operating frequency are typical properties that must be considered in the design of transmitting amplifiers. For receiving amplifiers, noise figure or noise temperature, gain, stability, biasing conditions and operating frequency are the important properties. Note that several of these properties are common to both types of amplifiers.

S-Parameters

Most of the properties are dependent upon the elec-

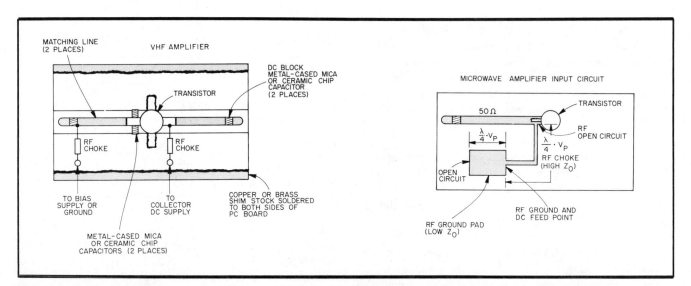

Fig 8—Construction techniques for VHF and microwave amplifiers. The various techniques illustrated are discussed in the text.

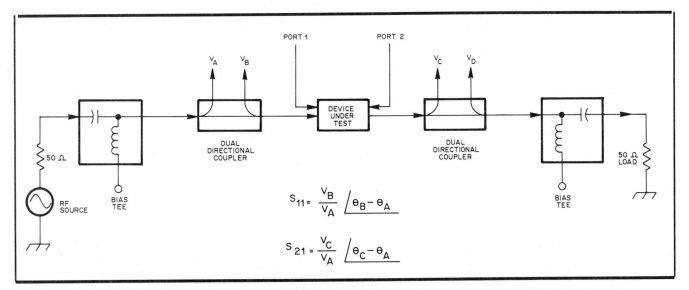

Fig 9—Typical test setup for measuring S_{11} and S_{21}.

$$S_{11} = \frac{V_B}{V_A} \ \underline{/\theta_B - \theta_A}$$

$$S_{21} = \frac{V_C}{V_A} \ \underline{/\theta_C - \theta_A}$$

trical characteristics of the transistor to be used in the amplifier. These characteristics are usually detailed by the manufacturer in the form of S-parameters (scattering parameters) for low-power transistors. For high-power devices intended for transmitting applications, however, there are many different methods of specifying transistor performance parameters.

It is not possible to include a theoretical discussion of S-parameters; those interested can find this material in two Hewlett-Packard application notes.[3,4] The best way to understand the physical concept of S-parameters, however, is to examine the method by which they are typically measured.

Fig 9 depicts a typical test setup for measuring forward S-parameters. The bias tees isolate the 50-ohm RF system from the dc power supplies. A 50-ohm RF source sends a signal to port 1, the input of the DUT (device under test), through a dual directional coupler. Voltage V_A from the

directional coupler is proportional to the incident signal to the DUT, while V_B represents the signal reflected back from port 1 of the DUT. The magnitude of the *input reflection coefficient*, S_{11}, is the ratio of the reflected voltage to the incident voltage (V_B/V_A), and will always be less than one. The phase difference between voltages V_B and V_A represents the phase angle of S_{11}.

Voltage (V_C) from the dual directional coupler connected to port 2 is proportional to the signal transmitted through the DUT. Because the test setup is terminated in a purely resistive load of 50 ohms, V_D should be zero. The magnitude of the *forward transducer gain*, S_{21}, equals the ratio of output voltage V_C to input voltage V_A, and should be greater than one for active devices. The phase angle of S_{21} is the phase difference between voltages V_C and V_A.

To measure reverse S-parameters, a test setup similar to that shown in Fig 10 is used. Here, the signal source is at the output, and the input is terminated in a 50-ohm

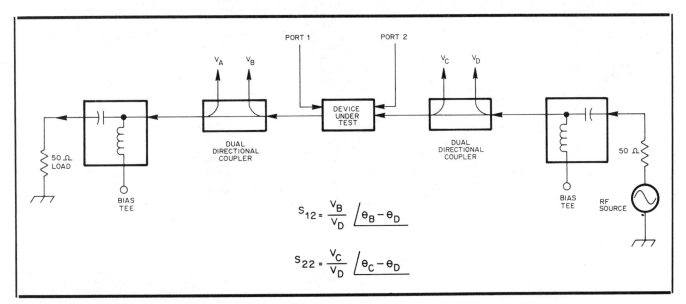

$$S_{12} = \frac{V_B}{V_D} \ \underline{/\theta_B - \theta_D}$$

$$S_{22} = \frac{V_C}{V_D} \ \underline{/\theta_C - \theta_D}$$

Fig 10—Typical test setup for measuring S_{12} and S_{22}.

load. The magnitude of the *reverse transducer gain*, S_{12}, is the ratio of reverse voltage V_B through the DUT to incident voltage V_D to the DUT. The phase difference between V_B and V_D is the phase angle for S_{12}. The magnitude of the *output reflection coefficient*, S_{22}, is the ratio of V_C to V_D, while the phase angle of S_{22} is the difference between those two voltages.

A vector voltmeter can be used to measure the voltages and phase angles from the coupler ports. These measurements are now highly automated by semiconductor manufacturers, using network analyzers, sweep frequency generators, and so on. S-parameters are generally shown in tabular form for bias values and frequencies applicable to the device. In other instances, S_{11} and S_{22} may be provided as curves plotted on a Smith Chart, while S_{21} and S_{12} are shown as polar plots.

Occasionally, S-parameters will be stated in decibels, presumably because many measurement systems provide the magnitudes in decibels. And because *voltages* are measured in a constant-impedance system, the conversion to absolute values is obtained from the formula

$$|S_{nn}|_{dB} = 20 \log|S_{nn}|$$

where nn represents the S-parameter subscript.

INPUT AND OUTPUT LOAD IMPEDANCES

Although S-parameters are sometimes supplied for power devices, especially those which are designed for class-A operation, the characteristics for such devices are more often given as input and output load impedances. Unfortunately, there is no recognized standard for such

data, so you must first ascertain the form in which the data are provided.

For example, output load impedance may be either (1) the output impedance of the device or (2) an impedance which is a conjugate match to the output of the device for either maximum power gain or for maximum device efficiency. Similarly, the specified input impedance is *generally* the transistor input impedance, but could be the required conjugate impedance. Furthermore, the impedances are *usually* stated in rectangular series form ($R \pm jX$)—but not always! Occasionally, they are given in rectangular parallel form. Often, impedance values are presented as Z_{in} and Z_{out} on a Smith Chart, but Z_{in} and Z_{out} are seldom defined. Most of the time they represent the device values, rather than the conjugates—but not always! To reiterate, you must ascertain the form in which the data are provided.

There may be purists who maintain (correctly so) that there is no such thing as the output impedance of a device. There is only a conjugate impedance that results in optimum power transfer or device efficiency. Regardless, the mathematically fictional Z_{out} is very useful in determining which circuit solution you may wish to employ.

A measurement method for power devices used by at least one transistor manufacturer appears in Fig 11. The DUT is placed in a test fixture, to which the desired bias voltages and RF input power are applied. The input and output three-stub tuners are adjusted for zero input reflected power and maximum gain at the rated output power. The DUT is then removed from the circuit, and the RF source is replaced by a 50-ohm load, as shown in Fig 11B. A vector voltmeter or a network analyzer is used to measure the

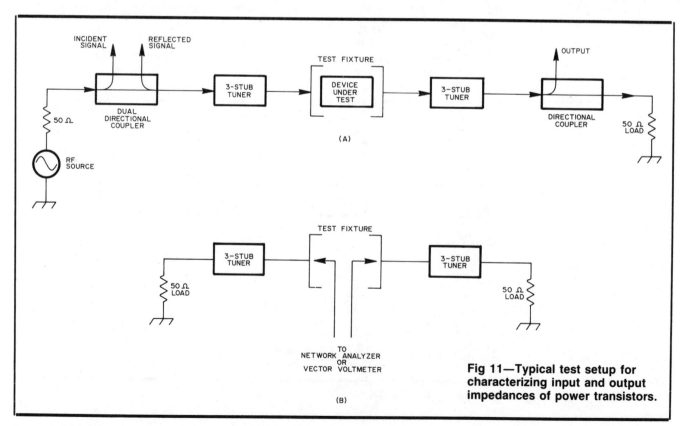

Fig 11—Typical test setup for characterizing input and output impedances of power transistors.

input-circuit and load-circuit impedances looking back to the source and load terminations. These measured impedances represent the conjugates of the input and output impedances of the DUT.

Note that this procedure does not actually characterize the transistor. The final large-signal impedance values represent a stable operating point for the device at its rated gain and power level.

AMPLIFIER DESIGN TECHNIQUES

The design techniques discussed are limited to transistor devices that are unconditionally stable. The variety of modern transistors available for different frequencies makes this a reasonable limitation. Also, by specifying transistors that are unconditionally stable, it is possible to utilize a simplified design method which requires a minimum number of calculations for low-level amplifiers. Methods for designing transistor amplifiers that are made conditionally stable by gain mismatching or resistor loading are described in several application notes.[3,4]

Designing with S-Parameters

When using S-parameters to design low-level amplifiers, where device impedances are relatively large, there are many different ways of accomplishing the actual board design. Practically any method you select will perform properly. For transmitter power amplifiers, where device impedances are generally low, large circulating RF currents and the attendant circuit losses must be considered. Low circuit Qs are required in order to keep losses to a minimum. Low Qs do not, however, necessarily mean wide bandwidth; other circuit elements such as tuned lines and stubs may result in limited bandwidths. On the other hand, the Q of the components should be as high as practical so that they do not represent loss elements.

Calculating Input and Output Impedances

Table 3 lists the equations that must be used to calculate the series input- and output-impedance values from

---

Table 3
Design Equations Using S-Parameters

Eq		Remarks
(1)	$MSG_{dB} = 10 \log \left| \dfrac{S_{21}}{S_{12}} \right|$	
(2)	$D = (S_{11} S_{22}) - (S_{12} S_{21})$	
(3)	$K = \dfrac{1 + |D|^2 - |S_{11}|^2 - |S_{22}|^2}{2|S_{12}| |S_{21}|}$	
(4)	$B_1 = 1 + |S_{11}|^2 - |S_{22}|^2 - |D|^2$	
(5)	$MAG_{dB} = MSG_{dB} + 10 \log \left(K \pm \sqrt{K^2 - 1}\right)$	Use minus before radical when B_1 is positive, and plus when B_1 is negative
(6)	$C_1 = S_{11} - (D \times S_{22}{}^*)$	$S_{22}{}^* = $ conjugate of S_{22}
(7)	$|\Gamma_{in}| = \left[\dfrac{B_1{}^2 \pm \sqrt{B_1{}^2 - 4 |C_1|^2}}{2 |C_1|} \right]$	Use minus before radical when B_1 is positive, and plus when B_1 is negative
(8)	$B_2 = 1 + |S_{22}|^2 - |S_{11}|^2 - |D|^2$	
(9)	$C_2 = S_{22} - (D \times S_{11}{}^*)$	$S_{11}{}^* = $ conjugate of S_{11}
(10)	$|\Gamma_{out}| = \left[\dfrac{B_2 \pm \sqrt{B_2 - 4 |C_2|^2}}{2|C_2|} \right]$	Use minus before radical when B_2 is positive, and plus when B_2 is negative.
(11)	$\Gamma_{in} = |\Gamma_{in}| \; \underline{/\theta\, C_1}$	
(12)	$\Gamma_{out} = |\Gamma_{out}| \; \underline{/\theta\, C_2}$	

Table 4
S-Parameters for the NE02135 Transistor

V_{CE} = 10 V, I_C = 5 mA

Freq (MHz)	S_{11}		S_{21}		S_{12}		S_{22}	
100	0.84	−36	13.82	156	0.02	73	0.94	−18
500	0.68	−126	7.18	106	0.08	35	0.51	−53
1000	0.66	−163	4.02	81	0.09	27	0.34	−66
1500	0.65	178	2.75	64	0.10	27	0.31	−74
2000	0.65	163	2.10	52	0.12	30	0.31	−83
2500	0.66	151	1.68	39	0.13	26	0.31	−95
3000	0.66	141	1.46	27	0.14	26	0.33	−106
3500	0.67	129	1.24	17	0.16	26	0.36	−116
4000	0.68	121	1.14	5	0.17	23	0.38	−127

V_{CE} = 10 V, I_C = 20 mA

Freq (MHz)	S_{11}		S_{21}		S_{12}		S_{22}	
100	0.62	−80	31.13	139	0.01	60	0.77	−37
500	0.64	−163	9.88	93	0.04	46	0.26	−79
1000	0.65	176	5.07	75	0.06	49	0.16	−95
1500	0.64	164	3.45	63	0.08	50	0.15	−101
2000	0.65	154	2.60	52	0.11	51	0.16	−111
2500	0.66	142	2.10	40	0.13	43	0.18	−121
3000	0.66	133	1.81	30	0.15	40	0.20	−129
3500	0.66	122	1.55	20	0.17	36	0.22	−136
4000	0.68	115	1.43	8	0.19	31	0.25	−144

V_{CE} = 10 V, I_C = 10 mA

Freq (MHz)	S_{11}		S_{21}		S_{12}		S_{22}	
100	0.73	−55	22.55	148	0.02	65	0.87	−27
500	0.64	−148	8.90	98	0.06	37	0.36	−66
1000	0.64	−176	4.71	77	0.07	39	0.23	−82
1500	0.64	169	3.19	63	0.09	40	0.21	−87
2000	0.65	156	2.42	52	0.11	42	0.21	−97
2500	0.65	145	1.95	40	0.13	37	0.22	−108
3000	0.66	135	1.69	29	0.15	35	0.25	−118
3500	0.66	125	1.43	19	0.17	32	0.27	−127
4000	0.68	117	1.34	8	0.19	28	0.29	−137

V_{CE} = 10 V, I_C = 30 mA

Freq (MHz)	S_{11}		S_{21}		S_{12}		S_{22}	
100	0.58	−95	35.35	134	0.01	59	0.72	−40
500	0.64	−169	10.11	91	0.03	50	0.22	−82
1000	0.65	173	5.15	74	0.06	55	0.14	−97
1500	0.65	162	3.49	62	0.08	53	0.14	−103
2000	0.66	152	2.63	52	0.11	54	0.15	−112
2500	0.66	141	2.10	39	0.13	46	0.17	−122
3000	0.66	132	1.82	29	0.15	42	0.19	−129
3500	0.67	122	1.54	20	0.17	38	0.22	−137
4000	0.68	115	1.44	9	0.20	31	0.24	−146

S-parameters, as well as other important performance characteristics for low-level applications. For a useful device, the maximum stable gain (MSG) should be at least 10 dB, since the maximum available gain (MAG) is typically 2 to 3 dB less than the MSG. The stability factor (K) must be greater than one for the device to be unconditionally stable.

To illustrate the use of these equations, a 2304-MHz amplifier using the NE02135, a readily available low-cost transistor made by NEC, will be designed. The S-parameters for this device are shown in Table 4. From the values of S_{21}, which are directly related to gain, it can be seen that there is little difference between the values of S_{21} at collector currents of 20 mA and 30 mA. Therefore, a collector-to-emitter voltage of 10 V and the lower collector current of 20 mA will be used as the bias point.

Linear interpolation between the S-parameters at 2000 and 2500 MHz yields the following values for 2304 MHz:

$$S_{11} = 0.656 \; \angle 146.7$$

$$S_{12} = 0.122 \; \angle 46.1$$

$$S_{21} = 2.3 \; \angle 44.7$$

$$S_{22} = 0.172 \; \angle -117.1$$

From Table 3, Eq 1,

$$MSG = 10 \log (2.3 \; \angle 0.122) = 12.8 \text{ dB}$$

and from Eq 2,

$$D = (0.656 \; \angle 146.7) (0.172 \; \angle -117.1) - (0.122 \; \angle 46.1)$$
$$(2.3 \; \angle 44.7)$$
$$= 0.102 - j0.225$$
$$= 0.247 \; \angle -65.6$$

Now the stability factor can be determined from Eq 3,

$$K = \frac{1 + 0.247^2 - 0.656^2 - 0.172^2}{2 \times 0.122 \times 2.3} = 1.07$$

which, being greater than 1, indicates the device is unconditionally stable.

From Eq 4,

$$B_1 = 1 + 0.656^2 - 0.172^2 - 0.247^2 = 1.34$$

Because B_1 is positive, a minus sign is used ahead of the radical in Eq 5 to calculate the maximum available gain:

$$MAG = 12.8 + 10 \log (1.07 - \sqrt{1.07^2 - 1}) = 11.2 \text{ dB}$$

Eqs 6 through 10 of Table 3 yield the results which follow. Conjugate values are required in Eqs 6 and 9:

$$C_1 = 0.656 \; \underline{\angle 146.7} - (0.247 \; \underline{\angle -65.6}) (0.172 \; \underline{\angle 117.1})$$
$$= -0.574 + j0.327$$
$$= 0.661 \; \underline{\angle 150.3}$$

$$\Gamma_{in} = \frac{1.34 - \sqrt{1.34^2 - (4 \times 0.661^2)}}{2 \times 0.661} = 0.85$$

$$B_2 = 1 + 0.172^2 - 0.656^2 - 0.247^2 = 0.538$$

$$C_2 = 0.172 \; \underline{\angle -117.1} - (0.247 \; \underline{\angle -65.6}) (0.656 \; \underline{\angle -146.7})$$
$$= 0.059 - j0.240 = 0.247 \; \underline{\angle -76.3}$$

$$|\Gamma_{out}| = \frac{0.538 - \sqrt{0.538^2 - (4 \times 0.247^2)}}{2 \times 0.247} = 0.66$$

$|\Gamma_{in}|$ is the magnitude of the transistor input reflection coefficient when the output is matched, while $|\Gamma_{out}|$ is the magnitude of the transistor output reflection coefficient when the input is matched. (Note the difference between these quantities and the magnitudes of S_{11} and S_{22}, which are measured with 50-ohm loads at the terminating ends.) Equations 11 and 12 of Table 3 annex the phase angles, which are equal to the phase angles of C_1 and C_2. Therefore

$$\Gamma_{in} = 0.85 \underline{/150.3}$$

and

$$\Gamma_{out} = 0.66 \underline{/-76.3}$$

Transistor input and output reflection coefficients can be transformed into transistor input and output impedances. Although this can be done mathematically, the equations are tedious to solve; using a Smith Chart is simpler and faster.

Because the reflection coefficients are vector voltage quantities, the voltage-reflection-coefficient scale is used to determine the radial distances represented by the magnitudes of these vectors. Each magnitude is plotted on a radial vector from the center of the chart to the angle on the peripheral scale which corresponds to the angle of the reflection coefficient.

Fig 12 shows the calculated reflection coefficients plotted on a normalized Smith Chart. The normalized series impedances which correspond to these points (from the resistance and reactance coordinates) are:

$$Z_{in} = 0.09 + j0.26$$

$$Z_{out} = 0.5 - j1.14$$

Multiplying the normalized impedances by 50 yields the following impedances for a 50-ohm system:

$$Z_{in} = 4.5 + j13$$

$$Z_{out} = 25 - j57$$

With this information, the actual operating circuit can be designed. Of the many available design methods, two will be presented. One technique will use quarter-wave lines and tuning devices to match into and out of the transistor. The second method will use an immittance chart to determine the microstrip line lengths and tuning devices.

Matching with Quarter-Wave Lines

To match the input and output of the transistor by means of quarter-wave lines, calculated device input and output impedances will be used. To transform the input impedance to a 50-ohm source using a quarter-wave section, the inductive input reactance must be tuned out. The simplest and most direct method is to place a capacitive reactance between the base of the transistor and ground.

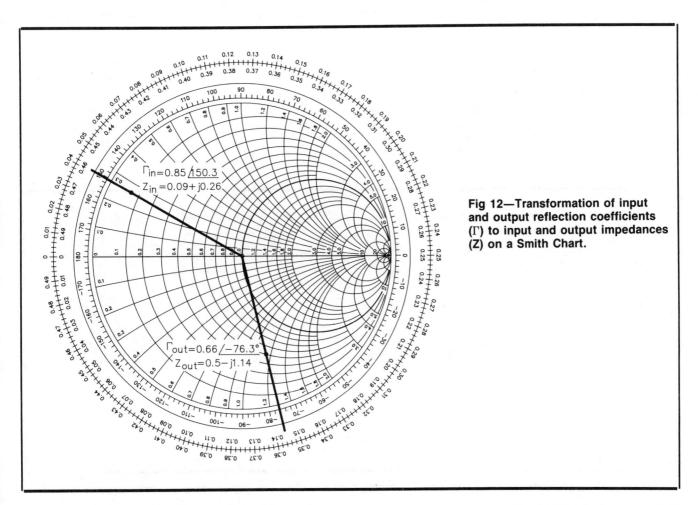

Fig 12—Transformation of input and output reflection coefficients (Γ) to input and output impedances (Z) on a Smith Chart.

First, however, the series input impedance must be transformed to an equivalent parallel impedance to find the value of capacitive reactance for parallel resonance. The following equations are used to convert from series to parallel form, and vice versa:

$$R_p = R_s \left[1 + \left(\frac{X_s}{R_s} \right)^2 \right] \quad \text{(Eq 13)}$$

$$X_p = \frac{R_s R_p}{X_s} \quad \text{(Eq 14)}$$

$$R_s = \frac{R_p}{1 + \left(\frac{R_p}{X_p} \right)^2} \quad \text{(Eq 15)}$$

$$X_s = \frac{R_s R_p}{X_p} \quad \text{(Eq 16)}$$

From Eqs 13 and 14,

$$R_p = 4.5 \left[1 + \left(\frac{13}{4.5} \right)^2 \right] = 42.1 \text{ ohms}$$

$$X_p = \frac{4.5 \times 42.1}{13} = 14.6 \text{ ohms}$$

Therefore, the required capacitance at 2304 MHz is 4.7 pF.

To determine the impedance of the quarter-wave line required to match the parallel input resistance of 42.1 to 50 ohms,

$$Z_0 = \sqrt{42.1 \times 50} = 45.9 \text{ ohms}$$

The mismatch using a 50-ohm line would, however, result in a VSWR of only 50/42.1, or 1.19:1.

For the output circuit, a quarter-wave line can be used as a reactance inverter. In this case, the simplest and most direct method is to series resonate the output reactance of the transistor. First, calculate the impedance value of the quarter-wave line required to match the 25-ohm resistive component of Z_{out} to 50 ohms:

$$Z_0 = \sqrt{25 \times 50} = 35.4 \text{ ohms}$$

This line will also transform the 57-ohm capacitive-reactance component to an inductive reactance whose value is determined as shown in Fig 5:

$$X_L = 35.4^2 / 57 = 22 \text{ ohms}$$

which can be series-resonated by a 3.1-pF capacitor at 2304 MHz.

The complete circuit, which includes shorted quarter-wave lines as RF chokes and open quarter-wave lines as RF grounding pads, is shown in Fig 13. The technique is a simple but powerful method of designing circuits for both receiver and low-power transmitter applications.

Designing with Immittance Charts

An immittance chart consists of two superimposed Smith Charts, oriented 180° apart. For clarity, such charts are generally printed in two contrasting colors. One of the colors, with its infinity point on the right, represents impedance coordinates. The second color, with the infinity point on the left, represents admittance coordinates—the constant-resistance circles become constant-conductance circles, and the constant-reactance lines become constant-susceptance lines. Because impedance (Z) and admittance (Y) are reciprocal functions, that is, Z = 1 / Y, the rules for working with their values on the chart are exactly opposite of one another.

In the examples that follow, we will follow a procedure of designing *from* the device *to* the load and source, using the device series input and output impedances, and will be governed by the following rules:

1) If a radial vector is rotated clockwise, the amount by which the vector is rotated, as measured by the difference between the starting and ending points on either

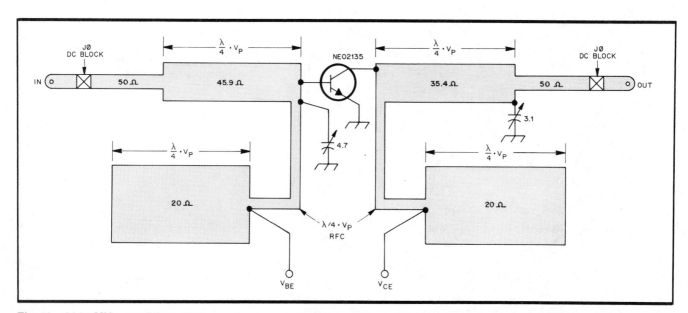

Fig 13—2304-MHz amplifier using quarter-wave matching sections. The line impedances are calculated in the text.

of the peripheral wavelength scales, represents the length of a series transmission line. If a normalized chart is used, the characteristic impedance of the line will be 1 ohm.

2) If a series-impedance point is rotated clockwise on a constant-VSWR circle until it intersects the constant-conductance circle that passes through the origin of the chart, the required shunt reactance can be determined by moving from the intersection to the periphery of the chart along a constant-susceptance line. The shunt reactance can be read directly from the value of the constant-reactance line at the periphery. If the origin of the chart is clockwise from the intersection on the constant-conductance circle, the shunt reactance is capacitive; if the origin is counter-clockwise, the reactance is inductive.

3) If a series-impedance point is rotated clockwise on the constant-resistance circle on which it is located, the difference between the starting reactance and the ending reactance represents a series-inductive reactance.

4) If a series-impedance point is rotated counterclockwise on the constant-resistance circle on which it is located, the difference between the starting reactance and the ending reactance represents a series-capacitive reactance.

Fig 12 shows the input and output impedances of the NE02135 transistor plotted on a Smith Chart. These points are also shown on the normalized immittance chart of Fig 14. Since the source and load impedances are to be 50-ohms resistive, it is necessary to rationalize all reactance and resistance values to 50 ohms by multiplying by 50. These values are shown on the chart.

To design the input circuit, rotate Z_{in} clockwise (using a compass based at the center of the chart) until, at point A, it intercepts the 20-mS constant-conductance circle which passes through the center of the chart. The distance that Z_{in} has been rotated is approximately 0.005 wavelength, as measured on the "WAVELENGTHS TOWARD GENERATOR" scale. Because the immittance chart has been converted to 50 ohms, this represents the length of a series 50-ohm line from the transistor input to a 50-ohm source.

The shunt reactance required to complete the input circuit is found by moving from point A to the periphery of the chart along a constant-susceptance line; this is designated point B. The reactance is equal to value of the constant-reactance line at the periphery and is capacitive, because the origin of the chart is clockwise from point A. On Fig 14, this is shown as a capacitive reactance of 16.1 ohms (obtained by multiplying 0.322 by 50), which is equivalent to a capacitance of 4.3 pF at 2304 MHz.

The output circuit is designed in a similar manner. However, when Z_{out} is rotated clockwise, it will intersect the 20-mS constant-conductance circle twice. This indicates that there are two possible solutions. At point C, a series

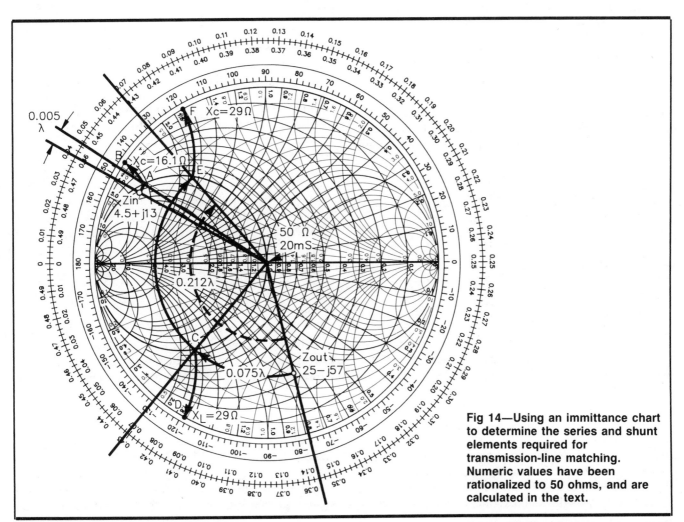

Fig 14—Using an immittance chart to determine the series and shunt elements required for transmission-line matching. Numeric values have been rationalized to 50 ohms, and are calculated in the text.

0.075-wavelength line is required. Moving to point D along a constant-susceptance line shows that a shunt reactance of 29 ohms is required, which must be inductive because the center of the chart is counterclockwise from point C along the 20-mS susceptance circle.

If Z_{out} is rotated to point E, the series line length becomes 0.212 wavelength, and a shunt capacitive reactance of 29 ohms will be needed. In this case, the shunt element found at point F can be a 2.4-pF capacitor at 2304 MHz.

Open and shorted stubs may be used in place of discrete reactive components as the shunt elements. The 29-ohm inductive reactance found at point D can be obtained from a shorted 50-ohm stub, using the relationships shown in Fig 4B

$$\theta = \arctan (X_L / Z_0)$$
$$= \arctan (29 / 50) = 30.1°$$

For Teflon board,

$$L2 = \frac{(3.25)(0.688)(30.1)}{90}$$

$$L2 = 0.74 \text{ cm}$$

If a 29-ohm open capacitive stub were to be used for the reactance determined at point F, then

$$\theta = \arctan (Z_0 / X_L)$$
$$= \arctan (50 / 29) = 59.9°$$

$$L1 = \frac{(3.25)(0.688)(59.9)}{90}$$
$$L1 = 1.49 \text{ cm}$$

The actual circuit can be implemented by the use of discrete capacitors and/or a mix of open stubs and shorted stubs. The choice is primarily determined by the design of the dc-feed circuit and/or the board layout. Fig 15 illustrates both solutions. Use either:

$$\frac{\lambda}{4} = \frac{29980}{(4)(f)} \text{ (cm)}$$

or

$$\frac{\lambda}{4} = \frac{11803}{(4)(f)} \text{ (inches)}$$

to obtain free-space quarter wavelength.

Although microstrip has been used for these amplifiers, because the use of discrete components other than capacitors is not very practical at 2304 MHz, *all* of the circuit elements can utilize discrete components at lower frequencies.

Transmission-line networks are really low-Q versions of L-networks that are capable of matching any complex impedance to a resistive source or load.

Fig 16 shows eight L-network configurations. If Z_{dev}, the complex impedance of the device, is within the un-shaded portion of the Smith Chart, the network can be

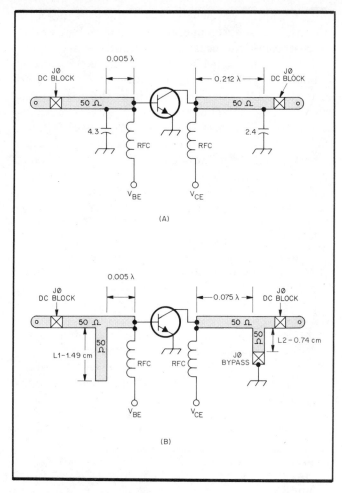

Fig 15—2304-MHz amplifier designed using 50-ohm lines as matching elements, as described in the text. In (A), the shunt elements are discrete capacitors whose design value is shown. Open and shorted stubs are used as the shunt elements in (B).

used to match that impedance to a resistive load (usually 50 ohms. This allows you to determine which of the eight networks can be used and which would be the most convenient to implement. It can be seen that the input circuits shown in Figs 15 A and B are equivalent to the network in Fig 16C. The output circuit of Fig 15A corresponds to the network in Fig 16C, while that of Fig 15B corresponds to Fig 16H.

The actual L-networks shown in Fig 16 are rarely used in UHF and microwave amplifiers because of the difficulty in realizing the discrete inductances normally required. However, use of the figure will preclude an invalid design. The methods by which the Smith Chart and immittance chart can be used to determine the L-network values are covered in the Hewlett-Packard application notes[3,4] and in Phillip H. Smith's book.[5] The latter includes overlays and a chart for each of the L-networks, which simplifies the design procedure considerably.

It may not be possible to find some immittance-chart solutions using L-network charts for two reasons. First,

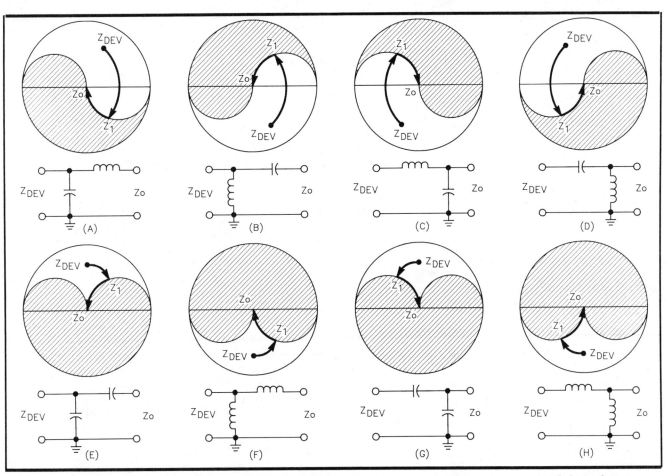

Fig 16—L-networks which will match a complex impedance (Z_{dev}) to Z_0, a resistive source or load. Impedances within the shaded portion of the simplified Smith Chart cannot be matched by the network. Z_1 represents the impedance which is transformed from Z_{dev} by the series element.

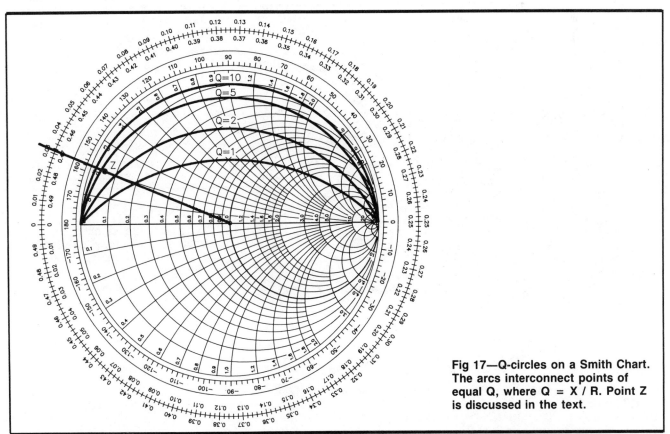

Fig 17—Q-circles on a Smith Chart. The arcs interconnect points of equal Q, where Q = X / R. Point Z is discussed in the text.

a 50-ohm line impedance does not provide an optimum transfer impedance in all cases. It is, however, an easy physical solution. Second, L-networks using discrete components are usually high-Q circuits, where the Q is 10 or more. In contrast, in microwave transistor amplifiers where 50 ohms represents a high impedance, the values of Q are normally considerably less than 10. The reader is referred to the *ARRL Handbook*[6] and Terman's *Radio Engineers' Handbook*[7] for detailed discussions of Q.

Since Q = X / R, it may be represented on a Smith Chart or an immittance chart by connecting points having equal values of X / R. The resultant lines are arcs of circles, commonly called Q-circles, and are shown in Fig 17. Note that impedance point Z has a value of 0.05 + j0.2, and therefore a Q = 0.2 / 0.05 = 4. If this impedance were rotated clockwise, as part of an impedance-matching procedure, it can be seen that the Q would increase. This is an important consideration in the design of high-power transistor amplifiers, which follows.

Designing with Large-Signal Impedances

Power amplifiers are usually designed by using large-signal impedance specifications provided by the manufacturer. As discussed previously, such data may be presented in several forms, one of which is a Smith-Chart plot. Fig 18 shows the large-signal impedances for a TRW52601 transistor, which is a 1.5-W linear device designed to operate in the 1- to 2-GHz region.

A major problem is to get accurate values from the Smith Charts and polar plots that are presented on the data sheets. However, careful scaling and replotting on a full-

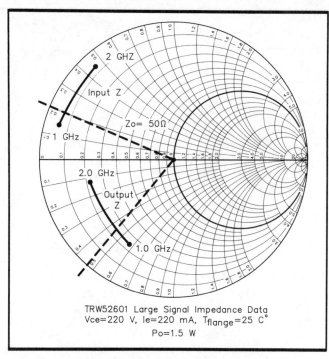

Fig 18—TRW52601 large-signal impedance data, as provided by the manufacturer, with dashed radial vectors added to intersect the plots of input and output impedance at the estimated 1.3-GHz points.

size Smith Chart will provide usable data. To start the design of a 1296-MHz amplifier, radial lines (shown as broken lines on Fig 18 are drawn to intersect the input-Z and output-Z plots at points which are estimated to be

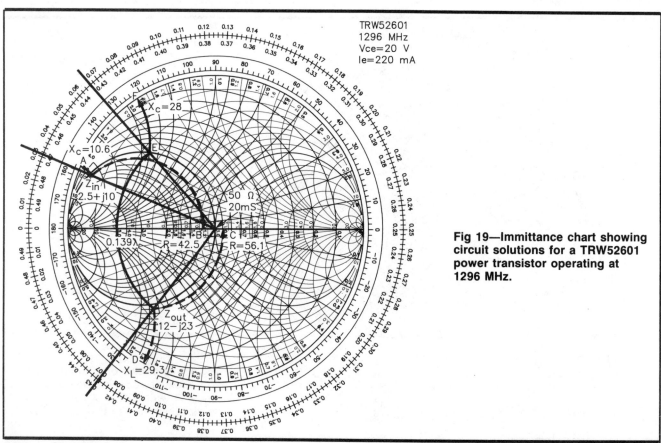

Fig 19—Immittance chart showing circuit solutions for a TRW52601 power transistor operating at 1296 MHz.

1.3 GHz on each curve. These points have been transferred to Fig 19 as $Z_{in} = 2.5 + j10$ and $Z_{out} = 12 - j23$, with their values rationalized to 50 ohms.

By inspecting the position of the plotted points on the immittance chart with respect to the conductance circles passing through chart center and by referring to Fig 16, we can see that we could solve this circuit in exactly the same way as for the small-signal amplifier—by using L-networks or quarter-wave matching sections for the input and the output.

Note that the magnitude of Z_{in} is close to the periphery of the chart and represents a low impedance. This impedance is also shown on Fig 17 as point Z; note that any clockwise rotation to the 20-mS conductance circle rapidly increases the Q of the input circuit. (The output circuit is less critical in this respect because of its smaller vector magnitude.) Power level and circuit Q are now the important criteria for determining the circuit design. For Z_{in}, $Q = X_{in}/R_{in} = 4$. Since we want low-Q solutions for power amplifiers to minimize circulating RF currents and thus minimize circuit losses, let us use a low-Q solution for the input circuit and show both solutions for the output circuit.

Since the input is inductive, it requires a shunt capacitor to tune out the reactance. From Eqs 13 and 14, the equivalent parallel input resistance is 42.5 ohms, and the equivalent parallel input reactance is 10.63 ohms. Thus, the required shunt capacitive reactance is −10.63 ohms, which is provided by 11.6 pF at 1296 MHz. A good practice to follow for power amplifiers is to use two capacitors in parallel from the transistor base to ground; one capacitor might be variable. For higher power levels, open shunt capacitive stubs would be a better solution.

The impedance of the quarter-wave line required to transform 42.5 ohms to 50 ohms is $\sqrt{42.5 \times 50}$, or 46.1 ohms.

The series-to-parallel conversion can also be solved graphically on an immittance chart. By following the susceptance line on Fig 19 from Z_{in} to the peripheral scale, you will find the required shunt reactance value of 10.6 ohms at point A. To find the equivalent parallel resistance, follow the conductance circle clockwise from Z_{in} to the real axis where a resistive value of 42.5 ohms can be read at point B.

For a low-Q output circuit, the same procedure is used. First, for a shorted shunt inductive stub required to cancel the capacitance of the output circuit, convert Z_{out} into its parallel impedance form. From points C and D of Fig 19, the equivalent parallel resistance is 56.1 ohms and the required parallel inductive reactance is 29.3 ohms.

A 53-ohm quarter-wave line will be needed to match 56.1 ohms to 50 ohms. For a shorted inductive stub at the output of the transistor, choose a stub impedance value (Z_0) so that

$$\theta = \arctan(29.3 / Z_0)$$

Then use the procedure shown in Fig 4B to obtain the length of the shorted stub (L1).

The L-network solution for the output circuit is obtained from the immittance chart by rotating Z_{out} on its radius vector clockwise until it intercepts the 20-mS conductance circle (point E on Fig 19). Simply read the shunt reactance value and the line length from the peripheral scales as before, and rationalize their values to 50 ohms. This results in a series 50-ohm line which is 0.139 wavelength long and a shunt reactance of −28 ohms (4.4 pF at 1296 MHz). By using Fig 16 and the location of Z_{out}, you can see that other L-networks can also be used. Fig 20 shows the circuit configurations which have just been calculated.

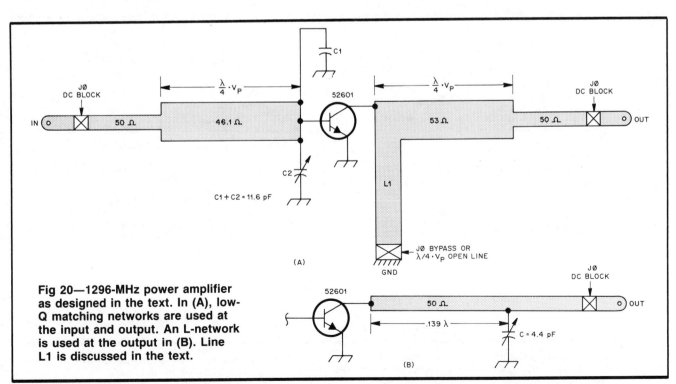

Fig 20—1296-MHz power amplifier as designed in the text. In (A), low-Q matching networks are used at the input and output. An L-network is used at the output in (B). Line L1 is discussed in the text.

An Experimental Design Approach

For those who do not like mathematical calculations and do not have access to computer programs, there is an experimental approach that will generally provide good results for *low-level*, gain-matched amplifiers. The only math required is the calculation of MAG and K, using Eqs 1 through 5 from Table 3. K must be greater than 1.0 for the bias and frequency you plan to use.

The amplifier can be built on a standard board with input and output lines, RF chokes, and grounding pads. The input and output lines can be 50-ohm lines that are slightly over a half-wavelength long, while the RF chokes and grounding pads are quarter-wave line sections. Place the dc blocking capacitors close to the input and output connectors.

The input circuit for most modern low-level, grounded-emitter transistors will require a capacitive reactance either very close to the base of the transistor, or a little less than a half wavelength away. The output circuit will generally tune with a capacitive reactance at some point along the output line. Observing either gain or power output, move a capacitive probe along the input and output lines to determine the point at which the gain or power output is at a maximum. (A capacitive probe can be made by gluing a small metal tab to the end of a toothpick, and insulating the metal with a coat of polystyrene cement.) Then tack solder a discrete tuning capacitor at that point and tune for best amplifier gain. If the MAG is close to the calculated value, the design is essentially finished. If not, slight adjustments of the locations of the capacitors on the 50-ohm lines will usually increase the amplifier gain to a value close to the calculated MAG.

After a little experience, this becomes a relatively simple process. However, the same can be said for using the design equations and Smith Charts. This experimental method is not recommended for power amplifiers because the transistor must be in a full operating configuration in terms of bias voltages and drive levels. The power transistor may not be stable until it is matched for maximum gain at rated power output. Even trying it with reduced bias values is dangerous, as it could easily be in an unstable region and might oscillate rather than amplify. For an expensive power transistor, using the equations and Smith or immittance charts is the only safe way.

BIAS SUPPLIES

Active Bias Supply for Class A Transistors

Fig 21 shows the schematic diagram of a recommended active bias circuit for linear, class-A, grounded-emitter transistors. It does not generate Zener diode noise, and can be used for either low-noise receiver preamps or high-power transistors.

Use of the circuit is predicated on two assumptions—the beta of the RF amplifier transistor is at least 20, and the base-to-emitter junction voltage of Q1 is 0.7 V. To determine the resistances of R1 and R3, select a value of V_1 which is typically 3V. Then

$$R3 = \frac{R2 \times V_{CC}}{V_1} - R2$$

and

$$R1 = \frac{V_1 - 0.7}{I_C} = \frac{2.3}{I_C}$$

where I_C = RF transistor collector current.

R3 is normally made up of a fixed resistor and a

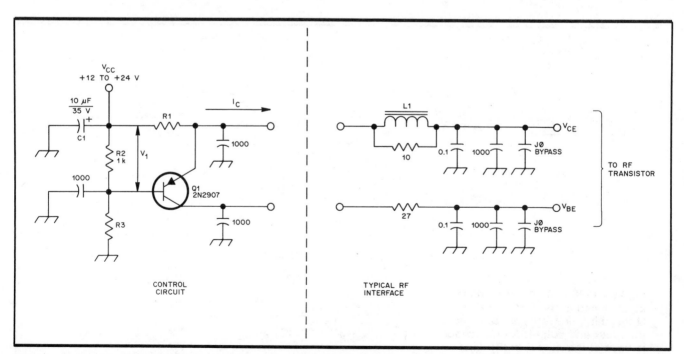

Fig 21—Active bias supply and RF interface for class-A transistors. L1, R1, R3, and V_1 are discussed in the text. C1 is a tantalum electrolytic. Q1 can be any silicon PNP transistor with a beta of 20 or more.

potentiometer that has sufficient range (typically 2 to 5 kΩ) to control the operating point for the RF transistor.

Be sure R1 has an adequate power rating. Note that V_{CE} will be less than V_{CC} by approximately 2.3 volts, so adjust V_{CC} accordingly to obtain the rated bias point.

Although the circuit is a dc control circuit, its interface with the RF transistor is extremely important. The interface is related to the frequency of operation and the low-frequency gain of the RF transistor. Fig 21 shows a typical 1296-MHz interface for minimizing low-frequency gain or oscillations, with adequate RF bypassing.

For low-power transistors, L1 can be a 1- to 10-μH toroid. The 10-ohm resistor effectively prevents low-frequency oscillations by swamping the low-frequency gain path. At higher power levels and higher collector currents, make sure that the core does not saturate. For high-power amplifiers, an alternative is to use an air-wound 10- to 12-turn coil of no. 26 wire with an inside diameter of 1/16 inch.

Self-Regulating Bias Source for Class A Power Transistors

Fig 22 shows a low-parts-count, self-regulating bias supply for class-A linear power transistors. The RF interface shown is typical for the microwave frequencies. V_{CE} will be approximately 1 V greater than the Zener voltage (V_Z) of D1. I is the sum of the transistor collector and base currents. Therefore,

$$R1 = \frac{V_{CC} - (V_Z + 1)}{I}$$

Adjust V_{CC} as required to obtain the desired operating point. D1 should typically have a power rating of 1 W.

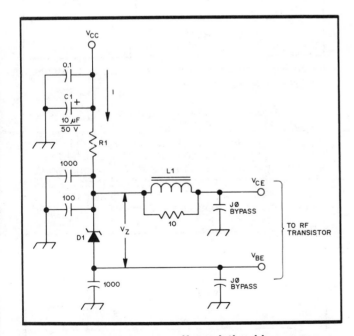

Fig 22—Low-parts-count, self-regulating bias source for high-power class-A transistors. D1 and R1 are discussed in the text. C1 is a tantalum electrolytic. L1 is the same as in Fig 21.

Bias Source for Class AB Power Transistors

The TRW BT500 is a bias source which is suitable for use with class-AB RF transistors, which require a stiff bias supply because of the large difference between idle current and peak current. A circuit using the BT500 is shown in Fig 23. The device should be mounted on the same heat sink as and as close as practical to the RF transistor to provide good thermal tracking. Similar bias sources are available from other manufacturers.

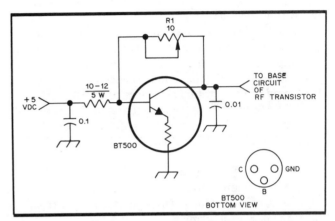

Fig 23—Bias source for class-AB power transistors. R1 is a 10-turn trimmer potentiometer used to adjust the RF-transistor collector current.

MISCELLANEOUS CONSIDERATIONS AND HINTS

For FM or CW operation, use a class-C device. If SSB operation is contemplated, a linear device will be required. In this case, be careful about using S-parameters for power amplifiers unless the device is specified for class-A operation at the power level to be used. Instead, use the large-signal impedances and an immittance chart.

For power levels up to several hundred milliwatts, S-parameters can generally be used. Expect, however, that the circuit may have to be trimmed to obtain maximum power gain. This is accomplished by probing the line with a capacitive probe as you watch the output power from the amplifier. If you find a point that increases the power, that is, the amplifier gain, a small change in the position of the main tuning device can be made.

It's important to keep in mind the heat-sink requirement of your power transistor. If your device is biased up to class AB (typically 50 to 100 mA with no drive), duty-cycle problems are nominal and related to key-down periods and drive levels. For medium- and high-power class-A operation, however, the device is drawing from hundreds of milliamps to more than an ampere at all times. Because of this, it's important to get as much information as possible from the manufacturer concerning its heat-sinking characteristics. It's a good idea to only key the amplifier when your system is in transmit mode by hooking up a keying relay to your rig's PTT or VOX circuit.

For low-noise receive preamps using bipolar transistors, many manufacturers supply optimum source and load impedances for best noise figure and gain. They are specified for bias condition and frequency. These values may be used in the same manner as the gain-matched amplifiers we have already discussed, for the quarter-wavelength solution or the line solution.

GaAsFET devices have not been discussed, but the theory and circuit techniques presented apply equally well to GaAsFET amplifier design throughout the microwave region.

If the measured amplifier gain is substantially less than the design figures indicate, do the following *before* replacing the transistor:

1) Check the operating bias conditions to be sure they are within specifications.

2) Reevaluate the RF grounding circuits to be sure they are effective RF grounds. This includes making certain that the chip capacitors which have been used are truly microwave capacitors, and that good soldered connections have been made to the metallic surfaces of the capacitors.

3) Experiment with the inductances of wire-wound RF chokes. If the RF tuning changes when the RF choke is changed, find a choke configuration that has a minimum effect on the tuning.

Occasionally, you will find a circuit design that will have one or more apparently extra tuning stubs on the input and/or output lines. These generally result from one or both of the following:

1) For class-C amplifiers, many designers use eighth-wavelength open stubs near the transistor collector in order to provide a low-impedance path for the second harmonic. This stub represents a quarter-wave open stub to the second harmonic and acts like a short circuit. Its position will normally be between the collector and a point one-eighth wavelength down the line. The eighth-wave stub will then normally have to be tuned out by another stub to eliminate its effect at the fundamental frequency.

2) Dc blocking capacitors and the connectors used for launching the signal on and off the board may represent impedance discontinuities on the line. Tuning stubs may be required to tune out their effects on SWR and gain.

Notes

[1]James R. Fisk, "Microstrip Transmission Line," *Ham Radio*, January 1978, pp 28-37.
[2]Frederick Emmons Terman, *Radio Engineers' Handbook* (New York: McGraw-Hill Book Company, Inc, 1943).
[3]*S-Parameters . . . Circuit Analysis and Design*, Application Note 95 (Hewlett-Packard Company, September 1968).
[4]*S-Parameter Design*, Application Note 154 (Hewlett-Packard Company, Revised May 1973).
[5]Phillip H. Smith, *Electronic Applications of the Smith Chart in Waveguide, Circuit, and Component Analysis* (New York: McGraw-Hill Book Company, Inc, 1969).
[6]*The ARRL Handbook for the Radio Amateur*, 67th ed (Newington: American Radio Relay League, 1989), pp 2-27 to 2-29, 15-5.
[7]Terman, pp 135-172.
[8]Nelson M. Cooke and Herbert F. R. Adams, *Basic Mathematics for Electronics*, 4th ed (New York: McGraw-Hill Book Company, Inc, Gregg Division, 1976).
[9]*The RF Capacitor Handbook* (Huntington Station, California: American Technical Ceramics, 1972).

Just What is an S-Parameter?

By H. Paul Shuch, N6TX
Copyright (C) 1986, Microcomm

Consider the typical microwave component, circuit or assembly as a two-port device, one which contains two connectors to which RF signals can be applied, or from which they can be extracted. Depending on the intended application, these ports may simply be labeled INPUT (or "gozinta"), and OUTPUT (or "gozouta"). Any active circuit is likely to contain as well one or more power connectors. However, these dc inputs are not "ports" for the purpose of signal analysis, merely a source of fuel that the circuitry will expend in doing its job, which is to massage RF signals in some specific way.

The ac behavior of any two-port device can be modeled at a given frequency, by a set of only four numbers or mathematical expressions, one each for forward gain, reverse gain, input impedance or match, and output impedance or match. Fig A illustrates this concept.

The use of parameter sets to model the behavior of a component or circuit is not unique to microwave or RF analysis. Consider the familiar h-parameters used to model the low frequency signal response of, say, a common-emitter bipolar junction transistor. There's h_{fe} for forward current gain, h_{re} for reverse voltage gain, h_{ie} for input resistance, and h_{oe} for output conductance. The h indicates hybrid, which means the model involves a combination of measured parameters. The first subscripts (f, r, i and o) are self explanatory, and the second subscript (e in this case) indicates the circuit configuration in which the transistor was employed to make the measurements (common emitter). Common

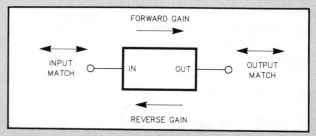

Fig A—A generalized set of four parameters that describe the behavior of a two-part device.

base or collector h-parameters would end in a, b or c, respectively.

The chief advantage of h-parameters is that they reduce the internal construction of the transistor to a simplified model for circuit analysis. One hybrid model of a common emitter bipolar junction transistor is shown in Fig B. Notice that the use of h-parameters has reduced the whole transistor to simple Thevenin input

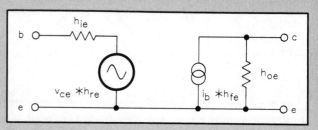

Fig B—One possible hybrid parameter model for a bipolar junction transistor.

and Norton output networks. Kirchhoff's laws will now facilitate the analysis of a complete circuit, employing such a transistor model.

Unfortunately, three very good reasons exist for not employing h-parameters in RF or microwave analysis. The first is that the variety of measurements involved (voltage ratio, current ratio, resistance and conductance) requires a like variety in instrumentation. Next, h-parameters involve magnitudes only, while most RF applications require phase information as well. Finally, h-parameter measurement involves terminating input and output ports in opens and shorts, a practice not conducive to longevity for microwave active devices.

Several other parameter sets exist for describing the forward gain, reverse gain, input match and output match of a two-port device, while overcoming the above objections. The most popular are Z-parameters, Y-parameters and S-parameters. Among these, S-parameters are probably the easiest to measure directly, and the combination of instruments and accessories used to measure them is called collectively a Network Analyzer.

In order to overcome the three limitations identified for the hybrid parameter set, three rules apply to the definition, measurement and application of S-parameters:

(1) All S-parameters are voltage ratios. Although it is difficult to accurately measure potentials at microwave frequencies, a comparison of the amplitudes of two different signals is relatively easy. Using suitable detectors, attenuators and indicators, voltage ratios can be accurately determined using audio substitution, RF substitution or power ratio techniques.

(2) All S-parameters are vectors. This will complicate the required instrumentation somewhat, but by providing phase as well as magnitude information, S-parameters facilitate accurate analysis of gain, stability, complex impedance and admittance, and a host of other pertinent vector quantities.

(3) All S-parameters are measured and specified with all ports terminated in a specified system characteristic impedance. That impedance may be 50 Ω for standard coaxial systems, 75 Ω in the cable TV industry, around 200 Ω in rectangular waveguide, or 377 Ω for measurements made in free space. But whatever system impedance is specified, it must be applied consistently, and uniformly. And all ports of any device, even those not involved in the measurement at hand, must be so terminated.

Once these three conditions are satisfied, we still need a way to express the data unambiguously, and this is done through the use of subscripts, one for each port of the device being described. Each S-parameter is a voltage ratio, the ratio of a potential out of a specified port, to that applied to a (perhaps different) specified port. The ratio, or fraction, can be described by two subscripts, the first for the numerator, and the second representing the denominator. For the general form "S_{xy}," think "x over y," or the voltage out of port x, divided by the voltage applied to port y.

Assume that a device's input port is arbitrarily labeled "1," and its output port "2," as shown in Fig C. The gain of this device, in the forward direction, can be called Forward Voltage Transmission Coefficient, and is found by dividing the output voltage from port 2, by the signal applied in to port 1. The corresponding S-parameter is S_{21}. Since two distinct subscripts are involved, this would be pronounced "S sub two, one," and *not* "S sub twenty-one." Similarly, the

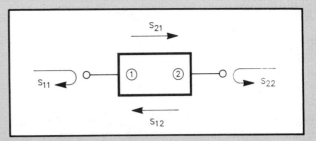

Fig C—The four scattering parameters for a two-port device.

reverse gain, or Reverse Voltage Transmission Coefficient, would be found by dividing the EMF taken out from port 1, by that applied to port 2, and the resulting S-parameter would be S_{12} (but *not* "S sub twelve"!) Remember that these are both voltage gains, expressed as vectors (that is, both an amplitude ratio and a phase difference between the two signals involved).

If the impedance of any port of our device under test is imperfectly matched to the previously specified system characteristic impedance, reflections will result upon applying a signal to, or taking one from, that port. This will give rise to forward and reverse propagated waves, whose amplitudes can be determined independently with a directional coupler, and whose phase difference can be found with a slotted line, using the null-shift method. This would define for us the remaining two S-parameters, S11 (for the voltage reflected out of port 1, divided by that applied to port 1), and S_{22} (similarly defined for port 2). You may recognize that such measurements represent simply voltage reflection coefficients, and in fact the names of these two S-parameters are Input Voltage Reflection Coefficient, and Output Voltage Reflection Coefficient, respectively.

It should be pointed out that S_{11} and S_{22}, though voltage reflection coefficients, are not the *only* possible voltage reflection coefficients associated with the input and output ports. For example, when designing transistor amplifiers, we frequently calculate γ_{11} and γ_{22} the input and output reflection coefficients each measured with the other port *conjugately matched*. Don't confuse these with S_{11} and S_{22}, which were measured not with the other ports matched, but rather with them *terminated* in a specified system characteristic impedance.

You can see that the above convention, although derived for two-port devices, can be generalized to three-port components (such as mixers and directional couplers), four-port devices (such as quadrature hybrid branch couplers), or any other number of ports, through the addition of the appropriate subscripts.

You may be wondering where the S in S-parameters comes from. It stands for the word "scattering," and to understand why, you need simply determine the S-parameters for a given device over a range of frequencies, and plot them graphically. You will notice that scattering parameters, as a function of frequency, are scattered all over the map. Hence their name.

Well, not really. "Scattering" actually refers to scattering matrices, a tool of matrix algebra from which S-parameters were derived. But you don't really have to utilize scattering matrices, or even understand matrix algebra at all, to apply S-parameters successfully. You need only apply a few basic rules of vector arithmetic to benefit from the convenience of S-parameter analysis and design.

Who is Phillip Smith and Why are We Afraid of His Marvelous Chart?

By H. Paul Shuch, N6TX

One of the most spectacular recurring themes in Electronics is the concept of Duality: There are two different ways to express any electrical phenomenon, and they are mathematically interrelated. We see Duality at work from the most simple to the most complex. For example, electromotive force (EMF), which we commonly call Voltage, is related to potential energy per unit charge. Thus EMF is a manifestation of potential energy, a statement borne out by our referring to EMF as "electrical potential."

Well, the Dual of EMF is current, the net motion of charged particles, which relates to kinetic energy per unit flux, and can thus be thought of as a manifestation of kinetic energy. The Duality between EMF and current allows us to evaluate circuits through their potential energy, or their kinetic energy, and to relate the two analyses mathematically. The connection between the two is called Ohm's Law.

Since resistance is the ratio of EMF to current, it can be thought of as the ratio of (or conversion from) potential to kinetic energy. The Dual of resistance is conductance, the ratio of (or conversion from) kinetic to potential energy. And if you thought conductance was the *reciprocal* of resistance, you're close: it's the *Dual* of resistance. The reciprocal is simply the mathematical tool used to convert one to the other.

If, on the other hand, you thought resistance was "the opposition to current flow," you're also close. That's one of the things a resistance *does*, but not necessarily what resistance *is*.

In a similar vein, the Dual of capacitance (the ability to store energy in electrostatic fields) is inductance (the ability to store energy in magnetic fields). The Dual of impedance (the ratio of potential to kinetic energy in a series ac circuit) is admittance (the ratio of kinetic to potential energy in a parallel ac circuit).

Kirchhoff's Voltage Law and Kirchhoff's Current Law are Duals, in that both state the concept of conservation of energy. The former stipulates that all the EMF around a loop must be accounted for, while the latter says all the current at a node must be accounted for. One application of Kirchhoff's Voltage Law is the Voltage Divider Theorem: The output EMF of a series circuit is a predictable fraction of the input EMF. Its Dual, the Current Divider Theorem, states the output current of a parallel circuit is a predictable fraction of the input current.

More Duality examples abound. The Norton Theorem allows us to express any signal source as a pure kinetic energy source with a shunt admittance. Its Dual, the Thevenin Theorem, models any signal source as a pure potential energy source with a series impedance. We could go on to show that low-pass filters are the Dual of high-pass filters, bandpass filters the Dual of band reject filters, etc. The list is endless. The point is, there's a marvelous symmetry to electronics, as there is to all the physical sciences.

That symmetry becomes apparent when we plot, for example, complex impedance on a rectangular coordinate system. Consider the Cartesian[1] Coordinate System depicted in Fig A, where the abscissa (horizontal or X axis) represents values of resistance, from zero ohms at the left to infinity on the right, and the ordinate (vertical or Y axis) represents values of reactance, inductive ($+j$, on the top half of the graph) or capacitive ($-j$, on the bottom). Note that we can express the complex impedance of any series circuit as a unique point on the graph, described either in rectangular ($R + jX$)

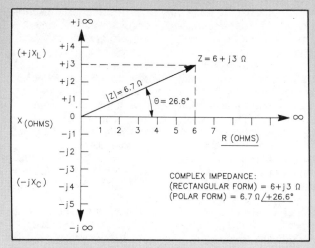

Fig A—Complex impedance plotted on Cartesian Coordinates.

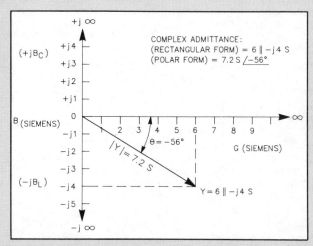

Fig B—Complex admittance plotted on Cartesian Coordinates.

or polar ($Z < 8$) form. We can readily convert between rectangular and polar notation, utilizing the Pythagorean Theorem and simple trigonometry.

It would be equally valid to utilize Cartesian coordinates to describe the complex *admittance* of a *parallel* circuit, as shown in Fig B. Here the horizontal axis represents a *conductance* continuum, extending from 0 siemens at the left to infinity at the right. The vertical axis represents values of capacitive ($+j$, on the top) and inductive ($-j$, on the bottom) *susceptance*. You may notice that in converting from series to parallel notation for a given circuit, the *sign of the imaginary operator changes*. This is because impedance and admittance are duals (hence numeric reciprocals), and when you take the reciprocal of a complex number algebraically (by rationalizing the denominator) the sign always changes.

Back in the 1930s, an RF engineer named Phillip H. Smith modified the familiar Cartesian Coordinate System, to avail himself of the duality between series (impedance model) and parallel (admittance model) circuits. The graphical calculator which resulted[2] is known as a Smith Chart, and is today one of the primary tools of microwave circuit analysis and design.

The origin of the Smith Chart is readily understood

by considering the modified Cartesian coordinate system depicted in Fig C. Here the vertical axis has been bent around so that $+j$ infinity, $-j$ infinity, and real infinity all converge. We have thus enclosed the chart into finite bounds. Let's utilize this coordinate system to plot complex impedances. The horizontal axis still represents values of resistance, extending from zero at the left to infinity on the right. The previously vertical (now curvilinear) axis still represents values of reactance, from zero at the origin, up (and around clockwise) to $+j$ infinity at the "top" (now right hand edge), and down (and around counter-clockwise) to $-j$ infinity at the "bottom" (same right hand edge!).

The mathematical process of distorting the coordinate system is called Conformal Mapping, and produces some useful results. The graph still encompasses all possible complex impedances, each uniquely identified as the intersection of a line (now arc) of resistance, and a line (now arc) of reactance. Furthermore, each point on the graph represents a unique, and identifiable, value of complex impedance. As you will observe in Fig D, we have produced a Smith Chart.

How can we convert the complex impedance of a given series circuit to the complex admittance of its parallel equivalent circuit? If you said "turn the impedance upside down," you're right. The two are duals, one being the mathematical reciprocal of the other. Well, the Smith Chart shown in Fig D is an impedance graph. How, then, do we turn it into an admittance graph? Simply by turning it upside down, as shown in Fig E! Now the horizontal axis represents values of *conductance*, the upper vertical axis values of capacitive *susceptance*, and the lower vertical axis values of inductive *susceptance* for any complex circuit described in the parallel model.

Actually, we can use the Smith Chart for both purposes without physically turning anything upside down. Take a look at the highlighted labels on the axes of Fig D. The horizontal axis is said to represent values of "Resistance Component (R/Z_0)" (more on what these fractions mean shortly), "or Conductance Component (G/Y_0)." The upper half of the vertical axis (actually,

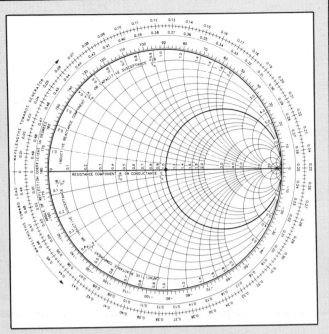

Fig D—The fully developed Smith Chart, with axes for plotting complex impedance and admittance. Note that the labels detail the normalization procedure.

circumference) is similarly labeled "Inductive Reactance Component (X_L/Z_0) or Capacitive Susceptance Component (B_C/Y_0)," and the lower half reads "Capacitive Reactance Component (X_C/Z_0) or Inductive Susceptance Component (B_L/Y_0)." The multiple "or" functions above suggest not Boolean Algebra or digital logic circuits, but rather that a single Smith Chart can do double duty, as either a series circuit (impedance) graph, or a parallel model (admittance) display. Since the Smith Chart is used to plot either complex impedance or complex admittance, it is sometimes called an "immittance" chart.

Considering the dual nature of the Smith Chart, we

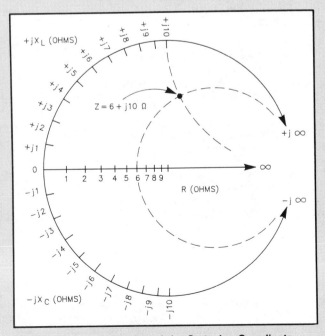

Fig C—Conformal mapping of the Cartesian Coordinate System produces the familiar Smith Chart graphical transmission line calculator.

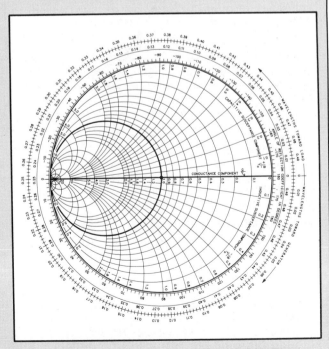

Fig E—Smith Charts intended for complex admittance (parallel circuit) analysis are sometimes oriented like this.

are now ready to perform our first Smith Chart manipulation: conversion of a series complex circuit to its parallel, or admittance, equivalent. Let's do the conversion algebraically first, to see what we'll be missing when we employ the graphical solution.

For a series combination of 1 ohm of resistance, and 2 ohms of capacitive reactance, what is the equivalent parallel circuit? In rectangular notation, our impedance equals:

$Z = 1 - j\,2$ ohms.

Since impedance and admittance are duals,

$Y = 1/Z = 1/(1 - j\,2)$.

We rationalize the denominator (that is, multiply it by its conjugate), but must multiply the numerator by the *same* value:

$Y = 1 * (1 + j\,2) / (1 - j\,2) * (1 + j\,2)$

$= (1 + j\,2) / (1^2 + j2 - j2 - j^2 4)$

$= (1 + j\,2) / (5) = (1/5) + j\,(2/5)$

$= 0.2 + j\,0.4$ siemens, or $200 + j\,400$ millisiemens.

Thus for a series combination of 1 ohm of resistance with 2 ohms of capacitive reactance, the equivalent admittance equals 200 mS of conductance, in parallel with 400 mS of capacitive susceptance. This is summarized in Fig F.

The same conversion on a Smith Chart is depicted in Fig G. First find the circle representing 1 ohm of resistance (a), and follow it down to the arc representing 2 ohms of capacitive reactance (b). Their intersection (c) is the complex impedance of interest. Draw a straight line from this impedance point, through the center of the chart (d), and out an equal distance on the other side to (e), which represents the complex admittance point. To interpret this point, read around to the real axis at (f) for the value of conductance, and up to the imaginary axis at (g) for the value of susceptance. The Smith Chart yields $0.2 + j\,0.4$ siemens, the same as the algebraic solution above. But which was easier?

Since we can graphically convert impedance to admittance on a Smith Chart, it stands to reason we can go the other way, converting admittance to impedance. The same procedures apply: plot what you know, reflect it through the middle of the chart, equidistant out the other side, and read the coordinates for the dual of the circuit you started with. A handy application of the Smith Chart, and you can't do it on Cartesian Coordinates!

There are numerous other conversions which we can perform on a Smith Chart, but all require that we first plot a known complex impedance (or admittance) on the Chart's coordinate system. In the foregoing example, with both resistance and reactance in the low ohms, direct plotting on the Chart was possible. But try plotting the two following complex impedances, and you're in for a bit of difficulty:

(a) $50 + j\,100$ ohms, and (b) $100 - j\,10$ ohms.

Obviously, the above two complex numbers represent significantly different impedances, thus should appear widely separated on an impedance graph, right? Surprise! When plotted directly on a Smith Chart, *both* impedances occupy nearly the same point, the extreme right-hand portion of the horizontal axis.

Three possibilities exist for rectifying the above difficulty: (1) limit ourselves to working with resistances and reactances ranging from fractions of an ohm to tens of ohms, (2) modify the axes of the Smith Chart to fit our data, or (3) modify our data to fit the Smith

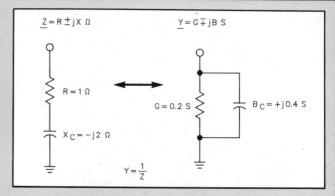

Fig F—Duality between series complex impedance and parallel complex admittance (see text for calculations).

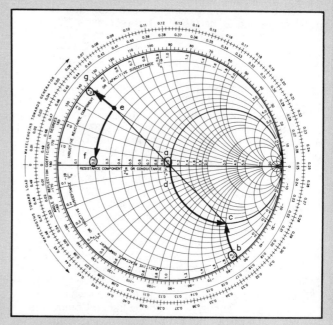

Fig G—Smith Chart conversion between complex impedance and complex admittance (see text).

Chart. The third alternative is consistent with industry practice. Prior to plotting a complex impedance on a Smith Chart, merely divide its resistive and reactive values by an agreed-upon constant. The same applies to plotting of complex admittances; divide the conductance and susceptance by a predetermined constant. The process is called normalization.

But what value should we use as a divisor when normalizing complex impedances or admittances? In order to differentiate between diverse data points which might otherwise converge toward "infinity" on the Chart, we should pick a number which is going to pull our data points in toward the center. And since, in order to reduce reflective losses, we usually desire to match circuit impedances to a specified system characteristic impedance, the characteristic impedance of the system itself makes an ideal normalization constant. (In the case of a parallel equivalent circuit, of course, it is the characteristic *admittance* of the system to which we would normalize our data.) Normalizing by the characteristic impedance, or admittance, of the measurement system, explains the denominators of the fractions found on the labels of each Smith Chart axis, as shown in Fig D and discussed above.

Consider the two complex impedances (a) and (b), used previously to illustrate the difficulty of direct Smith

Chart plotting. Assume that these represent the load impedances in which a standard coaxial measurement system (Z_0 = 50 ohms) is to be terminated. If we divide each resistance and reactance by 50 ohms (the normalization constant), we get:

(a) $Z_n = 1 + j\,2$, and

(b) $Z_n = 2 - j\,0.2$.

Plotting the above normalized impedances on a Smith Chart is relatively straightforward, and is illustrated in Fig H.

Note that normalized impedances are always *unitless ratios*, and are *not* measured in ohms. In dividing a complex impedance, in *ohms*, by a system characteristic impedance, also measured in *ohms*, the units cancel. The same reasoning holds when plotting complex *admittances* on a Smith Chart. Normalize by dividing the data by the system characteristic admittance (in the case of a 50-ohm coaxial system, this would be 20 millisiemens, the reciprocal of 50 ohms). The resulting normalized data would also be unitless.

An unexpected benefit of impedance or admittance normalization is that the Smith Chart will then present us with a qualitative assessment of the impedance (or admittance) match between the system and a device under test. Remember that it's generally desirable for a circuit, component or subassembly to have an impedance close to the characteristic impedance of the system in which used, to minimize reflective losses. Since normalizing the system complex impedance (dividing it by itself) produces a ratio of unity, the normalized value ($1 + j0$) on a Smith Chart represents a perfect match. And where does this value appear on the Chart? Precisely at its center.

The degree of impedance match achieved is illustrated by normalizing and plotting the complex impedance of any load. The closer the resulting point appears to the middle of the Chart, the better the match. Consider once more the two complex impedances which we normalized and plotted as Fig H. Which load impedance represents a better match to the 50-ohm system? Point (b) is closer to the center of the Chart than point (a), thus impedance (b) represents the better match.

What would it take to *quantify* the degree of impedance or admittance match? With a Smith Chart, not much. The degree of mismatch present in a transmission line system can be described in terms of such parameters as Voltage Reflection Coefficient ρ (the Greek letter rho), Power Reflection Coefficient (ρ^2), Return Loss, Reflection Loss, Voltage Standing Wave Ratio, Standing Wave dB, etc. And at the bottom of the Smith Chart, in the area marked "Radially Scaled Parameters," appear scales for graphically calculating each of these reflection terms.

Note in the middle of the scales at the bottom of Fig H, the word "center." This is there to remind you that, when using the Smith Chart to determine reflection terms, what you're interested in most is the distance of a normalized impedance (or admittance) point from the *center* of the Chart. Once this distance is measured (with either a ruler, a drawing compass or a set of draftsman's dividers—I call this latter my Smith Chart "solid state memory") it can be readily transferred to scales at the bottom of the Chart, remembering to measure distance outward from the point marked "center."

Consider the reflection terms corresponding to sample point (a) in Fig H. Measuring the distance from the center of the Chart to Impedance Point (a), then transferring the distance down to the left-hand side of the bottom scale (the one marked "Standing Wave, Vol

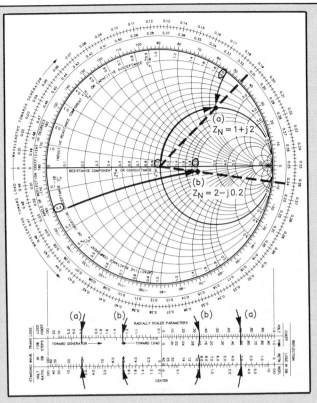

Fig H—Plotting normalized complex impedance (see text). Reflection terms are found for the "Radially Scaled Parameters" axes at the bottom of the chart.

Ratio"), we find a corresponding VSWR of about 5.8. Immediately above, on the scale marked "Standing Wave, in dB," we find that this corresponds to a 15-dB difference between peaks and nulls, when this particular load impedance is measured with a slotted line in a 50-ohm system.

Moving over to the scales on the right-hand side of the Chart, the top scale tells us that the corresponding "Refl. Coef, Vol" (Voltage Reflection Coefficient) is 0.70 while just below, we read a "Refl. Coef, Pwr." (Power Reflection Coefficient) of 0.49. Finally, the bottom two scales on the right-hand side confirm a Return Loss of about 3.2 dB, and a Reflection Loss of roughly 2.8 dB for our device under test. Now we could certainly have determined these values algebraically, given the complex impedance of the load and the characteristic impedance of the system, but the Smith Chart reduces complex arithmetic to simple distance measurement.

Now, try the same conversions for Point (b) in Fig H. Did you get a VSWR of 2.0 or 6 dB, a Voltage Reflection Coefficient of 0.34, Power Reflection Coefficient just under 0.11, 9.4 dB of Return Loss, and 0.53 dB of Mismatch Loss? If so, you're well on your way to mastering the Smith Chart.

Do you have the feeling we've left something out? You're right! Many of the reflection terms are vector quantities, and all we've discussed so far are their magnitudes. There are an infinite number of complex impedances which might share a particular Voltage Reflection Coefficient, for example, and we differentiate them by their reflection phase angles. A scale about the circumference of the Chart, highlighted in Fig H, indicates Phase Angle of Reflection Coefficient, in degrees. To read the phase angle for any normalized and plotted complex impedance, simply draw a straight line, or radial, from the center of the Smith Chart, through the impedance point, and out to this scale. In example (a), the phase angle of ρ comes to +45 degrees; for (b), the angle is −8 degrees, as indicated in Fig H.

Two more circular scales, Wavelengths Toward Generator and Wavelengths Toward Load, show how a complex impedance changes as we move along a transmission line. And two more Radially Scaled Parameters, Transmission Loss Coefficient and 1 dB Steps, relate to changes in measured reflections along lossy transmission lines. Their use is detailed elsewhere in this manual, and in the book cited in Note 3, probably the best treatment of Smith Chart use ever published.

The Smith Chart is a graphical transmission line calculator which allows us to plot any complex impedance or admittance, normalized to the characteristics of the system of interest. We can use it to convert between series and parallel circuit topology, to determine reflection terms, and to design networks to

Amplifier Design by Scalar Approximation

By H. Paul Shuch, N6TX
Copyright (C) 1987, Microcomm

Let's suppose you're planning to design and build a microwave amplifier around a transistor of known S-parameters. Unless you are blessed with an inordinate amount of available time and an unlimited supply of components, you will probably want to perform a few calculations before first you assail PC board with soldering iron. At the very least, it may be informative to determine in advance the gain available from your transistor, at the particular operating frequency and quiescent bias point which you have selected. Then too, there's the matter of stability. It's nice to know in advance whether the circuit you're building is going to end up oscillating ("If I had wanted an oscillator, I'd have designed an oscillator...") Fortunately, gain and stability prediction are readily achieved through S-parameter analysis.

Utilizing the full set of scattering parameters for your active device (that is, all four vectors at the frequency and bias point of interest), gain and stability prediction can be accomplished either by algebraic analysis, or through graphical calculation on Phillip H. Smith's ubiquitous Chart. The required procedures are detailed elsewhere in this book, and can be rather tedious.

At times a simple approximation of device performance will suffice, and this can be performed readily through scalar approximation (that is, through the analysis of the S-parameter magnitudes alone, independent of phase angles). Of course, like all approximations, the scalar analysis will introduce errors which some may find unacceptable. But the convenience of hand-calculator solutions, as opposed to vector algebra, makes scalar approximation a particularly enticing option where multiple analyses of various devices or bias points are required. Besides, as will be demonstrated in the example which follows, the results are sufficiently precise for most Amateur Radio applications.

The parameters of interest prior to building an amplifier include the device's Transducer Unilateral Gain (G_{tu}), Maximum Stable Gain (MSG), and Maximum Available Gain (MAG). Noise figure data is often a significant consideration as well. Unfortunately, I know of no method of predicting noise performance short of full vector analysis, and thus will confine this discussion to gain and stability approximations.

Transducer Unilateral Gain is simply a measure of the power gain, expressed in dB, which the active device will produce when it is terminated directly in the specified system characteristic impedance (that is, with no attempt to include impedance matching circuits at its input and output). Since obviously any impedance mismatch at the device's input and output will generate reflective losses, G_{tu} is a *worst case* specification, the *lowest* gain you should expect to see at your selected frequency and operating point.

You may recall that the conditions under which G_{tu} are specified are *precisely* those under which scattering parameters are measured. Thus G_{tu} would be expected to be closely related to S_{21}, forward voltage transmission coefficient (the scattering parameter for forward gain). Unfortunately, S_{21} is a vector voltage ratio, while we desire to express G_{tu} in dB. We can, however, convert the magnitude of S_{21} to G_{tu}, the way we always convert voltage ratios to dB: by squaring them (to get power ratio), taking their common logarithm, and multiplying by ten. Mathematically,

$$G_{tu} = 10 * \log_{10} |S_{21}|^2 \qquad \text{(Eq A)}$$

It is interesting to note that the average microwave active devices performs very much like a low-pass filter, with unilateral gain decreasing in a predictable manner with increasing frequency. A monotonic (1 pole) low pass filter has a gain slope above cutoff of −6 dB per octave (or −20 dB per decade), and G_{tu} for a typical microwave transistor can be expected to follow suit. In fact, an analysis of typical transistor data sheets indicates that for bipolar and field effect devices alike, the magnitude of S_{21} tends to vary inversely with frequency. Equation A indicates that this implies a 6-dB reduction in G_{tu} for each doubling of frequency, just what you would expect from a monotonic low pass filter.

In an actual circuit, however, the gain provided by a transistor will generally significantly exceed G_{tu}. This is because the typical circuit implementation generally contains impedance matching circuits to overcome the reflective losses at the input and output of the active device. Since S-parameters allow us to quantify input and output reflections, we can readily calculate the mismatch losses present at each port of the active device, and hence the additional gain which we can realize by eliminating such impedance discontinuities.

The scattering parameters corresponding to input and output voltage reflection coefficient are S_{11} and S_{22} respectively, and their magnitudes allow us to approximate the mismatch losses α_ρ (alpha subscript rho) suffered at each port. By using the magnitude of voltage reflection coefficients the corresponding reflection losses, in dB, can be readily determined on a Smith Chart. Alternatively, an algebraic solution lends itself readily to calculator analysis:

$$\alpha_\rho = -10 * \log_{10} (1 - \rho^2) \qquad \text{(Eq B)}$$

match complex impedances or admittances to a particular system. Computer software is today beginning to eclipse the Smith Chart in both resolution and popularity, but where a quick overview of impedance or admittance matching is required, the convenience of Smith Chart analysis is hard to beat.

Notes

[1]Cartesian Coordinates are named for Rene Descartes, the

Seventeenth Century French philosopher, scientist and mathematician who is credited with inventing analytic geometry. He is best known for the rather cryptic pronouncement *cogito ergo sum* ("I think, therefore I am.")

[2]Smith, Phillip H., "Transmission Line Calculator." *Electronics*, Vol 12 No. 1, Jan 1939, p 12.

[3]Smith, Phillip H., *Electronic Applications of the Smith Chart in Waveguide, Circuit and Component Analysis*. (c) 1969, McGraw-Hill, NY. 222 pp.

where α_ρ is the input or output reflection loss in dB, and ρ, the Greek letter rho, represents the magnitude of the input or output voltage reflection coefficient, S_{11} or S_{22}.

Since a properly designed matching circuit will be expected to eliminate all impedance mismatches (and hence all reflection losses), the achievable gain from an active device is the dB sum of its transducer unilateral gain and its input and output reflection losses. Algebraically,

$$MAG = G_{tu} + \alpha_\rho \text{ (in)} + \alpha_\rho \text{ (out)} \qquad \text{(Eq C)}$$

where MAG represents Maximum Available Gain, in dB, at that particular frequency and bias point.

But is that much gain really healthy? We have all experienced cases of amplifiers which oscillated because they were designed to produce too much gain. Oscillation is caused in part by an internal feedback path within the active device, which couples a portion of the output signal back into the input. This internal feedback path is described by the reverse voltage transmission coefficient S_{12}, the magnitude of which plays a role in stability analysis.

Maximum Stable Gain (MSG) is a measure of the greatest gain, in dB, which can be expected of a particular active device, without sacrificing unconditional stability. It is found by comparing the magnitudes of forward gain S_{21} and reverse gain S_{12}:

$$MSG = 10 * \log_{10}\left(|S_{21}| \, / \, |S_{12}|\right) \qquad \text{(Eq D)}$$

As long as the Maximum Available Gain does not exceed the Maximum Stable Gain, no internal oscillation path exists. (This does not mean, however, that the amplifier might not oscillate due to some *external* feedback path. Thus circuit layout is still important!)

As an example of how the above relationships might be applied, consider the scattering parameters of the popular Motorola MRF-901 bipolar junction transistor, at 1296 MHz, with V_{ce} of $+10$ Vdc and I_c of 10 mA:

$$S_{11} = 0.47 \, / \, +160° \qquad S_{21} = 3.1 \, / \, +63°$$

$$S_{22} = 0.43 \, / \, -40° \qquad S_{12} = 0.08 \, / \, +64°$$

For scalar analysis, we can ignore the phase angles of the above scattering parameter vectors, and deal with the magnitudes alone.

From Eq 1, we can determine transducer unilateral gain:

$$G_{tu} = 10 * \log_{10} (3.1)^2 = 9.8 \text{ dB}$$

Thus, if we employ no matching circuits whatever, merely applying 50-ohm microstriplines directly to the

input and output (base and collector, respectively), we can expect the MRF-901 to yield almost 10 dB of gain.

Eq 2 gives us the input and output reflection losses:

$$\alpha_\rho \text{ (in)} = -10 * \log_{10} (1 - 0.472) = 1.1 \text{ dB}$$

and

$$\alpha_\rho \text{ (out)} = -10 * \log_{10} (1 - 0.432) = 0.9 \text{ dB}$$

which suggests that properly matching the device will add about 2 dB additional gain to our amplifier circuit. From Eq 3, we now determine Maximum Available Gain:

$$\begin{aligned} MAG &= G_{tu} + \alpha_\rho \text{ (in)} + \alpha_\rho \text{ (out)} \\ &= 9.8 + 1.1 + 0.9 = 11.8 \text{ dB} \end{aligned}$$

which would certainly make for a nice amplifier.

Now for stability analysis, let's calculate Maximum Stable Gain from Eq 4:

$$MSG = 10 * \log_{10} (3.1 \, / \, 0.08) = 15.9 \text{ dB}$$

Well, the MRF-901 is certainly stable, and more than only marginally so. The Maximum Available Gain is less than the Maximum Stable Gain (a condition for stability), by roughly 4 dB. Though a change in S-parameters (perhaps caused by a change in temperature, or in bias point, or a variability in active device manufacturing) could vary the available gain, it probably wouldn't be by enough to exceed MSG. Which demonstrates why, at 1296 MHz, MRF-901 amplifiers seldom oscillate.

To determine the effectiveness of the above scalar approximation, consider the data for an MRF-901, generated by a full vector S-parameter analysis performed on a computer. G_{tu} and MSG agree almost precisely with the scalar approximation just performed, while MAG differs by a little more than a dB. The computer calculates K, the Rollet Stability Factor, at about 1.2, which indicates unconditional stability. Although our scalar approximation doesn't address K, our comparison of MSG to MAG led us to the same conclusion. The only thing our scalar method didn't provide that the vector analysis does is the determination of Z_{ms} and Z_{ml}, the source and load reflection coefficients for simultaneous conjugate match. These are certainly necessary to perform the required matching circuit design. Nonetheless, as a preliminary design step, scalar approximations alone will provide a valid indication of the type of performance to expect from a given microwave active device.

UHF/Microwave Oscillators

By Bill Troetschel, K6UQH

UHF/Microwave oscillator chains demand excellent crystal oscillator performance. For transmitter and receiver applications, the goals are:

1) Precise and stable operating frequency.
2) Low phase noise.
3) A minimum of spurious signals.

These goals will be examined in detail in the following sections.

OSCILLATOR BASICS

An oscillator is an amplifier circuit that uses an initial startup signal (noise) that is subsequently amplified. A portion of this amplified noise is returned to the input circuit and re-amplified. Circuit elements that make up the return (feedback) path vary among oscillator types, and can be made frequency selective.

Frequency components of the original noise signal are enhanced by the RF selectivity of the circuit elements and amplified until the circuit oscillates at its resonant frequency. For sustained and stable oscillation to occur, the amplified signal must be fed back to the input circuit with the proper phase and amplitude values.

For a crystal-controlled oscillator, the main element in the feedback path is the crystal itself. Other circuit elements serve to provide feedback energy of the proper amplitude and phase so that sustained and stable oscillation can occur. Since the crystal is the primary feedback element, the crystal characteristics have a profound effect on the performance of the oscillator. The crystal must be of high quality for microwave applications.

Other circuit elements cannot be ignored, as they affect oscillator characteristics, especially in terms of varying component impedances because of changes in temperature, humidity, aging effects, and so on.

Frequency Precision and Stability

The requirement for a precise and stable microwave frequency requires the use of crystals which are calibrated to at least six decimal places. This level of accuracy is necessary to provide accurate microwave LO injection frequencies. Further, the crystal must be used in an oscillator circuit that can be adjusted in terms of feedback phase, feedback amplitude, and the load impedance presented to the crystal.

To demonstrate the need for high-accuracy crystals, we will examine a 10-GHz system (using a crystal specified to six decimal places) with an IF of 144 MHz.

We start with a crystal frequency that will be multiplied by a factor of four (4), multiplied again by a factor of three (3), and then multiplied by a factor of nine (9) in an SRD multiplier, a total multiplication factor of 108. This will provide an LO injection frequency of 9856 MHz. Our required crystal frequency (to six decimal places) is

then 91.259259 MHz. There is a seventh uncalibrated digit which could range in value from zero to nine. (The above assumes it is 0.)

For this crystal, (108) (91.259259) = 9,855.999972 MHz —28 Hz low at 10 GHz. Let's try nine for the seventh digit: (108) (91.2592599) = 9,856.000069 MHz—or 69 Hz high at 10 GHz. Thus, the maximum uncorrected error at 10 GHz could range from 28 Hz low to 69 Hz high.

No quality crystal manufacturer would permit a value of nine for the seventh digit when calibrating a crystal to six decimal places. The most likely values would be four or five. In any case, the maximum required adjustment of the crystal frequency is 1/108th of 69 Hz at the overtone crystal frequency. This adjustment is almost negligible, and is well within the allowable crystal bandwidth adjustment range for crystal-controlled operation. This permits a precise 9856-MHz LO injection frequency with no frequency offsets.

For stability, the crystal-oscillator circuit should be lightly loaded and/or buffered. For low-level oscillator/multiplier chains, the load on the oscillator circuit is normally stable after tune-up, and buffer amplifiers are seldom required. If load variations occur during operation, however, a buffer amplifier may be necessary.

The dc power to the oscillator/multiplier/amplifier circuit should be well regulated, preferably by the use of "on-card" regulators such as a 7812 (12 V). Further, regulate the oscillator stage and the first doubler stage by using another regulator such as a 7808 (8 V). Using two regulators eliminates frequency variations because of voltage changes.

Oscillator components also affect oscillator stability. This means that good components are required, such as silver mica capacitors and carbon film resistors.

Temperature variations remain a major problem, especially when using large frequency multiplication factors. For home-station operation, a tight-fitting enclosure filled with cotton is adequate up to 10 GHz.

With this minimal thermal blanket, 10-GHz portable operation has posed no problems. Short-term thermal drift is on the order of a few Hz, and long-term drift, with normal temperature changes, is well within the IF passband of an SSB receiver. Installing the crystal in an oven only solves part of the problem, as external circuit component characteristics can vary widely as a function of temperature. A better solution is to thermally control the entire crystal oscillator/multiplier.

Phase Noise

Mathematically, phase noise is a complicated subject that will not be examined here. A more intuitive approach is used here.

Purely random noise (white noise) is a compilation of a large number of randomly occurring noise "energy spikes'' of various sizes and shapes, which generates a complex frequency/amplitude spectrum with a wide bandwidth. Frequency components of these noise spikes can be identical, but they will exist with random phase (time) relationships. See Fig 1.

Oscillator feedback circuits are frequency selective, and frequency components of these noise spikes that match the feedback circuit resonances are enhanced and amplified. Since there are a lot of randomly occurring energy spikes, the problem is that although the energy noise (within the circuit and crystal bandwidth) exists at nearly the same frequency, the phase (time) distribution of energy is totally random.

These frequency distributions will be amplified accordingly. The output from the oscillator will now consist of the energy at the crystal frequency, plus the random phase noise within a bandwidth determined by the circuit Q.

Fig 2A illustrates the effect of a high-Q crystal bandwidth and a high-Q circuit bandwidth and the resultant output spectrum of energy. This is typical of the output of a low-phase-noise oscillator circuit.

Fig 2B illustrates the effect of a lower-Q crystal bandwidth and a low-Q circuit bandwidth and the resultant output spectrum of energy. This is typical of the output of a high-phase-noise oscillator circuit. In oscillator circuits of this type, the crystal is usually connected from the base of the transistor to ground (a heavily loaded crystal), where the base impedance is quite low. If this type of oscillator circuit is used for a transmitter, you can waste a considerable amount of power in simply transmitting noise.

Spurious Signals

Spurious signals from a crystal oscillator can generally be traced to unwanted vibration modes of the crystal itself. These unwanted crystal vibration modes can be controlled

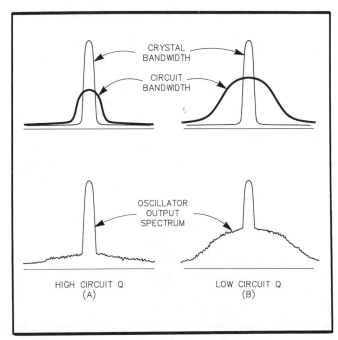

Fig 2—Depiction of the effects of high-Q (A) and low-Q (B) circuits on oscillator spectral output.

to some degree during the manufacturing process by doping and/or loading the crystal to suppress unwanted modes. Quality crystal manufacturers make every attempt to minimize these spurious oscillation modes, but in the end you get what you pay for, as the effort is time consuming and increases the cost of the crystal. The spurious signals that are produced by these unwanted vibration modes can usually be minimized by operating the crystal at a minimum required feedback level so the main ''calibrated mode'' is all that is excited.

Turn-Off/Turn-On Characteristics

Sometimes, an oscillator circuit can be perplexing. Even though it's tuned up and running smoothly—the next time you turn it on—nothing happens. Circuit supply voltages are normal, so what is the problem? A sluggish crystal and/or a heavily loaded oscillator circuit can be the culprit, but most of the time the problem has another cause. Some experimenters try to get away with using a crystal that's calibrated only to two or three decimal places. And, rather than accepting an offset at the operating frequency (because of the LO error), they try to ''rubber'' the crystal. For overtone crystals, this generally leads to completely unstable operation and poor turn-off and turn-on characteristics. The required amount of ''tuning'' may exceed the point that represents the proper phase and amplitude relationship for proper crystal operation.

As described previously, the best solution is to use a crystal that is calibrated to at least six decimal places. This necessitates only a small adjustment of the crystal frequency.

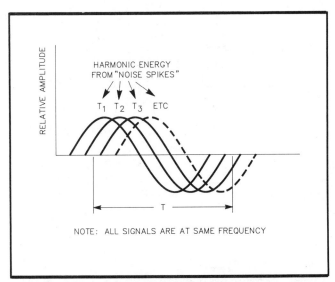

Fig 1—Phase relationship of multiple energy sources as observed in oscillator feedback circuits.

THE LOCAL OSCILLATOR CHAIN

Fig 3A shows a typical local oscillator chain for microwave applications. It consists of a crystal oscillator followed by frequency multipliers, filters and amplifiers. The length of the chain is determined by the multiplication factor needed to achieve the desired injection frequency. This is greatly affected by the frequency of the first crystal oscillator.

Fig 3B shows an alternate method of attaining LO injection using a diode multiplier module. Direct multiplication using a step-recovery diode is used to generate the required LO frequency.

The circuit shown in Fig 4 is recommended for use from 432 MHz to 10 GHz.[1] The crystal and circuit Q is high, thus reducing phase noise considerably. This circuit is occasionally seen with an RF choke wound on a low-value resistor across the crystal (which is intended to suppress various frequency resonance modes of the crystal). These spurious modes (discussed previously) are generally excited because of too much feedback to the crystal. If proper care is taken to ensure that the feedback amplitude is just sufficient to excite the main calibrated mode, the choke is unnecessary.

The crystal used in this oscillator is series-resonant, and is specified to six decimal places for the microwave frequency of interest.[2]

Fig 5 shows the complete schematic diagram for the recommended crystal-oscillator circuit, two doubler stages, and a class-C amplifier that can be used to generate frequencies in the 300- to 400-MHz range. Referring to Fig 5, you can see that a 3-dB (50-ohm) pad is used to isolate the crystal oscillator from the first doubler stage. Capacitive impedance matching is used between the doubler stages and the final class-C amplifier stage. The tuning

capacitors are mica trimmers that have been modified by removing the metal washers from the adjusting screws, and replacing them with insulating washers. The matching capacitors are miniature trimmers. This permits adjustment with a minimum of hand-capacitance effects. Note the use of silver-mica button feed-through capacitors for the second doubler, the class-C stage and the collector coil of the oscillator.

The final class-C amplifier is "turned on" by the second multiplier output signal. Other than the requirement for tuning, series-resonant overtone crystals from 70 to

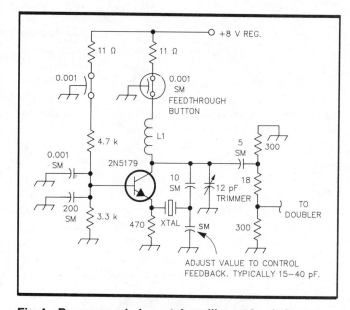

Fig 4—Recommended crystal oscillator circuit for use between 432 MHz and 10 GHz. See text for details.

L1—6½ turns no. 24 on no. 10-32 threaded Teflon form.

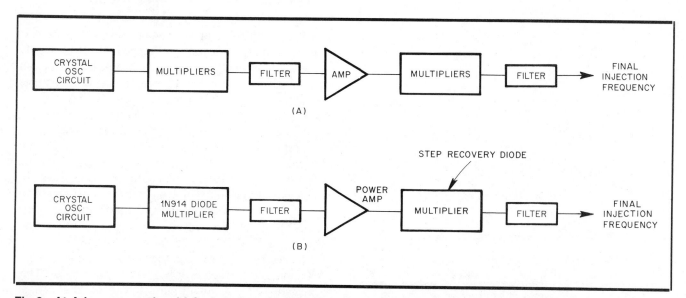

Fig 3—At A is a conventional LO chain for microwave applications. At B is a directly multiplied LO chain for microwave applications using an SRD multiplier.

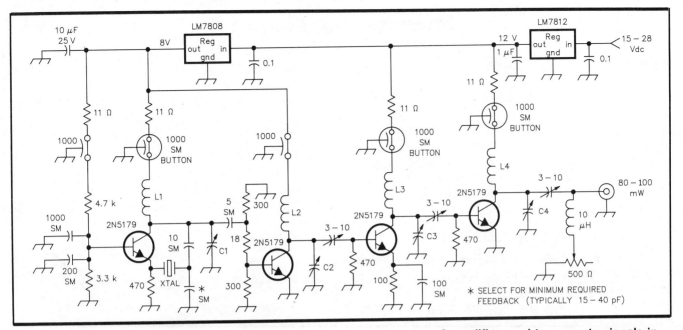

Fig 5—Recommended crystal oscillator circuit, doubler stages and a class-C amplifier used to generate signals in the 300- to 400-MHz range. See text for details.

L1—6-1/2 turns no. 24 on no. 10-32 Teflon screw.
L2—6 turns no. 22, close-wound on 1/8-inch-ID form.
L3,L4—1 turn no. 22, double-spaced on 1/8-inch-ID form.

C1—0-12 pF Johanson trimmer.
C2,C3,C4—1.5-20 pF trimmer. (ARCO 402).
Note: Circuit values are for a crystal frequency of approximately 95 MHz.

110 MHz can be used in this circuit. The transistors are 2N5179s, which feature an isolated collector that allows the case to be grounded by the fourth lead wire.

The output of the class-C amplifier is designed to capacitively match a coaxial line which goes to a 1N914 diode multiplier mounted in an external trough line. The 1N914 diode bias is adjusted from the osc/mult/amp unit by the 500-Ω potentiometer shown in the schematic.

A modification to reduce the length of the oscillator chain for higher microwave frequencies (10 GHz) is shown in Fig 6. The modification increases the output from the basic osc/mult/amp to approximately 200 mW. This drives a follow-on diode multiplier hard enough to achieve $(1/n)^2$ performance. At this drive level, the 500-Ω potentiometer shown in Fig 5 may not be required. The modification does require the addition of another 8-V regulator, replacing the 2N5179 with an MRF-571 and a slight retuning of the amplifier stage. This modification can also be made for lower-frequency applications to reduce your parts count.

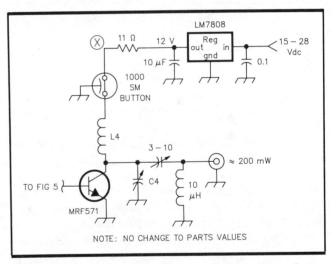

Fig 6—High-power output stage for the amplifier shown in Fig 5. See text for details.

[1]Lane, M., "Transistor Crystal Oscillators to Cover the Frequency Range from 1 kHz to 100 MHz." (Australian Post Office Research Laboratories, Report 6513).

[2]Croven Crystals Limited, 500 Beech St, Whitby, Ontario, Canada, tel 416-668-3324. Also available from Melvin Sales Inc, PO Box 5283, San Mateo, CA 94402, tel 415-349-7444.

Microwave Filters

By Bill Troetschel, K6UQH

The *ARRL Handbook* has extensive information on filters used at lower frequencies. We will not cover that information in this discussion. Our goal here is to describe the characteristics of various types of filters that have application at microwave frequencies, and to discuss some of the practical factors associated with various filter types. We will also provide an experimental design example for a 1296-MHz multielement interdigital filter.

GENERAL CONSIDERATIONS

There are three basic types of filters used extensively at UHF/microwave frequencies: low pass, band pass (narrow and wide), and high pass.

The methods used to obtain these features can be characterized as:

1) Low- and high-pass filters made from pi networks and/or L-pads (generally implemented with microstripline).

2) Narrow band-pass filters made from quarter- or half-wavelength stubs, coaxial cavities, trough lines or waveguide sections.

3) Wide band-pass filters that use interdigital configurations.

Some of these filter configurations have special features, such as the ability to be tuned or adjusted to provide a proper impedance match to the input and/or output lines. Selection of the proper filter for your requirements should be made carefully and consider several factors:

1) Single-frequency applications—where your interest is in developing a single, fixed-frequency filter for use in oscillator chains, or for spot-frequency operation, such as a repeater receiver/transmitter. This category also applies to the case of having to reject a high-power signal outside the ham bands, such as a radar or a nearby satellite microwave transmitter, which can desensitize your receiver and could cause severe cross-modulation products on received signals.

2) High-density RF areas where there are literally thousands of signals on the air. This situation can create a need for effective band-pass filtering.

3) To fulfill the requirement that amateur transmitters and receivers do not interfere with other services. This is generally accomplished by making sure you do not radiate the LO signal from your receive mixer, or your LO and image sideband signals from your transmit mixer circuit.

Fig 1 shows a typical microwave pi network (in microstripline). Note that one or more of the shunt capacitance elements could be a discrete tuning capacitor for adjustment.

The resonant lines and cavities that are used for filters are normally designed to operate at the lowest "mode"

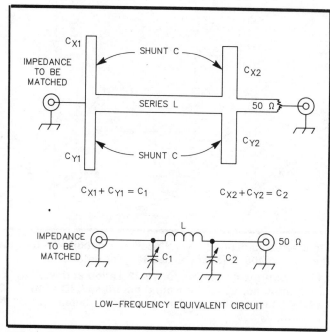

Fig 1—Representation of a microwave microstripline pi network.

that is practical (a quarter wavelength or a half wavelength). This establishes the "structure" of the electric and magnetic fields on or in the filter. Other resonant modes are possible with different electric and magnetic field structures, but are seldom used.

Narrowband Filters

Figs 2A and 2B show two commonly used filters for narrow-bandwidth applications. By looking at these filters as coaxial sections, the outside diameter of the inner conductor (d), and the inside diameter of the outer conductor (D), are normally chosen to provide a coaxial impedance between 50 and 100 ohms. Optimum Q is obtained at a coaxial cavity impedance of approximately 77 ohms. To calculate the coaxial cavity impedance use

$$Z_0 = 138 \log \frac{D}{d}$$

The filter shown in Fig 2A is a coaxial filter with a center-conductor length which is less than a quarter wavelength, typically 15% less, to permit tuning by a capacitive disc. The voltage field in a filter of this type is radial from the center conductor to the filter walls, and varies from zero intensity at the bottom of the filter to maximum intensity at the capacitively tuned top. The magnetic field is perpendicular to the electric field and

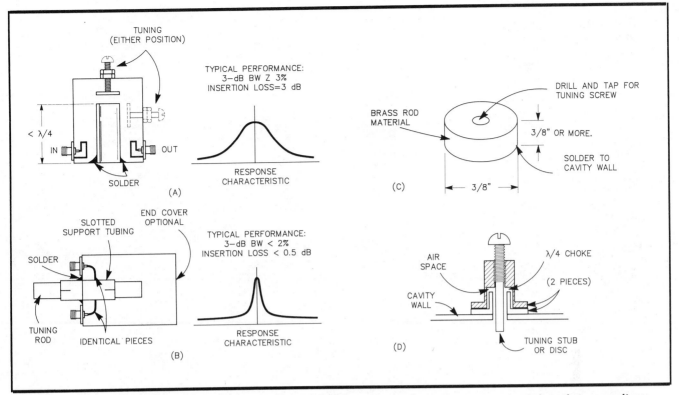

Fig 2—At A is a coaxial filter with a center-conductor length that is less than a quarter wavelength to permit tuning. A soldered brass rod (C) can eliminate some of the tuning instabilities of the tuning screws shown at A. At D is an RF-choke mounting arrangement that can also reduce tuning-screw instabilities. B shows an easier-to-build version of the filter shown at A.

varies from maximum intensity at the bottom of the filter to zero intensity at the top. Magnetic-field link coupling is shown at the bottom. Voltage-field coupling by means of probes could, however, be used at the top of the filter.

This type of filter has several drawbacks. The determination of the parameters of a link or probe at microwave frequencies is not very precise. They are generally determined experimentally. The resulting links and the degree of coupling generally cause the filter to exhibit lower Q (broader bandwidth), and to have a greater insertion loss than other methods of construction. In addition, the tuning discs are normally supported by a single (soldered) nut and a locking nut, which can cause erratic tuning because of the few screw threads available. The use of a brass standoff, which is drilled and tapped for the tuning screw to improve the number of contact threads, in conjunction with a nylon locking nut can improve this tendency considerably. See Fig 2C.

At higher microwave frequencies, the tuning screw can be mounted in an RF-choke mounting (similar to a waveguide choke flange), effectively removing the screw thread contacts from the RF circuit. See Fig 2D.

The filter shown in Fig 2B has similar electrical characteristics. This filter is easier to build and has a higher Q and lower insertion loss than the filter in Fig 2A. Tuning is much smoother because the slotted tubing provides good

mechanical support and electrical contact. Tuning is accomplished by varying the length of the center (adjustable) tubing.

The length of the center rod above the bottom of this filter will be very close to the free-space quarter wavelength of the frequency for which it is adjusted. The tubing is thin-wall, telescoping brass tubing, available at most hobby shops.

This filter uses a direct connection to the center conductor. A rule of thumb is to connect to the center conductor at a height above ground which is approximately 1/15 of the wavelength at the operating frequency. This is a narrow-bandwidth filter and has a low insertion loss, typically less than 0.5 dB.

Figs 3A and 3B show two versions of a high-Q filter that provide the ability to match into a given line impedance, (nominally 50 ohms). This type of filter may be constructed as either a trough-line or a coaxial-cavity filter. Coaxial-cavity filter impedance can be calculated as described previously, while trough-line impedance can be approximated by using:

$$Z_0 = \left(138 \log \frac{D}{d}\right) + 3.54$$

Fig 3A is a quarter-wavelength version using a coaxial cavity, while Fig 3B is a grounded half-wavelength version

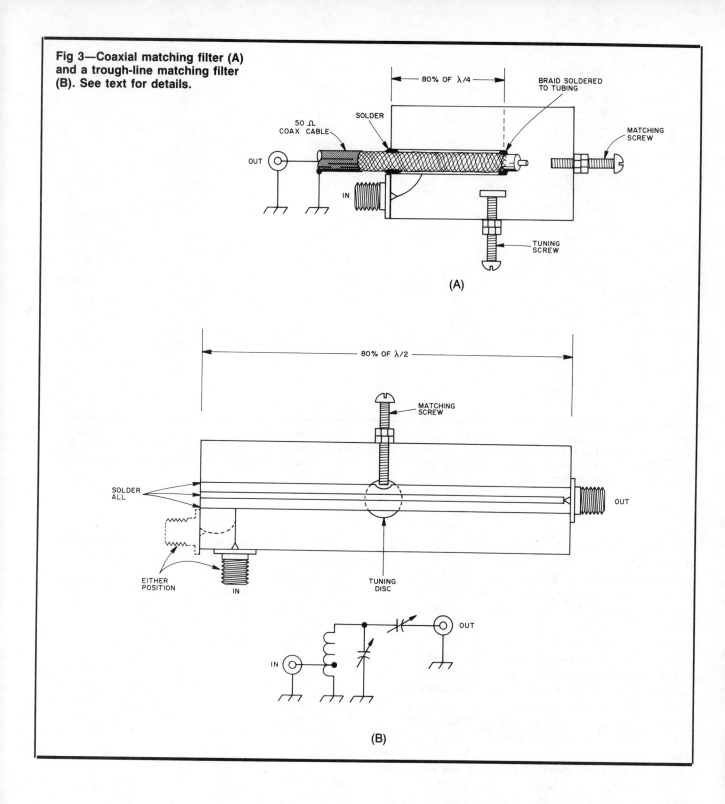

Fig 3—Coaxial matching filter (A) and a trough-line matching filter (B). See text for details.

using a trough-line. For the quarter-wavelength version, the output line can be coaxial cable as shown, with the braid soldered to the center tube, or constructed with a type-N fitting and a center rod. For this case, the outer diameter of the inner rod (d) and the inner diameter of the outer rod (D) should be chosen to exhibit the desired characteristic load impedance, nominally 50 ohms. Tuning for either version is accomplished by the disc capacitor, while matching is accomplished by the screw-probe that "looks" at the center line and represents a small capacitor.

These adjustments are interactive, but easy to accomplish. Simply adjust them for maximum power transfer to the load.

Band-pass Filters

Figs 4A and 4B show two methods that have been used to obtain narrow, band-pass coupled filters at microwave frequencies. They may be implemented as copper rods or tubing, or flat copper strips above a ground plane, and are generally grounded half-wavelength lines. See Fig 4A.

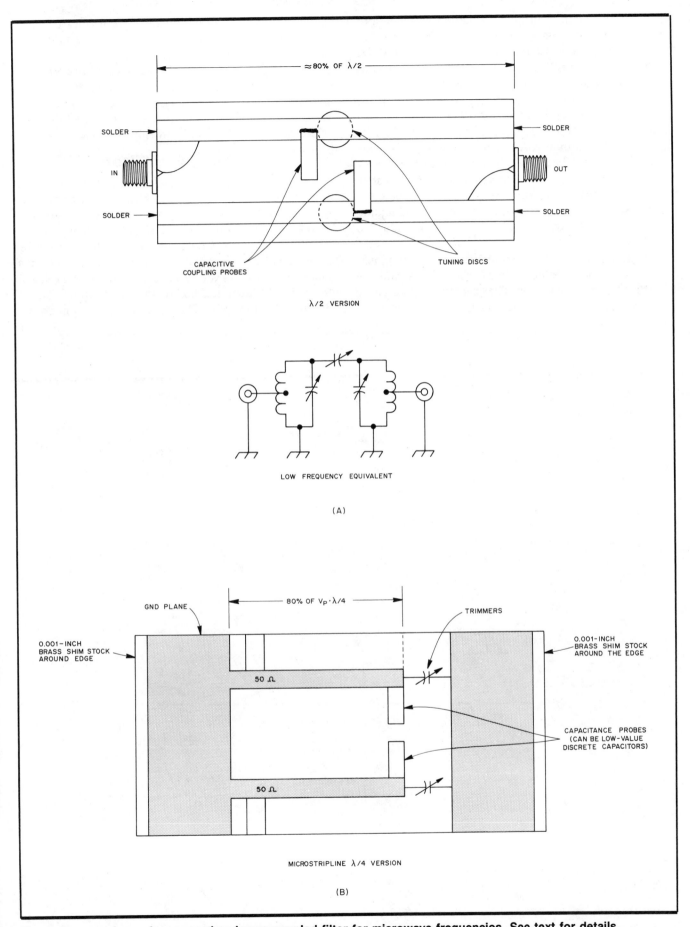

Fig 4—Two versions of a narrow band-pass-coupled filter for microwave frequencies. See text for details.

They can also be implemented as quarter-wavelength or half-wavelength lines using microstripline. See Fig 4B. The degree of coupling is determined by the position and size of the capacitive probes soldered to the lines. The low-frequency equivalent circuit is also shown.

The key to using filters of this type is to keep the resonant lines well separated so that the degree of coupling is determined by the capacitive probes, rather than by inadvertent line coupling. A rule of thumb for lines made from tubing would be to keep them separated by approximately three diameters; for microstriplines, approximately three line-widths apart. The resonant lines can be completely isolated as long as you can control the coupling between the lines by capacitance probes or inductive coupling.

Figs 5A and 5B show two methods of coupling isolated lines made of tubing. Fig 5A shows a method for inductive (aperture) coupling. The aperture height is equal to the base for critical coupling. The height of the aperture is typically 1/15 of a wavelength at the design frequency. The degree of coupling can be controlled by the adjustment screw as shown in the insert.

Fig 5B shows a typical method of capacitive coupling. A sweep-frequency generator can be used to tune these narrow band-pass filters and to set the degree of coupling (normally slightly over-coupled) to establish the 3-dB bandwidth and the desired in-band ripple.

Waveguide Filters

A useful "utility" waveguide filter is shown in Fig 6A. It uses two inductive partitions which are tuned by capacitive screws to couple in and out of the waveguide half-wavelength cavity. This cavity is slightly less (approximately 10%) than a waveguide half wavelength at the desired frequency, to accommodate a tuning screw. The two matching screws, located a waveguide quarter wavelength from the SMA connectors, are matching screws. The inductive partitions should be thin brass to perform proper-

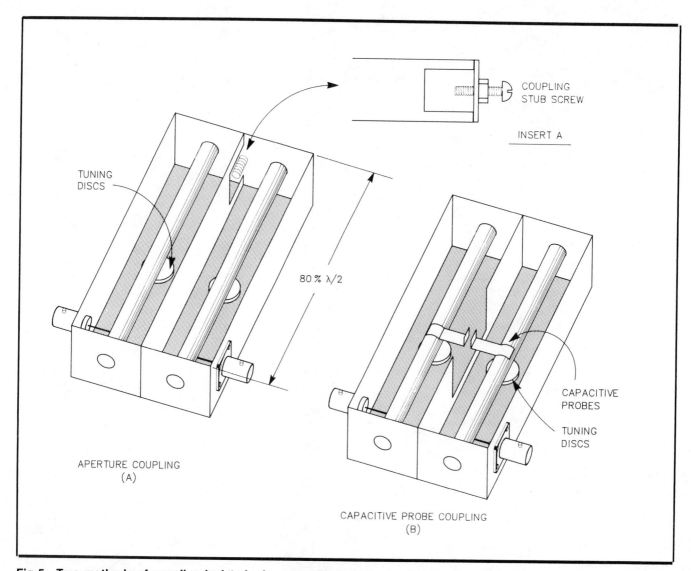

COUPLING STUB SCREW

INSERT A

TUNING DISCS

80 % λ/2

APERTURE COUPLING
(A)

CAPACITIVE PROBES

TUNING DISCS

CAPACITIVE PROBE COUPLING
(B)

Fig 5—Two methods of coupling isolated microwave filter elements. See text for details.

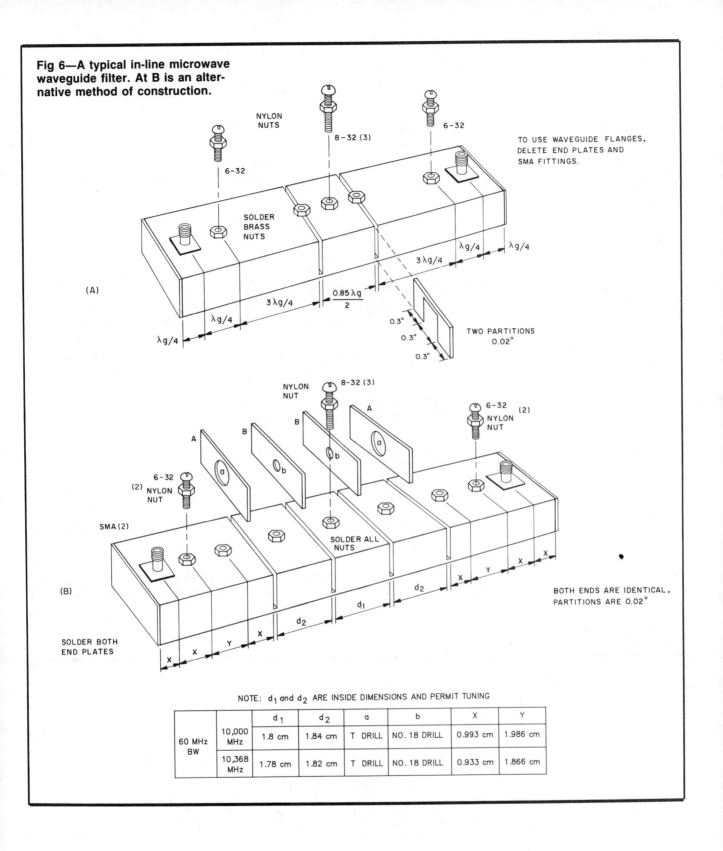

Fig 6—A typical in-line microwave waveguide filter. At B is an alternative method of construction.

NOTE: d_1 and d_2 ARE INSIDE DIMENSIONS AND PERMIT TUNING

60 MHz BW		d_1	d_2	a	b	X	Y
	10,000 MHz	1.8 cm	1.84 cm	T DRILL	NO. 18 DRILL	0.993 cm	1.986 cm
	10,368 MHz	1.78 cm	1.82 cm	T DRILL	NO. 18 DRILL	0.933 cm	1.866 cm

ly, typically 0.020 inch. If you cut the slots in the waveguide for the partition with an X-acto® saw blade rather than a hacksaw blade, you can use thinner brass. X-acto also makes a small aluminum mitre box for use with its saw blades that simplifies the cutting of slots in the waveguide. The dimensions shown will provide easy adjustment. Be sure to frequency-sweep the filter for tune-up, or pre-tune the filter to the desired frequency. This is a narrow-bandwidth filter (typically 2% bandwidth).

An excellent waveguide band-pass filter for 10 GHz was developed by G3JVL, and is shown in Fig 6B as modified by this author. This filter has an insertion loss of approximately 0.5 dB, and an excellent band-pass characteristic. The tabular data shows the dimensions that were used for the filter for 10000 MHz and 10368 MHz. The filter offers a band-pass of approximately 60 MHz (less than 1%) at either frequency and is ideal for eliminating LO and undesired sideband energy. When used in an SSB system with an IF of 144 MHz, the only signal transmitted or received is the desired sideband signal. It is an easy filter to construct with simple hand tools. When you assemble the filter, work from the inner partitions to the outer partitions, which will maximize your ability to check the solder seams.

Note in Figs 6A and 6B that either filter has the option of using coaxial connectors or waveguide flanges. When using coaxial connectors, solder end-plates on the waveguide ends a waveguide quarter wavelength from the pick-up probes. An SMA connector is recommended, but type-N connectors may be used by filing one flange on the connector to accommodate the matching screw nylon lock-nut.

The Interdigital Filter

A popular band-pass filter is the interdigital filter. Different physical versions of this type of filter offer a wide range of capabilities. The filter consists of rods or tubing mounted in a flat plane, in an interdigital configuration. The input and output rods are not normally considered as active elements (poles) as their function is to provide an impedance match from the active elements to the outside world.

Few active elements (typically one pole) represent limited capability, but easy reproducibility. With a single active element (pole), this type of filter does not outperform some of the filters already discussed. When several active elements are used, however, this type of filter offers superior performance.

Mechanically, multielement versions of this type of filter are reasonably easy to construct, and filter performance is very good, as long as the dimensions are closely followed. This type of filter is analytically quite complicated, and multiple-element filters of this type are either computer designed or graphically designed.

Because of construction accuracy errors such as the use of "nearest-size" diameters for the active elements and the problem of estimating the fringing capacitance required to resonate the rods, it is necessary to tune multielement interdigital filters for optimum performance.

If you do not have access to a lathe, many small machine shops will turn down brass or copper rod stock to your dimensions at a minimal cost, especially if you do your own drilling and tapping. A recommended alternative is the use of appropriate sizes of telescoping thin-wall brass tubing that is sold in hobby shops. Use of this type of construction permits much easier tuning of the filter and eliminates problems associated with solid rods and tuning screws. By using the appropriate telescoping sizes that are properly "slotted" for a tight fit, you eliminate tuning screws and provide smooth tune-up and stable operation.

To optimize filter performance, tune-up of a multielement interdigital filter is best done by using a sweep-frequency generator and an oscilloscope. It is the fastest and most accurate method. A less accurate and more tedious method is to use a tunable signal generator and a detector.

For multielement filters, the center elements have the most effect on "centering" the passband around the desired frequency. The outer elements have the greatest effect on the overall shape of the response curve and the insertion loss of the filter. If you quickly sweep (tune) the signal generator and observe the detector output, you can visualize the shape of the response curve, providing the signal generator output is relatively constant. They are all

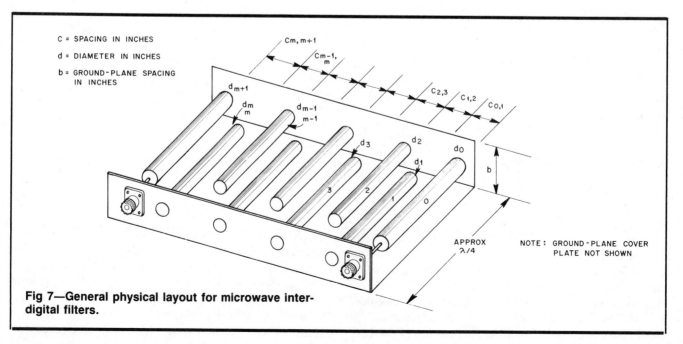

Fig 7—General physical layout for microwave interdigital filters.

interactive adjustments, so a lot of patience is required when using a point-by-point tuning method.

Interdigital filters come in various configurations which determine their fundamental filter characteristics. Perhaps the interdigital filter of most interest for amateur use is the configuration consisting of round elements of various diameters and variable spacing that produces a Butterworth band-pass response.

Fig 7 shows the general physical layout for a filter of this type, and the dimensional symbols used. The critical dimensions are rod or tubing diameter (d), spacing (c), and the ground-plane spacing dimension (b). The length of the rods is typically 85% to 90% of a quarter wavelength to permit tuning. If telescoping tubing is used, the outer tubing length can be typically 85%; the adjustable tubing will provide the correct length.

Graphical design curve "pairs" for d/b ratios (diameter), and c/b ratios (spacing), are provided in Fig 8 for interdigital filters with three to eight active elements.

These graphs were derived from computer programs based on the original equations.[1,2] By reading the graphs carefully and using the diameters and spacings as derived, actual filter performance v theoretical filter performance is in excellent agreement, if you have access to equipment for tuning the filter properly.

1296-MHz DESIGN TUTORIAL

Let's use the graphs in Fig 8 to design a 5-active-element filter for 1296 MHz. This is an experimental design, so we can take some "liberties" with the dimensions —just to see what happens. Assume we want a 40-MHz, 3-dB bandwidth to cover 1260 to 1300 MHz. Because 1280 MHz is the center of this range, we will use that value as the design center. This is $(40/1280) \times 100 = 3.1\%$ bandwidth. This value is the vertical ordinate to be used on the graphs.

We will use nearest-size element diameters and control the other dimensions to approximately 1/100th of an inch. From the graphs for the five-active-element filter, note that the three center elements are essentially the same diameter. We will arbitrarily choose their diameter to be ¼ inch. Note carefully that dimension (b) is a key dimension. The element diameter and spacing values from the graphs are the (d/b) and the (c/b) ratios, where d is the element diameter and c is the element spacing.

If (b) is chosen to have a value of one (1), you can read the values from the graphs directly; you then, however, have the problem of getting all the rod or tubing diameters to the specified values. Since three of the five active elements have the same diameter, and we have chosen these values to be ¼-inch diameter, we will use telescoping tubing. Working backwards, (b) turns out to be 0.651 inch: (from the graph) the (d/b) ratio = 0.384 inch, and (d/b) = (0.25 / b) = 0.384 inch, so b = (0.25 / 0.384) = 0.651 inch.

For the first and fifth active element: (from the graph)

(d/b) = 0.365 and (d) = (0.365) (0.651) = 0.238 inch. Since there are no machine shops in our town, we will again use ¼-inch element diameters so all five active elements are now ¼ inch in diameter, made from telescoping tubing.

For the input and output coupling elements: (from the graph) (d/b) = 0.524 and (d) = (0.524) (0.651) = 0.341 inch. Hobby-shop tubing is available in 11/32-inch-OD sizes (0.3438 inch), so we will also use 11/32-inch-diameter tubing for the input and output elements.

Using the same procedure for the spacing (c/b ratios):
d0 to d1, and d5 to d6 = 0.46 inch.
d1 to d3, and d4 to d5 = 0.85 inch.
d2 to d3, and d3 to d4 = 0.98 inch.

A quarter-wavelength element at 1280 MHz would normally be 2.3 inches long, but to allow for tuning you should use at least 85% of that length, which is approximately 1.95 inches. Remember, this length is the length within the filter. Allow at least an extra quarter of an inch to extend beyond the bottom of the filter partition to permit slotting of the tubing. The tubing length in the filter is basically non-critical for telescoping tubing, but it should be as long as feasible to permit tuning and to minimize the effect of element-diameter variations. Also, since we are using tubing, all of the outer tubing for the elements is simply soldered in place. Be sure to slot both ends of the tubing before you solder it in place. Use a spacer block under the lines to make sure they all lie in the same plane, and check visually for vertical symmetry when soldering.

Fig 9 shows the filter layout with dimensions. Fig 10A shows a typical filter response prior to tuning. Fig 10B shows the filter response after tune-up. It shows a 3-dB bandwidth of approximately 34 MHz instead of the anticipated 40 MHz. The less-than-1-dB insertion loss bandwidth is approximately 30 MHz from 1270 to 1300 MHz, and can be easily tuned for 1265 to 1296 MHz.

Considering we used graphical methods, and imprecise element diameters, the filter response is extremely good. The resultant (although slightly less than optimum) bandwidth is quite usable. By using these graphs and following the dimensions closely, you can design multi-element bandpass filters with approximately 1-to-10% bandwidths that are tailored to your requirements.

2304-MHz DESIGN

By following a similar approach, an effective filter for 2304-MHz can be designed. Construction details and dimensions for a 5-active-element filter are shown in Fig 11. Other than the difference in frequency, the performance of this filter is similar to the 1296-MHz design.

Notes

[1]Cristal, E. G., "Coupled Circular Cylindrical Rods Between Parallel Ground Planes," *IRE Transactions*, *MTT-13*, July 1964.
[2]Metcalf, W. S., "Graphs Speed Design of Interdigital Filters," *Microwaves*, Feb 1967.

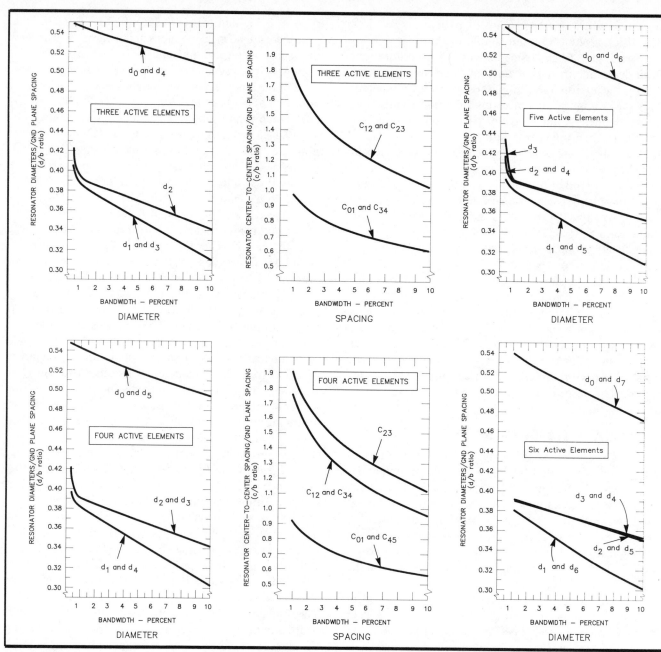

Fig 8—Graphical design curve "pairs" showing d/b and c/b ratios for designing interdigital filters with three to eight active elements. See text for details.

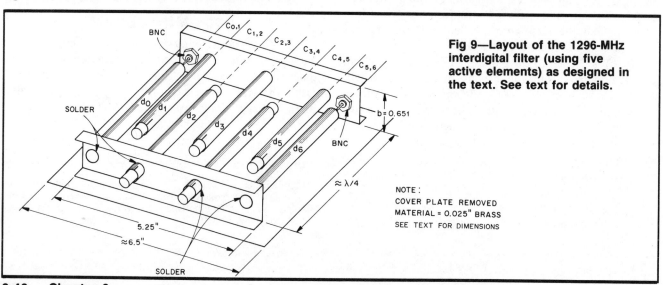

Fig 9—Layout of the 1296-MHz interdigital filter (using five active elements) as designed in the text. See text for details.

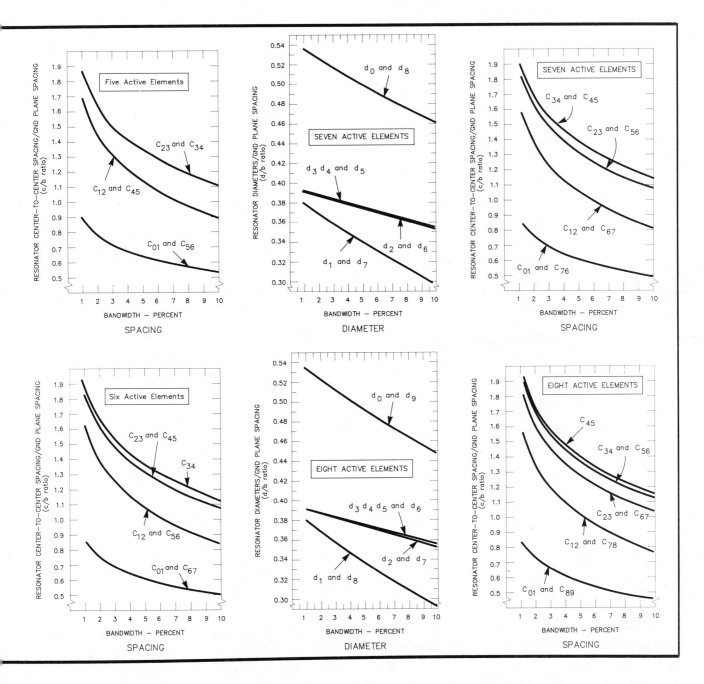

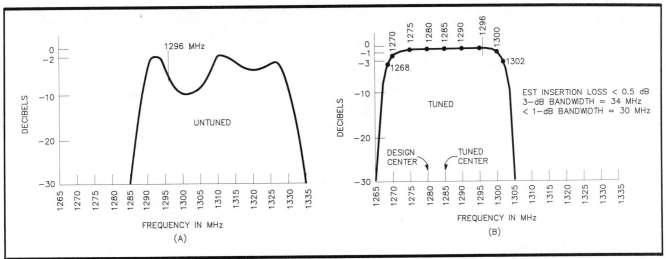

Fig 10—Frequency response of the interdigital filter shown in Fig 9 before (A) and after tune-up (B).

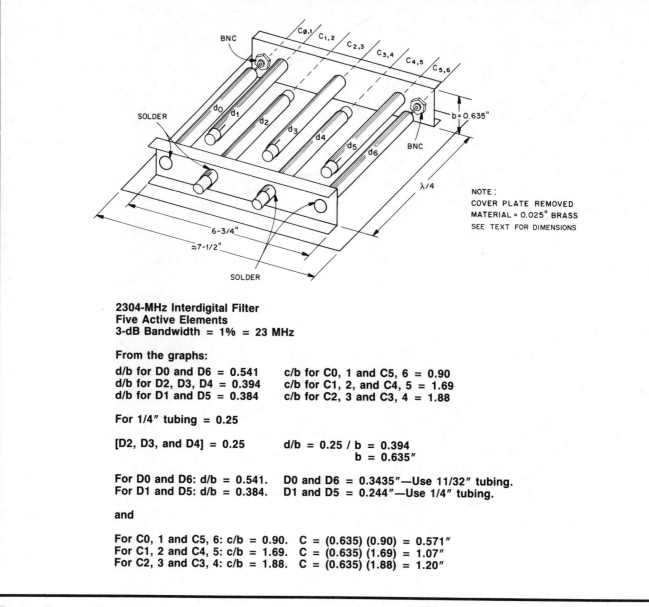

2304-MHz Interdigital Filter
Five Active Elements
3-dB Bandwidth = 1% = 23 MHz

From the graphs:

d/b for D0 and D6 = 0.541   c/b for C0, 1 and C5, 6 = 0.90
d/b for D2, D3, D4 = 0.394   c/b for C1, 2, and C4, 5 = 1.69
d/b for D1 and D5 = 0.384   c/b for C2, 3 and C3, 4 = 1.88

For 1/4" tubing = 0.25

[D2, D3, and D4] = 0.25   d/b = 0.25 / b = 0.394
                                     b = 0.635"

For D0 and D6: d/b = 0.541.   D0 and D6 = 0.3435"—Use 11/32" tubing.
For D1 and D5: d/b = 0.384.   D1 and D5 = 0.244"—Use 1/4" tubing.

and

For C0, 1 and C5, 6: c/b = 0.90.   C = (0.635) (0.90) = 0.571"
For C1, 2 and C4, 5: c/b = 1.69.   C = (0.635) (1.69) = 1.07"
For C2, 3 and C3, 4: c/b = 1.88.   C = (0.635) (1.88) = 1.20"

Fig 11—Construction details for a 5-active-element 2304-MHz interdigital filter.

UHF/Microwave Mixers

By Bill Troetschel, K6UQH

A mixer is an important circuit element in amateur UHF/microwave receivers and transmitters. In this section we will examine diode mixers that are used at UHF and microwave frequencies. We will try to provide enough information so you can decide which microwave mixer type is the best for your applications. We will not discuss mixer terms and definitions (except where pertinent to microwave applications), as the *ARRL Handbook* provides an excellent practical discussion of general mixer theory, and is recommended reading.

MIXER OPERATION

The only element in a mixer that permits us to "mix" signals is the diode. It is the only element that provides the nonlinear and switching characteristics that enable us to convert energy at one frequency into energy at another frequency. Signal mixing can only be accomplished by devices that are nonlinear or time variant (that is, their characteristics change as a function of time). Under RF conditions, the diode also acts as a switch that is either open or closed as a function of the amplitude and polarity of the RF signal. The conversion of energy from one frequency to another can be utilized to "down-convert" a microwave frequency to a lower IF that can be easily amplified (a receive mixer). Conversely, a lower-frequency signal can be "up-converted" to the microwave region (a transmit mixer).

Other than the direction in frequency of the energy transfer, there are few differences in requirements between receive and transmit mixers. For example, the dynamic range required for a receive mixer that is preceded by high-gain, low-noise preamp is about the same value required for a transmit mixer to provide a useful, undistorted output signal. Figs 1A and 1B show typical configurations for

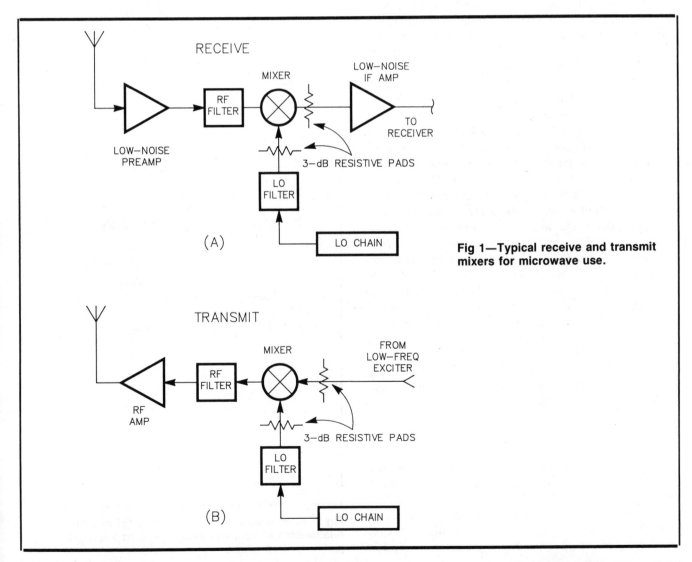

Fig 1—Typical receive and transmit mixers for microwave use.

receive and transmit mixers and their associated components.

MIXER CHARACTERISTICS

The two primary signals in a mixer are the local oscillator and the signal to be either up- or down-converted. In any mixer circuit (receive or transmit), the strongest signal must be the local oscillator signal. The LO signal determines the "switching rate" of the diodes and how far it swings on the diode-transfer curve. These two primary signals cause current flow through the diode which is expressed as a mathematical power series expansion of the exponential characteristic of the diode. The mathematical terms of this power series expansion represent the various and numerous outputs of the mixer. Also, since the diode is acting like a switch at the LO frequency, there is a spectral amplitude distribution of energy which is found by using Fourier analysis.

For a transmit mixer, it is recommended that the power level of the LO signal be at least 10 dB greater than the power level of the low-frequency signal to be up-converted. This is done to maintain a good dynamic range and to minimize the energy levels of unwanted mixer products.

For receive mixers, the LO/RF power ratio is seldom an issue. If you are bothered by strong local signals that appear to be transmitting on multiple frequencies, or if you can hear another signal along with a signal you are listening to, read carefully the discussion of high-level doubly balanced mixers. These problems could be caused by the lack of sufficient dynamic range in your mixer.

The mixer output signals of most interest for amateur applications are the IF signal for receive, and the sum signal of the local oscillator and the low-frequency transmit signal, for transmitter applications. This process is called "low-side injection" which means that the LO frequency is lower than the desired microwave RF frequency. High-side injection (LO frequency above the desired microwave RF frequency) is seldom used for amateur applications.

Harmonic mixer signals, which are generated primarily by harmonics of the local oscillator, are generally of low amplitude. These signals are attenuated by a factor of $1/N$, where N is the harmonic number. In addition, for well balanced mixers, even harmonics are strongly attenuated by the balancing circuits. The remaining odd harmonic signals generally do not represent a serious problem because of their low amplitudes.

The "undesired" IF image response from the LO signal is simply the IF response that you don't want to use. For a receive mixer with a filter on the RF port, the potential signal response will not exist. In this receive mixer, however, there are still two mixer-generated signals at the IF port. They are the sum of the RF and LO signals, and the difference between the RF and LO signals and, as such, have a considerable effect on how the mixer's conversion loss is specified. See Fig 2A.

For a lossless mixer, each signal represents half (3 dB) of the RF signal. The sum signal is normally eliminated by filters at the IF port which provide a conversion loss

3 dB greater than the double-sideband specification. Typical mixer losses of 3 dB will provide the common mixer specification of approximately 6 dB SSB conversion loss.

In transmit mixers, the IF image response *is* a mixer product that, if amplified, can be a *real* RF signal that can cause "out-of band" operation. In addition, the undesired signal will show up as false (too high) RF power readings at the desired frequency. It is normally eliminated by using the proper filter at the RF output port.

Fig 2B shows the relationship of the various mixer signals when the mixer is used as a low-side receive mixer. For a transmit mixer, the IF would be the 30-MHz signal

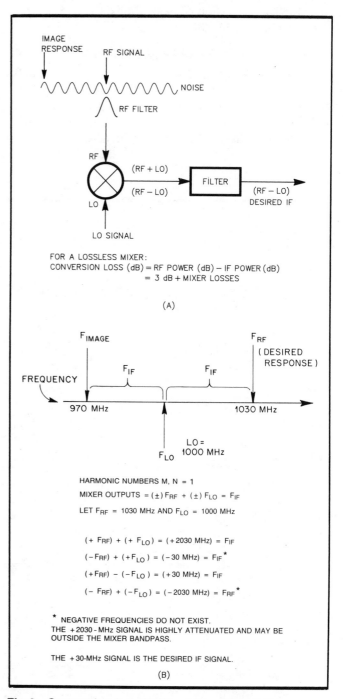

(A)

FOR A LOSSLESS MIXER:
CONVERSION LOSS (dB) = RF POWER (dB) − IF POWER (dB)
= 3 dB + MIXER LOSSES

(B)

* NEGATIVE FREQUENCIES DO NOT EXIST.
THE +2030-MHz SIGNAL IS HIGHLY ATTENUATED AND MAY BE OUTSIDE THE MIXER BANDPASS.

THE +30-MHz SIGNAL IS THE DESIRED IF SIGNAL.

Fig 2—Conversion loss in RF mixers (A) and the relationship of various mixer signals in a low-side injected receive mixer.

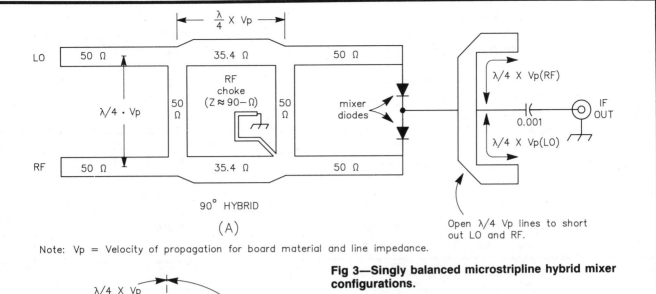

Note: Vp = Velocity of propagation for board material and line impedance.

Fig 3—Singly balanced microstripline hybrid mixer configurations.

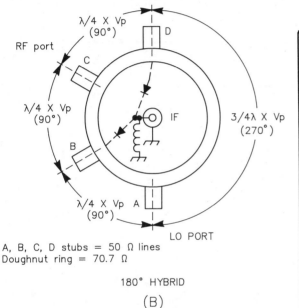

A, B, C, D stubs = 50 Ω lines
Doughnut ring = 70.7 Ω

180° HYBRID

(B)

to be up-converted to 1030 MHz. For this case, rewrite the formula as: $(\pm)F_{LO} + (\pm)F_{IF} = F_{RF}$, and again, ignore negative frequencies.

MIXER CIRCUITS

The important thing to remember about microwave mixers is that all of the circuits used are assumed to be linear, reciprocal and lossless methods of phase-shifting RF signals, and that only the diodes do the mixing. Identification of mixer types can be confusing. In one case they are identified by the function performed, and in another case they are identified by the circuit which is used to perform the function. Then, of course, there are other categories of mixers, such as waveguide mixers, that can fall into either category. Let's look at them in that order. In the first category we have:

1) Single-ended mixers with one diode.
2) Singly balanced mixers with typically two diodes.
3) Doubly balanced mixers with typically four diodes.
4) Harmonic mixers with either two or four diodes.

5) Image-rejection mixers.
For the second category:

1) Ninety-degree hybrid—a lossless, reciprocal four-port device which is also known as a 3-dB coupler, a 90° branch coupler or a quadrature hybrid.

2) One-hundred-eighty-degree hybrid—a lossless, reciprocal, four-port device that can act like a Wheatstone Bridge. It's also known as a magic tee, a 3-dB coupler, a hybrid junction, a hybrid coil, a power divider, a power combiner or a rat-race.

Other categories include waveguide mixers which can be single-ended, singly balanced, or magic tees.

Single-Ended Mixers

Single-ended diode mixers have been around for years and have been widely used in amateur applications from HF to microwave frequencies. They are characterized by their low dynamic range and low LO power requirements, and are generally used for narrow-band applications. If proper band-pass and low-pass filters are used, they can perform well in small-signal applications. They are seldom used as transmit mixers because their limited dynamic range will only produce a low-level undistorted output signal which requires several stages of linear amplification.

Singly Balanced Mixers

Singly balanced mixers have been used extensively in amateur applications—particularly at UHF and microwave frequencies. They are characterized by an average dynamic range, as the LO power required is greater for a singly balanced mixer to properly set the operating point for two diodes. They have good LO-to-IF and LO-to-RX isolation. They also provide better intermodulation product suppression and, because of the balancing circuits, provide a considerable reduction of even harmonic signals. Performance is determined by the particular circuit used, that is, microstripline, waveguide, and so on.

Figs 3A and 3B show typical configurations for

microstripline singly balanced hybrid mixers. Fig 3A shows a 90° hybrid circuit. Notice in Fig 3A that there is a high-impedance grounded quarter-wavelength line shown as a dc return path for the diodes, rather than the use of conventional wirewound RF chokes and dc blocking microwave chip capacitors. Since we are using LO power to properly bias the diodes, J0 bypassing can be used as an RF ground for the quarter-wavelength line, and a low-value resistor to dc ground can be used so diode performance can be monitored. The use of open quarter-wavelength lines at the RF and LO frequencies at the output is an additional measure to ensure that these signals are eliminated at the IF port.

Fig 3B shows a 180° hybrid mixer. Keep in mind, however, that microstripline on a circuit board does not have to be either straight lines or circles—just accurately dimensioned.

There are some important considerations to be aware of if you plan to use microstripline hybrids for mixer applications:

A) The use of appropriate filters at the RF ports is essential in order to eliminate IF image responses for either transmit or receive operation.

B) The selection of the center design frequency of the hybrid should be carefully considered. If you want maximum rejection of the LO frequency, the center design frequency should be the local oscillator frequency rather than the arithmetic mean frequency.

C) The bandwidth of the hybrid mixer must be considered in terms of the IF you want to use. For example:

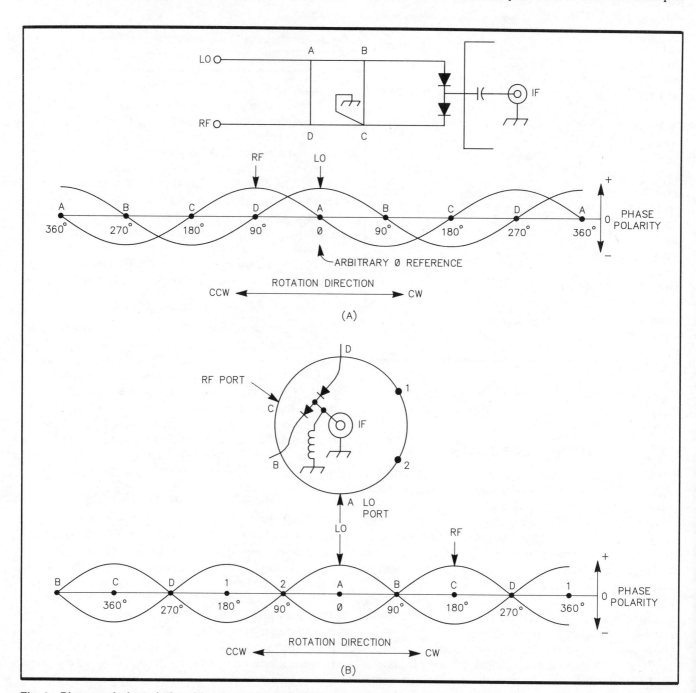

Fig 4—Phase polarity relationships for 90° and 180° hybrids.

for a 1296-MHz mixer, if you choose an IF of 144 MHz, the required LO frequency is 1152 MHz. The arithmetic mean center frequency is then 1224 MHz. By using this frequency as the hybrid center design frequency, it represents a bandwidth requirement of 144 / 1224(100) = 11.8%. This is just about the maximum bandwidth available for a microstripline hybrid, and represents a trade-off in terms of the degree of rejection of the LO frequency by the phasing lines.

If you design for maximum LO frequency cancellation, and use a 144-MHz IF, the design center would be 1152 MHz, and the bandwidth would be 288 / 1152(100) = 25%. This represents an unreasonable mixer bandwidth.

This potential problem represents a good reason to consider using a 28- or 50-MHz IF for microstripline hybrid mixers at 1296 MHz.

For the case of a 28-MHz IF, and the LO frequency as the design center, the bandwidth requirement would be 56 / 1152(100) = 4.9%, a value well within the expected bandwidth capability. For a 50-MHz IF, the value would be 100 / 1152(100) = 8.7%, and is still a reasonable value.

In summary, if you want optimum LO fundamental and even-harmonic rejection at the RF and IF ports, design your microstripline mixer for the LO frequency and consider using a 28- or 50-MHz IF for frequencies up to 2304 MHz (using microstripline mixers). The losses at the RF port are easily made up with RF amplifiers. Otherwise, use the arithmetic mean frequency and accept the compromise, or consider using broadband doubly balanced mixers.

The key to understanding how any hybrid circuit works, is to look closely at the phase polarity relationships that exist for a given configuration. Figs 4A and 4B show typical phase polarity relationships. The phase polarity is presented so it is obvious that one hybrid is 90° and the other hybrid is 180°. Note carefully that the drawings only represent polarity v wavelength or degrees.

A point that sometimes causes confusion is the realization that the RF and LO signals are asynchronous (not in phase with each other). Regardless of the initial phase displacement between the incoming signals, the hybrid will force a fixed phase displacement between the signals within the hybrid. The value of the fixed phase displacement is determined by the hybrid used.

For the 90° hybrid, either signal enters the network 90° out of phase with respect to itself through the quarter-wavelength (90°) leg A—D. For the 180° hybrid, the signal is 180° out of phase because of the half-wavelength (180°) represented by legs A—B and B—C.

To use the drawings, trace each primary signal separately around the hybrid in both a clockwise and counterclockwise direction. Check the phase polarity at each port for the signal you are tracing and determine if you are at an "in-phase" point. If you are at a "phase-opposition" point (hybrid networks are assumed to be lossless), signal magnitudes will be equal and total cancellation will occur at that port.

Doubly Balanced Mixers

Doubly balanced mixers are being used more fre-

quently in amateur circuits. They offer superior dynamic range and a further reduction of IM products. They require more LO power than the preceding mixers, but this is not a problem with today's circuits. For 432 MHz on down, doubly balanced mixers are within the constructional capability of most hams. Commercially made doubly balanced mixers for the lower frequencies are inexpensive, however, so it's hardly worth the effort of making them yourself.

One mixer manufacturer (Watkins-Johnson) specifies classes of mixers and the approximate LO power required. This is shown in Table 1. Note that the circuits shown typify only one leg of the diode ring. For microwave mixers, these are not discrete diodes; they are matched diodes built on the same substrate material. Fig 5 shows a typical schematic diagram for a class-2, type-1 DBM.

Table 1

MIXER CLASS AND TYPE	CIRCUIT	TYPICAL LO POWER FOR DBM
CLASS 1		+7 dBm TO +13 dBm
CLASS 2, TYPE 1		+13 dBm TO +24 dBm
CLASS 2, TYPE 2,		+13 dBm TO +24 dBm
CLASS 3, TYPE 1		+20 dBm TO +30 dBm
CLASS 3, TYPE 2		+20 dBm TO +30 dBm
CLASS 3, TYPE 3		+20 dBm TO +30 dBm

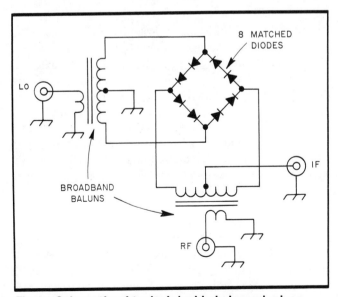

Fig 5—Schematic of typical doubly balanced mixer.

As LO power requirements increase, dynamic range and intermodulation (IM) products suppression improves considerably. The resistors and capacitors used in conjunction with the diodes in certain mixer classes serve to suppress particular IM products, and to keep the mixer conversion losses relatively constant versus frequency. For the microwave bands, constructing broadband doubly balanced mixers is generally beyond the capabilities of most amateurs. Commercially made units are becoming less expensive, and are recommended. (Many components and parts available at flea markets may contain doubly balanced mixers.)

Harmonic Mixers

Harmonic mixers evolved because of the original problem of obtaining adequate and stable LO power at the proper frequency. They use the LO second harmonic to produce mixing with the RF signal. Harmonic mixers may use either two or four diodes. They require sufficient second-harmonic power to properly bias the diodes, and have higher conversion losses than a fundamental mixer. Oscillator stability is important, as its effect is doubled in the second harmonic.

Image-Rejection Mixers

The image-rejection mixer (SSB up/down converter) has been extensively used for single-frequency conversion methods in satellite TVRO systems. Image rejection is accomplished by using hybrid phasing systems in conjunction with single or doubly balanced mixer circuits. See Fig 6. Amateur construction of mixers of this type is probably limited to 432 MHz. The phase and amplitude balancing that is required to achieve good image rejection above this frequency generally requires thin-film techniques, fused-silica substrates and ultra-expensive test equipment.

This type of mixer has not been used often even for the lower microwave frequencies, as it represents a considerable increase in mixer complexity and board design. Component-wise, it requires well-matched diodes, the use of microwave chip resistors to properly terminate many of the ports, as well as microwave chip capacitors. The mixer-circuit components must be carefully matched to maintain the required phase relationships. The main feature of this type of mixer is to properly phase the signals so that either the upper or lower fundamental IF response from the output can be eliminated by terminating the proper port. It can also be used to generate an SSB signal when used as an up-converter. Their use in an amateur system preceded by high gain, low-noise GaAsFETs would be highly effective. Image-rejection mixers are readily available commercially.

Waveguide Mixers

Figs 7 and 8 show a waveguide magic tee (180° hybrid) for a 10-GHz receive mixer. Since it is a reciprocal device, it may also be used as a transmit mixer. As a receive mixer, the LO signal is applied to port A, and the microwave RF signal is applied to port B. As shown in the figure, the RF signal would be vertically polarized. Note that LO energy

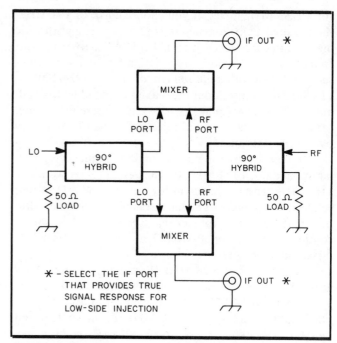

Fig 6—Configuration of a doubly balanced image-rejection mixer.

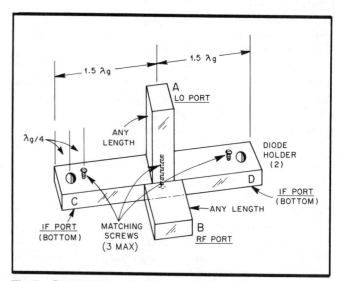

Fig 7—General layout of a waveguide·"magic-tee" hybrid mixer for 10 GHz.

is effectively eliminated from port B because the waveguide sections are cross polarized. The two legs (C and D) that contain the diodes are typically 1.5 waveguide wavelengths long.

Note the use of the term "waveguide wavelength." There are three wavelength terms that are used to describe waveguide performance: free-space wavelength (λ), waveguide cut-off wavelength (λ_c) and waveguide wavelength (λ_g). The most commonly used 10-GHz waveguide, RG-52U, has an internal width of 0.9 inch (2.286 cm), and an internal height of 0.4 inch (1.016 cm). The normal operating mode for this waveguide is $TE_{1,0}$, wherein the

Fig 8—Hybrid "magic-tee" mixer for 10 GHz.

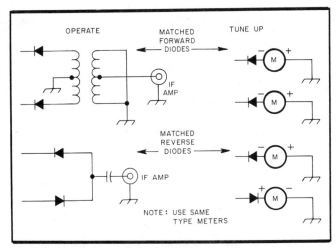

Fig 9—Typical circuits for coupling mixer diodes to successive circuit elements.

electric field goes from the top to the bottom of the guide height, with maximum intensity at the center of the width. The magnetic field is perpendicular to the electric field.

The width of the guide determines the guide cut-off frequency in terms of wavelength. The cut-off wavelength = 2(width). If width = 0.9 inch (2.286 cm), 2(width) = 4.572 cm, which corresponds to 6557 MHz. Any frequency below 6557 MHz will not propagate through the waveguide and will be severely attenuated. This property is used extensively for excellent microwave attenuators, which are named "below cut-off attenuators."

Waveguide wavelength is equal to:

$$\lambda_g = \frac{\lambda}{\sqrt{1 - \left(\frac{\lambda}{\lambda_c}\right)^2}}$$

The diodes are mounted electrically, a waveguide quarter wavelength from the closed ends of sections C and D. Matching stubs (screws) can be mounted at waveguide eighth-wavelength intervals starting one guide quarter wavelength in front of the diodes. One is generally sufficient. Three of them, however, will match practically any impedance, as they represent a 3-stub tuner.

There are discontinuities where the waveguide sections are joined. One is easily tuned out by a screw that protrudes into the LO waveguide, a waveguide quarter wavelength from the back of the RF waveguide. See Fig 7. Another adjustment is an inductive iris in the LO waveguide. It is normally ignored in amateur applications. Some commercially made magic tees also use similar inductive irises for matching in legs C and D, instead of using matching screws.

Fig 9 shows typical circuits for coupling the IF signal from the diodes. Matched-forward or matched-reverse diode configurations can be used. The circuits assume the diodes are properly matched and are being driven equally. Use either of the tune-up circuits shown for setting the initial drive levels.

Other Mixer Considerations

There are (at least) two important mixer operating conditions that will minimize IM products:

1) Make every attempt to properly terminate the mixer ports, especially the IF port. If the various ports of the mixer are not properly terminated, the energy reflected back into the mixer diodes acts like additional source signals and produces additional, unwanted mixer products

2) Apply relatively high LO power for a given mixer so that it operates further up on the diode transfer characteristic curve.

Diode Selection

If you choose to build single-ended or singly balanced mixers, the first problem you run into is the selection of a diode that will operate at the available LO injection power, operate at the desired frequency, and provide a minimum mixer conversion loss. Diode selection is dependent upon a number of factors:

    1) Mixer circuit design:
        A) Microstripline hybrid.
        B) Waveguide.
        C) Number of diodes required.
        D) Other factors.
    2) Available LO injection power.
    3) Noise figure of the IF amplifier. Note: many diode manufacturers assume an IF NF of 1.5 dB at 30 MHz.
    4) Ability to match the output impedance of the diode.
    5) Desired noise figure or conversion loss.
    6) Physical diode configuration.
    7) Operating frequency.

Selection of a usable diode from manufacturer's data books, once you have this information, is pretty straightforward.

Frequency Multiplication with Step-Recovery Diodes

By Bill Troetschel, K6UQH

Step-recovery diodes have been identified by many different names, such as snap diodes, and misnamed as varactor diodes, which they are not. They are, in fact, quite similar to PIN diodes—with a slightly different junction treatment. Perhaps the most descriptive name is the Switching Reactance Multiplier, SRM, used by Hewlett-Packard.

SRD MODEL

The theory behind SRDs is still being studied by solid-state physicists and engineers, so we will use the theory described in Hewlett-Packard's application notes *AN-920* and *AN-928* for this discussion.

The SRD may be modeled as a charge-controlled switch that switches between two (capacitive reactance) impedance states. These two states will be developed as a function of the ac input waveform and the "diode" characteristic. A (large forward capacitance) low-impedance state will occur during nearly the entire period of the input waveform. During the positive portion of the input cycle, charges will be stored in the device; during the negative portion of the input cycle, these charges will be withdrawn, resulting in a large current flow during almost the entire input cycle. This represents the low-impedance state.

At the end of the input cycle, all of the charge is withdrawn and a (very small reverse capacitance) high-impedance state abruptly occurs. This switching from the low-impedance state to the high-impedance state occurs in a extremely short interval of time, typically 100 picoseconds for a 10-GHz device. This single cycle of operation permits the circuit to store an appreciable amount of energy in a series inductance) during the low-impedance state, and release that energy as a high-amplitude, narrow pulse when switching occurs. It is this pulse that is our prime concern.

There is diode resistance, diode case capacitance and diode case inductance associated with this model, which we will acknowledge, but ignore for this discussion.

This very narrow pulse of energy is the basis of the high harmonic content spectrum that is generated, which can be used as a frequency comb or as a single harmonic frequency. The main emphasis in this discussion is to use one of these harmonic signals to generate a 10-GHz LO signal.

We will describe the theory, design and tune-up of a 10-GHz LO chain using an SRD to generate sufficient power to operate any type of diode mixer (including doubly balanced mixers) for receive and transmit applications.

SRD Theory

If we could generate a pulse that had a near-zero pulse width (time domain), it could be represented as a nearly infinite number of equal-amplitude, harmonically related lines in the frequency domain. This spectrum represents the Fourier transform of the time-domain pulse. It would be an ideal comb generator. In practice, a zero-width pulse is not possible, so let us assume that we can generate a very narrow sinusoidal pulse with a pulse-width of T_p. Fig 1 shows the spectral distribution of energy represented by this pulse.

At point A, the energy level is zero. This point is called the first-zero crossover point and represents the limit of our interest. This point occurs at a frequency which is $3/2T_p$ for our sinusoidal pulse. For example: if the pulse-width is equal to 100 picoseconds, (100E-12), the frequency at point A would be $3/2(100E-12)$ or 15 GHz. Its amplitude would be zero. Spectral lines to the left of point A would have energy levels shown by the curve. This curve represents the idealized output of a comb generator for this sinusoidal pulse, where stray circuit resonances have not affected the energy distribution. The total energy of all the spectral lines under the curve to the first-zero cross-over point nearly equals the total energy contained in the sinusoidal pulse because the energy to the right of the first-zero point is quite small.

If this energy is terminated with a resistance, we would have an effective comb generator with a first-zero point of $3/2T_p$. Comb generators have their applications, but we are looking for a single spectral line with plenty of energy for application in an LO chain.

The obvious approach is to use a tuned circuit (a filter) to select the spectral line we want and eliminate all other lines. This brings up an interesting and often neglected point. If we use a filter—what happens to the energy that was represented in the other spectral lines? The basic answer is that the other spectral lines are not generated to any great degree when the resonant circuit is used. The

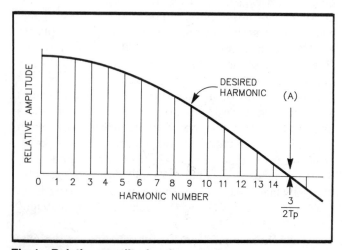

Fig 1—Relative amplitude of spectral energy generated by the SRD's narrow-bandwidth pulse.

energy of the desired line has an energy level of approximately $1/n$, where n is the harmonic number of the line you choose. See Fig 2.

There are several unstated assumptions in the previous statement. The filter (shown in Fig 3) is a tuned circuit with a definite Q. It is being excited by a pulse that has a specific width. We will call this tuned circuit a "ringing circuit" because we will make it "ring like a bell" with one strike

of the gong (which would produce a loud ringing sound which gradually diminishes in amplitude, that is, a damped waveform).

Optimum loaded Q for the filter is given as $(pi/2)n$, which simply means that a greater harmonic frequency output requires a greater Q. The Q of the ringing filter is adjusted by the loading of the circuit.

The filter will sustain a damped waveform at its resonant frequency every time it is pulsed as (a function of its Q). If the loaded Q of the filter is adjusted so that the energy in the pulse is delivered in a time interval equal to n cycles of the desired harmonic signal (one cycle of the input frequency), most of the energy in the pulse will be delivered as (energy$_{in}$ / n = energy$_{out}$).

It is also true that the ringing filter bandwidth normally will not completely reject the n − 1 and the n + 1 harmonic lines, so additional filtering may be necessary for a given application.

CIRCUIT ELEMENTS

Fig 3 shows a block diagram and a schematic of a typical SRD multiplier and identifies the various elements we will discuss. The letters A, B, C and D refer to Fig 4 which shows the waveforms developed by the various elements. This particular configuration is called a shunt

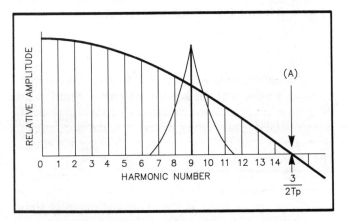

Fig 2—Relative amplitude of spectral energy by the SRD's narrow-bandwidth pulse when a tuned filter is used to eliminate unwanted harmonic responses.

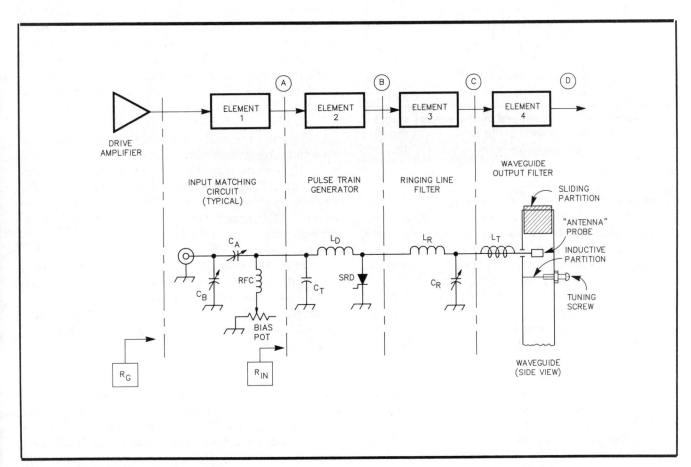

Fig 3—Typical SRD multiplier setup.

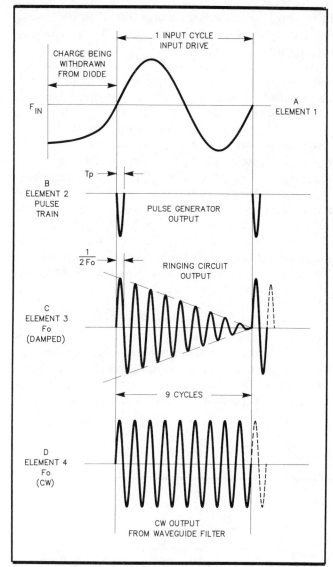

Fig 4—Waveforms as developed by the various stages of the SRD set-up as shown in Fig 3.

Within the figure:
1 INPUT CYCLE INPUT DRIVE

CHARGE BEING WITHDRAWN FROM DIODE

F_{IN}

A ELEMENT 1

T_p

B ELEMENT 2 PULSE TRAIN

PULSE GENERATOR OUTPUT

$\frac{1}{2F_o}$

RINGING CIRCUIT OUTPUT

C ELEMENT 3 F_o (DAMPED)

9 CYCLES

D ELEMENT 4 F_o (CW)

CW OUTPUT FROM WAVEGUIDE FILTER

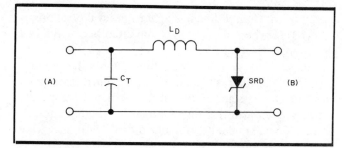

Fig 5—Schematic for a simple shunt multiplier.

Within the figure: L_D, C_T, SRD, (A), (B)

It is important to keep in mind that we are trying to generate a pulse that has a width which is optimized for the generation of a chosen harmonic frequency at approximately 10 GHz. This pulse is generated by the diode switching its state during the final portion of the input waveform. The main criterion for the pulse is that its width, T_p, is such that $3 / 2T_p$ is a frequency well above our desired harmonic frequency, and that T_p has a pulse width of approximately ½ cycle at the desired harmonic output frequency.

Since the pulse is generated when the diode switches to its high-impedance, reverse-capacitance state, *that* capacitance value and L_d should resonate at the proper frequency. This resonant frequency (f_o) is the key to generating the proper pulse width because the time, (pulse width − T_p), is simply $1/ f_o$, and for ½ cycle of the resonant output frequency, $T_p = 1 / 2f_o$. At this point we have the output of the "driving inductance circuit" producing a train of pulses. We need to convert this to a single-frequency, damped waveform through the use of a tuned ringing-line filter. We will then convert this damped waveform to a steady-state CW waveform with an additional filter. Fig 4 shows the entire process in detail.

There is a range of pulse width duration times that are suitable for generating the desired harmonic. One limit is $1 / 2f_o$, and the other limit is $1 / f_o$. Circuit Q, circuit values, and efficiency get involved in the selection. $1 / 2f_o$ represents a pulse width of ½ cycle of the output frequency, while $1 / f_o$ represents one cycle of the output frequency. Normally, $1 / 2f_o$ (½ cycle) is chosen for the design. As an equation: $1 / 2f_o < T_p < 1 / f_o$.

For the lower microwave frequencies (below 10 GHz) you can design your system using almost any value between either limit. *Your design choice will, primarily, determine component values.* If we need a frequency of approximately 10 GHz, the range of acceptable pulse-width durations would be from $50 < T_p < 100$ picoseconds. Diodes for amateur applications are available with transition times of approximately 70 picoseconds. Obviously, a $1 / 2f_o$ design for 10 GHz is not practical because 50 picoseconds represents a pulse width that the diode cannot produce. From a practical point it is generally easier to generate a longer pulse, so a design pulse width (T_p) in this case would be chosen at about 85 picoseconds. That cor-

multiplier because the diode is shunted (in parallel) with the line. This configuration is commonly used up to about 10 GHz. Above 10 GHz, a series multiplier is generally used to accommodate the package inductance of the diode.

Fig 5 shows the diode as a shunt multiplier with the driving inductance (L_d) and a capacitor (C_t). A low-frequency source (approximately 1100 MHz for a 9× multiplier) is applied at point A. A "train" of pulsed signals is generated at point B.

We will discuss specific diode characteristics later; all you need to remember now is that the diode represents a large capacitor during most of the drive cycle (C_{fwd}), a small capacitor during the transition period (C_{vr}), and that the change takes place in a very small time interval. L_d has various names used by different manufacturers. The most common name is "driving inductance," which we will use here.

responds to a frequency of about 12 GHz. It also corresponds to a 3 / 2T$_p$ frequency of approximately 18 GHz for the first-zero point, which is well above our desired harmonic frequency.

Hewlett-Packard *Application Note 920* has a series of computer-derived design curves for optimum pulse width v frequency and multiplying factors. A pulse width of 85 picoseconds represents the design frequency, (1 / T$_p$ — 12 GHz) for L$_d$ and C$_{vr}$ to resonate for the 10-GHz SRD multiplier.

Since the value for C$_{vr}$ is provided by the manufacturer for a given diode, L$_d$ can be easily calculated. It will, at 10 GHz, normally be in the range of 1 nanohenry—and therein lies a problem. Although you can calculate the required inductance to any number of decimal places, realizing that inductance at 10 GHz is another matter.

We will discuss the subject of determining L$_d$, L$_r$ and L$_t$, along with the effect of diode choice and line impedance later in this section.

To summarize, L$_d$ and C$_{vr}$ are a resonant circuit at a frequency that corresponds to a pulse width (T$_p$) that can generate the desired harmonic in the tuned, ringing-line filter, and that 3 / 2T$_p$ is a frequency well above the desired harmonic. Additionally, L$_d$ must also resonate with C$_t$ at the input driving frequency. This is required so the diode has the time to experience a complete polarity reversal during the ac input cycle, and thus go through its two-state condition.

C$_t$ is an important consideration. For a 10-GHz generator, it will normally be approximately 30 picofarads (at resonance), which assumes an 1100-MHz driving frequency (a 9× multiplier). More importantly, it must

provide essentially an ac short at all harmonic frequencies. At 10 GHz, it will generally be constructed as a "flat plate" disc capacitor that is less than a quarter wavelength in radius at a frequency which is equal to 1 / 2T$_p$.

It must be carefully constructed to pass all the harmonic energy up to the first-zero point of 3 / 2T$_p$. To obtain the capacitive value required within these constraints, a thin-dielectric material such as Teflon® must be used. When C$_t$ is essentially an RF short at the harmonic output frequencies, L$_d$ and the SRD's C$_{vr}$ can be visualized as a parallel resonant circuit at the proper frequency to generate the correct pulse width.

Element (4) in Fig 3 is the waveguide filter—an important component. It is a resonant section of waveguide consisting of an adjustable, RF-shorting partition, a capacitively tuned inductive iris, and an antenna stub which couples into the E field of the waveguide section. The significant part of this section that requires careful construction is the adjustable partition. The waveguide filter is very high Q, and when tuning the filter by adjusting the sliding partition, you will find that it tunes quite sharply. The partition should fit snugly so that it doesn't wobble around as it is adjusted. A brass or copper slug about 1 inch long that fits snugly into the waveguide can be made to work, however, the use of "finger stock" as shown is highly recommended. The Q of this filter and its mechanical stability is important in terms of obtaining excellent single-frequency operation and acceptable power output from the multiplier.

Element (1) in Fig 6, the input-matching section, can be any matching network that will provide a match from the 50-ohm (approximately 1100 MHz) feedpoint—shown

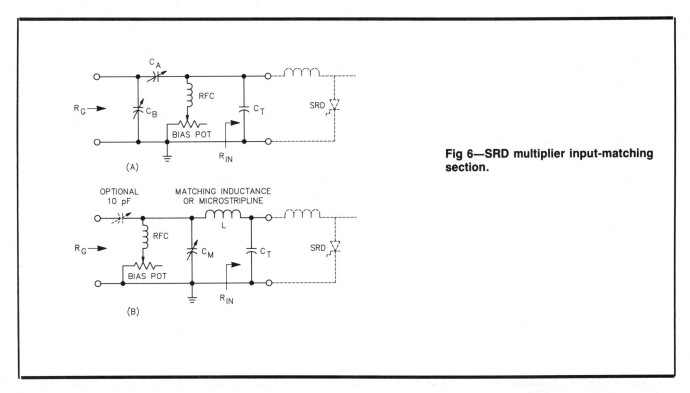

Fig 6—SRD multiplier input-matching section.

as R_g—to the input of the SRD. Since the SRD input point is resonant at the drive frequency, it is essentially a low-resistance point, typically 5 ohms or less. This is shown as R_{in}.

Two matching networks are shown. The first is a capacitive matching section that has been used by several experimenters, and works well for narrowband applications.

The second is a recommended matching network shown in H-P's *AN-920*. It also works well. Equations for calculating the component values of this network are shown in Fig 7.

At low driving frequencies this matching section can consist of discrete components. At higher driving frequencies it may be easier to use a quarter-wavelength microstripline matching section that matches R_g to R_{in}. The microstripline impedance for this matching section is

SCHEMATIC REFERENCE

TYPICAL COMPONENT CALCULATIONS			
CIRCUIT COMPONENT	EQUATIONS USED	values for $1/2\,F_O$ = 50 pSEC, C_J = 0.75 pF	values for: T_p = 85 pSEC, C_{vr} = 0.75 pF
L_d	$\left(\frac{T_p}{\pi}\right)^2 \cdot \frac{1}{C_{vr}}$	0.34 nH	0.98 nH
C_t	$\frac{C_{vr}}{(2\,F_{in}T_p)^2}$	62.5 pF	21.6 pF
L_r	normally $L_d = L_r$	0.34 nH	0.98 nH
C_r	$\frac{1}{(2\pi F_O)^2\,L_r} - C_c$	C_c—not used 0.77 pF	C_c—not used 0.27 pF
R_g	normally = 50 Ω	50 Ω	50 Ω
R_{IN}	$\approx 2\pi F_{in} L_d$	2.34 Ω	6.74 Ω
L_m	$\frac{\sqrt{R_G R_{in}}}{2\pi F_{in}}$	1.6 nH	2.7 nH
C_m	$\frac{1}{2\pi F_{in}\sqrt{R_G R_{in}}}$	13.5 pF (variable)	7.9 pF (variable)
RFC		6T no. 26 on 1/16" ID form, single spaced	
BIAS POT	1–2 kΩ	—	—

F_{in} = 1095.111111 MHz, F_O = 9856 MHz } m = 9

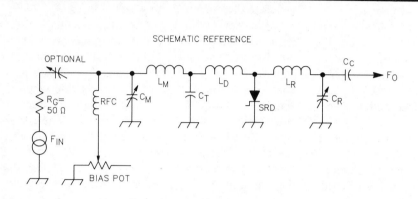

Fig 7—Equations used to calculate component values for the SRD input-matching network.

nominally 15 ohms, and Z = SQR(R_g × R_{in}). If you use the quarter-wavelength input matching section, the ratio of R_g / R_{in} should be approximately (10) for the equations to provide proper answers.

Use of an electrical half-wavelength (or integer multiple) coaxial line from the driver stage to the SRD multiplier is recommended to minimize coax lead-length sensitivity.

There is one important parameter for any of the input matching networks you use. The bias choke must be a good choke at the input frequency and have a minimum of stray resonances over a wider range of frequencies. Do not bypass the bias choke. Some stray series resonances in the bias choke circuit can show up as negative resistance and cause oscillations that will fill the waveguide section with all sorts of unwanted energy. This energy will radiate locally, and probably break the squelch on your receivers!

The electrical distance in wavelengths between the RF choke and the SRD also must be considered. Since a good choke acts like a shorted quarter-wavelength circuit at the RF input frequency, if the SRD is an electrical quarter wavelength away from the choke, it "sees" an RF short circuit. A rule of thumb is to make your choke "long,

skinny and single-spaced" at the drive frequency and attach it directly to C_t.

A potentiometer is provided to set the proper diode bias for the available drive level. Use a carbon pot rather than a wire-wound pot—you don't need any extra "undefined" chokes.

Fig 8 shows the transistor amplifier that is used as the driver stage for the SRD multiplier. It uses an inexpensive Motorola MRF-571 bipolar device which can be used as a class-A linear amplifier up to about 2.0 GHz. The circuit shown can be tuned from approximately 1000 to 1300 MHz, and produces 200 mW output with 20 mW of drive.

The circuit board contains an RF-to-dc interface that permits stable operation. This is an important consideration for driving an SRD, because an SRD multiplier is anything but a constant load. The design frequency for this amplifier was 1095.111111 MHz. The experimental SRD multiplier supplied a 9856.000000-MHz LO signal for a 10-GHz SSB system using a 144-MHz IF. Slight retuning of this amplifier to use other LO or intermediate frequencies is easily accomplished.

For the experimental system, the design goals were to put the drive stage, the SRD multiplier, the mixers and

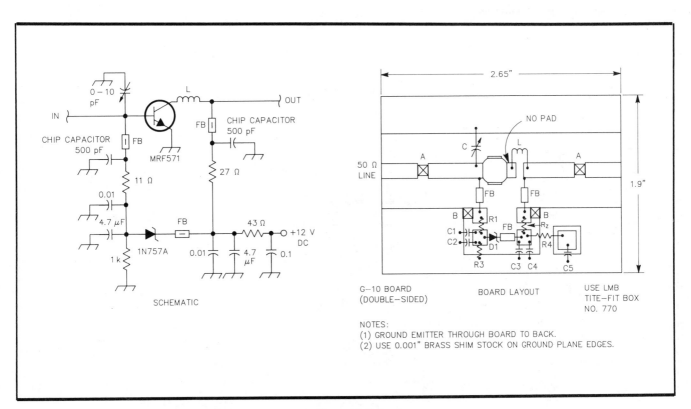

Fig 8—Transistor amplifier stage used to drive an SRD multiplier.

R1—11 Ω.
R2—27 Ω.
R3—1 kΩ.
R4—43 Ω.
C1,C3—0.01 µF.
C2,C4—4.7 µF tantalum.
C5—0.1 µF ceramic.
A—100 pF chip cap.

B— 500-1000 pF chip cap.
C—1-10 pF Johanson variable.
FB—4 turns no. 30 enamel wire on Amidon 64-101 ferrite bead.
L—2 turns no. 30 enamel wire wound on no. 57 drill bit.
D1—1N757A or 1N5239B 9.1-V Zener diode.
Q1—MRF-571 transistor.

λ_o = FREE-SPACE WAVELENGTH

λ_c = WAVEGUIDE CUT-OFF WAVELENGTH

λ_g = WAVEGUIDE WAVELENGTH

$$\lambda_g = \frac{\lambda_o}{\sqrt{1 - \left(\frac{\lambda_o}{\lambda_c}\right)^2}}$$

CALCULATIONS FOR 9856 MHz (RG-52 WAVEGUIDE)

$$\lambda_o = \frac{29980}{9856} = 3.042 \text{ CM } (1.198'')$$

$$\lambda_c = 4.572 \text{ CM } (6557 \text{ MHz})$$

$$\lambda_g = \frac{3.042}{\sqrt{1 - \left(\frac{3.042}{4.572}\right)^2}}$$

$$\lambda_g = 4.075 \text{ CM } (1.6'')$$

$$\frac{\lambda_g}{2} = 2.038 \text{ CM } (0.8'')$$

$$\frac{\lambda_g}{4} = 1.02 \text{ CM } (0.4'')$$

Fig 9—Typical waveguide calculations. See text for details.

GaAsFETs at the antenna. This requires running dc, IF and low-level 1095.111111-MHz signals to the antenna. The 1095-MHz signal can be generated in the shack by using another MRF-571 stage to overcome losses. Only about 25 mW of drive is needed for the antenna-mounted stage.

The equations for calculating component values are shown in Fig 7, which shows the calculated values you would get if you could use the ½-cycle mode ($1/2f_o$), and the actual values for the experimental model that used a T_p of 85 picoseconds. Fig 9 shows typical calculations for the waveguide dimensions. Figs 10 through 15 show the construction details of our 10-GHz SRD multiplier.

Choosing An SRD

There are several SRD parameters to examine when determining if a particular diode is suitable for your application:

1) Lifetime—a measure of the time a charge will remain in the transition region. It must be long enough to permit the RF current to reach a negative peak in the diode. This value should be greater (approximately 10 times) than the period ($1/f$) of the input frequency. It is normally given in nanoseconds ($10E^{-09}$).

2) Diode transition time (T_t)—the time required for a device to switch from a low-impedance to a high-impedance state. This time should be less than the period

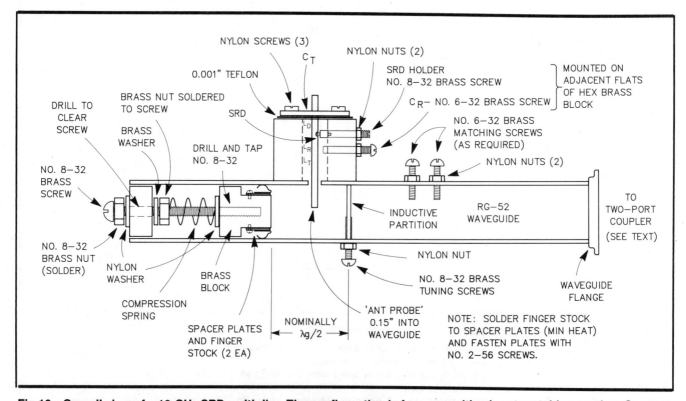

Fig 10—Overall view of a 10-GHz SRD multiplier. The configuration is for a capacitive input-matching section. See text.

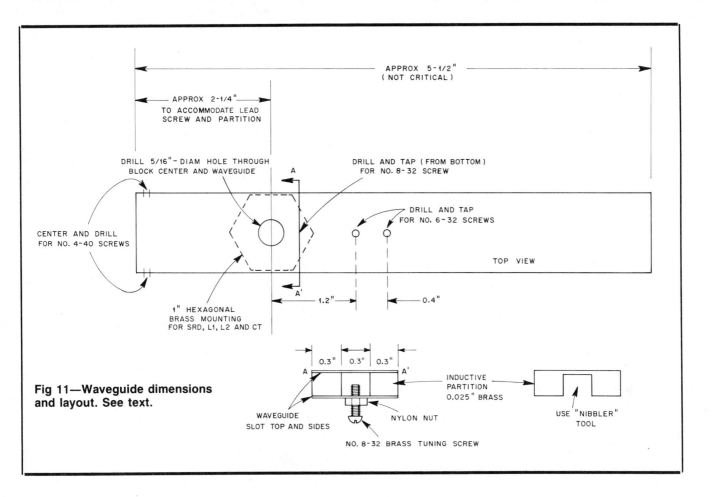

Fig 11—Waveguide dimensions and layout. See text.

(1/f) of the output frequency. It is normally given in picoseconds (10E^{-12}).

3) Breakdown voltage (V_b or V_{br})—usually provided for a reverse current of 10 microamperes, and will typically vary from 15 to 30 volts for single diodes. It sets the absolute limit of output power for an assumed 50-ohm system.

4) Junction capacitance (C_j or C_{vr})—normally provided for a given reverse bias voltage. It is generally given as a min/max value. It is typically expressed as C_j or C_{vr} in picofarads. Use its nominal value to calculate L_d.

These performance parameters are provided in the manufacturer's data sheets.

A Design Example

The first step is to acquire about 12 inches of RG-52 waveguide (0.4 × 0.9-inch ID), and a few inches of 1-inch hexagonal "yellow brass" stock. If you decide to make the two-port coupler as a separate unit, you will also need a couple of waveguide flanges. Hexagonal brass stock is versatile in that you can mount components through its flat surfaces, and finding "center" is much easier than with cylindrical sections.

Diode Selection

For our design example, we'll use DVB 6100- and DVB 6101-series SRDs from Alpha Microwave Semiconductors. They have typical input frequency ratings of 0.5 to 3.0 GHz, and output frequency ratings of 9.0 to 18 GHz for the 6100 series, and from 5 to 15 GHz for the 6101 series.

Diode lifetime for either series is listed as 10 nanoseconds minimum (diode lifetime should be at least 10 times the period of the input frequency).

The drive frequency we have selected, 1095.111111 MHz, has a period of 0.9 nanoseconds. Because the ratio of diode lifetime v input frequency is greater than 10:1, it represents a suitable drive frequency. Transition time pulsewidth, T_t, is listed as a maximum of 70 picoseconds for the 6100 series, and 100 picoseconds for the 6101 series. The data does not, however, indicate the minimum pulsewidth.

Experimental Models

Several working models have been built using different diode types to assess the validity of the design concept. The "Mark 1, Model 3" used the DVB 6100B diode, which has a reverse capacitance, C_{vr}, of from 0.5 to 1.00 pF, and a pulsewidth, (T_t max) of 70 picoseconds. A value of 0.75 pF was used for the component calculations as shown in Fig 7. The design pulsewidth was chosen as 85 picoseconds. Fig 9 shows typical waveguide dimensions used for the frequency selected.

As shown in Fig 7, L_d and L_r would normally have the same inductive value if we were able to use the optimum 1 / 2F_0 design (50 picoseconds). Because the drive inductance, L_d, and the ringing inductance, L_r, are going to operate at slightly different frequencies, we assume the

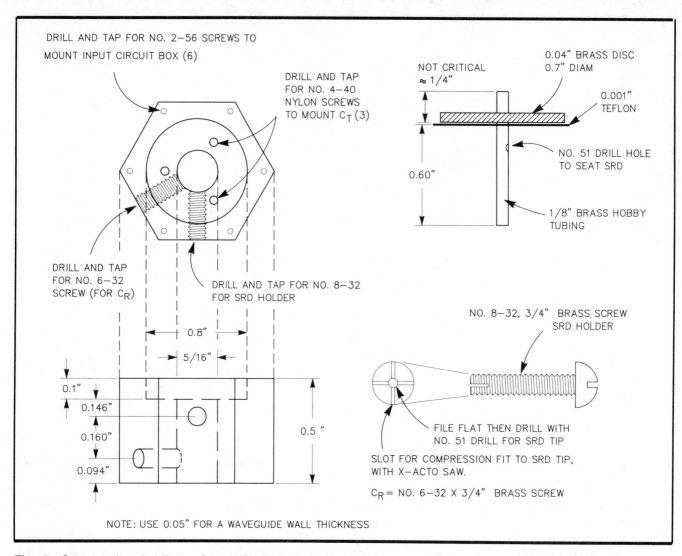

Fig 12—Construction details for C_T and C_2. The 0.1-inch cutout is not required for capacitive matching. See text for details.

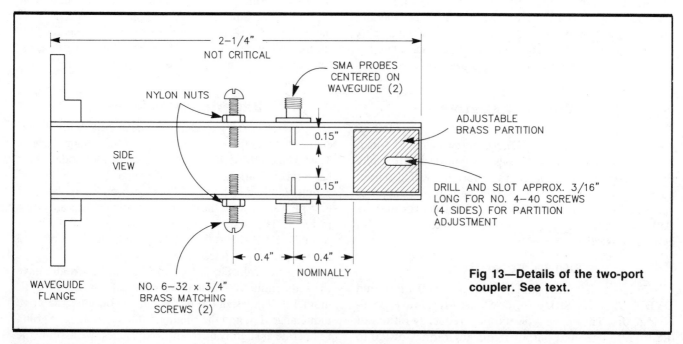

Fig 13—Details of the two-port coupler. See text.

inductive values will stay the same—but at different frequencies! The goal is to derive physical dimensions for these inductances.

The use of a normalized Smith Chart or immittance chart makes this easy. The impedance of the coaxial line making up L_d and L_r is 54.9 ohms (for the dimensions used), so a chart centered at 55 ohms is also suitable. Using the normalized chart, convert the required inductance into an inductive reactance ($X_L = 6.28$ f L). Then, normalize this value by dividing by 50 ohms. The resultant can be found on the periphial reactance scale of the chart. The wavelength can then be read from the periphial wavelength scale.

Because the coaxial line making up L_d and L_r has an air dielectric, multiplying the wavelength value by the free-space wavelength in centimeters or inches will provide the required line length. In this case, for L_d and C_{vr} to resonate at 12 GHz, the line length is 0.146 inch, or 0.371 cm.

As an alternative to the Smith Chart, you can use the equation for shorted lines less than a quarter-wavelength long to get the answer directly. (See the Design Techniques section earlier in this chapter.)

In this case:

$$\theta = \arctan(jX / Z_0)$$

where $Z_0 = 54.9$ ohms,
$jX = 73.9$ ohms,
$\theta = 53.39°$

Because one cycle = $360°$ and the wavelength (12 GHz) = 0.984 inch, L is the required line length:
(L / 0.984) = (53.39 / 360)
L = 0.146 inch.

Note: extreme precision is not required for these calculations because we are assuming the nominal value for C_{vr} is 0.75 pF, and an 85-picosecond pulse corresponds to a precise frequency of 11.765 GHz, not 12.0 GHz. Tune-up will accommodate most errors.

A similar solution applies to the tuned ringing line, L_r. This line should resonate at the desired harmonic frequency of 9856 MHz, and is 0.160 inch as determined by either method. It is also tunable by C_r.

One dimension remains to be found. By referring to Fig 16 in the Design Techniques section, you can see that L_r and C_r represent a network that matches a capacitive value to a low-value resistive point. We want to continue this line as a transition line, L_t, and extend it into the waveguide where it will represent a high impedance radiating probe in the E field of the waveguide. The length of L_t should be a free-space quarter wavelength at the oscillator's harmonic frequency. This length, from C_r, is 0.2994 inch.

These dimensions establish the height of the hexagonal brass section that "houses" the concentric line for the frequency of operation and the diode chosen.

SRDs tested in various 10-GHz models were Alpha Industries DVB 6100As, DVB 6100Bs, DVB 6101As and DVB 6101Bs. The main difference between the 6100s and the 6101s is that the 6101s have a higher breakdown voltage (30 V versus 15 V for the 6100s). Neither voltage represents a breakdown problem for the power levels at which this SRD multiplier operates. Alpha uses the term C_j for diode capacity (measured at 6 V, reverse bias) rather than C_{vr} as we have been using. Alpha also uses T_t for pulsewidth. All of these diodes worked well in various experimental units with slight adjustments of the component values. Similar diodes from other manufacturers should work equally well.

Tune It Up!

Tuning an SRD multiplier requires at least an RF power meter and a method of frequency measurement—such as a calibrated waveguide "suck-out" cavity that provides a "dip" in the power-meter reading. The author uses a well-calibrated HP-431C power meter with a 478A coaxial thermistor head and an HP-X532A "dip" wavemeter, plus several calibrated attenuators.

Keep in mind during the tune-up process that at 10 GHz it is fairly easy to tune an SRD multiplier to other undesired modes (frequencies). The cut-off frequency of the waveguide is 6557 MHz, and modes within the waveguide to well over 12 GHz can be excited. So *any* time you see a power reading, check its frequency! If it is a "clean" frequency, the dip on the power meter will be quite deep (typically 2 dB for the wavemeter used). If the signal is not "clean," the dip will be shallow. A spectrum analyzer makes this job easier—but it is not essential. Use the waveguide dip meter to verify that lower and higher harmonics (n − 1 and n + 1) are virtually eliminated (no dip on the meter).

The first step in the tune-up process is to verify that you have a *clean, single-frequency* drive signal at a power level of approximately 200 mW. If you do not have a clean, single-frequency signal, trying to tune up an SRD is an exercise in futility. The use of a reentrant filter *prior* to the MRF-571 stage may be required.

Because there are a lot of screws to adjust, some "presets" are in order. First, adjust the sliding partition in the waveguide filter to a waveguide half wavelength for the desired frequency and set all other matching screws in the waveguide to a "full-out" position, *except* for the capacitive tuning screw in the waveguide filter. Preset it for a little less than half penetration into the waveguide filter inductive partition. Preset the ringing-line filter screw (C_r) to its mid-capacitance range.

With the power meter on a low-power scale and the wavemeter connected, apply drive and adjust the tuning of the input-matching section in conjunction with the diode bias pot and look for an indication of power output. Be prepared to shut things off fast—you might be close enough to being tuned up to "pin" the power meter until you set it to a higher-scale value.

Once output power is indicated, verify the frequency! If it is the wrong frequency, or the dip is shallow, readjust the sliding partition in the waveguide to less than a waveguide half wavelength, as the antenna probe will tend to capacitively load the waveguide filter and require a shorter length. You should find a sharply tuning adjustment point that provides output power with a good dip

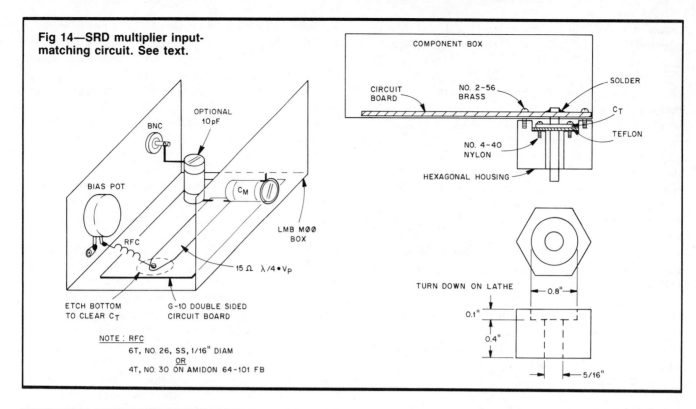

Fig 14—SRD multiplier input-matching circuit. See text.

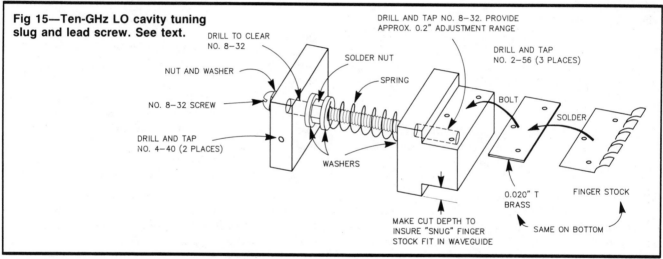

Fig 15—Ten-GHz LO cavity tuning slug and lead screw. See text.

at the correct frequency. Readjust the inductive partition tuning screw for maximum power at the *correct* frequency, along with the tuned, resonant ringing-line capacitor (C_r). Be careful—they are capable of tuning to the wrong harmonic. Judge their setting by the depth of the dip on the power meter.

These adjustments are nearly "set and forget" once they are set at the correct frequency. After that, it is a matter of simply peaking everything for maximum power output while constantly verifying that you're at the correct harmonic. 200 mW input should produce about 20 mW output. If you have a nice dip (2 dB or better) on the power meter, you can be reasonably sure that the power is all at the proper harmonic. Check the $n-1$ and $n+1$ frequencies to be sure.

Now, turn the drive on and off and verify that everything is working normally and reliably. If not, slightly

readjust the diode bias and matching network tuning for solid operation.

During the tune-up process, having a 10-GHz signal source is helpful. With the SRD connected to a mixer/IF amplifier and your receiver, you can listen to the tune-up results as you proceed.

You will find that you can generally hear the signal source even when the SRD is not completely tuned to the correct harmonic. The signal, however, will be weak and the unwanted harmonic energy will make the S meter read high when the receiver is detuned from the source frequency. As you approach the correct harmonic in the tune-up process, the signal will become loud and the background noise as seen on the S meter will drop to a level established by the IF amplifier gain. The effect is dramatic and gratifying; you know the unit is on 10 GHz and the mixer is operating with the correct LO frequency!

Once it's tuned and all of the adjustments are tightened down, the multiplier is extremely stable and reliable. If you connect a spectrum analyzer at this point, you will see a strong, clean, single line with nothing but normal spectrum analyzer noise on the baseline, down approximately 60 dB. When you put the two-port coupler on the waveguide you should get essentially equal power from each port, with perhaps slight readjustments of the waveguide matching screws and the sliding partition. With 20 mW of total power, each port will provide about 10 mW. This power level permits you to use a short coax run to the mixers and still have enough power to operate even a doubly balanced mixer. If you are using mixers that don't require that much power, reduce the drive level to the SRD by attenuating the *input* to the MRF-571 stage, or use a longer piece of coax to the mixers. RG-58 coax makes an excellent 10-GHz attenuator!

Comments

In other versions of the SRD multiplier, the RF flanges used to fasten the two-port coupler to the SRD have been eliminated. The two-port coupler is an integral part of the waveguide section. Use a piece of waveguide approximately 6 inches long for the complete unit and build the two-port coupler on the end. In addition, the sliding adjustment on the two-port coupler is eliminated by simply soldering an end plate exactly one waveguide quarter wavelength from the coupler probes.

At present, there is little available and understandable tutorial literature on the use of SRDs. *Hewlett-Packard Application Note 920* is probably one of the best and most detailed source of information on the subject.

SRD multipliers can also be used for the lower-microwave frequencies. The methods described for 10-GHz SRDs generally apply to lower frequencies as well. Just be sure to select the right diode for your input and output frequencies—the theory of operation is the same. Other modes, such as narrowband FM for simplex operation, can be generated directly by simply phase-modulating the crystal oscillator. Construction methods at lower frequencies utilize microstripline techniques rather than waveguide, and power outputs are greater because the required multiplying factor is smaller. SRDs also produce more power at lower frequencies.

Coaxial RF Cavities

By Buzz Miklos, WA4GPM

1678 Pioneer Rd
Salt Lake City, UT 84104

Resonant circuits for vacuum-tube amplifiers and oscillators used below 100 MHz have traditionally employed lumped-constant elements to achieve resonance. As the frequency is increased beyond 100 MHz, however, a significant amount of capacitance and inductance necessary to tune the circuit is contained within the tube, resulting in the need for only small amounts of additional reactance to achieve the desired resonant condition. By employing stripline, the upper frequency limit of vacuum-tube circuits can be extended to 2000 MHz. These stripline designs, however, must be fully shielded to prevent additional radiation losses, and circuit Q is usually difficult to control. Coaxial and radial circuits offer another alternative which can provide satisfactory performance for vacuum tubes up to 9 GHz. These circuits offer excellent control of Q, minimum radiation losses, simplicity and repeatability.

At frequencies above 300 MHz, coaxial circuits are often used in amplifier and oscillator circuits to achieve a high degree of efficiency. See Fig 1. Coaxial line resonators have their entire electromagnetic field contained within the outer conductor. Radiation losses and undesired coupling to other circuit elements are therefore avoided, and resonator Q is greater than with conventional lumped constant or stripline resonators. The resonant frequency can be changed by a movable short-circuiting element or plunger, or by means of a lumped capacitance placed across the resonator at a point of high electric-field strength.

Since the mode of propagation in coaxial resonators is TEM, there is no lower limit to possible operating frequencies, and there is usually no interference from resonances associated with higher modes of propagation. This advantage is not shared by radial cavity resonators. Consequently, coaxial-line circuits present fewer optimization problems.

Circular or rectangular resonators are radial circuits, capacitively loaded at their center by the tube. See Fig 2. Because propagation in this type of resonator can take place in more than one direction and in various modes, cavity resonators have a large number of possible resonant modes. For a half-wavelength resonator with the tube in the center, the TE_{110} mode is predominant. The electric field is maximum in the active region of the tube, and the tube capacitance, therefore, loads the cavity and reduces its size for a given frequency. The electric field lines are parallel to the axis of the tube and are zero at the circumference of the resonator. Resonators of this type are

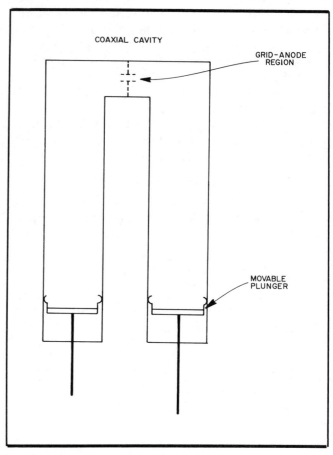

Fig 1—Simplified coaxial circuit.

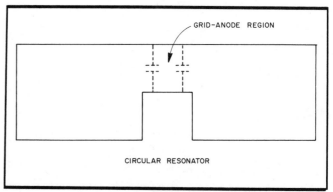

Fig 2—Capacitively loaded circular resonator.

usually provided with a movable wall or slug placed in an area of high electric-field intensity for tuning adjustment. These types of resonators are, however, fairly narrow-band devices which are susceptible to undesired resonances that reduce efficiency and give rise to spurious oscillations.

Because of the complexity related to the design of radial line and waveguide resonators, the best choice for amplifier circuits is the coaxial line type. Although some machine work is necessary, a large variety of stock tubing sizes is available that make it possible for the home builder to fabricate an efficient cavity at a reasonable cost. The design of such cavities is straightforward and requires only a minimal amount of mathematics. Many of the parts can be fabricated with simple hand tools. For this reason, the rest of this chapter will be devoted to the theory, design and fabrication of these types of circuits.

COAXIAL CAVITY FUNDAMENTALS

The coaxial-cavity resonator can be thought of as an extension of a low-frequency L-C tuned circuit. The inductor becomes the walls of the cavity and the capacitor becomes the distributed capacitance along the cavity walls. See Fig 3. The high inherent Q of concentric lines as resonant circuits, the extremely low radiation and the ability to isolate these configurations from other circuit elements contribute to successful designs using coaxial cavities.

To understand how a coaxial resonator actually works, we have to rely on transmission-line theory. The coaxial cavity resonator is actually a short section of coaxial transmission line. A quarter-wavelength short-circuited line appears as an open circuit and can be considered as a parallel resonant circuit. Similarly, a short-circuited line one-half-wavelength long appears as a short circuit and behaves electrically as a series resonant circuit.

Consider, for a moment, a more detailed look at the behavior of a quarter-wavelength line short-circuited at one end. The input impedance of this line will then be observed as the line length is varied for a fixed frequency. From transmission line theory the input impedance for this line is equal to

$Z_{IN} = jZ_0 \tan \theta$

where

Z_0 = the characteristic impedance of the line
θ = the length of the line in electrical degrees

If $\theta = 90°$, or ¼ wavelength, the tangent approaches infinity and the impedance of the line will be extremely high, just as is the case with a parallel resonant circuit. As θ becomes less than 90° (shorter than a ¼ wavelength) the impedance falls rapidly and becomes inductive because the sign of the tangent is positive for angles 0 to 90°. If the line is longer then 90°, the impedance still falls off rapidly, but the circuit now appears capacitive because the sign of the tangent is negative for angles 90 to 180°. See Fig 4.

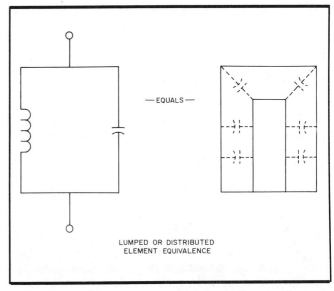

Fig 3—A coaxial resonator cavity is similar to a low-frequency L-C circuit.

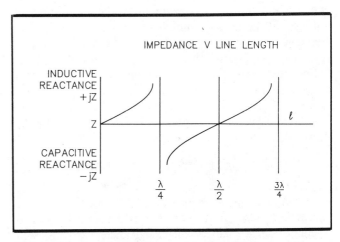

Fig 4—Graph of impedance v line length as used to tune UHF resonant circuits.

Looking at the impedance graph of Fig 4, another interesting point should be noted. The impedance of the ¼-wavelength line repeats every half wavelength. Thus, if the frequency is very high and the wavelength very short, the line can be lengthened in half-wavelength steps and still retain its resonant characteristics. This characteristic is almost always used for tuning UHF circuits since the first quarter wavelength of line is part of the tube and, therefore, cannot be changed.

To make practical use of coaxial resonators as circuit elements in amplifiers and oscillators, they must be connected to vacuum tubes. Since the input or output impedance of a tube is predominantly capacitive by nature of its grid-cathode or gird-plate capacitance, we can achieve resonance by foreshortening the coaxial line and making its impedance appear inductive. If the impedance of the line is made to match the impedance of the tube (but of opposite sign), resonance will be achieved. This qualitative explanation yields the familiar formula

$$jX_c = jZ_0 \tan \theta$$

where

  jX_c = the reactance of the tube
  jZ_0 = the characteristic impedance of the line and
  θ = the foreshortened length of line in electrical degrees

COAXIAL LINE CHARACTERISTICS

Several characteristics of coaxial lines are important to consider when designing amplifiers and oscillators. Q, bandwidth, voltage and current distribution and characteristic impedance are all important parameters which will have an effect on the final performance of the circuit.

Voltage and Current Distribution

For a quarter-wavelength line short-circuited at one end, current will be at a maximum at the short end and voltage will be at a maximum at the open end. Such a distribution is shown in Fig 5.

When the lines are extended to 3/4 or 5/4 wavelength, voltage and current distribution along the line will repeat at half-wavelength intervals. The significance of understanding these distributions will be important in determining the placement of coupling and tuning probes or the design of fingers for tuning plungers.

Characteristic Impedance

The characteristic or surge impedance of coaxial lines is a function of the diameter ratios of the conductors. The expression found in most texts provides an easy way to calculate line impedances when the diameters are expressed in any self-consistent set of units.

$$Z_0 = 138 \log_{10} \times \frac{D_{\text{outside}}}{D_{\text{inside}}}$$

The physical length of coaxial lines used as resonant circuits is mainly dependent on frequency. The characteristic impedance of the line also is a factor since θ is inversely proportional to Z_0 as is shown when the standard formula for resonance is solved for line length in degrees

$$\theta = \tan^{-1}\frac{(jX_c)}{(jZ_0)}$$

In other words, as the characteristic impedance of the line decreases, the length of the line increases. See Fig 6.

The distributed capacitance of the line is also dependent on the characteristic impedance of the line, and will be higher for lower-impedance line. Because of the increased stored energy in the distributed capacitance of the lower-impedance line, the operating Q (loaded Q) will be higher than for a high-impedance line. If circuit efficiency

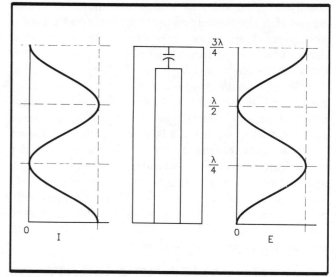

Fig 5—Current and voltage distribution along a ¾-λ line.

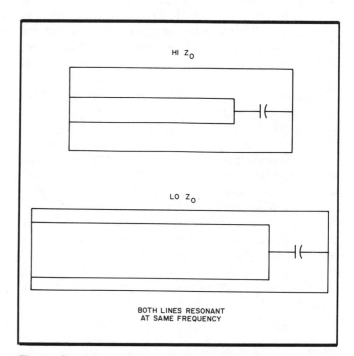

Fig 6—Graphic depiction of characteristic impedances of two different resonant lines. Both lines are resonant at the same frequency.

is of prime importance, such as in the output circuit of an amplifier, higher line impedances (70 to 90 ohms) will provide for lower loaded Q and better circuit efficiency.

Higher-mode operation introduces complications when considering loaded Q on the basis of stored energy and energy delivered per cycle to the load. The stored energy is greatly increased by the additional length of line in 3/4- and 5/4-modes of operation. There is, however, a question as to whether a high- or low-impedance line will have more or less stored energy for a given load impedance.

It was stated that stored energy is a function of line capacitance. The square of the voltage across this capacitance must also be considered when determining the total stored energy.

Consider two lines of the same resonant impedance, but of different characteristic impedances. The low-characteristic-impedance line (Z_01) will be longer than the high-impedance line (Z_02) since both resonate the same C_{gp}. Since both lines are driven by the same voltage, E_2 is larger than E_1:

$$e = E_1 \sin\theta_1 = E_2 \sin\theta_2$$

or

$$E_2 = E_1 \frac{\sin\theta_1}{\sin\theta_2}$$

and

$$\sin\theta_1 > \sin\theta_2$$

The increase in voltage in the added half wavelength of line (by the increase in characteristic impedance) frequently increases the stored energy more than the reduction in capacitance will reduce it. Practically speaking, the designer must find an impedance that will minimize stored energy while considering both line length and characteristic impedance. If θ_2 is less than 40° with 3/4-mode operation, or 25° with 5/4-mode operation, the lower characteristic impedance should be sought. Impedances of 20 to 30 ohms are, therefore, quite efficient for input-line circuits.

BANDWIDTH AND Q CONSIDERATIONS

So far, only ideal cavities have been discussed, that is, cavities that have perfectly conducting walls. Real cavities, however, have finite resistance, which depends largely on the conductivity of the bulk material, the depth of penetration when considering the skin effect, and the effectiveness of contact fingers and mechanical joints. To optimize cavity performance, an understanding of these concepts is necessary.

Because RF currents flow on the surface of the conductor, thus reducing the cross-sectional area available for current flow, some consideration must be given to the choice of material for cavity walls and components. As the frequency is increased, the depth of penetration of the RF current flow decreases, thus increasing losses. The skin depth, defined as the point where the electric field intensity is 37% less than the field intensity at the surface of the conductor, is given by

$$\delta = \frac{1}{\sqrt{\pi f \mu \sigma}}$$

where
δ = skin depth
σ = the conductivity of the material
μ = the permittivity of the material in free space
f = frequency

The above equation is convenient for comparing the skin depths of various materials. Fig 7 compares skin depth of several common cavity materials as a function of frequency.

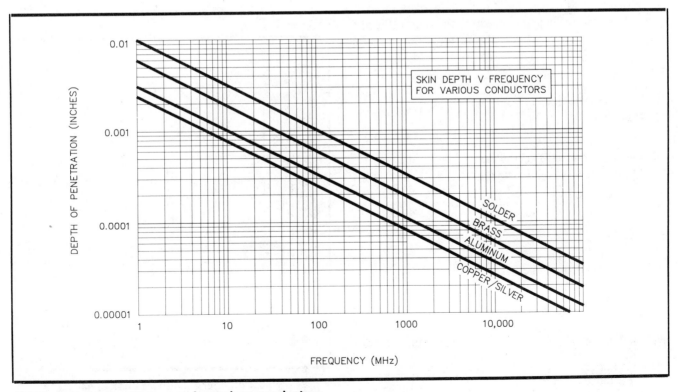

Fig 7—Skin depth v frequency for various conductors.

As shown by the graph, copper and silver are ideal choices for cavities, based on their conductivity. Silver and gold plating are typically found in most commercial cavities to reduce surface resistance. Aluminum and brass are the economical choices for base materials since they are easily plated. Plating thicknesses of 0.0002 to 0.0004 inch are sufficient for cavities operating as low as 50 MHz, since the depth of penetration at this frequency is only 0.00035 inch.

Besides the conductivity of the cavity walls, the mechanical joints contribute to the overall efficiency of the circuit. For a quarter-wavelength cavity, the connection of the center and outer conductors to the base at the shorted end is especially critical because the peak circulating current must flow through this joint. To appreciate the significance of this fact, consider a cavity designed to operate at 432 MHz at 1 kW. The circulating current in the output circuit can be estimated to be the peak fundamental current of the anode times the loaded Q of the circuit. If the loaded Q is 20 and the peak RF current is 1.5 amperes, then 30 amps of RF circulating current must flow through the area in the cavity where the impedance is minimum. Since resistive losses are I^2R losses, only a small resistance will be required to significantly reduce circuit efficiency. A poorly constructed joint combined with reduced cross-sectional area (because of skin effect) can ruin an otherwise efficient circuit.

Finger stock or helical spring contacts are also potential trouble spots which can increase the resistance in the cavity circuit. When these items are used as connecting points for tube flanges or plungers, care should be taken to ensure a tight fit around the entire contact surface. A properly plated, clean surface will prevent erratic performance and overheating, which could destroy the fingers.

Armed with some basics about conductivity in UHF cavities, we can begin to understand the relationships of bandwidth, Q and efficiency. Resonator efficiency, the efficiency of the tube and cavity as a tuned circuit, is defined as

$$\eta = \frac{Q_u - Q_l}{Q_u} \times 100\%$$

where

Q_u = unloaded Q of the cavity
Q_l = loaded Q of the cavity

Q can also be defined as

$$Q = \frac{\text{frequency}}{\text{bandwidth}}$$

or, in terms of stored energy, as

$$Q = 2\pi f \frac{\text{energy stored per cycle}}{\text{energy lost per cycle}}$$

in the RF circuit. This can also be compared to the equation

$$Q = \frac{\text{reactance}}{\text{resistance}}$$

since energy can only be stored in the pure reactance of the circuit, and all losses are be related to the resistance of the circuit. To increase circuit efficiency, we must make the unloaded Q as high as possible by reducing all ohmic losses in the cavity walls, joints, and the anode ceramic. Second, we must make the loaded Q as low as possible by properly coupling the load to the cavity. This will require a fairly wide bandwidth, but will result in maximum circuit performance. By using the relationships between Q, bandwidth and efficiency, we can look at cavity performance quantitatively, and make the right changes to optimize performance.

COAXIAL RESONATOR TUNING

The principal method of tuning coaxial resonators is by the use of a movable plunger which changes the length of the cavity as the frequency is varied. The plunger is usually made of beryllium copper spring fingers which are in intimate contact with the wall of the cavity. See Fig 8. This type of plunger works well for amplifier applications where the frequency must be varied over several hundred megahertz.

In some oscillator applications where the frequency must be varied rapidly over a large range, the conventional contact plunger is usually inadequate. Noise, introduced by dirty fingers, corrosion, and wear requires a modified plunger design. To prevent damaging effects, non contact plungers are usually employed. The simplest types are the bucket and choke plunger illustrated in Fig 9. These plungers can be explained with the aid of transmission-line theory. The gaps between the plunger and the line con-

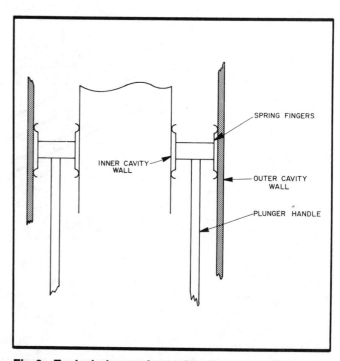

SPRING FINGERS

INNER CAVITY WALL

OUTER CAVITY WALL

PLUNGER HANDLE

Fig 8—Typical plunger for tuning coaxial cavities.

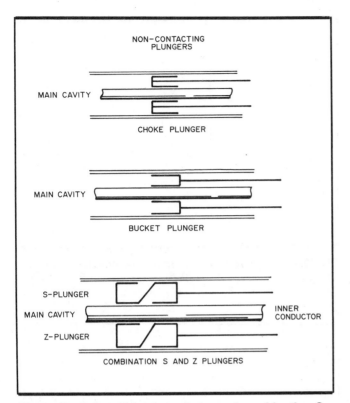

Fig 9—Depiction of bucket, choke and combination S and Z plungers for tuning coaxial cavities.

ductors form low-impedance transmission lines. If the plunger, and hence, the gap lines are made a quarter wavelength long, the high impedance in which the gap lines are terminated will be transformed to a low impedance at the plunger face. By decreasing the impedance of the gap lines, the impedance at the plunger face will decrease. Thus, the main cavity will see a short at the plunger, despite the lack of a dc connection.

Combinations of bucket and choke plungers to form S and Z plungers improve upon this basic concept. They reduce RF leakage in the dead space behind the plunger, and assure that the plunger face is presenting a short to the main cavity. Non-contacting plungers, however, require precision parts to hold the gaps in tight tolerance, since air is usually the chosen dielectric. Consequently, non-contacting plungers are usually found only in high-reliability military and laboratory applications.

For amateur cavities that only operate over a narrow range of frequencies, tuning discs or slugs are employed. These devices add capacitance to the coaxial line and will adequately tune out the variations introduced by inter-electrode tube capacitances and loading. For lower frequencies, a brass disc soldered to a flat-head screw with a fine thread is all that is necessary. A tensioning device such as a spring or jam nut will minimize erratic operation. For L-band and higher, a simple slug will provide adequate capacitance to tune the circuit.

To be effective, the tuning disc or slug must be placed at the high-voltage point along the cavity. For a quarter-wavelength line, that will be right up against the tube. For higher-mode lines, the tuning capacitance is placed a quarter wavelength above the short. Typical tuning positions for several line lengths are shown in Fig 10.

COUPLING

The purpose of coupling is to transfer RF power in to, or out of, the coaxial circuit. To do this efficiently, the coupling must also accomplish an impedance transformation, have low internal losses, and be capable of tuning out its own internal reactance. Being able to conveniently adjust the coupling while the circuit is in operation is also another point that makes cavity adjustment much simpler.

Loop (inductive) coupling couples RF energy via the magnetic field, and is most effective when used at the maximum-current point of the line. Such a loop will act as an impedance transformer and perform a matching function between the coaxial line and the load. The insertion of a series capacitor in the loop will tune out the loop's internal reactance and provide a better match for the outgoing transmission line. See Fig 11.

For tuned or untuned coupling circuits, the degree of coupling is determined by the area formed by the loop and its placement relative to the center conductor. A suitable means of adjusting loop positions is helpful in setting up a cavity for the first time. The series capacitor is, however, usually all that is necessary to optimize the coupling circuit once placement of the loop has been adjusted for maximum power transfer. Coupling probes or capacitors can also be used for coupling, but like tuning capacitors, must

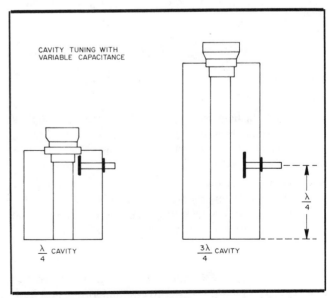

Fig 10—Typical cavity tuning positions for two commonly used cavity sizes.

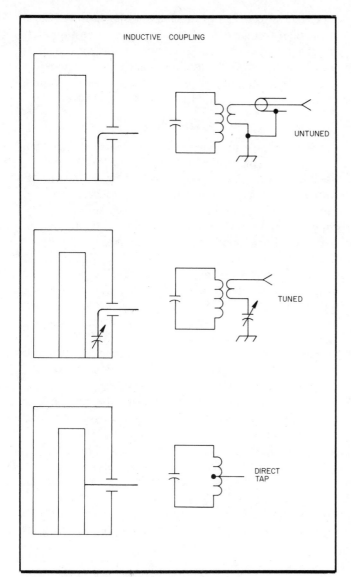

Fig 11—Three types of inductive coupling for coaxial cavities.

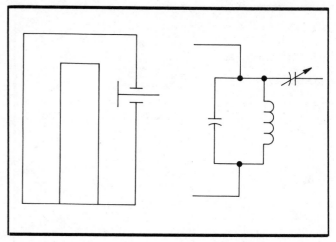

Fig 12—Capacitive probe coupling for coaxial cavities.

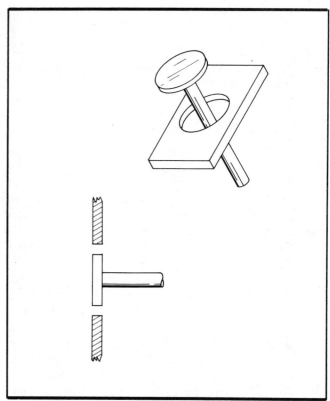

Fig 13—Probe-Loop coupling for coaxial cavities.

be placed at the high-voltage point of the line. The coupling is varied by moving the probe nearer to, or farther from, the center conductor of the coaxial line. The capacitor probe also provides an impedance transformation from the line to a low impedance load. The value of the capacitance is usually only a few picofarads. See Fig 12.

In some cases, where a coaxial line is made to tune over a wide frequency range, the coupling device must move along the line to be efficient. Sometimes, a loop will be fixed to the plunger and will remain at the high-current point, regardless of frequency. In cases where this is impractical, it might be easier to combine probe and loop coupling. An example of probe-loop coupling is shown in Fig 13.

When the probe is close to the fixed arm, the coupling is similar to loop with a variable amount of series capacitance. As the probe is moved away from the fixed arm, the coupling becomes more capacitive. This type of coupling is found in many military-surplus cavities and will provide effective coupling over several hundred megahertz.

CAVITY DESIGN

The best way to strengthen our understanding of cavity theory is to actually design, build, and test an actual cavity. We normally begin such a task by setting a design goal, choosing a device, and designing the metal work to meet the requirements—within the constraints of cost and technological capability. The following reinforces the theory introduced in the previous section.

We desire to construct an RF amplifier for 1296 MHz, capable of more than 200 W output which can be easily tuned and constructed. Several planar triodes manufactured in Europe and the United States are likely candidates for this type of operation. We will choose the EIMAC YU-129. The cavity will be a coaxial type using a 3/4-λ anode line and a 5/4-λ line for the grid cathode. The general design is shown in Fig 14.

The following is a step-by-step procedure for the cavity design.

1) Determine the wavelength for 1296 MHz,

$$\lambda = \frac{11808}{1296} = 9.111 \text{ inches}$$

2) Determine the anode line impedance. This will be a function of the available tubing sizes for the grid and anode, as well as the dimensions of the grid/anode contact surfaces. If 4-inch-diameter tubing is chosen for the anode, and 2-inch-diameter tubing for the grid, then anode ID = 3.75 inches

grid OD = 2.00 inches

$$Z_0 = 138 \log_{10} \frac{3.75}{2.00}$$

$$= 37.7 \text{ ohms}$$

3) From the YU-129 data sheet, read the output capacitance, C_{gp}, and calculate its reactance at 1296 MHz:

$$X_c = \frac{1}{j\omega C_{gp}}$$

$$= 15.35 \text{ ohms}$$

4) Now use the general formula for coaxial lines to determine the length of the anode line:

$$jX_c = jZ_0 \tan \theta$$

$$\theta = \tan^{-1} \left(\frac{15.35}{34.94} \right)$$

$$\theta = 23.71°$$

The line length in degrees must now be converted to inches by the relationship

$$\frac{\theta \times \lambda}{360} = \text{inches}$$

or

$$\frac{23.71 \times 9.1111}{360} = 0.6001 \text{ inch}$$

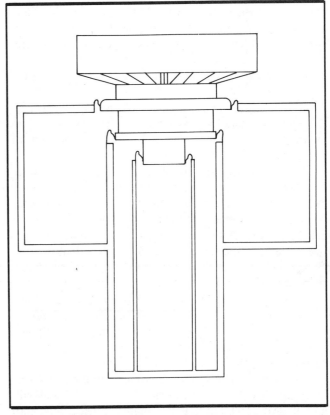

Fig 14—General outline of a 1296-MHz coaxial cavity. This design is based upon the EIMAC YU-129.

5) Since 0.6001 inch is an impractical length for a plate line, we will add a half wavelength and use ¾-wavelength line. 0.6001 + (9.1111/2) = 5.156 inches.

6) Design the input line. Follow the same procedure for the grid/cathode line using the appropriate value for C_{in} and a practical Z_0:

ID of grid line = 1.75 inches

OD of cathode = 1.125 inches

C_{gk} = 18 pF

Calculated $Z_0 = 138 \log_{10} (1.75 / 1.125) = 26.48$ ohms

Calculated $X_c = (1 / j\omega C_{gk}) = 6.82$ ohms

Calculated length of ¼-wavelength line in electrical degrees:

$\theta = \tan^{-1} (6.82 / 26.48)$

Calculated line length in inches:

$(14.443 \times 9.1111) / 360 = 0.3655$ inch

Since 1/4-wavelength line is too short to be practical, use 5/4-wavelength line. This will allow the input tuning controls to be below the end of the anode line. Length is then 0.3655 + 9.111 = 9.4766 inches.

7) Output tuning and coupling. Since the cavity is designed to operate over a narrow frequency range, a single capacitive element will be added to the anode line rather than changing the length of the line with a plunger. Not more than 1 to 1.5 pF will be required. This is accomplished

with a ¾-inch disc soldered to the end of a 3/8 × 24 screw in the anode line side wall. It must be placed at a voltage maximum, which would be ¼ wavelength above the bottom end of the anode line. Therefore, the tuning cap should be 9.1111 / 4 = 2.27 inches above the bottom of the anode.

Likewise, the output probe is placed ¼ wavelength above the cold end of the cavity; a ¾-inch disc will provide the required capacitance. The output probe is shown in Fig 15.

8) Input tuning and coupling. To accomplish a good input SWR, a plunger is chosen to tune the grid/cathode line, and a capacitive probe is used to match the input to the line. The placement of the input probe has to be estimated to some extent, since the final position of the plunger is variable. It still must be placed ¼ wavelength above the plunger position. For this cavity, that's 2.227 inches above the predicted position of the plunger. See Fig 16.

9) Bypassing and voltage feed. There are numerous ways and materials available to construct bypass and blocking capacitors. Typical materials include mica, mylar, Teflon® and Kapton®. All four have advantages, depending upon application, cost, and availability.

For plate blocking and bypassing, Kapton is perhaps the best choice. It has a dielectric constant of 3.6 and will hold off over 2500 V/mil. It is available in sheet, tape, and clad forms, can be easily cut and does not cold flow. For the YU-129 cavity, a 5-mil Kapton bypass was etched from clad material. This capacitor had a value of 200 pF, which is equivalent to 0.6 ohm of reactance at 1296 MHz.

Always use ample clearance between the anode contact plate and the screws holding it in position. Teflon shoulder insulators with no. 6-32 screws are often used to secure anode plates where the diameter of the insulator is at least 3/8 inch. Remember that the crests of screw threads will be more susceptible to arc-over for a given clearance than a smooth cylinder. Also, the edges of the contact plate and anode cavity top plate should be machined with a radius to prevent breakdown at sharp edges and corners.

The cathode bypass should be designed to have low reactance at the operating frequency. Capacitors can be made with concentric insulated sleeves or, as in this cavity, an insulating block with lumped capacitance placed over the gap. Try to keep the inductance low by placing several capacitors in parallel. Disc ceramics are okay to use, even at 1296 MHz, although chip capacitors are probably better. Eight 100-pF chip caps equally spaced around the circumference of the cathode line works quite well in this application.

10) Finger stock and contact surfaces. Finger stock provides a flexible, low-inductance contact as well as allowing for easy tube installation and removal. When designing collets for finger stock, use the dimensions supplied by the manufacturer and the tube outline drawing. Provide 0.015 inch to 0.025 inch interference per side (between the fingers and the tube) to assure a snug fit. Avoid the use of a torch when soldering the fingers in place. The intense heat of the flame will destroy the temper in the fingers. Use a hot plate to heat the work. An

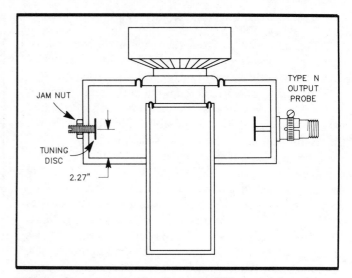

Fig 15—Output probe for the 1296-MHz coaxial cavity.

aluminum plug, the same diameter as the contact surface, makes an ideal fixture for pushing the fingers against the collet while soldering.

11) Cooling and ducting. Tubes designed for UHF amplifier service are not extremely efficient, and considerable energy must be dissipated as heat. Choose a blower that will supply the required volume of air at the back pressure specified in the tube's data sheet. It is better to err by using too big a blower than one too small.

There are no specific rules for the cavity top hat or air chamber. Their shape and size are almost always dependent upon available material. Round designs work as well as square. There are only two precautions.

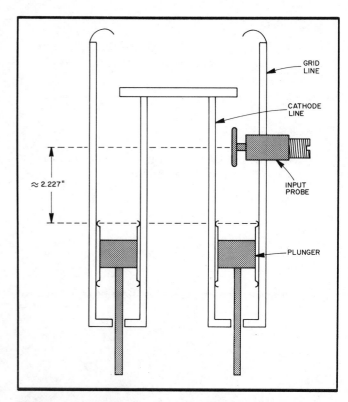

Fig 16—Input probe for the 1296-MHz coaxial cavity.

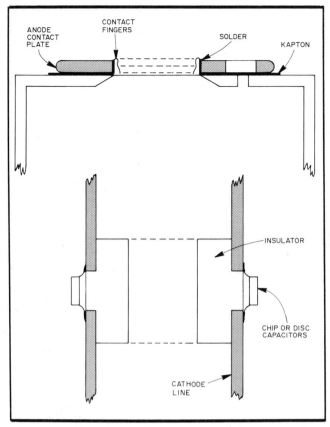

Fig 17—Typical cavity bypass and blocking techniques.

First, make sure there is adequate shielding in the ducts. Both inlet and outlet should be screened or better yet, honeycombed with shielding material.

There should also be a tight fit between the anode top plate and the top hat. Small gaps should be avoided since they make excellent slot radiators. All fastening points should be clean and tight. Some designs will use mesh gaskets to assure a tight contact.

TESTING AND OPERATION

No cavity design is complete until it is tested and made operational. Because of subtle design changes, or in the case of a new design, most cavities require some tinkering to optimize performance.

Fig 17 shows a block diagram of an ideal test set-up for initial cavity alignment. Although such a setup is probably beyond the reach of many, it will be instructive to set up a cavity with this system and demonstrate its usefulness. Many of the measurements that will be mentioned can be done with nothing more than a signal generator and RF voltmeter. Such low-budget configurations are, however, extremely time consuming and prone to inaccuracy.

Connect the cavity as shown in Fig 18. The use of directional couplers at the input and output will make the alignment move along rapidly. Make sure that the cavity is terminated in a 50-ohm load. Many dummy loads are not purely resistive above 400 MHz. It is also a good idea

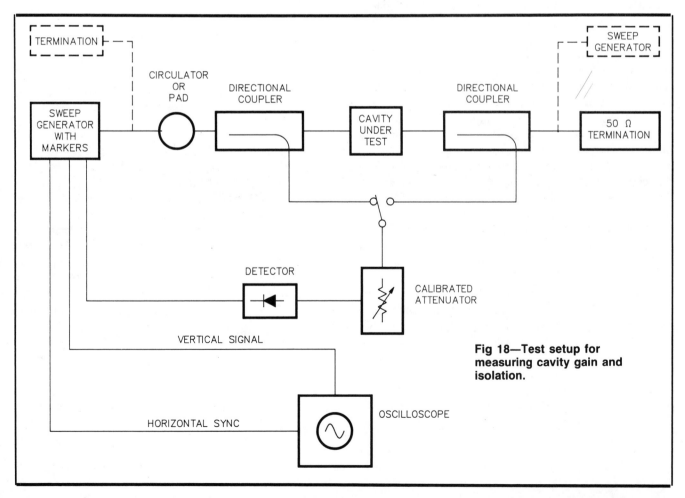

Fig 18—Test setup for measuring cavity gain and isolation.

to use a 3-dB pad or isolator at the input to prevent damage to the signal generator if the cavity should break into oscillation.

Apply filament voltage, air and high voltage to the cavity. Adjust the bias to produce 50 to 100 milliamperes of plate current. If testing another type of tube, obtain enough plate current to allow the tube to operate in Class AB, below the dissipation rating of the anode.

Couple the sweep generator to the input and monitor the output on the oscilloscope. Adjust the input and output tuning controls to resonate at the same frequency. Look at the reflected signal at the input. Adjust the input coupling and tuning for the best notch at the desired operating frequency. At the output, adjust the coupling and tuning for bandwidth, usually about one percent of the operating frequency. See Fig 19.

Measure the gain. For triodes, 10- to 20-dB gain is practical, depending on the tube type and frequency.

Now, connect the sweep generator to the output port of the cavity and terminate the input. Measure the reverse gain or as it is more commonly called, isolation. This gain will be negative and may be in the order of 0 to 40 dB. The important consideration is the isolation relative to forward gain. To assure stability, the isolation should be at least 10 dB greater than the gain.

Most cavity amplifiers are usually under-neutralized and show high gain and poor isolation. Instability may or may not be observed at various settings of the tuning controls, or when the input or output are unterminated. The method employed to neutralize these amplifiers is to increase the inductance in the grid circuit. This can be done by taping over the grid fingers and reducing the grid contact area. Forward gain and isolation measurements are repeated until the isolation peaks at the operating frequency. This will not occur at maximum gain, but will in most cases, guarantee unconditional stability. For the YU-129 cavity, four to eight grid fingers are typically taped using Teflon or Kapton tape. In some cavities, fingers are removed. Although there is variation in interelectrode capacitance from tube to tube, the effect on neutralization is usually negligible. Once the neutralization is set, there is usually no need for readjustment.

Neutralization will also reduce the interaction of input/output tuning. The SWR null at the input should now be easily obtained at the operating frequency, and the cavity should be stable and free of oscillations.

Replace the sweep generator with a high-power drive signal and terminate the output with a dummy load rated for the correct power and frequency. Adjust the bias for the class of operation desired. Increase the drive signal until plate current is observed and adjust the tuning controls for maximum output. The output loading control should be adjusted for the proper grid current while the input coupling is adjusted for lowest SWR. Work the power output up slowly until the desired operating conditions are

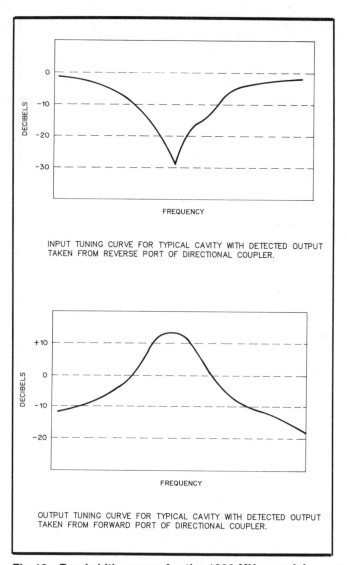

INPUT TUNING CURVE FOR TYPICAL CAVITY WITH DETECTED OUTPUT TAKEN FROM REVERSE PORT OF DIRECTIONAL COUPLER.

OUTPUT TUNING CURVE FOR TYPICAL CAVITY WITH DETECTED OUTPUT TAKEN FROM FORWARD PORT OF DIRECTIONAL COUPLER.

Fig 19—Bandwidth curves for the 1296-MHz coaxial cavity.

met. Grid dissipation is usually the limiting factor in UHF triodes, and maximum ratings should be observed.

For high-power cavities such as the YU-129, it is also a good idea to refrain from long key-down periods during tune-up. A safer method makes use of an automatic keyer set for high-speed dots—thus creating a pulse signal. Peak power can be read on the power meter if you know the pulse length and duty cycle, or an oscilloscope can be used in conjunction with the couplers, a detector diode and a calibrated attenuator. Either method is acceptable and will surely reduce the risk of tube damage during tune-up.

TECHNICAL DATA

The YU-129 is a planar triode of ceramic/metal construction and rugged design. It is intended for use in linear-amplifier applications up to 1.3 GHz.

The '129 may be used as an amplifier or CW oscillator in grid or plate-pulsed modes.

Chapter 7

Notes on UHF and Microwave Systems Design

By Geoffrey H. Krauss, WA2GFP
16 Riviera Dr
Latham, NY 12110

System—a group of artifacts working together, in accordance with a selected set of rules, to bring about a common goal or purpose.

The basic purpose of any communications system is to move information (of some variety, with the exact type being relatively unimportant) from one location to another. In a radio communications system, this information, no matter what its nature, is transferred by variation of some selected characteristic of an electromagnetic signal traveling through free-space (Fig 1).

The information to be sent is input to a source of electromagnetic energy; the source energy, after variation (or, to use the word we more commonly associate with this process, modulation) of at least one signal parameter (amplitude, frequency, phase, and so on), is coupled to the transmission medium. The coupling can be direct, or can require an intermediary coupling transducer (the transmitting antenna). If the energy can travel through free space to the second location, the energy is received at a detector; another transducer (the receiving antenna) may be required to couple the received energy to the detector. If the signal has certain characteristics, the detector will be able to extract some portion of the information and provide that information to some "user," in other words, the ears of a ham operator.

A SIMPLE SYSTEM

The simplest system need have no more than an energy

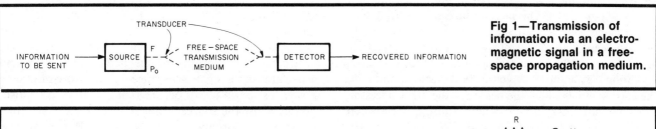

Fig 1—Transmission of information via an electromagnetic signal in a free-space propagation medium.

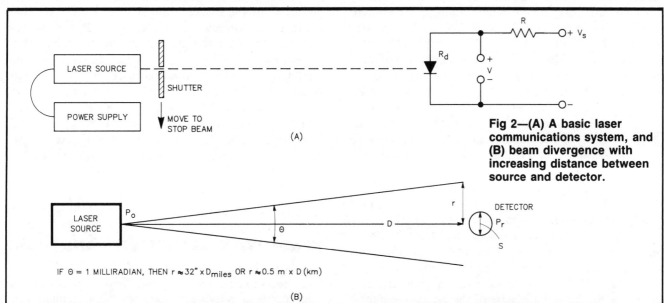

Fig 2—(A) A basic laser communications system, and (B) beam divergence with increasing distance between source and detector.

IF Θ = 1 MILLIRADIAN, THEN $r \approx 32'' \times D_{miles}$ OR $r \approx 0.5$ m $\times$ D (km)

source and an energy detector. The relevant characteristics of the source are its output power P_o and its frequency F; the frequency must not only be within the working range of the detector, but must also be within a legal amateur band. While bare oscillator sources are presently operated on several different wavelength bands, a bare detector is commonly used on only one band: the band of light wavelengths (visible or infrared), that is, typically of between about 550 nanometers (nm or 1×10^{-9} meters) and about 1100 nm. This wavelength octave range may be expressed in terms of angstrom (A) units, that is, 5500 A-11000 A. Using the well-known frequency-wavelength relationship ($c = F \times \lambda$, where c is the speed of electromagnetic energy in a vacuum, 2.998×10^8 m/sec, F is the frequency in hertz (Hz) and λ is wavelength in meters (m), the 632.8-nm red light output from a helium-neon (HeNe) gas laser corresponds to a frequency of 473.8 THz (a terahertz = 1×10^{12} Hz), or 473,800 GHz.

This system is shown in Fig 2A; the source is a laser oscillator, coupling light waves directly to the atmospheric medium, and the detector is any one of a large class of light detectors. The particular detector here is a light-sensitive semiconductor diode, which changes resistance with a change in the amount of light falling upon its surface. The detector functions as a simple voltage divider; the output voltage $V = + V_s R_d \times (R_d + R)$, where R_d is the detector diode resistance at any time, and is a function of the amount of light received. The present record for Amateur Radio communications in the band above 300 GHz is held by stations not much more complex than that shown.

Of course, a simple station of this type will only tell you whether the beam is being received or not, so some additional mechanism is required if other information is to be communicated. This mechanism can be nothing more complicated than a mechanical shutter, that is, a light-blocking card with a hole through it; move the card to let at least part of the beam through the hole for one signal condition (say an up-scale voltmeter deflection) and move the card again to block the beam for the other necessary signal condition (say no meter deflection). Move the card back and forth by hand to send CW; use an electro-magnetic shutter and send faster CW, and so on. Note that this simple modulation scheme may require that the sender be able to see the light beam, in order to set up the shutter to alternately block and pass it. This is fine with an HeNe red-line laser, but would be quite another story with almost all of the infrared semiconductor lasers presently available (luckily, they can be electronically pulsed on/off to send CW). In addition, cost is much greater for semiconductor diode lasers, although the information transfer rate can be much higher with a diode laser. The paramount reason, however, for using a laser with a visible-light output is SAFETY!! Go back to Chapter 2 and reread the safety material, particularly that information concerning the maximum radiation intensity necessary at the most vulnerable part of the human body, the eye. Then consider that UHF and microwave radiation is basically dissipated in the aqueous part of the eye, while light is transmitted through that part of the eye to the light-to-nerve impulse conversion portion of the eye—a much more dangerous condition. Is it any wonder that almost all serious amateur laser work is done with visible light rays!

While we are considering communication at >300 GHz, we can note that the frequency of the emitted electromagnetic radiation (light) is very stable, being related to the electron-orbit transitions in neon gas (essentially as stable as an atomic clock!). Let us also consider the other factor, the output power, that is, the amount of energy being output from the laser tube source, and then consider how much of that energy actually reaches the detector.

A look at Fig 2B will show you that even if we know nothing about the atmospheric attenuation of the beam, the radius r of the beam spreads out by an amount which increases with increasing distance D between source and detector. This happens because the beam edges are not perfectly parallel and a real beam diverges by some amount. A typical beam divergence angle θ is about 1 milliradian (mrad, or 0.001 radian; a radian is approximately 57.3°) for a gas laser, but is about 1 full radian for most ham-affordable diode lasers. (While it is true that both types can be collimated to be parallel at some range of distances D, this would unnecessarily complicate our consideration of some simple system effects. It is mentioned here merely because optical communication systems are not considered in any other portion of this book.) Simple trigonometry tells us that $\tan(\theta/2) = r/D$; therefore, the beam diameter $2r = 2D \times \tan(\theta/2)$ at the detector. Let us provide a detector with an active, light-sensitive area represented by a circle of diameter S. If the detector size factor S is less than the beam diameter 2r, then we can see that all of the source output is not received at the detector. This loss can be appreciable: the beam might have a total area of about 0.8 square meters at a distance of one km, even for an approximately 1-mrad divergence, and most affordable diode detectors have an active area in the square-cm range—an aperture-mismatch power loss of 30-60 dB occurs. That is, all of the power output P_o of the source is not received by the detector. However, the amount of received power P_r will increase as the beam angle θ is decreased; this is equivalent to increasing the "gain" G_s of the source coupling "antenna." The received power increases if the detector area increases to intercept more of the beam; this is the same as increasing the "gain" G_d of the detector coupling "antenna." Therefore, we can say that $P_r = (P_o) \times G_s \times G_d \div L_p$, where L_p is the signal loss over the chosen path between source and detector. If we convert each of the numbers to their logarithm, we can add and subtract, rather than multiply and divide, terms:

$$P_r \text{ (dBm)} = P_o \text{ (dBm)} + G_s \text{ (dB)} + G_d \text{ (dB)} - L_p \text{ (dB)}$$

SENSITIVITY, SELECTIVITY AND NOISE

The attenuation of the signal due to path loss L_p might seem to be not all that bad, because one might consider merely amplifying the detected signal to increase its

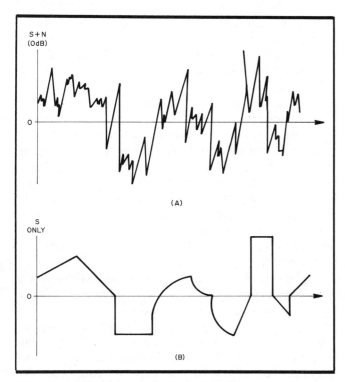

Fig 3—(A) Desired signal mixed with noise, at a 0-dB S/N ratio, and (B) the recovered signal.

amplitude until it is large enough to be useful. At this point we encounter two factors, applicable only to the receiving portion of the system, which pose problems. These factors—sensitivity and selectivity—have to do with the detector output signal, which also contains other components besides the signal received from the source. These unwanted signal components are noise and interference signals serving only to mask the desired information signal. Ignoring, for the present, interference signals and non-natural noise sources, we can concentrate on only two forms: the noise received along with the desired signal by the detector from the transmission medium, and the noise added to the detected incoming signal and noise by the detector itself.

For a real detector, there is thus some minimum amplitude of signal which must be present at the detector before the detector can retrieve any information from that signal, even if the desired information is as limited as the knowledge of whether any signal at all is present at the detector. Why is this so? It is because of the presence of random noise signals (here, any light) which have a total amplitude great enough to mask a desired small-amplitude signal. Even if the signal-to-noise ratio of the incoming signal is just sufficient for equal signal and noise to be present at the detector input, the additional noise internally generated in the detector will cause the total noise amplitude to exceed the detected signal (assuming that the detector has perfect conversion efficiency, which never occurs in a real system). Thus, there is some minimum signal, which is related to the amplitude of random noise at the detector, which must be present before the signal can itself be discerned. The factors which determine how small we can make this minimum discernible signal (MDS)

are additional limitations which a radio operator, as the designer of at least one end of the system, must consider. Look at the detector output voltage waveform in Fig 3A, for a 0-dB signal-to-noise ratio, S/N, of the desired received signal power, P_r, to the undesired noise power, P_n, at the detector. Is it apparent to you that the transmitted "information" is the Fig 3B waveform? Query: How can this ratio be improved? What happens if either (1) the signal power can be increased, or (2) the noise power can be decreased?

To increase the received signal power, the output power P_o of the source could be increased; the distribution of the power coupled to the transmission medium could be modified so that more of the power is directed toward the location of the receiver (decreasing the divergence angle θ is equivalent to increasing antenna directivity and therefore increasing gain G_s) by the first transducer; the second transducer could be modified to intercept more of the signal arriving at the reception location (increased interception = increased gain G_d); or the distance D between the locations, and hence the signal-attenuation loss L_p, could be reduced. One can see that, for a fixed path over a fixed distance D (with a fixed path-loss attenuation L_p), there is some maximum P_r value attainable, when source output power P_o is at a maximum legal/attainable level and the antenna gains are as large as possible for the available space, cost and other factors. The question invariably shifts to: Can the amount of noise power be reduced?

The total noise power is made up of several contributions: thermal noise, man-made noise, atmospheric noise, solar/stellar noise, and the like. Temporary noise, such as that from certain atmospheric sources (thunderstorms), can be minimized by merely waiting for conditions to change. Man-made noise can be minimized by selecting your operating QTH to be shielded by terrain, distance, and so on, from the noise sources. Solar/stellar noise can be minimized by selection of frequency, operating time, pointing direction of antennas, and like considerations (see Fig 4).

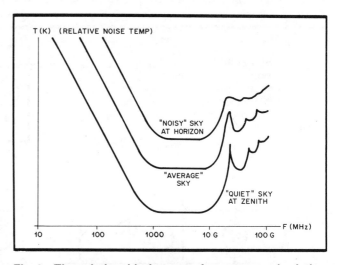

Fig 4—The relationship between frequency and relative noise temperature under different conditions.

Thermal-noise signals are caused by random motion of electrons due to heat energy agitation; the higher the temperature, the greater the thermal agitation and the more noise-producing movement of electrons. A movement of electrons is a current; a thermal movement of electrons is a noise current, I_n. By Ohm's Law, any current passing through a non-zero resistance generates a voltage across that resistance; a noise current, I_n, passing through a non-zero resistance generates a noise voltage, E_n. Therefore, a noise current, I_n, will flow through, and a noise voltage, E_n, will be present across, any non-zero resistance which is at a non-zero temperature; the resistance appears to be a source of noise power, P_n.

The actual value of the noise-producing resistance, R_n, need not be as large as the total dc physical resistance R. (This is due to the presence of a "correlation" coefficient between the noise current and noise voltage, somewhat analogous to the phase angle of reactive power in low-frequency ac power circuits, which can be—and generally is—less than 1. The noise resistance is then the product of the real dc resistance and the noise correlation factor.) Noise power, noise voltage and noise current are all of zero magnitude only at absolute zero, that temperature at which all molecular motion ceases; the resistance of any conductor becomes zero only when the conductor is at a physical temperature so near to absolute zero that the effective temperature T_e of the normally resistive conductor is essentially zero, and the conductor is said to become superconductive. Absolute zero is 0 kelvin (0 K = −273.16 °C).

As the effective temperature T_e is increased, the noise power increases, for a resistance of constant noise value; the noise power also increases as the noise resistance increases, if the resistance is held at a constant temperature above absolute zero. Because noise signals occur at random times, the noise energy is evenly distributed at all frequencies; the wider the band of frequencies looked at by the receiving detector, the greater the included noise power. Thus, the total noise power, P_n, against which the received signal power, P_r, must be compared, is also determined by the bandwidth B over which the noise and the signal are observed; this is the second, or selectivity, factor. The noise power $P_n = k \times T_e \times B$, where k is Boltzmann's constant, 1.38×10^{-23} joule/K, and T_e is the effective temperature, in K, of the noise-receiving element(s).

To answer the previous question then, the effect of thermal noise power can be reduced by (1) reducing bandwidth B; for example, by using medium-speed CW (with a bandwidth of 100-250 Hz) instead of SSB (with a bandwidth of 1800-2300 Hz); (2) reducing the effective temperature T_e of the noise-receiving or noise-generating elements in the receiving portion of the system; or (3) reducing the required signal-to-noise ratio, as by using an integrating filter (especially the one between your ears!) to pick out information closer to, or even under, the prevailing level of the noise.

The sensitivity of the receiver is the magnitude of input signal which must be provided at the receiver input to cause the information on the incoming signal to be detected in accordance with some predetermined criterion. In digital-data transmission, the criterion is typically the bit error rate (the rate at which a bit of data is incorrectly detected, may be as low as 1×10^{-9} for high S/N ratios and with the use of error-correcting codes).

Analog transmissions are generally different, as the criteria are somewhat subjective, that is, can the recovered information be interpolated to fill in any dropouts and make sense of the message (commercial radio communications actually have a quality factor which is determined by having a group of listeners of known capabilities extract information from taped, on-the-air transmissions).

The selectivity of the receiver is the frequency-domain counterpart of the amplitude-domain sensitivity, and is the effective bandwidth of the receiver. Note that the effective bandwidth is the bandwidth of a perfect filter having the same noise-power response as the total real receiver, and may be narrower than the most frequency-selective circuit in the receiver.

Noise Factor

Any physical circuit we can build will be at some

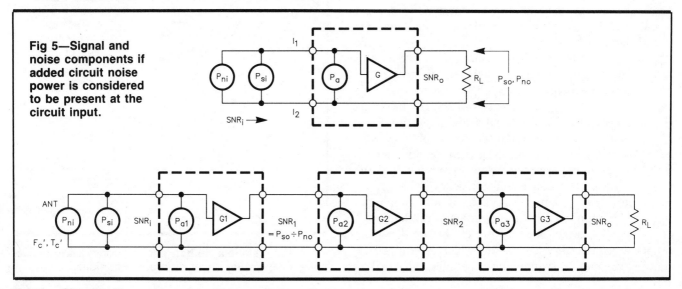

Fig 5—Signal and noise components if added circuit noise power is considered to be present at the circuit input.

temperature above absolute zero, and the electrons in the atoms of its wiring and elements have noise-generating random motion, causing some circuit noise power, P_{ckt}, to be present. If we consider all of this added circuit noise power to be present as noise power P_a at the circuit input, then the signal and noise components will be as shown in Fig 5A; the external signal power P_{si} and external noise power P_{ni} are both supplied to the circuit input terminals I_1 and I_2, while the circuit-added noise power P_a appears across the input of the circuit internal amplification block, having a gain G which is noise-free, since we have deliberately placed all of the circuit noise in the input noise source power P_a. The input signal-to-noise ratio, SNR_i, is then equal to P_{si}/P_{ni}, while the output signal-to-noise ratio, SNR_o, which must be worse than the input SNR_i in any real-world circuit (because no circuit removes random noise, but all real circuits do add circuit noise power P_a), is equal to P_{so}/P_{no}. A standard factor F can be defined to tell us just how much SNR deterioration occurs; this noise factor F is the ratio of SNR_i to SNR_o; that is

$$F = (P_{si}/P_{ni})/(P_{so}/P_{no}) \qquad \text{(Eq 1A)}$$

or

$$F = (P_{si}/P_{so}) \times (P_{no}/P_{ni}) \qquad \text{(Eq 1B)}$$

We know that: (1) the output signal power, whatever its actual magnitude, is only the input signal power multiplied by the gain G, so that $P_{so} = G \times P_{si}$; and (2) the output noise power is the total input noise power, to the noise-free gain block, multiplied by the gain, so that $P_{no} = G \times (P_{ni} + P_a)$. Rewriting Equation 1B, we get:

$$F = \frac{P_{si}}{G \times P_{si}} \times \frac{G \times (P_{ni} + P_a)}{P_{ni}} \qquad \text{(Eq 1C)}$$

o r

$$F = \frac{P_{ni} + P_a}{P_{ni}} \qquad \text{(Eq 2)}$$

This simplifies, by removing like terms in numerator and denominator, to a simple equation:

$$F = 1 + (P_a/P_{ni}) \qquad \text{(Eq 3)}$$

The lowest possible noise factor F is exactly 1, which can only occur in the ideal case when absolutely no noise power P_a is added by the circuit (which could be the entire receiver). In any real circuit/receiver, non-zero noise power P_a is always added and causes the output SNR to be lower than the input SNR. Note that an amplifier adding as much noise power P_a as the noise power P_{ni} already present at its input has $P_a = P_{ni}$, or $F = 1 + (P_{ni}/P_{ni}) = 2$.

Noise Figure and Noise Temperature

Query: Is the use of *noise factor* the only measure by which one can compare the noise-power adding capacities of several circuits of the same general type? No. At least two other measures are used: *noise figure* and *noise temperature*.

Noise figure, NF, is nothing more than a logarithmic conversion, in decibels (dB, implying the use of base 10)

of the noise factor ratio F (which, being a ratio, is a "pure" number having no dimensional units associated with it):

$$NF = 10 \times \log(F) \qquad \text{(Eq 4)}$$

Thus, the perfect amplifier (F = 1) has a noise figure NF $= 10 \times \log(1) = 10 \times 0 = 0$ dB; this makes a lot more sense to many people—adding zero noise power is the same as a 0-dB change! The amplifier that adds noise power P_a equal to the input noise P_{ni} has F = 2, for a noise figure NF $= 10 \times \log(2) = 10 \times 0.2998 = 2.998$ dB, commonly rounded off to 3 dB.

In the past, when noise figures of 3-6 dB were considered very good at UHF and above, use of noise figure for comparison of circuit noisiness was perfectly acceptable; two circuits might be measured with widely different noise figures, say 4.1 dB and 5.7 dB, which were easy to distinguish between, whether one took their difference (1.6 dB) or their ratio (5.7/4.1 = 1.39). But modern-day amateur state-of-the-art UHF (and above) amplifiers and receivers can have noise figures under 1 dB. Comparison between two under-1-dB circuits becomes more difficult.

For example, how much difference is there between a first 432-MHz preamplifier with $NF_1 = 0.42$ dB (or, using F = antilog(NF/10) $F_1 = 1.10154$) and a second 432-MHz preamplifier with $NF_2 = 0.39$ dB (and $F_2 = 1.09396$)? The noise-factor difference of 0.00758 is slightly more meaningless than the ratio of noise factors $F_1/F_2 = 1.00693$; the noise-figure ratio $NF_1/NF_2 = 1.077$ and noise-figure difference of 0.03 dB both seem to say that the two units are almost exactly the same in performance. However, since the added noise power that we seek to minimize is due to the circuit apparent temperature being above absolute zero, let us use that temperature as the indicator. We can define noise-equivalent temperature T_e as:

$$T_e = 290 \text{ K} \times (F - 1) \qquad \text{(Eq 5A)}$$

or

$$T_e = 290 \text{ K} \times [\text{antilog(NF/10)} - 1] \qquad \text{(Eq 5B)}$$

The perfect amplifier (F = 1 and NF = 0 dB) will have $T_e = 290 \times (1 - 1) = 0$ K, adding, exactly as one might expect, the same noise power as a resistance at absolute zero (0 K). From our example, the first preamplifier has $T_{e,1} = 290 \times (1.10154 - 1) = 29.5$ K and the second preamplifier has $T_{e,2} = 290 \times (1.09396 - 1) = 27.3$ K; a clear 2.2 K difference is now apparent. As a percentage, the second preamplifier is (2.2/29.5) $\times 100\% = 7.5\%$ better than the first. We can now see that the two preamplifiers are not even close to being the same!

Query: How should we find the loss of sensitivity, or change in minimum discernible signal (MDS), due to a non-perfect circuit with a noise factor F greater than 1? The actual noise power $P_{ni, act}$ is now not just $P_{ni} = k \times T \times B$, but is increased by the added circuit noise power P_a, so that $P_{ni, act} = P_{ni} + P_a = P_{ni} \times F$ (from Eq 2). Therefore, accounting for the non-ideal noise factor F > 1,

$$P_{ni, act} = k \times T \times B \times F \qquad \text{(Eq 6)}$$

Numerically, at MDS where $P_s = P_{ni}$, sensitivity is

$$P_{sens} = k \times T_e \times B \times F$$

or, in dB,

$$P_{sens} = 10 \times \log(k) + 10 \times \log(T) \\ + 10 \times \log(B) + 10 \times \log(F) \quad \text{(Eq 7)}$$

but, using $10 \times \log(k = 1.38 \times 10^{-23}) = -228.6$ dBW, at the standard "room" temperature $T = 290$ K, yielding $10 \times \log(T) = 24.6$ dB, and $10 \times \log(F) = $ NF, this reduces to:

$$P_{sens} \text{ (in dBW)} = -204 \text{ dBW} + 10 \times \log(B) + \text{NF} \quad \text{(Eq 8)}$$

where noise bandwidth B is in Hz and the sensitivity is in dB relative to 1 W (dBW). In the more frequently used terms of dBm (dB relative to 1 mW):

$$P_{sens} \text{ (in dBm)} = -174 \text{ dBm} + 10 \times \log (B) \text{ [in Hz]} \\ + \text{NF (dB)} \quad \text{(Eq 9A)}$$

or

$$P_{sens} \text{ (in dBm)} = -144 \text{ dBm} + 10 \times \log (B) \text{ [in kHz]} \\ + \text{NF (dB)} \quad \text{(Eq 9B)}$$

Several examples of receiver MDS sensitivity appear in the table elsewhere on this page.

If you have ever attended a VHF hamfest at which noise-figure measurements were made, you may have noticed that the measured noise figures for preamplifiers were considerably better than the noise figures measured for complete receivers or converters. We should understand that the whole is worse than the best stage, because even if the lowest noise figure/temperature amplifier is used in the first stage of the converter/receiver, the subsequent stages must make some noise contribution.

The noise contribution of each stage to the total for the system is affected by the gain of the preceding stages because that gain increases the signal level to which the noise is added. Thus, the gain of each stage "isolates" (somewhat) the noise contributions of following stages from the desired signal.

Let us look at the signal-to-noise ratios in successive stages of an amplifier chain (see Fig 5B). The chain input SNR_i is given as P_{si}/P_{ni}. If the second stage were replaced with a load, the first amplifier output SNR_1 would be $(G_1 \times P_{si}) \div (G_1 \times P_{ni} + G_1 \times P_{a1})$ and we could stop here and reduce this expression to $SNR_1 = P_{si}/(P_{ni} + P_{a1})$. Because an *active* load (the second stage) is present, its input added noise component P_{a2} is part of the load on the first stage and must also appear in the actual SNR_i; therefore,

$$SNR_{12} = \frac{G_1 \times P_{si}}{G_1 \times (P_{ni} + P_{a1}) + P_{a2}}$$

which reduces to

$$SNR_{12} = \frac{P_{si}}{P_{ni} + P_{a1} + (P_{a2}/G_1)}$$

This is the same as saying that the input noise factor F_i is:

$$F_i = F_1 + [(F_2 - 1)/G_1] \quad \text{(Eq 10A)}$$

Similarly, as the second stage output is *actively* loaded with a stage producing an input noise component P_{a3}, then SNR_2 must include this noise power and the effects of the intervening "isolation" gain G_2:

$$SNR_2 = P_{si}/[(P_{ni} + P_{a1}) + (P_{a2}/G_1) + (P_{a2}/G_1 \times G_2)].$$

This leads to

$$F_i = F_1 + [(F_2 - 1)/G_1] + [(F_3 - 1)/(G_1 \times G2)] \quad \text{(Eq 10B)}$$

The general formula eventually becomes:

$$F_i = F_1 + [(F_2 - 1)/G_1] + [(F_3 - 1)/(G_1 \times G_2)] + \dots \\ [(F_k - 1)/(G_1 \times G_2 \times G3 \dots \times G_{k-1})] + \dots \quad \text{(Eq 10C)}$$

The formula for system noise temperature T_i is identical, if the k-th stage noise-factor F_k is replaced by the effective stage temperature T_k for that same stage.

The application of the system noise-factor equation can be illustrated with a typical receiver front end, as in Fig 6. The antenna is coupled by a length of coaxial cable, with a loss of L_a (dB), to a first amplifier. This amplifier has a given noise figure NF_b and gain G_b (both in dB). The signal goes through a second amplifier, also with a given noise figure NF_c (dB) and gain G_c (dB); then through a third stage with a given loss L_d (dB); and finally

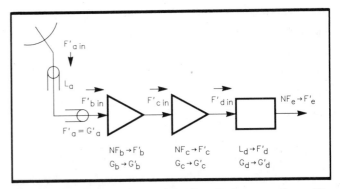

Fig 6—Application of system noise factor equation with a typical receiver front end.

Some examples of MDS sensitivity:

B (KHz)	1.8 (SSB)			00.5 (Wide CW)			0.1 (Narrow CW)		
NF (dB)	3.0	1.0	0.3	3.0	1.0	0.3	3.0	1.0	0.3
P_{sens} (dBm)	−138.4	−140.4	−141.1	−144.0	−146.0	−146.7	−151.0	−153.0	−153.7

This receiver has 15.3 dB worse sensitivity than this one!

into an end stage having a known noise figure NF_e (dB). We want to first find the noise factor $F_{in, d}$ at the input to the lossy stage; applying Eq 10A, this should be

$$F'_{d, in} = F'_d + [(F'_e - 1)/G'_d)].$$

IMPORTANT: Note that noise *factors* and *numerical* gains are being used, not noise figures or decibel gains; all terms must be purely numeric and *not* dB ratios! This is the most common mistake system designers make. To indicate the difference, the primed quantities F' and G' are used for noise factor and numeric gain.

We can easily find $F'_e = \text{antilog}(NF_e/10)$, but what is the numeric "gain" G'_d and the noise factor F'_d of a lossy circuit with a loss L_d (dB)? If it is remembered that the loss is a negative gain, that is, a loss of L_d dB is a gain of $-L_d$ dB, and that subtraction of log numbers is equivalent to division of "pure" numbers, then it will be seen that a numeric loss of $L'_d = \text{antilog}(L_d/10)$ becomes a numeric gain of $G'_d = 1/L'_d$, where L'_d is always greater than 1 and G'_d is always less than 1! The noise figure of most lossy, passive circuits is equal to the loss itself; some lossy circuits, like diode mixers, have a noise figure greater than the loss alone, due to extra noise from the diodes. The noise factor becomes $F'_d = \text{antilog}(L_d/10)$. Thus

$$\begin{aligned} F'_{d, in} &= F'_d + [(F'_e - 1)/G'_d] \\ &= L'_d + L'_d \times (F'_e - 1) \\ &= L'_d \times (1 + F'_e - 1) = L'_d \times F'_e \end{aligned}$$

The noise factors $F'_{c, in}$, $F'_{b, in}$ and $F'_{a, in}$ are now easily calculable, once the gain stage NFs and Gs are converted to F's and G's, as are the lossy cable stage "gain" $G'_a = 1/\text{antilog}(L_a/10)$ and noise factor $F'_a = \text{antilog}(L_a/10) = 1/G'_a$.

$$F'_{c, in} = F'_c + [(F'_d - 1)/G'_c] + L'_d \times [(F'_e - 1)/G'_c]$$

or

$$F'_{c, in} = F'_c + [(F'_{d, in} - 1)/G'_c]$$

$$F'_{b, in} = F'_b + [(F'_c - 1)/G'_b] + [(F'_d - 1)/(G'_b \times G'_c)] + L'_d \times [(F'_e - 1)/(G'_b \times G'_c)]$$

or

$$F'_{b, in} = F'_b + [(F'_{c, in} - 1)/G'_b]$$

and

$$F'_{a, in} = L'_a \times F'_{b, in}$$

Example: If
(A) cable loss $L_a = 0.3$ dB ($L'_a = 1.071$),
(B) $NF_b = 0.4$ dB ($F'_b = 1.094$) and gain $G_b = 16$ dB ($G'_b = 39.6$),
(C) $NF_c = 1.0$ dB ($F'_c = 1.26$) and $G_c = 20$ dB ($G'_c = 100$),
(D) $L_d = 6.8$ dB ($L'_d = 4.78$), and
(E) $NF_e = 7$ dB ($F'_e = 5.0$), then, working forward:

$$F'_{d, in} = 4.78 \times 5.0 = 23.9 \text{ and}$$
$$NF_{d, in} = L_d + NF_e = 13.8 \text{ dB}$$

$$F'_{c, in} = 1.26 + [(23.9 - 1)/100] = 1.489 \text{ and}$$
$$NF_{c, in} = 1.41 \text{ dB}$$
$$F'_{b, in} = 1.094 + [(1.489 - 1)/39.6] = 1.105 \text{ and}$$
$$NF_{b, in} = 0.44 \text{ dB}$$
$$F'_{a, in} = 1.071 \times (1.105) = 1.183 \text{ and}$$
$$NF_{a, in} = L_a + NF_{b, in} = 0.74 \text{ dB}$$

Note the relatively small final effect of the larger noise figures of stages (D) and (E), due to these terms being at the end of the chain, where the relatively high isolating effect of the stage (B) and (C) gains take effect. Also note the direct addition of d loss for lossy stages (A) or (D) to the total input dB NF of the following stages, to obtain the noise figure at the lossy stage input.

If we were to take the equivalent noise temperature T_a at the cable input, where $T_a = 290 \times (F'_{a, in} - 1)$, we could add this to the antenna equivalent temperature T_{ant} to get the system total temperature $T_{sys} = T_{ant} + T_a$. For example, here $T_a = 53.1$ K; if the antenna is pointing above the horizon and has an effective $T_{ant} = 100$ K, then $T_{sys} = 153.1$ K, $F_{sys} = 1.528$ and $NF_{sys} = 1.80$ dB. Conversely (and analogous to HF usage), if the antenna is pointing toward a higher-temperature region, T_{ant} may be sufficiently high (say, $500+$ K) that the receiver total input noise temperature contribution has almost no effect on the system noise figure, and the minimum discernible signal MDS is set substantially by the environment.

It must also be remembered that the MDS, at which the received signal power is equal to the receiving system noise power, sets only a rough minimum for reception; a good CW operator can make out a signal about 20 dB below the noise, while various threshold factors require SSB or FM signals to be 4 or 6 dB, respectively, above the noise level for reasonable detection.

Query: What, if anything, sets the practical maximum signal which a UHF-and-up receiving system must be designed for? Certainly, most front ends cannot withstand any significant portion of a watt of RF power for any length of time. As many operators of higher-power stations can tell you, sooner or later one of the system T/R relays may hang up, allowing too much transmitter power to leak into the station preamplifier and thereby blowing out the amplifier device. (As pointed out elsewhere in this book, a GaAsFET is less prone than a silicon transistor to this type of input-overload damage.)

Overload and IMD

This still leaves the question: Is there an upper signal level, less than the catastrophic power, at which signal recognition becomes difficult, if not impossible? Yes, there are at least two ways in which this can happen: overload, where one or more undesired signals are strong enough, alone or in combination (with the desired signal or among themselves), to block at least one receiver stage; and intermodulation distortion (IMD), where one or more extra signals, other than the signal to be received, can combine with each other or with the desired signal to generate IM products which are both (1) close enough to the desired signal frequency and (2) of sufficient amplitude to make recognition of the desired signal difficult or impossible.

On our UHF-and-above bands, the only practical situations in which overload blocking is encountered are physical proximity of at least two stations on the same band (in other words, station A's transmitter is on 432.033 MHz, working EME with 900-W output, and nearby station B's receiver is tuned to 432.035 MHz); physical proximity of two stations on bands in harmonic relationship (in other words, station B gives up on 432 and tries his new 23-cm receiver, on 1296.100 MHz, only to be blocked by station A's third harmonic at 1296.099 MHz); or caused by a signal from one's own station (in other words, your 1296-MHz receiver is tuned near the output frequency of your 1296-MHz transmitter in which only the amplifiers are turned off while receiving, allowing oscillator-multiplier chain signals to reach the receiver with sufficient amplitude to blanket reception of anything else).

In each of these actual cases, the solutions used (although perhaps not the only ones possible) were: first case—gentlemen's agreement to operate on frequencies as far removed from each other as practical, and use of sharp notch cavities tuned to each other's frequency to reduce spurious signal level as much as possible; second case— station A adds a third-harmonic filter with very low insertion loss at 432 MHz, but high loss at 1296 MHz; and third case—turn off as many multiplier stages as possible and, if necessary, the oscillator, to completely remove all transmitter signals during reception.

IMD problems are somewhat more difficult to conquer; luckily, the requirements for IMD (high amplitude undesired signal at exactly the wrong nearby frequency) are still rarely encountered on UHF-and-above amateur bands in most parts of the US and the world. Even so, the problem should be understood by every UHF/microwave operator.

Referring to Fig 7A, a desired signal is at frequency F_1, slightly below an undesired signal at frequency F_2. The operator tunes the station receiver such that the passband, PB, is below the undesired F_2 signal, but finds another undesired signal is now in the passband at a lower frequency $(2 \times F_1 - F_2)$. What has happened is that some nonlinearity in the receiver (maybe even the desired nonlinearity in the mixer!) has mixed the original desired and undesired signals $M \times F_1$ and $N \times F_2$ (where M =

N = 1 for first-order) and produced a new third-order signal (the difference between the second harmonic of F_1, with M = 2, and the fundamental of F_2) which falls in the receiver passband.

Any combination of two times one signal frequency and one times another nearby signal frequency will produce a third-order product. Because only two signals are involved, the other third-order product here is at $(2 \times F_2 - F_1)$, which is of higher frequency than F_2 and is thus not in the passband (if positioned as shown). Other IM products of order M + N have the general form of $N \times F_1 \pm M \times F_2$. In general, the sum products of any order, such as the illustrated second-order product $(F_2 + F_1)$ and third-order products $(2 \times F_1 + F_2)$ or $(2 \times F_2 + F_1)$, are at frequencies far above the desired frequency and can be ignored. Even-order difference products, which will have relatively small frequencies, can also be ignored. Only odd-order difference products will be in, or near, the passband, and even then only if both (1) the sum M + N of the multipliers is fairly low (below about 10, due to reduced amplitudes of higher orders), and (2) the multipliers N and M have a difference of 1 (that is, M − N = 1 or N − M = 1). Therefore, the products of interest generally are: third-order products $(2 \times F_2 - F_1)$ or $(2 \times F_1 - F_2)$, illustrated above; fifth-order products $(3 \times F_2 - 2 \times F_1)$ or $(3 \times F_1 - 2 \times F_2)$; seventh-order products $(4 \times F_1 - 3 \times F_2)$ or $(4 \times F_2 - 3 \times F_1)$; and possibly the ninth-order products $(5 \times F_1 - 4 \times F_2)$ or $(5 \times F_2 - 4 \times F_1)$.

The third-order IM products are usually the ones with greatest amplitude, and therefore will have the greatest effect on receiver overload. Thus, they will be the products used to characterize the degree of nonlinearity of any stage, or the entire system, of a receiver or transmitter. This sets a measure of maximum signal-handling capability; that is, an intercept point can be defined to occur when (as with the use of an undesired noise signal to set a lower signal limit) the amplitude of the undesired (third-order product)

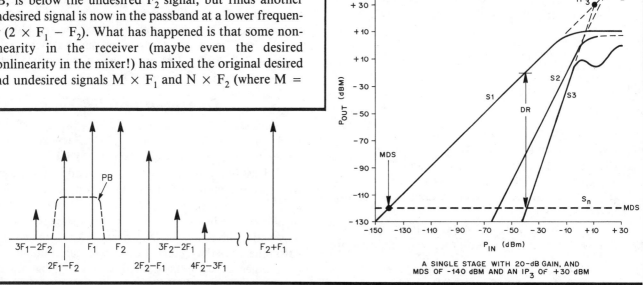

Fig 7—(A) IMD relationships for frequencies F_1 and F_2, and (B) an illustration of third-order intercept point.

signal is as great as the amplitude of the desired signal (which is the first-order signal with $N + M = 1$ and $1 \times F_1 + 0 \times F_2$).

However, the maximum useful desired signal level does not, as might be thought, occur at this third-order intercept point IP_3 (see Fig 7B) when the desired signal S_1 amplitude curve (or a linear extension of the linear portion of that curve) is equal to the third-order signal S_3 amplitude curve (or its linear extension). The maximum useful input signal S_1 really occurs close to the point when the third-order signal just becomes large enough to be heard, that is, when the third-order signal S_3 power is equal to the noise-power S_n signal. Because the third-order signal S_3 amplitude curve changes three times as fast as the first-order desired signal S_1 amplitude curve, the top of a spurious-free dynamic range is reached when S_1 is only two-thirds of the distance from MDS, which is calculable as $-144 + NF + 10 \times \log(B)$ (in kHz) dBm, to IP_3 dBm.

$$DR = (2/3) \times (IP_3 - MDS) \qquad \text{(Eq 11)}$$

In the illustrated case:

MDS = -120 dBm (out) and $IP_3 = +30$ dBm (out),

so that

$$DR = \frac{2[+30 - (-120)]}{3} = 100 \text{ dB}$$

A measurement of the dynamic range (the difference between the maximum and minimum "usable" signal amplitudes) can be made for each stage, or for the entire system of a receiver (to determine the overall susceptibility to overload/IMD, and which stage is most susceptible) or of a transmitter (to determine overall linearity, and so on, and in which stage the limiting distortion occurs). The

amateur UHF/microwave experimenter should be aware that other forms of IMD (such as that relating to second-order intercept point IP_2) exist, and that formulas are available to calculate multi-stage IMD effects and the like, even though these topics are believed unnecessary for most amateur work at this time and are, in any case, beyond the scope of this book.

Stability and Spurious Signals

Two other important factors, which occur in either the source (transmitter) portion or the detector (receiver) portion of a system, are (1) the frequency-domain stability, which is the ability to continue operation within some band of frequencies, including the desired frequency in use (if the stability of the detector is insufficient to keep the source signal, with its own degree of stability, within the selectivity bandwidth of the detector, the information cannot be provided at the detector output and the system no longer operates), and (2) the non-production of spurious signals, which are any signals produced in the system and adversely affecting the ability of the detector to recover the transmitted information.

Use of Characteristic Factors

As an example, let us apply the four criteria (sensitivity, selectivity, stability and lack of spurious signals) to the qualitative design of a simple laser-photodetector system to gain some understanding of basic behavior before considering more complex systems.

Sensitivity: Like the UHF/microwave portion of the electromagnetic spectrum, the light radiation portion is continuous; all frequencies (colors) will appear in the "noise." To achieve maximum signal-to-noise ratio, the total amount of non-source-produced light at the detector must be reduced to the minimum. Query: Is there a

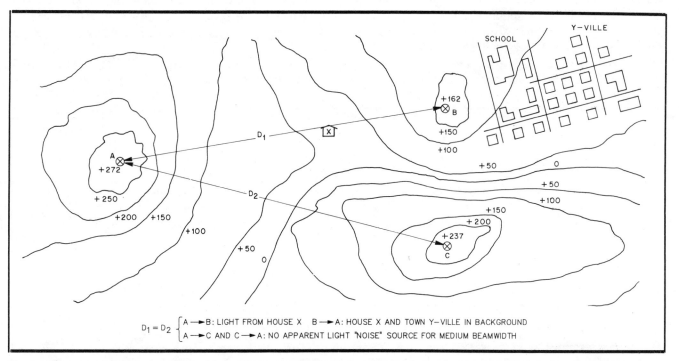

Fig 8—Two equal-distance paths which offer very different results.

more desirable time to operate and are there more desirable path characteristics to look for? Operation late at night, when the amount of atmospheric light (noise!) is low, and perhaps in winter (when background radiation T_e contributions from objects along the transmission path may be less) might be factors to consider.

While all optical communication is likely to be line-of-sight (LOS), and use of mountaintops is going to provide added range capability, you might also want to make sure that there are no other (spurious) light sources located at any point along a line extended through the location of the source and the detector and taking into account the light-acceptance angle of the detector (see Fig 8, and consider which of the two equal-distance paths is better, and why!). Additional sensitivity can be obtained by other limiting of the noise power $P_n = k \times T_e \times B \times F$. First, we could limit the wavelength bandwidth of the light allowed to reach the detector; if the transmitter emits red light (in other words, a HeNe laser), then we could put in something, like a sheet of red glass, to act as a bandpass filter which allows only the red wavelengths of light to get to the detector and which stops all other colors. Result—reduced B and reduced noise, but about the same signal, to the detector. Note that this may now require increased source and/or detector frequency stability, as the range of allowable operating frequencies is reduced. If combined with winter-night operation, to reduce system (and not just detector) temperature, a double increase in SNR results. Second, decrease the effective receiver temperature T_e and subsequent amplifier noise factor F; this may be as simple as using a jacket of dry ice around the detector to reduce the average ambient 290 K temperature to about 240 K, or may be as complex as using a low-noise photomultiplier tube (PMT) in a liquid-nitrogen Dewar flask (T_e = 77 K) and with special high-voltage supplies, and so on (here, the PMT has such a high gain that the noise factor of any post-amplifier is almost unimportant). Other schemes, such as the use of synchronously chopped transmitter beam and lock-in signal processing at the receiver, exist and are equally applicable to all weak-signal systems, but are beyond the scope of this book.

Now that we have a very basic idea about what characteristics we should be looking for, let's get more specific about actual workable systems. The first portion of a system will likely be a source of signals, that is, an exciter. Today, a fairly stable, non-spurious-producing source is not particularly difficult to design and build.

UHF/MICROWAVE SOURCES

The simplest manner in which a UHF/microwave signal can be generated is by use of a free-running oscillator at the output frequency F_o. Such sources were often encountered as recently as 10 years ago on all bands above 500 MHz; even today, this is the most popular method for generating signals above 6 GHz. As in any oscillator, the frequency is determined by a tank circuit; the higher the loaded quality factor Q_l of this tank circuit, the better the frequency stability of the oscillator. Since a high loaded Q requires an even higher unloaded Q_u, the lower the losses in the frequency-determining portion of the oscillator, the better its stability. In addition to a tank circuit, the oscillator needs an active device to supply power. This device functions as an amplifier and usually has three terminals, as a power gain greater than unity (0 dB) is needed. At frequencies above about 6 GHz, a two-terminal device which provides a negative resistance can be used to cause oscillations to occur across a tank circuit.

As a first example, the vacuum-tube power oscillator of Fig 9 is one that often shows up on the surplus market. The probe in the plate cavity feeds some output power back into the cathode circuit to sustain the oscillations which are shock-excited into existence by the initial current flow at turn-on; the tuned plate cavity is the primary frequency-control element, and is often fabricated from a solid block of a material with a very low coefficient of temperature expansion. In addition, the unloaded Q is increased by silver plating of the seamless milled cylindrical cavity; typical frequency stability of ±0.005% (0.05 MHz/GHz/°C), or better, can often be achieved, if operated at a reasonably constant voltage from a well-regulated power supply.

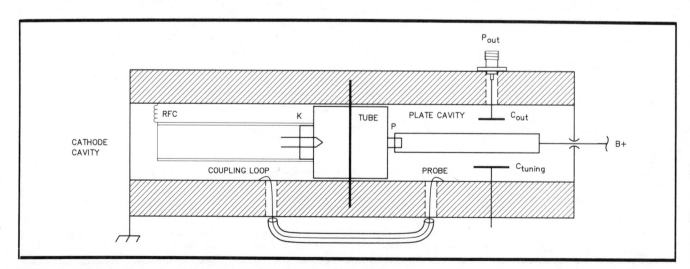

Fig 9—A vacuum-tube power oscillator often seen on the surplus market.

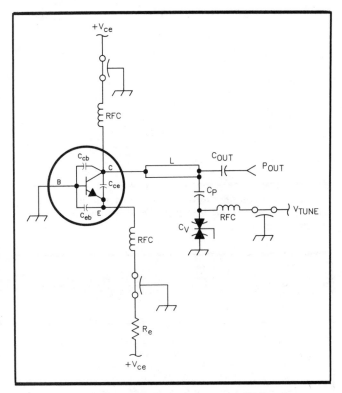

Fig 10—A voltage-variable transistor oscillator.

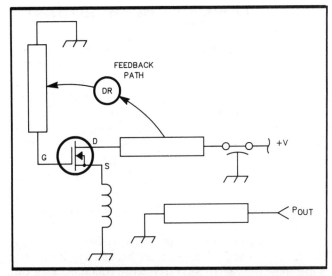

Fig 11—A 10-GHz oscillator with a ceramic resonator.

The voltage-variable transistor oscillator of Fig 10 is also often available on the surplus market; here, the feedback is provided by the device parasitic capacitances C_{ce} and C_{eb}. The unloaded Q of the tuning varactor C_v is relatively low and frequency stabilities on the order of even $\pm 0.1\%$ (1 MHz/GHz/ °C) are not easy to obtain in amateur-built units. However, the ease of modulating such oscillators over large frequency bands makes this configuration useful for quickly building cheap wideband-FM transmitters, sweep generators and similar applications. This type of oscillator finds special use in a phase-locked loop (PLL), such as in frequency synthesizers, where very good frequency stability can be given to the free-running oscillator (more about PLLs later).

The oscillator's active device can be a GaAsFET, and the feedback can be taken through a lightly coupled high-Q element, such as the ceramic resonator DR of the 10-GHz oscillator of Fig 11 (patterned after a commercially available 10-GHz unit from Mitsubishi Corp). A typical stability of $\pm 0.003\%$ (0.03 MHz/GHz/ °C) is obtainable with a very simple regulator.

Another class of free-running oscillator (Fig 12) is the type using a negative-resistance device (typically a two-terminal diode) across the frequency-determining tank circuit; the negative resistance supplies the energy necessary to sustain oscillations (in an opposite manner to a positive resistance, which dissipates power and tends to prevent oscillations). One such source is the Gunn-diode oscillator in the 10-GHz and 24-GHz Gunnplexer™ transceivers available from M/A-COM. A typical unit uses a waveguide portion, with "adjusted" backshort and a coupling iris, as a resonant cavity. These units have stabilities on the

order of $\pm 0.01\%$ (0.1 MHz/GHz/ °C); the high-current requirement and low efficiency of the diode contribute to large temperature changes at turn-on, and several tens of minutes are often needed as a warm-up period before fairly stable operation is possible. This same type of oscillator can be pulsed by pulsing the dc supply, and pulsed diode oscillators are a staple of operation above 30 GHz—here, frequency stability is not primarily affected by the dissipation of the diode, as the diode is pulsed with a fairly low duty cycle (the ratio of on-time to the total of on-and-off-time) on the order of 1% (on for 1 μsec and off for 99 μsecs, and so on).

Each type of oscillator can be made with many different device types, and with many different circuit configurations, so the number of possible different UHF/ microwave power sources is very large. Those most knowledgeable about what can and cannot operate on our bands above 300 MHz can often find items of interest which will not be recognized by the less experienced; as the last word states, this knowledge only comes with study and experience.

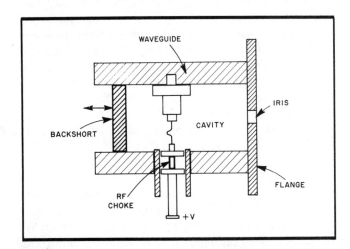

Fig 12—A free-running oscillator which employs a negative-resistance device (in this case, a two-terminal diode).

HIGH-STABILITY UHF/MICROWAVE SOURCES

As we have seen, for best sensitivity, the bandwidth B of the receiver should be as narrow as practical. This requires that the source have the best possible frequency stability, to remain in the narrow passband of a pre-detection filter and the like, in the receiver. It would be nice to have source stability, with temperature and voltage changes, and so on, on the order of 1 part per million (PPM or ±0.0001%), or even better! This translates to the maintenance of a frequency within not more than ±1 kHz for every GHz of the operating frequency. At 432 MHz, a 1-PPM stability puts your signal within 432 Hz of where it is expected; once found, slow drifts of a hundred Hz still allow use of a 250-Hz band-pass filter. Here, use of even a 100-Hz filter becomes possible. It's a different story at 10.384 GHz, where the signal can still drift over 20 kHz, if the extremes of factors setting stability are encountered. Query: How can such stabilities be achieved with Amateur Radio equipment? At present, only if crystal-controlled sources and a great deal of patience in temperature-compensation/thermal design are used.

Common crystals, and the oscillators containing them, cannot operate directly at any frequency approaching the UHF/microwave frequencies which are the subject of this book. How then do we obtain a crystal-controlled signal at the final desired frequency? By multiplying the output of an oscillator which operates at the highest possible sub-multiple of our desired output frequency. Thus, the oscillator output will be multiplied by some integer number N, after the output is buffered to reduce the frequency-destabilizing effects of the subsequent frequency multipliers. How shall we choose N? It is generally a number which is itself the product of some low-order prime integers, that is, 2, 3 or, at most, 5. Some simple rules are used, which will be illustrated by several oscillator/multiplier-chain frequency tree examples for the weak-signal frequencies 432 MHz (420-450 MHz band), 903 MHz (902-928 MHz band) and 1296 MHz (1240-1300 MHz band), as shown in Figs 13-15.

Rule #0 (yes, even more important than any first rule!): If at all possible, build each stage of equipment, all equipment, separately and then interconnect the stages after each is separately checked out. This may require a bit more expense in good connectors and cables, but is well worth it; you repay yourself the first time a previously working stage or unit goes bad and has to be isolated in a system of many stages or units.

Rule #1: Only frequency doublers (2×) and triplers (3×) are considered, or are actually needed, below 5 GHz. Reason: the next-highest prime multipliers (×5, ×7, ×11, and so on) are too inefficient. Non-prime multipliers, such as ×4, ×6,... are better realized with more than one stage, such as ×4 = ×2 ×2 and ×6 = ×3 ×2, for most sources generating appreciable power (that is, above 1 mW, or 0 dBm). Also, the higher-output frequency multipliers may be more easily realized as doublers.

Rule #2: Always consider discarding irrational base

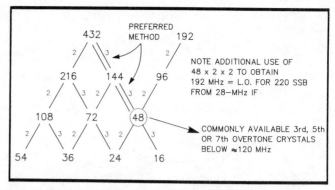

Fig 13—An oscillator/multiplier-chain frequency tree for 432 MHz. The circled frequency is the most common starting frequency.

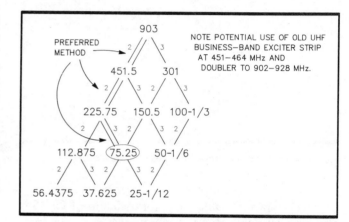

Fig 14—An oscillator/multiplier-chain frequency tree for 903 MHz.

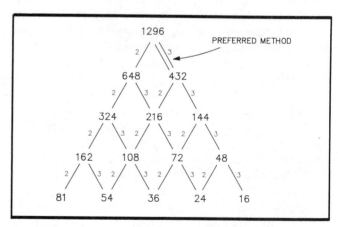

Fig 15—An oscillator/multiplier-chain frequency tree for 1296 MHz.

frequencies (that is, any N/3, N/7, N/9,... MHz, where N is an integer less than the denominator of that fraction). Reason: it is difficult, if not impossible, to obtain crystals exactly at these frequencies. While it is true that all oscillators should provide some frequency adjustment capability, even if relatively small, it is hard to adjust frequency, using frequency counters available to most amateurs, if that frequency is irrational even after several multiplications. See, for example, Fig 14, where frequencies of 50-1/6 MHz and 100-1/3 MHz might be considered (but should be disregarded).

Rule #3: The highest possible base frequencies, below about 120 MHz, should be used. Reasons: First, the frequency range of the better fifth-overtone crystals currently available to the amateur market is about 30-120 MHz. Second, the greatest separation in frequency is desirable to allow the best filtering of unneeded harmonics after each, or all, multiplications (you might want to consider these signals as being spurious, in the sense of being unwanted).

Rule #4: Where possible, filter and buffer-amplify each multiplication-stage output. Reason: Filtering will lower the undesired harmonics. Buffering will reduce the effect of the next multiplier stage on the present multiplier; this can be very important when a multiplier is finicky about the load needed for proper operation (yes, we do always want unconditionally stable multiplier stages, but we must occasionally use only conditionally stable stages because technology has not yet made better multipliers available for amateur use).

Rule #5: Allow for losses in coupling between stages and for practical filters. Reason: Unlike HF circuits with often negligibly small losses, much of the power developed in a UHF/microwave stage (multiplier or amplifier) can be easily lost in coupling, filtering and the like. If you allow for fairly high loss, you can rarely be unpleasantly surprised; it is easier and cheaper to add some attenuation (an extra few inches of RG-58/U or RG-174 coaxial cable) than to add another stage of amplification.

No specific high-stability oscillators are covered here; many examples will be found in the band-by-band construction articles in Volume 2. Do not be afraid of obtaining excellent crystal oscillators as complete units in the surplus market (some may require minor modification, often discussed in the "special-interest" journals such as *QEX*, *VHF Communications*, and so on). Also look

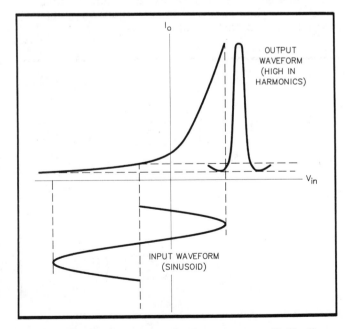

Fig 16—Input/output curve for frequency multiplication.

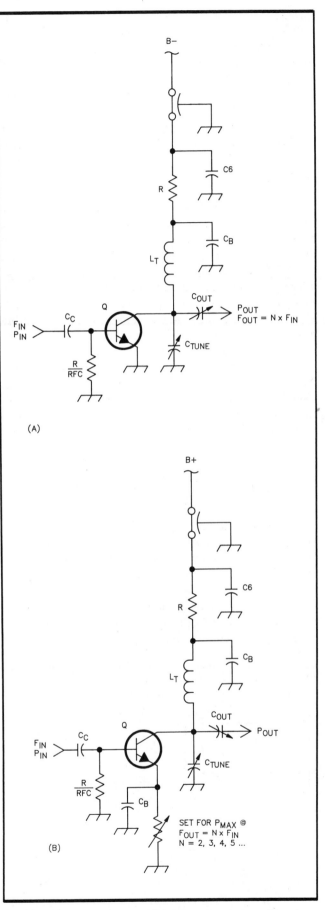

Fig 17—Two frequency multipliers; the emitter bias in (B) can be varied to maximize output at the desired harmonic.

through professional RF/microwave magazines, if you can obtain them (from friends, club members, libraries, and so on), for new ideas. While many multiplier stage examples will be shown in the band-by-band sections, it is worthwhile discussing one important characteristic of frequency multipliers at this time: all multipliers operate in a nonlinear manner!

Look at the input/output curve of Fig 16; this form of curve (literally, a nonlinear line!) is required to generate harmonics. The most efficient multipliers are operating with output current flowing for not more than 180°. Generally, the best multipliers operate with conduction angles of about 360/N degrees, where N is the desired multiplier harmonic. However, every device, even among those of the same type, will not turn on and turn off at exactly the same level of input signal; if necessary, some provision for varying the conduction angle (possibly by varying the stage device bias) should be provided. Compare the multipliers of Fig 17, where a variable emitter bias in the (B) circuit can be adjusted to maximize the output at the desired harmonic. Whatever the form of multiplier, the resulting pulse of current flows from the multiplier device to be typically transformed to a sinusoidal voltage by a subsequent resonant circuit. The Q of this resonant circuit is not infinite, so that undesired harmonics are going to be present. Determining the degree of additional required harmonic suppression will be a large part of your system design time and will also determine how much filtering will be required.

A Magic Frequency and a Multiplier Chain Therefor

If you look at the present amateur bands up to 30 GHz, you might notice that several harmonic relationships occur. Interestingly, by design of many people involved at many frequency-allocating conferences, our bands between 1300 MHz and 24,250 MHz all have at least one frequency (almost always used, by common sense and common agreement, as the center of the primary weak-signal sub-band in that band) which is a multiple of one special frequency:

1152 MHz (see Fig 18). This "magic" frequency and set of frequency relationships allow us to build one oscillator-multiplier chain to use as a common basis for all higher bands. Instead of five complete chains being needed to operate at 2304, 3456, 5760, 10,368 and 24,192 MHz, only one 1152-MHz chain and five multipliers are needed. The savings in cost and time can be partly put back into making the common 1152-MHz unit the best possible. A frequency tree for 1152 MHz is also shown in Fig 19, and one possible chain block diagram is shown in Fig 20.

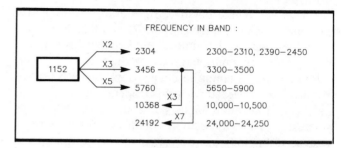

Fig 18—Multiples of 1152 MHz, a "magic" frequency.

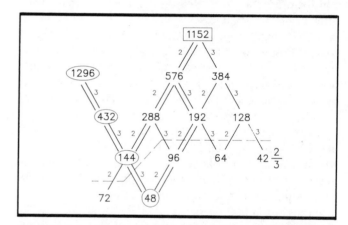

Fig 19—A frequency tree for 1152 MHz. Use a starting frequency below the dashed line (common overtone crystals). A good choice is 48 MHz; it allows multiple use (see circled harmonics).

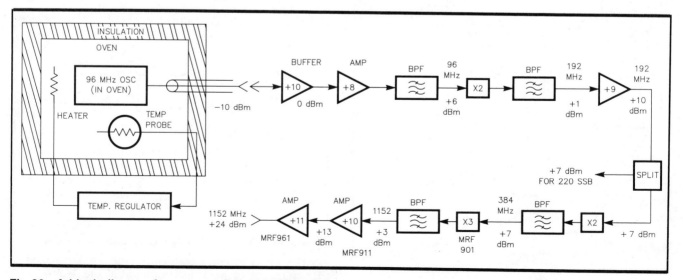

Fig 20—A block diagram for one possible 1152-MHz chain.

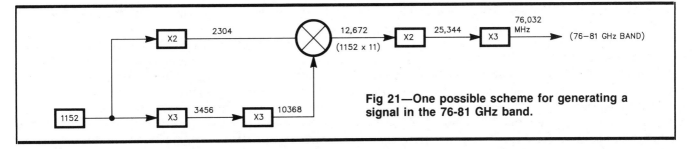

Fig 21—One possible scheme for generating a signal in the 76-81 GHz band.

Query: Are there any other methods we can use to generate a UHF/microwave signal? How can signals for even higher bands be generated? One method is "self-heterodyning," where the final frequency is a high-order multiple of a more easily obtained lower-frequency signal, and the multiple contains a prime factor greater than 5. For example, one scheme being considered for generating a signal in our new 76-81 GHz band is shown in Fig 21; the 66th multiple of the magic 1152 MHz is desired. But, while the first pair of factors ($\times 2$, $\times 3$) fit in nicely with commercial state of the art equipment, a $\times 11$ multiplier is more difficult than combining $\times 9$ and $\times 2$ signals, especially since the $\times 2$ signal is at 2304 MHz and the $\times 9$ signal is realized by a $\times 3$ signal at 3456 MHz being multiplied to 10,368 MHz, all of which are also in our bands! Thus, frequency addition is carried out by mixing. Note that a signal at 147.456 GHz, in the 142-149 GHz band, is the 64th harmonic (6 successive doublers) of 2304 MHz and the 128th harmonic (7 successive doublers) of 1152 MHz.

Another method uses phase-locked loops (PLLs). While the theory and practice of UHF/microwave PLLs deserves at least its own thick book, a PLL acts by feedback control of the exact frequency F_{osc} and phase of the output of an oscillator to maintain that oscillator at a high, but not necessarily integer, multiple of a highly stable reference frequency F_{ref}, that is, $F_{osc} = N \times F_{ref}$. The multiple N can be very much less than 1, or in the hundreds or thousands, and so on. In Fig 22, a general form of PLL signal generator is shown. The output of the UHF voltage-controlled oscillator (VCO) can itself be multiplied by a

factor xP to obtain the output frequency F_{out}. The oscillator frequency is divided by at least one frequency-divider stage (three stages are shown here, each dividing the previous frequency by a divisor N, M or L) to obtain the divider output frequency F_D for comparison to the divided-down-by-K reference frequency in the phase detector. Any phase/frequency error in one direction generates an error voltage, which is amplified and used to change the VCO frequency in the opposite direction, that is, that direction serving to reduce the error toward zero. Therefore, $F_{out} = F_{ref} \times P \times N \times M \times L \div K$. Low-cost integrated phase detectors (like the Motorola MC4044) and UHF dividers (like the RCA CA3179T divide-by-64-or-256) can be obtained without too much trouble. This allows signals at 1152 MHz to be generated using the top set of numbers shown in the figure, while a 47,185.92-MHz signal, in our 47.0-47.2 GHz band, could be generated using the lower set of numbers.

AMPLIFICATION

The average source-multiplier chain might provide a continuous output power in the range of 0 to + 10 dBm (1-10 milliwatts). While this is enough for many purposes, and contacts over distances of many dozens (and even hundreds) of miles have been made with a source signal of no higher power, there are often reasons for desiring a higher power level. Of course, once the magnitude of realizable output power P_o is determined and the driving (input) power P_{in} is known, the amplifier power gain G_p is easily obtained from their ratio: $G_p = P_o/P_{in}$. This

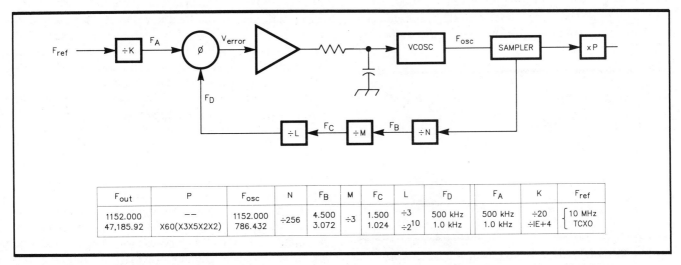

F_{out}	P	F_{osc}	N	F_B	M	F_C	L	F_D	F_A	K	F_{ref}
1152.000	--	1152.000	$\div 256$	4.500	$\div 3$	1.500	$\div 3$	500 kHz	500 kHz	$\div 20$	10 MHz
47,185.92	X60(X3X5X2X2)	786.432		3.072		1.024	$\div 2^{10}$	1.0 kHz	1.0 kHz	$\div 1E+4$	TCXO

Fig 22—A generalized PLL signal generator.

amount of amplification may not be available in one amplifier stage; an amplification chain of several stages may be required.

It is usually best to first separately optimize each individual stage, by building a separate module for each stage and tuning each module to operate from, and into, a standard impedance (50 ohms is the general standard in the US). Each stage must have an amplifying device, usually selected from vacuum tubes, power UHF silicon transistors and power GaAsFETs. The tubes are generally triodes, although some more exotic varieties, such as klystrons, traveling-wave tubes, and the like, occasionally are available. The amplifier can be "linear," which usually means operation in class A (with its associated relatively high dc power dissipation whenever enabled, even if not providing actual output power), unless power vacuum tubes are available for the frequency of use, in which case class AB or class B linear operation is possible. The use of class AB or B is advantageous in any linear power amplifier, as the amount of added distortion is desirably lower than in class C amplifiers, while the resting power dissipation is desirably less than in a class A amplifier. Use of a linear mode of amplification is mandatory, at the frequencies of interest, for any form of information transmission based upon varying the carrier amplitude in a non-switched manner. While transistors *can* be used in class AB or B linear service, if the base-emitter junction is properly forward-biased, the actual amount of distortion is highly sensitive to adjustment of resting bias and/or drive level and is best done under the same constraints as HF or VHF linear amplifiers; that is, using proper instrumentation for optimizing each module. Many UHF/microwave power transistors are designed and packaged for common-base operation (see Fig 23), which requires an additional low-voltage/ high-current power supply for forward-biasing the emitter-base junction. This further complication is avoided if a power GaAsFET device is used in the amplifier, but these devices are relatively expensive and presently hard to obtain. Alternatively, an amplifier can be operated in non-linear class C (without any appreciable resting dc power dissipation). This class of operation is fine for signals conveying information by changing a carrier parameter other than amplitude; even the amplitude can be changed to transmit information, if the amplitude

change is of binary nature (as in CW—the carrier is either there or it is not).

The number and nature of the required amplifier stages in an amplifier chain can only be determined by conservative calculations. In addition to stage gain and output power level, some attention must be paid to input/output standing-wave ratios, as a power loss will be encountered when a circuit attempts to provide incident power P_{inc} to a load with an actual load impedance Z_L other than that load impedance Z_{out} to which the stage was tuned. The power loss is, of course, related to the power P_{ref} reflected by the mismatched load Z_L; reduce the mismatch, or reflection, coefficient φ [where $\varphi = (Z_L - Z_0)/(Z_L + Z_0)$] and reduce the magnitude of reflected power [$P_{ref} = \varphi^2 \times P_{inc}$] lost from the actual output. The amount of loss, in watts or dB as needed, can be calculated once the magnitude of the reflection coefficient is known. If you would rather not do the calculations (with or without a scientific calculator), the amount of attenuation loss for a given reflection coefficient φ can be obtained from the scales at the bottom of a Smith Chart.

VSWR Review

A source, with an output voltage V_s, is connected to a load impedance Z_L by a transmission line of length l and characteristic impedance Z_0. The transmission line (of whatever type, see Fig 24A) can be modeled as a chain of cascaded sections (see Fig 24B), each having some series impedance $R + j\omega L$ component per unit length and some shunt admittance $G + j\omega C$ component per unit length. The characteristic impedance $Z_0 = (R + j\omega L)/(G + j\omega C)$. However, at lower frequencies (say, up to several hundred MHz) and with "heavy" conductors, where the skin depth d is much less than the conductor thickness (see Fig 24C), the value of both R and G are very low, so that the characteristic impedance equation reduces to the familiar textbook form $Z_0 = L/C$. However, at UHF and higher frequencies, skin depth is sufficiently low that some non-negligible attenuation occurs over almost any usable length of transmission line and cannot be ignored. With some amount of source power ($P_{inc} = V_s \times I_s$) provided to the line and incident on the load, some amount of power P_{ref} will be reflected by the load if $Z_L \neq Z_0$; the remaining power $P_{fwd} = V_L \times I_L = P_{inc} - P_{ref}$ will be absorbed by the load (see Fig 24D). Any reflected power will set up a pair of traveling waves on the transmission line: one (incident) wave travels from the source towards the load; the other (reflected) wave travels from the load towards the source. These waves form a *standing wave* pattern, with voltage and current periodically varying with distance from source and/or load (see Fig 24E).

We define standing-wave ratio (SWR) as the ratio of maximum to minimum field strength at a point, as that point varies by a distance of at least one-half of a wavelength on the transmission line. By convention: (1) this ratio is always greater than 1; and (2) we usually use the voltage ratio VSWR(s), because we generally detect the voltage amplitude of standing waves, using diode/square-law detectors. Thus, VSWR $= E_{max}/E_{min}$ and, because of

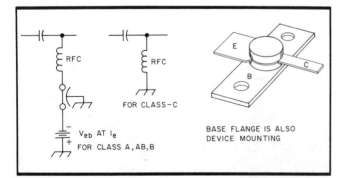

Fig 23—Many UHF/microwave power transistors are designed and packaged for common-base operation.

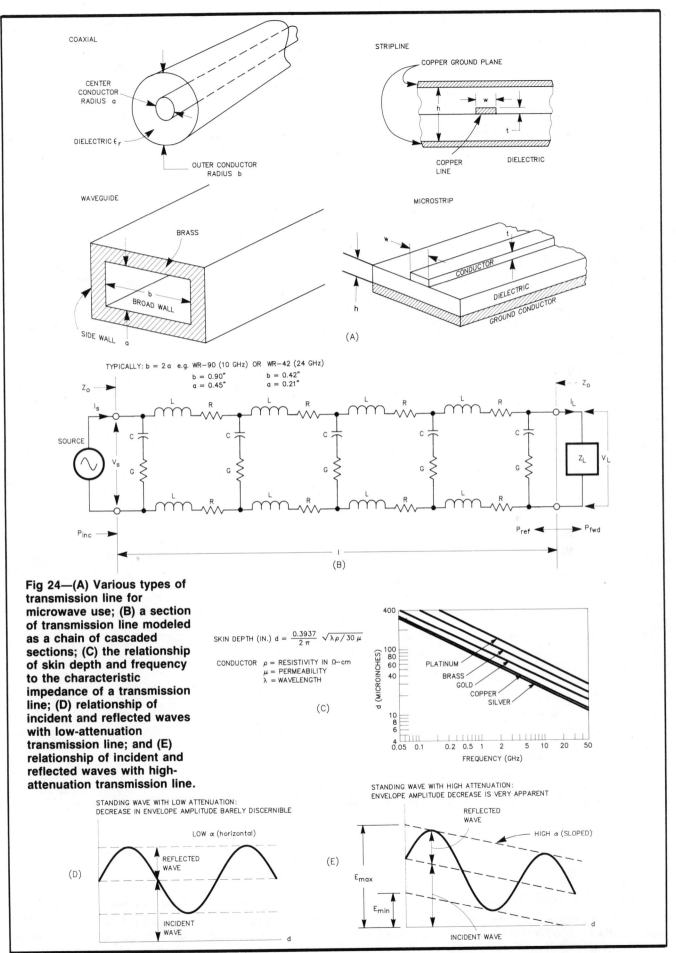

SKIN DEPTH (IN.) $d = \dfrac{0.3937}{2\pi} \sqrt{\lambda\rho / 30\,\mu}$

CONDUCTOR ρ = RESISTIVITY IN Ω–cm
μ = PERMEABILITY
λ = WAVELENGTH

(C)

Fig 24—(A) Various types of transmission line for microwave use; (B) a section of transmission line modeled as a chain of cascaded sections; (C) the relationship of skin depth and frequency to the characteristic impedance of a transmission line; (D) relationship of incident and reflected waves with low-attenuation transmission line; and (E) relationship of incident and reflected waves with high-attenuation transmission line.

convention (1), VSWR $= Z_1/Z_0$ if $Z_1 > Z_0$, and VSWR $= Z_0/Z_1$ if $Z_1 < Z_0$. In either case, if the VSWR ratio is given as (s), then VSWR (dB) $= 20 \times \log(s)$.

A reflection coefficient $\varphi = (s - 1)/(s + 1) = (Z_L - Z_0)/(Z_L + Z_0)$ is also usually used: $\varphi = 0$ if there is a perfect line-load impedance match ($Z_L = Z_0$); $\varphi = 1$ if a complete mismatch occurs and $P_{ref} = P_{inc}$, as by the load being an open-circuit, a short-circuit, or any impedance having a zero or infinite real (resistive or conductive) part. The VSWR-to-ρ change need not be done by calculations; most Smith Charts have scales interrelating these and several other factors.

What are some of these other factors which we can obtain from the VSWR (by calculation or Smith Chart)?

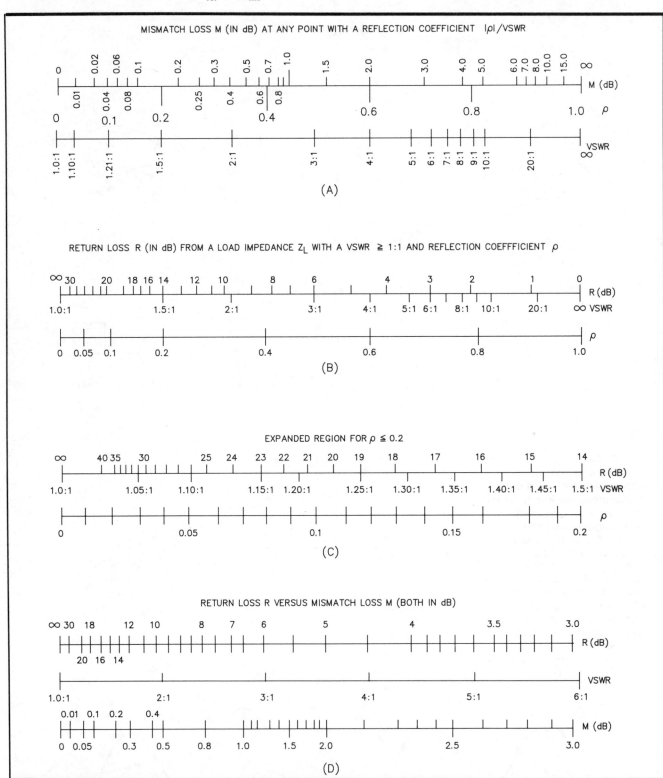

Fig 25—(A) Mismatch loss M (in dB) at any point with a reflection coefficient p; (B) return loss R (in dB) from a load impedance Z_L with an SWR $\geq$ 1:1 and reflection coefficient φ; (C) expanded region for $\varphi <$ 0.2; and (D) return loss R vs mismatch loss M (both in dB).

At least two other factors are of interest: the mismatch loss M and its companion, the return loss R. An effective power loss M occurs at any location where an additional power reflection occurs; as the reflected power P_{ref} increases, the remaining, forward-going, usable power must decrease, since the amount of incident power is constant.

Almost all components have a VSWR greater than 1.00000:1 and introduce some mismatch. The forward power P_{fwd} remaining after a mismatch loss is then equal to $P_{inc} \times (2/(s + 1)) = (1 - \varphi) \times P_{inc}$; the "lost" power is $P_{inc} \times \varphi$, so that mismatch loss M can be defined as $M = P_{ref}/P_{fwd} = \varphi/(1 - \varphi)$ or $M(dB) = -10 \times \log[(1 - \varphi)/\varphi]$.
Mismatch loss M can be obtained from the graph of Fig 25A. A low value of φ is desirable at any component acting as a load on a transmission line; we can tell if this load has a low mismatch loss by checking its $P_{ref}/P_{inc} = \varphi$ ratio. This ratio may be inverted, as $1/\varphi = P_{inc}/P_{ref}$, and is now called the return loss R. The return loss is a measure of how well the load is matched to the transmission line impedance: the higher the return loss, the *less* the reflected power and the better the match (also, the lower the mismatch loss M). Refer to Figs 25B and 25C for graphs of VSWR versus return loss, and to Fig 25D for a graph of return loss versus mismatch loss; note that a return loss R of 20 dB ($P_{ref} = 0.01 \times P_{inc}$) is generated by a load with a VSWR of about 1.21:1 and causes a mismatch loss of about 0.04 dB.

Sample Design

At this point, it should be mentioned that a neophyte UHF/microwave enthusiast need not have the engineering/math background necessary to actually design the desired circuits and the even-more-important mechanical layouts, but must be able to understand what is shown in a set of plans and be willing to exactly follow those plans. It is only at a somewhat higher level that one acquires the ability to design equipment, even with the use of aids such as Smith Charts, and so on. It is, in fact, now easier to design individual stages of a system using a personal com-

puter and S-parameter analysis/optimization programs (the latter obtainable, for some machines, for under $15), than to do the repetitive calculations and/or curve drawing formerly associated with stage-by-stage design. However, use of any aid still requires at least some understanding of system basics. With that in mind, let us do a sample amplifier chain design:

Frequency: 2304 MHz
Available input power: 5 mW (+7 dBm), into any VSWR < 1.2:1
Usage: Home QTH CW station
Desired output power: 20-30 W (+43 to +45 dBm)
Load impedance: 50 ohms
Load VSWR (max) = 3:1 (This is the maximum mismatch presented to the transmitter output, by the subsequent load of TR relay/feed line/antenna/ and so on)
REQUIRED GAIN:
$G_{min} = P_o(min) - P_{in} = +43\,dBm - (+7\,dBm) = 36\,dB$
$G_{max} = P_o(max) - P_{in} = +45\,dBm - (+7\,dBm) = 38\,dB$

The only single stage of amplification which can provide this much gain, at this frequency and/or output power level, would be an exotic tube. Assume one is not routinely available. Therefore, plan for the use of several triode and/or solid-state stages. How many stages? We must first determine how to obtain the needed output power magnitude and work backward from the output.

Output Stage

While it may be possible to obtain the desired amount of output power P_o with the combined output of several identical stages of amplification using solid-state devices, it is probably beyond the budget, if not the capabilities, of a strictly amateur effort. Use of a power vacuum tube is recommended; such amplifiers as the military-surplus TRC-29 and several commercially made units successfully use one of the so-called "lighthouse" triode tubes of the 2C39-3CX100A5-7289 type, operating in a grounded-grid circuit (see Fig 26 for one example). How does one find

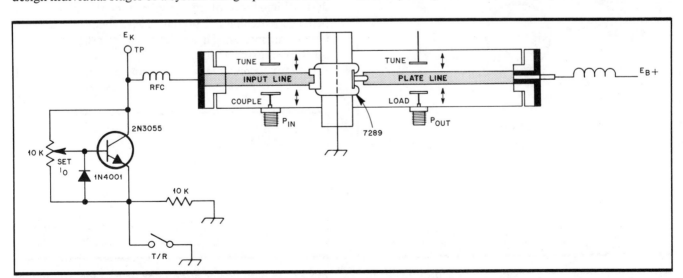

Fig 26—A "lighthouse" triode operating in a grounded-grid circuit.

out about goodies like this? By reading, discussions with other UHF/microwave enthusiasts, reading some more, and so on. Now, knowing that at least 20-30 watts can be attained with a triode tube, one can either calculate typical operational data or, more successfully at a neophyte level, obtain actual data from someone who has already made at least one such amplifier work. (The more units made to work by more experimenters, the better your chances of making one work, too.)

Using a 7289, at 900 V dc and with sufficient cathode bias for an average plate current of 125 mA, one should obtain:

Gain (at 20-W P_o) = 7 dB (5×); P_{in} of 20/5 = 4.0 W needed
(at 30-W P_o) = 6 dB (4×); P_{in} of 30/4 = 7.5 W needed

Therefore, plan on supplying between 4 and 7.5 watts to the final amplifier input. However, these input power levels will only drive the amplifier to supply the desired 20-30 W output level into a well-matched load.

We will assume that the amplifier output loading cannot be varied to accommodate a load deviating to any great degree from 50 ohms (if your amplifier output has a variable loading control, you may not actually need to use the following information, but should be aware of the types of problems and general direction of solution). Because a 3:1 load VSWR causes 50% of the output power to be reflected back to the amplifier and lost, the actual presence of a load impedance somewhere between Z_0/VSWR (max) = (50/3) = 16.66 ohms and Z_0 × VSWR (max) = 50 × 3 = 150 ohms may make it impossible to tune the output stage to supply the required output power!

Before considering any other part of the amplifier design, we must reduce the *apparent VSWR* of the load. We can do this by the use of a non-reciprocal device, which only allows power to flow in one direction (see Fig 27); one such device is the circulator. The power applied to any of the three connectors (each usually called a "port") can only go to the next port in the indicated "easy" direction of flow. *Ideally*, the power cannot flow in the opposite (or reciprocal) direction, against the "easy" transmission direction shown by the arrow. Therefore, the incident and reflected powers at each of the input, output and isolated ports shown in Fig 27 are obtained. Note that the amplifier output (which is at the circulator *input*) sees a reflected power which is reduced by the amount of isolation of the non-reciprocal device, so that the reflection coefficient is reduced and a very low actual VSWR is, in fact, present at the amplifier output. At the same time, the forward power is reduced only by the relatively low insertion, or forward, loss L of the circulator in the direction opposite to the direction in which the high isolation "loss" occurs; these are the best conditions for minimizing VSWR. Unfortunately, the mismatch at the circulator/transmitter output is still present and 50% of the output power is still reflected to the isolation resistance R_{iso} (by now, it should be apparent that the non-reciprocal device known as an isolator is nothing more than a circulator with a dedicated isolation-port resistive load). The 10-15 watts of possible reflected power is considerably more than the 0.5- or 1-W dissipation rating of the terminating resistor used on many isolators (these units are intended for reception or very low power operation); the resistor can often be carefully removed and replaced with an SMA connector; a high-power termination can be fabricated with a length of high-attenuation coaxial cable and a low-power termination, as shown in Fig 28.

We have solved the problem of making the amplifier provide full output power into the input port of the circulator, but must still get much more of that amplifier output power into the actual load. This must be done by matching, or transforming, the actual load impedance to the system design impedance of 50 ohms. The mathematics of impedance matching are presented elsewhere in this book; here we are interested in a practical mechanism for carrying out this transformation.

Many forms of impedance transformers are available

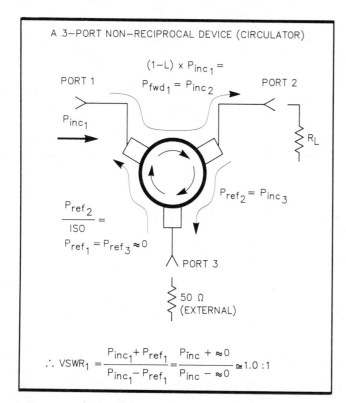

Fig 27—A circulator is a device which allows power to flow in only one direction.

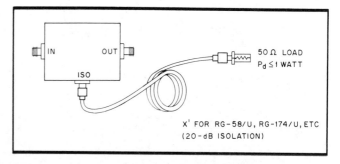

Fig 28—A high-power attenuator using high-attenuation coaxial cable and a low-power termination.

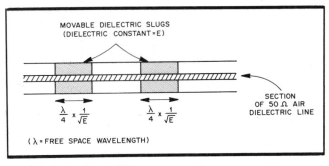

Fig 29—A double-slug tuner.

for the UHF/microwave bands. Many transformers have fairly narrow bandwidth, which is normally not great for commercial equipment, but is generally quite adequate for amateur use. The double-slug tuner is one transformer I find to be fairly easy to fabricate, mechanically rugged and capable of transforming any load with up to a 3:1 VSWR to 50 ohms; a simple example of one such unit is found in Fig 29. As shown in Fig 30A, a forward/reflected power monitor coupler can be placed between isolator and tuner, to aid in adjusting the tuner. This power monitor has a very small coupling value (usually less than -20 dB, just large enough to provide some discernible meter deflection) and need not be even moderately accurate, as long as each detector output voltage is monotonic (single-valued—see

Fig 30B) for all values of associated forward or reflected power. Since the reflection coefficient φ is merely the ratio of the reflected power to the incident power, one tunes to maximize forward power (greatest up-scale reading on the FWD meter) and to minimize reflected power (least up-scale reading on the REV meter). Since solid-state amplifier designs do not always have variable output loading, this sort of subsystem is often used. In fact, this form of output load control is useful and *practical* for all bands between 600 and 6000 MHz, for all types of amplifiers, and (depending upon the dielectric constant of the slugs) a very broad range of load impedance.

The final amplifier will provide an output power magnitude which depends upon the input power magnitude; the amplifier input may itself need a good impedance transformer to match to the system impedance. This matching device may not be necessary if the driver-amplifier is capable of tuning to the actual input impedance of the final amplifier, although this does require some trading-off of several advantages of the interchangeable/separate stage/module concept against the lower cost if impedance matching-metering-isolation is not used between each stage. Assume that the chosen approach is to separately adjust the final amplifier input VSWR to as close to 1.0:1 as practical. The amount of drive power now needing to be supplied, through an associated tuner and forward/

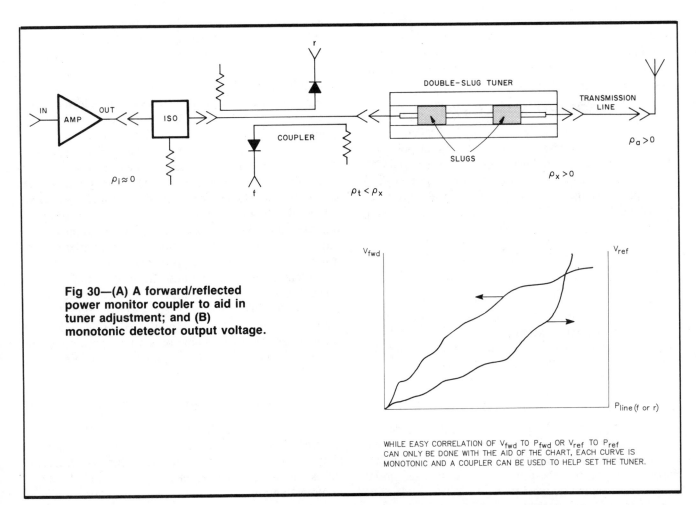

Fig 30—(A) A forward/reflected power monitor coupler to aid in tuner adjustment; and (B) monotonic detector output voltage.

WHILE EASY CORRELATION OF V_{fwd} TO P_{fwd} OR V_{ref} TO P_{ref} CAN ONLY BE DONE WITH THE AID OF THE CHART, EACH CURVE IS MONOTONIC AND A COUPLER CAN BE USED TO HELP SET THE TUNER.

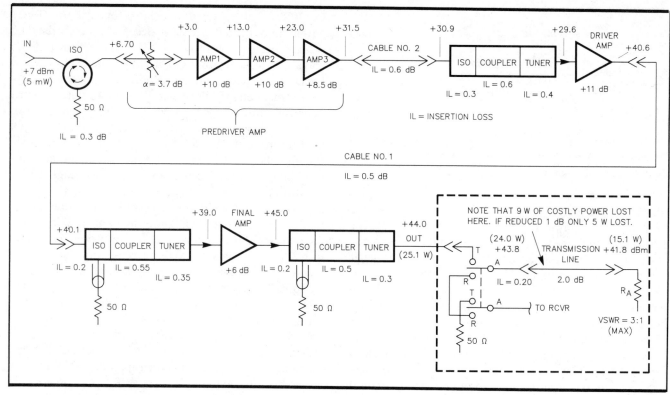

Fig 31—A block diagram for calculating drive power required.

reflected coupler (for obtaining meter readings), must be worked out, as shown in Table 1 and/or Fig 31. As with all components at microwave frequencies, we must account for the real power losses L in these components in any stage-by-stage power budget.

DRIVER AMPLIFIER

The driver amplifier can be any stage capable of supplying 4-8 watts into the low-VSWR input port now provided for the final amplifier. This could be realized with a second triode amplifier, in other words, another 7289 with a plate voltage of 800 Vdc and a cathode current of up to 80 mA. Such an amplifier may have a power gain of 10-13 dB, requiring input powers of:

$$P_{in} \text{ (max)} = P_{out, max}/G_{min} = 8/10 = 0.8 \text{ W}$$

$$P_{in} \text{ (min)} = P_{out,min}/G_{max} = 4/20 = 0.2 \text{ W}$$

This approximately 4:1 range is not too large to deal with using a variable output load control with current amateur state-of-the-art drivers. Alternatively, a solid-state driver may be quite cost-effective to provide 4-8 W of driving power. A 10-W P_{out} class-C silicon transistor (Motorola MRF-2010 in a 28-Vdc circuit) can provide 5 dB of power gain; a pre-driver (using an MRF-2003 transistor, for example) can add gain of 6 dB, so that an input power P_{in} of slightly more than 1 W is again needed. Of course, the class-C operation of the silicon UHF power transistors will not allow very linear operation, so use of a more-costly linear transistor or tube driver may be a better initial project, especially if your eventual goal is 2304-MHz SSB.

Use of a single power GaAsFET is presently not feasible at this power level, at new-device prices.

Another pair, or trio, of stages can provide the additional 23 + dB of power gain to raise the level of the + 7 dBm input to at least 1 W. Solid-state stages can provide good cost vs performance factors at these lower power levels; silicon transistors and GaAsFETs are available from many manufacturers. The amount of power actually provided to the input of the driver-amplifier can be set, if desired, by use of an attenuator made from a short length of a thin coaxial cable (RG-174/U has a suitably high attenuation constant). The attenuator should be preceded, if possible, by an amplifier-chain input isolator to maintain the input VSWR less than the relatively stringent 1.2:1 requirement. Note that the amount of input attenuation, if used to set the power level, provides an isolation of twice that attenuation. This is because the incident *and* reflected power levels are each reduced by the amount of the attenuation, so that the actual reflected power is reduced twice. One will see that the forward power reduction makes this form of isolation acceptable only where an appreciable power loss can be normally tolerated. A complete sample amplifier chain is shown in Fig 31.

MODULATION

FM or PM

If the sample amplifier chain was designed and implemented in the simplest manner, with a set of class C stages, the carrier signal frequency or phase could be varied in almost any manner (usually at, or near, the oscillator

Table 1

Based on *Known* Facts: Amplifier P_out and Drive P_in

Power conventions	Gains −; losses +
Final amplifier output	+45 dBm (30 W)
Amplifier gain	− 6 dB
Input power	+39 dBm
Tuner loss	+0.35 dB
Coupler loss	+0.55 dB
Isolator loss	+0.20 dB
Power required at input	+40.1 dBm
Cable #1 loss	+0.5 dB
Driver power required	+40.6 dBm
Driver amplifier gain	− 11 dB
Power required at input	+29.6 dBm
Tuner loss	+0.40 dB
Coupler loss	+0.60 dB
Isolator loss	+0.30 dB
Driver input power required	+30.9 dBm
Cable #2 loss	+0.6 dB
Power required from pre-driver	+31.5 dBm
Amplifier 3 gain	− 8.5 dB Total gain
Amplifier 2 gain	−10.0 dB of pre-driver
Amplifier 1 gain	−10.0 dB = 28.5 dB
Pre-driver input power required	+3.0 dBm
†Input power to pre-driver	+7.0 dBm
Pre-driver input power required	+3.0 dBm
Pre-driver input loss allowable (− 0.3 dB input isolator loss, and 3.7 dB input attenuation from 1-10 dB variable attenuator)	4.0 dB
†Final amplifier output	+45 dBm
Output isolator loss	−0.20 dB
Coupler loss	−0.50 dB
Tuner loss	−0.30 dB
Amplifier output power	+44.0 dBm (25.1 W)
T/R relay loss	−0.20 dB
Transmission line loss	−2.00 dB
Power to load	+41.8 dBm (15.1 W)

†System reference point changes here.

end of the exciter chain), and no special factors would need be considered at allowable amateur modulation indices and deviations.

AM

The only form of amplitude-varying modulation which can be fairly faithfully reproduced in the class C amplifier is CW (on-off keying). Even this binary form of amplitude modulation is not without problems in a state of the art amplifier chain: the higher the magnitude S_{21} of the forward scattering coefficient of the amplifier device

in the "turned-off" mode, the greater the amount of drive signal fed through the amplifier. Thus, a practical limit to the signal on/off ratio is set by the ratio of $S_{21\,on}/S_{21\,off}$. The value of $S_{21\,on}$ depends on the bias point of the turned-on device, and can be easily found on the device data sheet. Don't look for the value of *any* scattering parameter for a turned-off device! Only experience will tell what the keying ratio (that is, the ratio of forward gains in the on and off states) will be for an amplifier stage with at least one solid-state device. A vacuum-tube stage may have a high enough keying ratio, especially if keyed bias is used, but the quality of modulation should be checked in an actual moderate-to-weak signal situation and should not be assumed. Since the output of any stage may not have an acceptable keying ratio, it may be necessary to also modulate (key) at least one driving stage. This may lead to a keyer circuit which is necessarily more complex than those encountered in equipment operating at lower (HF) frequencies, where the off-state forward scattering coefficient may be vanishingly small.

SSB

The future of Amateur Radio at UHF/microwave frequencies will depend upon our ability to use voice-modulation signals for contacts which do not need the greater weak-signal capabilities of CW. At this time, the predominant voice mode for DX work is suppressed-carrier single sideband. How can we provide a source for transmitting an SSB signal on a UHF/microwave band? One method of SSB generation is the phasing method, which will work as well at microwave frequencies as at lower frequencies, if (and only if) one can adjust carrier phase shift sufficiently fine to obtain the desired rejections of both the carrier and the unwanted sideband (almost always the lower sideband). A second method is the filtering method in which the unwanted sideband is filtered from the desired sideband. The need to provide an undesired-sideband suppression of even 40 dB (and carrier suppression of at least 20 dB) at frequencies only a few hundred cycles removed from the unattenuated frequencies of the desired sideband is difficult enough at the relatively low frequencies (up to about 10 MHz) in present SSB exciters. At higher frequencies, due to the greater frequency-selectivity requirements, one cannot presently obtain filters sharp enough to allow SSB generation directly at the frequency of transmission.

Heterodyne Conversion

The only presently viable solution is to heterodyne to the final use frequency a single-sideband signal generated at a lower frequency, where the SSB signal can be generated by available components. Linear amplification is required, if the power level of the heterodyned signal amplitude is to be increased prior to transmission. A basic heterodyne up-conversion mixer is shown in Fig 32A; this mixer is not only substantially amplitude-linear, but is also frequency-linear, in the sense that the separations of several incoming frequencies are maintained in the output frequencies. This mixer can be operated in a reciprocal

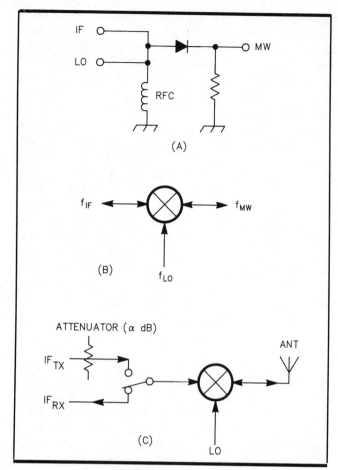

Fig 32—(A) A basic heterodyne up-conversion mixer; (B) the mixer of [A] operated in a reciprocal manner, thereby becoming a receiving down-conversion mixer; and (C) an attenuator/switch configuration for use when the IF TX power is greater than the mixer's RF power-handling capability.

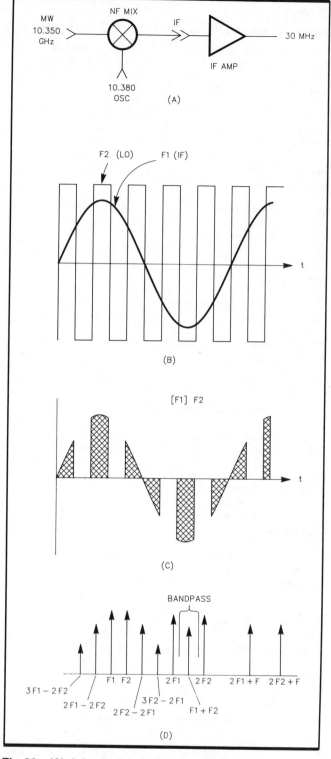

Fig 33—(A) A basic heterodyne mixer; (B) the "chopping" of one frequency (F1) by another (F2); (C) the signal resulting from the "chopping" in [B]; and (D) the frequency spectrum resulting from the "chopping" in [B].

fashion, as shown in Fig 32B, and becomes a receiving down-conversion mixer. Note that a received microwave signal, at F_{mw}, enters the RF port of the mixer and is mixed with the *same* local oscillator energy as in the transmit use of the mixer; the resulting difference frequency F_{if} is made available to an IF SSB receiver (or receiver portion of an SSB transceiver). With suitable switching, a single mixer (and a single local oscillator chain) can be used both to up-convert an IF signal to obtain a UHF/microwave signal for transmission and to down-convert a UHF/microwave signal to the IF for reception. If a single RF jack serves as both the RX input and low-level TX output in a transceiver, no switching may be needed. Conversely, if the TX signal power level at a common IF connection is greater than the maximum RF power-handling capability of the mixer, the attenuator/switch configuration of Fig 32C will be required.

The basis of all heterodyne mixing (see the mixer of Fig 33A) is the "chopping" of a first signal, at a first frequency F1 (see Fig 33B), by a second, generally larger amplitude, signal at a second frequency F2; the resulting signal (shown as [F1]F2 in Fig 33C, meaning that the signal in [] is chopped by the other signal) not only has com-

ponents at the two original frequencies, but also has components at all of the sums and differences of all integer N multiples of the first frequency (N × F1) and all integer M multiples of the second frequency (M × F2), as shown in the frequency spectrum of Fig 33D.

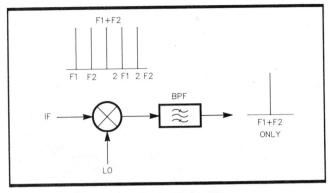

Fig 34—The action of a band-pass filter.

To clear up what may become a language problem, these new sum/difference frequencies are often called "products" or "product frequencies," because the resulting mathematical terms have products in which trigonometric functions (sine and cosine) are multiplied together; however, these terms all simplify to math expressions in which the final frequencies are in terms of sums and differences. No matter what the various writers call these terms, we can separate them into two groups: some terms have vanishingly small amplitudes, especially for very large values of N and/or M, and can usually (but not always) be ignored; other terms have very much larger amplitudes and must be carefully considered in a properly designed system. The question may be asked: "Which terms go into which category?" The best answer may be: If you use high enough starting frequencies for both signals, and then pass the mixing products through a proper band-pass filter (see Fig 34), it does not matter in most practical situations. What, then, is a proper band-pass filter to follow an up-converting (adding F1 to F2) frequency heterodyne converter (or frequency mixer) for amateur UHF/microwave use? This filter (BPF) will be one which has a center frequency F_c at the desired sum frequency ($F_c = N \times F1 + M \times F2$), where both N and M are usually, but *not always*, equal to 1. The BPF will have as low an insertion loss as possible, to minimize the loss of the hard-to-obtain UHF+ output signal. (Note: the loss through the filter from a first, or input, port to a second, or output, port is known as its insertion loss, usually abbreviated IL; the BPF, like

almost all passive lossy components above 300 MHz, may be reciprocal and usable with either port named input or output. However, some components do not show reciprocity and care must be taken in their selection and use.)

To be able to even consider ignoring any product term, the BPF must have a band-pass which is sufficiently narrow to attenuate any undesired product frequencies by as large an amount as possible; this indicates a bandwidth F_{bw} such that frequencies removed from that center frequency by the smaller F1 of the two input frequencies, in other words, at frequencies $F_{low} = F_c - (F_{bw}/2) = F2$ and $F_{hi} = F_c + (F_{bw}/2) = F2 + 2 \times F1$, be attenuated at least 40 dB with respect to the amplitude of the desired signal in the passband. Many systems designers will demand much higher unwanted-product attenuation; some systems have attenuations upwards of 120 dB in the transmitter, to ease potential receiver problems.

A top-of-the-line, yet totally practical, transmitting converter (transverter) designed for construction in one-function-per-module fashion is shown is Fig 35. Let's assume that the HF/VHF input frequency F1 is known, and that the local oscillator frequency F2 has been selected; the mixer is then selected to handle reasonable amounts of power at each of these frequencies and at the desired output product frequency. What is a reasonable power level depends, to some extent anyway, on the particular use. No one, for example, should seriously expect to use the full 100-200 W PEP output power of a 28-MHz SSB exciter/transceiver to directly drive a transistor mixer, for any UHF+ band output, without causing a catastrophic mixer burnout; however, *relatively* high drive power can be used to good advantage in many tube-type mixers. One rule might be: tube mixers can usually accept power levels of +0 dBm to +20 dBm (1-100 mW) at the grid, and up to several watts at the cathode; solid-state mixers generally want no more than +13 dBm (20 mW) at any input, unless the mixer is especially built to take higher power (even then, the highest power signal is generally the one at the LO input, and usually cannot be greater than about 6 dB above the normal specification level). A diode-based doubly balanced mixer (DBM) spec'd for a high-drive LO of +17 dBm should still never see more than about +23 dBm (200 mW) at any port. If you are duplicating an

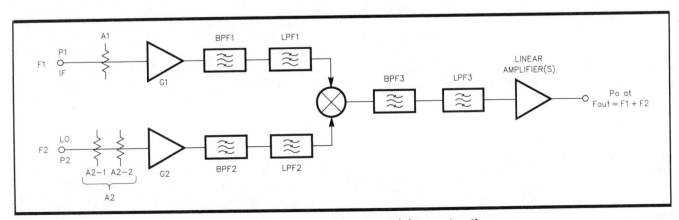

Fig 35—A transmitting converter designed for one-function-per-module construction.

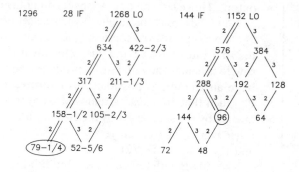

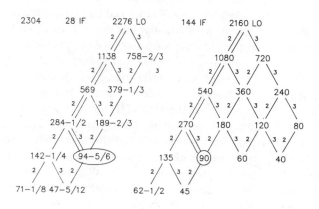

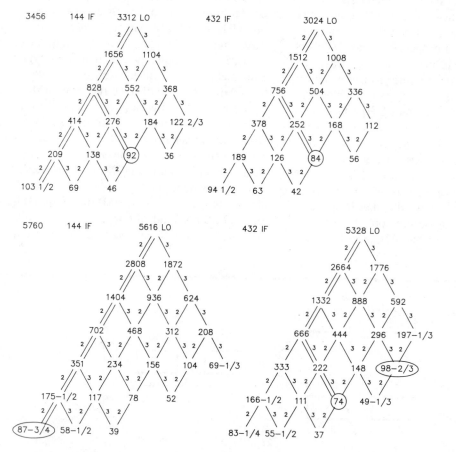

Fig 36—Sample frequency chains for transmitting up-conversion for some UHF/microwave bands. Circled frequencies are commonly used starting frequencies. Double lines are easier paths to desired end frequencies.

existing design, try to use the recommended mixer; if it is unavailable, try to match its specifications to another available unit. If designing your own unit, read all you can about each model of mixer available to you for the job, and pick a unit with the best specs for *your* job. As for the other blocks, let's consider why each block is present and what the proper basic design procedure is if that block is used:

1) An attenuator A1 and/or A2 is needed before either mixer input, if the power level P1 or P2, respectively, at that input is higher than the average level specified for the associated mixer input. If the average level is also the peak power, as with a local oscillator signal (which is a CW signal), then the attenuation value is fairly easy to chose. For a varying average level, as in an SSB driver input, use the peak level to set the attenuation. The attenuation in each input circuit (IF or LO), if needed, can be placed in one attenuator (in other words, as in attenuator A1) or in several physically separate attenuators (in other words, a first attenuator A2-1 and a second attenuator A2-2) to make up a total attenuator A2. This is particularly advantageous when a large amount of attenuation is needed. For example, a 100-W PEP exciter is to drive a transverter needing 100 mW of 28.1-MHz drive; a total of 30 dB of attenuation is needed, with the attenuator having to dissipate 99.9 W peak. This is not the kind of attenuator you build with ¼-W carbon resistors! A first attenuator A2-1 might use a cable attenuator, that is, a coaxial cable having at least 100-W power-handling capability at 28 MHz and having a length cut to cause a desired amount of cable loss (say, 20 dB), and therefore a desired output power level (1 W PEP for this example). This suggests that the cable attenuator can be "cut to length" by use of a power meter. The second attenuator A2-2 can now be a pi-pad or T-pad unit, built with small, discrete resistors, or can be a commercial/surplus 1- or 2-W unit of about 10-dB attenuation.

2) One or more amplifier(s) may be needed, as gain block G1 and/or G2 to provide enough drive, even if the associated attenuator A1 or A2, respectively, has a zero value, if the input power P1 or P2 is too low. For example, you have a very stable LO chain for providing F2 with a power $P2 = +10$ dBm, but the mixer needs a very high level drive signal at $+27$ dBm; an additional 17 dB of gain G2 is needed here. Note that if, instead of $+17$ dB of gain, a commercially available unit with $+22$ dB gain and $+30$ dBm of output power is available, an attenuation of 3 dB is needed after the amplifier (to reduce $+30$ dBm to the required $+27$ dBm), and the needed $+8$ dBm input power ($= +30$ dBm $- 22$ dB gain) may require 2 dB of attenuation before the gain G2 block, if that block is not capable of being slightly overdriven.

3) A band-pass filter BPF1 or BPF2 and/or a low-pass filter, in each of the two drive lines, helps to prevent harmonics of that signal from entering the mixer (because the undesired mixing products generated directly in the mixer are hard enough to get rid of, without added amplitude from unnecessary input signals). It also reduces any of the other drive signal which spills over due to less-than-perfect signal isolation between the two inputs (isolations of better than 20 dB may reduce the significance of this).

4) A band-pass filter BPF3 at the output of the mixer is almost always necessary to reduce the LO, image (that is, the "lower sideband" at F2-F1) and other mixer output signals at frequencies near the desired output frequency. While image-rejection mixers do exist (see receive mixers, below), they are complex and do not remove the LO and other unwanted signals from the output, so that a band-pass filter is still required after the mixer. The band-pass filter BPF3 must present the lowest possible attenuation (insertion loss) to the desired output frequency F_o, and as high an attenuation to the undesired images, local oscillator responses, and so on. A low-pass filter may be required after the band-pass filter, if one of the types of UHF + band-pass filters is used in which odd band-pass harmonics are not attenuated; certain forms of comb-line and interdigital filters have this form of attenuation characteristic.

5) At least one linear amplifier may be used to increase the desired signal amplitude, before feeding the output power P_o, at the desired output frequency F_o, to the T/R relays, antenna, and so on. The gain and power output of each stage will depend upon the state of the art at any time; this constantly changes and cannot possibly be predicted in advance. The output stage of the day as this is being written may be the pre-driver for the driver/final amplifier of the day you read these words.

With heterodyne conversion, because the IF signal frequency F1 is mixed with the frequency of a high-stability local oscillator, the LO chain output frequency F2 is not the desired frequency F_{out}, but is that frequency F2 offset from the desired frequency F_{out} by the first frequency F1. Thus, $F2 = F_{out} - F1$. Since F1 is almost always several times less than F_{out} (typically about $10\times$, by an old rule-of-thumb), and both F1 and F2 are lower in frequency than F_o (because it is usually easier to generate a lower-frequency signal), a new (LO) chain frequency can be specified and new trees drawn. Sample chains for transmission up-conversion are shown, for some UHF/microwave bands, in the different parts of Fig 36. A careful study of these trees will aid in your own attempts to design proper mixing schemes.

RECEPTION OF UHF/MICROWAVE SIGNALS

It will be apparent that whatever (such as a lower frequency signal) goes up, as to a higher UHF or microwave frequency, can (not *must*) come back down. While direct detection of received signals is occasionally used, it is almost invariably in cases where a receiving down-converter cannot, for one reason or another, be provided. Indeed, in any system using heterodyne up-conversion for signal transmission, it is almost unheard of to not also use heterodyne down-conversion for reception. The same high-frequency-stability oscillator/multiplier chain is used for providing local oscillator drive for both mixers. Dependent upon required power levels, the transmit side of the chain may require additional amplification.

Even if a CW, FM or other nonheterodyne transmis-

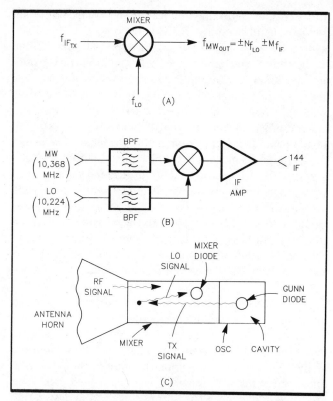

Fig 37—(A) A usable 10-GHz system; (B) a 10-GHz system with band-pass filtering added; and (C) a Gunnplexer transceiver, with part of the transmitted signal serving as the local-oscillator signal.

sion apparatus is used, it is desirable to use a down-converter for reception, because:

(1) the bulk of signal processing (gain, filtering, and so on) can be done at a lower and more appropriate IF frequency, and

(2) if the converter is built in single-function-per-module fashion, then improvements can be added, as available. This is not as potentially useful in a nonheterodyne scheme.

Superheterodyne Reception

Let us begin our look at receiving down-converters with a *usable* present-day station, say for 10 GHz (Fig 37). Fig 37A shows that the absolute minimum receiver is nothing more than a mixer; in actual use, say in a Gunn-plexer transceiver, the local oscillator signal is a bit of the transmit signal, generated by a Gunn-diode cavity oscillator and reflected from a screw projecting into the mixer waveguide. The microwave received signal enters the mixer from the antenna through the same waveguide end that emits the transmitted signal to the antenna (see Fig 37C). This same scheme is the way that almost all 24-GHz work is done, and is also used in a lot of simpler equipment for low-microwave (3400- or 5650-MHz) work over medium distances (out to 50-80 miles).

$$\text{Sensitivity (in dBm)} = -144 + 10 \times \log \text{BW (kHz)} + \text{NF}$$

Since the mixer noise figure NF_{mix} is at least equal to the mixer conversion loss *plus* whatever noise is added by the

mixer diodes, it *was* common practice to try to minimize the noise figure by building a mixer with the lowest conversion loss you could get, and to use the best (and usually the most expensive) mixer diode(s) available. This still yielded NF_{mix} of not less than about 5 dB at 432 MHz and 11 dB at 10 GHz. Because the first stage (the mixer) has a loss, the total receiver noise figure NF_{total} then becomes the sum of the stage NFs:

$$\text{NF}_{total} = \text{NF}_{mix} + \text{NF}_x$$

where NF_x is the noise figure of any following IF receiver. The IF receiver noise figure may also be on the order of 10 dB (for a typical HF receiver), for a total NF of 21 dB or so.

It was typical to include a low-noise, high-gain IF amplifier to reduce the effects of NF_x. If the IF amplifier has a gain about 10 dB greater than the following noise figure (say, $G = 20$ dB for $\text{NF}_x = 10$ dB), then the total NF is approximately the sum of the mixer and IF amplifier noise figures ($\text{NF}_{total} \approx \text{NF}_{mix} + \text{NF}_{amp}$, or, if $\text{NF}_{amp} = 1$ dB, $\text{NF}_{total} \approx 11 + 1 = 12$ dB). This is 9 dB better than the mixer-directly-into-receiver scheme, and is therefore eight times more sensitive. Today, it is still difficult and relatively expensive to build a low-loss/low-NF UHF/microwave mixer, although really good IF amplifiers are relatively easy. As will be shown later in this chapter, almost *any* working mixer, with conversion-loss/noise-figure up to 10, 12 or even 15 dB, can get you on the air, and can even be used in a high-quality system by addition of the proper preceding stages; a simple 3-dB coupler-type mixer, with Schottky diodes in microstrip on high-loss G-10 PC board, is often more than adequate. (Many contest QSOs over paths up to 70 miles, at 2304 and 3456 MHz, have been made to mobile/portable stations equipped with a few hundred milliwatts of transmitter power, a tincan antenna and such a mixer, with 12-15 dB loss, into a simple 5.595-MHz IF strip. In fact, signals have occasionally been so strong that the antenna had to be placed under the car!)

Front-end selectivity is, however, essentially non-

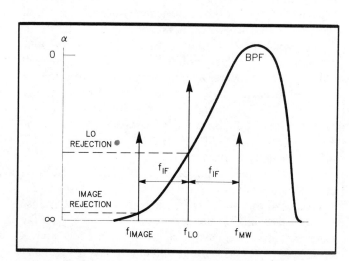

Fig 38—Response curve of a microwave band-pass filter designed to eliminate the image frequency.

existent, and any incoming signal is limited only by the frequency response of the antenna! Stability is that of the oscillator, which is here a free-running and very temperature-sensitive unit. Spuriosity is high, as there is no filtering to speak of. Thus, this simple receiving converter can be improved upon.

Let us now look at what the same station becomes in the case of state of the art improvements affordable by many amateurs. The mixer is now a physically separate unit, allowing other stages or subassemblies to be connected between each of the mixer connectors and any non-mixer assembly. The local oscillator will now be a crystal-controlled oscillator/multiplier chain, for added stability. Only two simple additions (Fig 37B) need be made to raise the converter performance level: a local oscillator band-pass filter can be used, since the LO frequency is now much more stable and will stay within a relatively narrow range of frequencies; and a band-pass filter can be placed in front of the mixer MW input. This MW filter must let the desired MW frequency pass with as little attenuation as possible, but attenuate the image frequency as much as possible (see Fig 38) to reduce the amount of noise power allowed into the mixer at the image frequency. This form of down-converter, with image-filter/mixer/LO filter, is the basis for the well-known Reed Fisher, W2CQH, 1296- and 2304-MHz converters of the '70s and G3JVL's 10-GHz waveguide-based reception mixer. In the 'CQH units, the two filters were opposite halves of a multi-resonator interdigital BPF, formed of sheet metal and heavy copper rods; not the easiest unit to build, but worth it at the time. In the 'JVL unit, the two filters are sections of a common waveguide, with irises and tuning posts; also not a simple unit to build, but still worth it for serious narrow-band work at 10,368 MHz at this time (late 1989). The obvious

reason why the 'JVL unit is still state of the art is the higher frequency involved.

Sensitivity should be up to almost 3 dB better than the bare mixer of Fig 37A, as the image noise is removed, with only a small reduction (due to the insertion loss of the MW BPF) in the signal at the desired frequency. The low-NF, high-gain IF amp is still required.

Selectivity is obviously greatly improved by the effective selectivity of the MW band-pass filter; in addition to the image being attenuated, other undesired and spurious signals outside of the filter passband are also desirably reduced at the MW input to the mixer. Stability is increased because the LO is no longer free-running, while the presence of the LO filter removes LO harmonics and other spurious signals at the mixer's LO input.

Now, consider the improvements possible for a best receiver (Fig 39) realizable in the decade of the '90s!

In this receiver, the local oscillator chain includes an amplifier, after the final multiplier (here, a tripler to 9936 MHz from 3312 MHz, which is also the LO frequency required in a 3456-MHz system with a 144-MHz IF range). Such an amplifier is available in a discrete GaAsFET unit, with microstrip impedance-matching circuits at the input and output; one such unit was shown in an article by Al Ward, WB5LUA, on page 31 in May 1989 *QST*. The tripler will probably be a diode type, as active multipliers at this frequency are generally beyond the amateur state of the art. The 3312-MHz amplifier driving the multiplier is somewhat easier to realize, as it is now possible to obtain MMIC (monolithic microwave integrated circuit) units with several dB of gain at 3 GHz; while MMICs available in 1989 have output power less than that usually required as the power level (say, +20 dBm) for a diode multiplier, it is possible to follow the MMIC(s) with a stage or two of fairly high

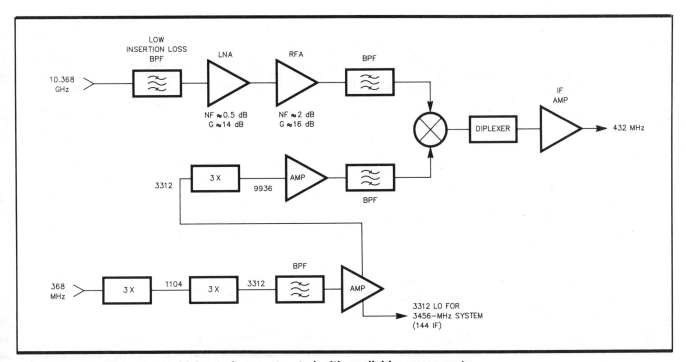

Fig 39—A "best" receiver which can be constructed with available components.

gain GaAsFET amplification to obtain the diode drive power. It is expected that such a power level will be available directly from an MMIC, in an amateur-affordable unit, in the early 1990s.

The same type of amplifier as may be used before the final LO filter can also be used as an RF amplifier before the mixer signal input filter; present designs (with a GaAsFET device in microstrip) can provide a 2-3 dB noise figure and 8-12 dB gain, so that 2-dB NF and 16-dB gain units are not far away. Even better amplifiers, with true LNA specifications (say, 0.5-dB NF and 14-dB gain) *are* presently available, if you can afford the hundred-plus dollars for the device, a so-called *HEMT* (high-electron-mobility transistor, which is a more specialized form of the already special microwave GaAsFET). Of course, with all this gain and low noise figure, an input band-pass filter, with very low insertion loss, is necessary to keep other, out-of-the-amateur-band microwave signals (say, police speed

radar) from overloading your front-end! Just how sensitive is a receiving converter of this style? Suppose that the input band-pass filter has an insertion loss of 0.2 dB and the pre-mixer filter has an insertion loss of 1 dB. Calculating the overall NF and gain, in both case A: a state of the art mixer/diplexer/IF amp (7-dB NF and sufficient gain so that the noise figure of the following receiver does not matter); and case B: a really mediocre home-brew unit (say, 15-dB NF, but good enough IF gain to still allow the following receiver NF to be neglected), we find

$$F_{total} = L_{bpf1} \times F1' + [(F2' - 1)/G1'] + [(L_{bpf2} - 1)/G1_m' \times G2_m'] + [(F_c' - 1)/G1_m' \times G2_m']$$

where L_{bpf1} and L_{bpf2} are the insertion loss ratios of the respective first and second band-pass filters; $F1'$, $F2'$ and F_c' are the noise *factors* of the respective LNA, RFA and mixer stages; and $G1'$ and $G2'$ are the gain ratios of the LNA and RFA stages. We also have to use the modified

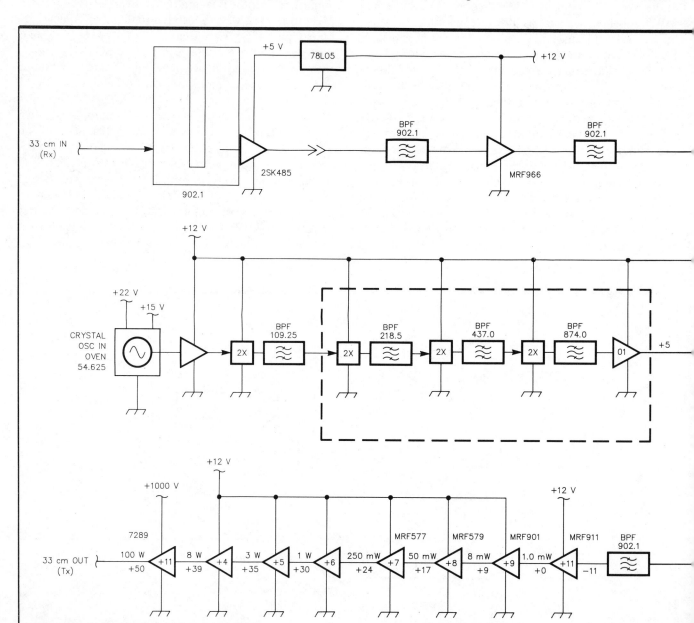

Fig 40—Block diagram of a 902-MHz station.

gain ratios $G1' = G1' \times L_{bpf1}$ and $G2' = G2' \times L_{bpf2}$, to account for the small, but real, gain reductions due to the filter losses. Note that only the last term changes with a change in mixer noise figure/conversion loss. Thus,

$$F_{total} = 1.17490 + 0.02438 + 0.00027$$

$$+ \frac{(F_c' - 1)}{10^{[(30\ dB - 0.2\ dB - 1.0\ dB)/10]}}$$

or

$$F_{total} = 1.19955 + (F_c' - 1)/748.8$$

where the gain of 28.8 dB = 748.8 prior to the mixer; the total converter gain is $28.8 - L_c + IF_{gain}$.

For the 7-dB mixer, $F_{total} = 1.20484$ or $NF_{total} = 0.81$ dB and $G_{total} = 21.8 + IF_{gain}$.

For the 15-dB mixer, $F_{total} = 1.23992$ or $NF_{total} = 0.93$ dB and $G_{total} = 13.8 + IF_{gain}$.

CONCLUSION

A receiving converter with enough gain and a low enough noise figure for any use (even EME communications) can be built around almost any mixer, *if* the proper low-noise amplifiers are used.

Two of the most-often encountered problems concern: (1) the loss of the pre-mixer band-pass filter needed to reduce the image response by 20+ dB, which can be solved by use of a so-called image-rejection mixer, which uses a special arrangement of signal, LO and IF phasings to cancel out the unwanted image. (This technique was relatively obscure until used in the 1980s as part of many TVRO converters for the 3.7-4.2 GHz band.) (2) the difficulty in generating the needed LO power at microwave frequencies, which can be solved by use of a so-called harmonic mixer, which accepts a larger-amplitude signal at an integer subharmonic of the desired LO frequency and uses one, or more, of the mixer diodes to then generate the desired harmonic signal.

All of the foregoing theory can be combined to design the hardware of a modern UHF/microwave station, such as the 902-MHz station in Fig 40. The selection of an antenna for this system will be governed by the desired end use, and is covered in the material on EME systems.

VHF and Microwave Applications of Monolithic Microwave Integrated Circuits

By Al Ward, WB5LUA
2375 Forest Grove Estates Rd
Allen, TX 75002

A monolithic microwave integrated circuit (MMIC) can best be described as a broadband untuned amplifier stage. Depending on the application it can use either silicon-bipolar or gallium-arsenide (GaAs) technology. The wide-band nature of these devices makes them ideal replacements for once state of the art thin-film hybrid feed-back amplifiers. Generally, silicon MMICs have usable gain to approximately 4 GHz while GaAs technology has usable gain to beyond 18 GHz.

The state of the art is progressing rapidly in the fabrication of single-package RF ICs, and the term MMIC applies to devices other than single-stage amplifiers. For applications where a low noise figure is not critical, a MMIC may be used as a "front end." In transmitters, MMICs can be used for all low-level stages up to 50 mW or so, depending on the device chosen. Manufacturers have demonstrated that complete receiver front-end assemblies —including RF amplifier, mixer and even the local oscillator—are possible on a single chip.

MMIC chip-manufacturing processes are very similar to those used for silicon bipolar transistors. By using nitride self-alignment techniques and ion-implantation techniques for precise doping control, a high degree of uniformity among wafers is guaranteed. (Nitride passivation ensures high reliability by minimizing oxidation build-up on the chip.) Additional benefits are high-volume production and low cost. Precision thin-film resistors are fabricated directly on the chip. The small reactances associated with the internal feedback resistors enhance the high-frequency characteristics of the MMIC.

Here I will describe the application of the Avantek MODAMP™ MMIC, which uses silicon technology. MODAMPs are gain blocks with nominal 50-Ω input and output impedances. Each contains a single-stage, Darlington-connected, transistor pair with internal biasing and a combination of series and shunt resistive feedback (see Fig 1—everything inside the shaded lines is contained inside the MMIC package). With the exception of one special series, internal feedback is set to ensure un-conditional stability. The input and output are matched to 50 Ω. This allows us to easily cascade multiple stages. Low-frequency performance is limited only by the value of the external coupling capacitors.

PACKAGING

MODAMPs are supplied in a variety of standard low-power, stripline transistor packages (see Fig 2). MODAMPs have part numbers that indicate the die, package and options (see "MMIC Nomenclature").

The plastic package (MSA-xx04) may be most desirable for commercial and amateur applications where temperature extremes are limited, between −25 °C to +85 °C. It has two common terminals that must *both* be connected to circuit ground.

The "Micro-X" ceramic package (MSA-xx35) is an industry standard for microwave transistors. This package is ceramic and offers acceptable performance over a wider temperature range (−55 °C to +125 °C) than the 'xx04 package. It also offers improved RF performance above 2 GHz because of lower package parasitics, when compared to the 'xx04.

MODAMPs are also available in a "micro-plastic" (MSA-xx85) package that combines the low-cost advantage of the 'xx04 with some of the microwave performance of the 'xx35.

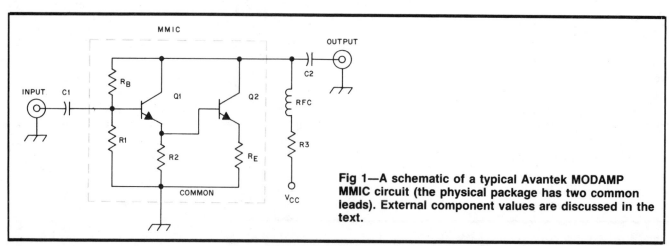

Fig 1—A schematic of a typical Avantek MODAMP MMIC circuit (the physical package has two common leads). External component values are discussed in the text.

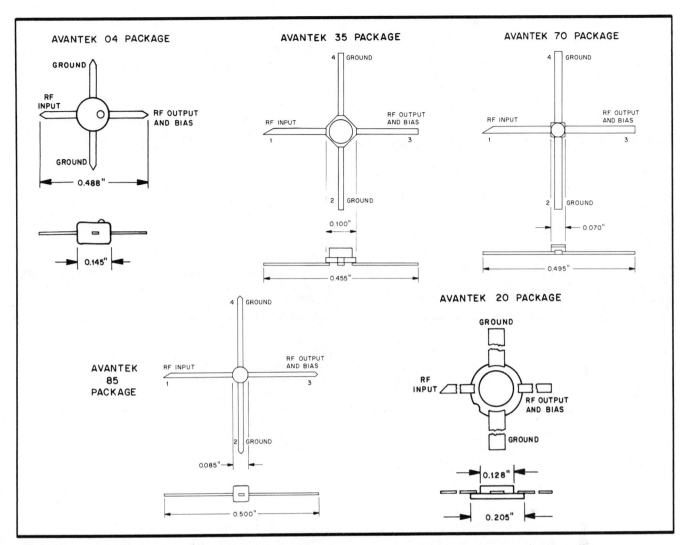

Fig 2—Avantek MMICs are available in a variety of package styles. The package makes a significant difference in MMIC gain at higher frequencies.

Thermal resistance, $\theta_{J\text{-}C}$, indicates how well heat (dissipated power) can be transferred from the device to a heat sink. MODAMPs are rated at approximately 85 °C/W for the 'xx04 package, 140 °C/W for the 'xx35 package and 90 °C/W for the 'xx85.

The 'xx04, 'xx35 and the 'xx85 packages are adequate for most commercial and amateur applications. While it seems a waste to use these components below 500 MHz, their low cost makes them attractive for a lot of applications at HF and below. Single-unit prices are about $3, $8 and $4, respectively, for the 'xx04, 'xx35 and 'xx85 packages. I recommend the 'xx85 series because they work well and cost only a few dollars each. Avantek components are available through a number of distributors nationwide. Contact Avantek for the name and address of the distributor for your area.[1] You should have no trouble buying MMICs in small quantities from any distributor.

For more rugged environments that require military screening, the Avantek .200 SOE (Stripline, Opposed Emitter, with 0.200-inch-wide leads, MSA-xx20) package or the 70-mil stripline package (MSA-xx70) are available. The MSA-0420 has a $\theta_{J\text{-}C}$ of 40 °C/W, which makes it capable of greater power dissipation, and hence greater

power output, than the other packages. $\theta_{J\text{-}C}$ for the MSA-0470 package is 115 °C/W. Prices for these high-reliability 'xx20- and 'xx70-series packages start at approximately $30.

Some MMICs are available in other packages, however, the best performance above 500 MHz can only be achieved with microwave packages.

INSIDE THE PACKAGE

As we discuss the circuitry, please refer again to Fig 1. The series- and shunt-feedback resistors are shown as R_E and R_B, respectively. These resistors, along with R1 and R2, set the amplifier quiescent bias point. The design option we will discuss requires an external "T" network to supply power and couple output to the succeeding stages. This arrangement offers the greatest bandwidth and highest gain. (Some MODAMPs have an internal bias resistor that allows direct V_{CC} connection, but results in reduced performance at higher frequencies.)

EXTERNAL COMPONENTS

C1 and C2 block dc to and from the adjacent circuits; they should be chosen for low reactance (less than 1 Ω) at

MMIC Nomenclature

The Avantek MODAMP MMICs each have a part number like: MSA-AABB-CD. The part number gives some important information about the device. Here's a guide to some characteristics of the various device families.

The number designated by AA defines which MODAMP die is used. The primary differences among the die types are maximum power output, gain and noise figure (NF). The performance numbers given here are approximate and will vary with package style and frequency. There are presently six dies available:

Dies Characteristics

01xx Low power (+1 dBm), high gain (18 dB) and moderate NF (5 dB).

02xx Medium power (+4 dBm), medium gain (10 dB) and moderate NF (6 dB).

03xx High power (+10 dBm), medium gain (10 dB) and moderate NF (5.5 dB).

04xx Highest power (up to +17 dBm), low gain (8 dB) and moderate NF (6 dB).

07xx Similar to 02xx except lower operating voltage and lower NF (4.5 dB).

08xx Highest gain (30 dB at 100 MHz), medium power (+12 dBm) and low noise figure (3 dB) (Note: This device is not unconditionally stable and care must be given to bias-decoupling design.)

BB designates package configuration. There are five package options:

Package Style		Comments
xx04	Plastic	0.145″ circular, low cost, reduced performance above 1 GHz.
xx20	BeO	0.205″ mil-spec circular Berylium-oxide (ceramic), excellent thermal conductivity.
xx35	Micro-x	0.100″ square, excellent performance beyond 1 GHz.
xx70	Stripline	0.070″ square, hermetic, gold-plated package, high reliability.
xx85	Micro-plastic	0.085″ circular plastic, low-cost, excellent performance beyond 1 GHz.
xx86	Surface mount	A xx85 package with leads formed for surface mounting, decreased high-frequency performance above 1 GHz.

Options

Some of the ceramic MMIC families have a suffix (-CD) tacked onto the end of the part number. An example is the MSA-0335-21. A "1" for the first digit of the suffix indicates that the series-bias resistor (R3 of Fig 1) is part of the MMIC. Such MODAMPs need a +12-V dc supply. The four leads are then: input, output, V_{CC} and common (ground). A "2" indicates that an external bias resistor is required (the chip operating voltage is typically 5 to 6 V), and there are two common (ground) leads.

The second digit of the suffix is used to designate a premium part, usually with better high-frequency response. For example, the gain of the MSA-0235-11 is 1 dB less at 1 GHz than it is at 100 MHz versus 800 MHz for the MSA-0235-12. This is quite a difference in performance!

These options apply to the '01xx, '02xx and '03xx geometries in the 'xx35 and 'xx70 packages. The '04xx series (for example, the MSA-0470 or MSA-0435) has no bias or frequency-response options and therefore no suffix.

The 'xx04 and 'xx85 package styles have two common leads for best high-frequency performance. Power is connected via output connection, and there is no internal-bias-resistor option. This is the standard arrangement, so these parts have no suffix after the package style (for example, MSA-0104).

the frequency of operation. Silver-mica capacitors are fine for HF, VHF and UHF operating frequencies. Use good low-loss ceramic chip capacitors above 1 GHz.

It is important to choose the right values for R3 and RFC if we are to get the maximum gain and power output from the MMIC. RFC provides a high reactance, while R3 helps set the required operating point for a specified V_{CC}. Together, RFC and R3 should yield more than 500 Ω at the operating frequency. If RFC is omitted, gain will suffer by approximately 1 dB, depending on frequency. This is caused by the parallel loading of the resistor across the nominal 50-Ω output impedance of the amplifier.

R3 helps the "on chip" resistors set the amplifier operating point, but also has several other important functions:

• High values for R3 load the amplifier output less and allow greater gain.

• It provides temperature compensation to prevent thermal runaway. That is, as the device current gain (β) increases with temperature, the greater current drawn through R3 increases the R3 voltage drop and decreases voltage across the MMIC.

• A carbon resistor at R3 has a positive temperature coefficient (resistance increases with temperature) that helps counteract the negative temperature coefficient of the on-chip resistors.

A value for R3 is calculated with the following equation (actual values will be discussed later):

$$R3 = \frac{V_{CC} - V_{MMIC}}{I_{MMIC}} \qquad \text{(Eq 1)}$$

where V_{CC} = available supply voltage. V_{MMIC} and I_{MMIC} are specified on the device data sheet. As V_{CC} increases, so will the value for R3. Avantek recommends a 2-V difference between the supply and chip requirement for best performance over a wide temperature range. (If there was no R3, thermal runaway would destroy the chip at 100°C.)

PERFORMANCE

Typical gain and 1-dB gain-compression performance data for the MSA-0104 through MSA-0404 (plastic package) MMICs is shown in Table 1 (including several cascade and parallel arrangements). Performance data for several "Micro-X" "xx35 and" xx85 versions appears in Tables 2 and 3, respectively. By comparing single-device figures in

Table 1
Typical Gain and 1 dB Compression Point (P$_{1dB}$) for Avantek 04-Package MODAMPs

Device (MSA-)	30	50	144	220	432	902	1296	2304	3456	
0104	19	19	19	18	17	14	12	9	6	dB Gain
	+8	+8	+7	+6	+4	†	†	†	†	dBm P$_{1dB}$
0204	13	13	13	13	12	11	10	8	6	dB Gain
	>+7	>+7	>+7	>+7	+7	+5	+4	+2	†	dBm P$_{1dB}$
0304	13	13	13	13	12	11	10	8	6	dB Gain
	>+13	>+13	>+13	>+13	+13	+11	+10	+5	†	dBm P$_{1dB}$
0404	8	8	8	8	8	8	7	6	5	dB Gain
	>+13	>+13	>+13	>+13	>+13	+13	+13	+13	†	dBm P$_{1dB}$

For Cascaded xx04-Packages

Device (MSA-)	30	50	144	220	432	902	1296	2304	3456	
02/03	26	26	26	26	24	22	20	16	12	dB Gain
	>+13	>+13	>+13	>+13	+13	+11	+10	+5	†	dBm P$_{1dB}$
02/03/04	34	34	34	34	32	30	28	††	17	dB Gain
	>+13	>+13	>+13	>+13	+13	+13	+13	††	†	dBm P$_{1dB}$
03/04/04	†††	†††	†††	†††	†††	†††	†††	22	16	dB Gain
	†††	†††	†††	†††	†††	†††	†††	†13	†	dBm P$_{1dB}$

For Four Parallel Connected '0404s

Device (MSA-)	30	50	144	220	432	902	1296	2304	3456	
04/04	>+19	>+19	>+19	>+19	>+19	+19	+19	+19	†	dBm P$_{1dB}$

†Not specified.
††Combination not desired for 2304 MHz because of gain compression in the 03xx stage.
†††Not analyzed.
Note: Data obtained from Avantek data sheets and represent typical performance at current specified for continuous operation.

Table 2
Typical Gain and 1 dB Compression Point (P$_{1dB}$) for Avantek 35-Package MMICs

Device (MSA-)	902	1296	2304	3456	
0135	17	15	11	9	dB gain
	†	†	†	†	dBm P$_{1dB}$
0235	12	11	10	8	dB gain
	+11	+9	+6	†	dBm P$_{1dB}$
0335	12	12	10	7	dB gain
	+12	+10	+6	†	dBm P$_{1dB}$
0435	8	8	7	5	dB gain
	+12	+10	+6	+5	dBm P$_{1dB}$
††	+15	+13	+9	+6	dBm P$_{1dB}$
0835	24	20	15	12	dB gain
	+13	+14	+12	+10	dBm P$_{1dB}$

†Not specified
††The '0435 is capable of greater power output when operated at higher current (70 mA) in intermittent service.
Note: Data obtained from Avantek data sheets and represents typical performance at current specified for continuous operation.

the tables, you can see that the microwave packages do offer superior performance above 2 GHz and that the 'xx85 package does offer a good compromise between performance and price. It's readily apparent that gain above 902 MHz is approximately 1 to 2 dB greater with the 'xx85 package than the 'xx04 package; the 'xx85 and 'xx35 packages offer similar gain above 902 MHz. The 'xx85 package is certainly the choice for economy, yet it still retains the high-frequency performance of the 'xx35 package.

Input and output SWR for this family of MMICs are usually less than 2.0:1 with noise figures in the 5- to 7.5-dB range—with the exception of the MSA-0835; it is capable of 3- to 4-dB noise figures up to 3 GHz because it uses minimal feedback. According to the data sheet, it is capable of more gain than any of the other devices, but it is *not* unconditionally stable. The impedances of its source and load must be set to retain stability—more on this device later.

SOME WORKING AMPLIFIERS

Series-Connected (Cascade), Two-Stage Amplifiers

A simple HF/VHF test amplifier built with MSA-0204 and MSA-0304 MMICs and readily available components is shown in Fig 3. The capacitors are dipped-mica components. Table 4 gives calculated values for the series resistor (for continuous operation at the specified current level). RFCs were not used in this circuit. 0.1-μF bypass capacitors were added to suppress low-frequency oscillations in the bias/coupling network. (Remember that MMICs have significant low-frequency gain; good bypassing is a must.) When installling the MMIC, use the lead of a 1-W resistor as a form (see Fig 3B) to bend the common leads down, and then away, from the package so that the device will lay flat when soldered to the ground plane.

Table 3
Typical Gain and 1 dB Compression Point (P_{1dB}) for Avantek 85-Package MMICs

Device (MSA-)	Frequency (MHz)									
	30	50	144	220	432	902	1296	2304	3456	
0185	18	18	18	17	17	15	14	10	7	dB Gain
	>+7	>+7	+7	+5	+4	+3	+2	†	†	dBm P_{1dB}
0285	12	12	12	12	12	12	11	10	8	dB Gain
	>+9	>+9	+9	+7	+5	+5	+5	†	†	dBm P_{1dB}
0385	12	12	12	12	12	12	11	10	7	dB Gain
0485	8	8	8	8	8	8	8	7	6	dB Gain

†Not specified.
Note: Data obtained from Avantek data sheets and represent typical performance at current specified for continuous operation.

One version of the amplifier was built on a piece of 0.015″ hobby brass, bolted to the inside of a standard mini-box. The brass sheet allows the MMIC common leads to be tack soldered directly to the ground plane. (I purposely made the lead lengths long on version A—3/8″, versus 1/4″ for option B—to see the effect on higher-frequency performance.)

Fig 3D shows gain measurements made on a swept network analyzer. Curve A is for the amplifier using 3/8-inch leads, while curve B is for the amplifier using 1/4-inch leads. Both versions have usable gain well above 1 GHz. Use good VHF assembly techniques (short lead lengths) to assure usable gain beyond 1 GHz. The noise figure below 1 GHz is about 6 dB.

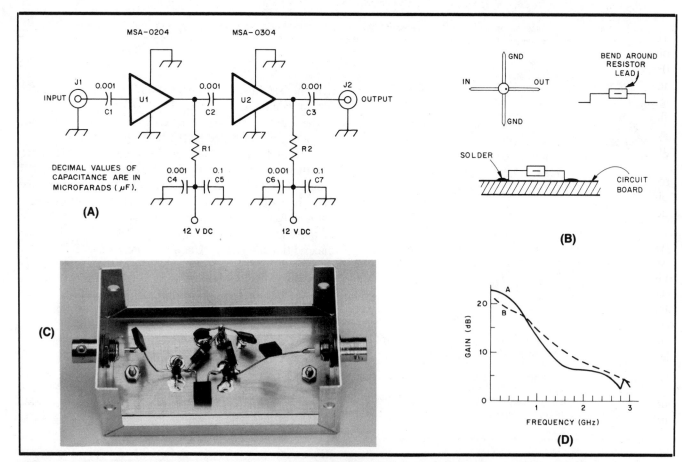

Fig 3—A simple HF and VHF MMIC amplifier circuit. (A) shows the schematic diagram. Capacitors are silver-mica or ceramic; values are expressed in μF. The resistors are ½-W carbon. Details for mounting the MMICs to double-sided PC board appear in (B). (C) is a photo of the completed amplifier, built on sheet brass inside a small aluminum box. All ground points are soldered to the brass sheet, which is electrically connected to the box. Gain is plotted against frequency for both versions of the amplifier at (D). Curve A is for version A with 3/8-inch leads, while curve B is for version B with 1/4-inch leads.

J1, J2—Female, chassis-mount BNC. U1—Avantek MSA-0204 MMIC.
R1, R2—See Table 4. U2—Avantek MSA-0304 MMIC.

Table 4
Bias-Resistor Values for V_{CC} = 12 V

(MSA-)	Optimum Current (mA)	Resistance / Dissipation (Ω) / (W)
0104	20	330 / 0.13
0204	30	220 / 0.20
0304	40	180 / 0.29
0404	50	130 / 0.33
0135	22	270 / 0.13
0235	40	150 / 0.24
0335	50	120 / 0.30
0435†	50	130 / 0.33
0835	35	120 / 0.15
0185	17	410 / 0.12
0285	25	280 / 0.18
0385	35	200 / 0.25
0485	50	140 / 0.35

†The 0435 is capable of greater power output when operated at higher current (70 mA) in intermittent service.

Table 5
MMIC Amplifier Performance at HF (Circuit of Fig 3)
With 0.001-μF Blocking Capacitors

Frequency (MHz)	Gain (dB)
28	21.4
7	20.6
3.5	19.0
1.2	19.0

With 0.1-μF Blocking Capacitors

Frequency (MHz)	Gain (dB)
28	21.7
7	21.4
3.5	21.5
1.2	22.0

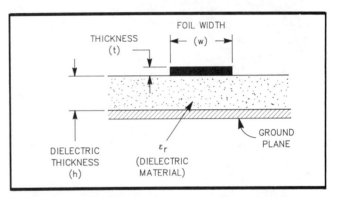

Fig 4—A cross-section view of typical microstripline construction.

Since the swept network analyzer plots only characterize the amplifier down to 50 MHz, additional point-by-point data was taken to evaluate performance at specific HF frequencies. This data is shown in Table 5. The low-end gain rolloff is below 7 MHz when using 0.001-μF blocking capacitors. Calculations predict that 0.1-μF capacitors will extend the low-end rolloff below 100 kHz, but may impact performance above 50 MHz, depending on capacitor parasitics.

You can find many uses for this basic test amplifier around the amateur station: as an IF amplifier for converter noise-figure measurements, or as a preamplifier for a frequency counter or spectrum analyzer.

If maximum gain is desired at amateur frequencies greater than 902 MHz, use microstripline techniques. A cross-section view of a microstrip transmission line is shown in Fig 4. The actual impedance of the microstripline depends on the line width (w), the height of the line above the ground plane (h), and the dielectric constant (ϵ_r) of the material separating the line from the ground plane. Microstripline impedance calculations are beyond the scope of this article, but you can learn more about them from several good articles that have appeared in the amateur literature.[2,3,4]

A schematic, etching pattern, component layout and photo of a microstripline circuit are shown in Fig 5. The microstripline PC board can be etched, or you can use a sharp knife and hot soldering iron to remove copper and create isolated pads on any piece of scrap PC board. Common glass-epoxy material is fine for most applications below 2 or 3 GHz. Standard 0.062″, double-sided, glass-epoxy PC-board material has ϵ_r of about 5.0. A microstripline with a characteristic impedance of 50 Ω is about 0.100″ wide on this material. The line lengths needed for an MMIC amplifier are short enough that the loss of glass-epoxy material is acceptable, even at 3456 MHz.

Good quality 0.05″- or 0.10″-square chip capacitors are used for coupling to adjacent circuits. The capacitors are necessary for good gain performance at frequencies above 1 GHz. Use a 15-W soldering iron when installing the chip capacitors to avoid removing the metallization during assembly. (An excellent article on the selection and use of chip capacitors appeared in *QEX*.[5]) SMA coaxial connectors provide a simple low-loss way to "feed" a microstripline circuit. Homemade RF chokes were designed to enhance performance above 1 GHz.

To ensure a low-loss, low-inductance path to ground for the common leads of the MMIC, pieces of thin copper or brass foil (preferably no greater than 0.005″ thick) are used to tie the ground areas on the top of the board to the bottom ground plane. First wrap the edges of the board. Then drill a hole, where the MMIC mounts, that is big enough to wrap a piece of the foil under the common leads, through the hole, down to the ground plane. Solder the foil on both sides of the board. Alternatively, drill small holes through the board under the ground leads of each device. Pass the leads through the small holes and solder each lead to both the top and bottom ground areas.

When cascading two or more MMICs in a receiver or

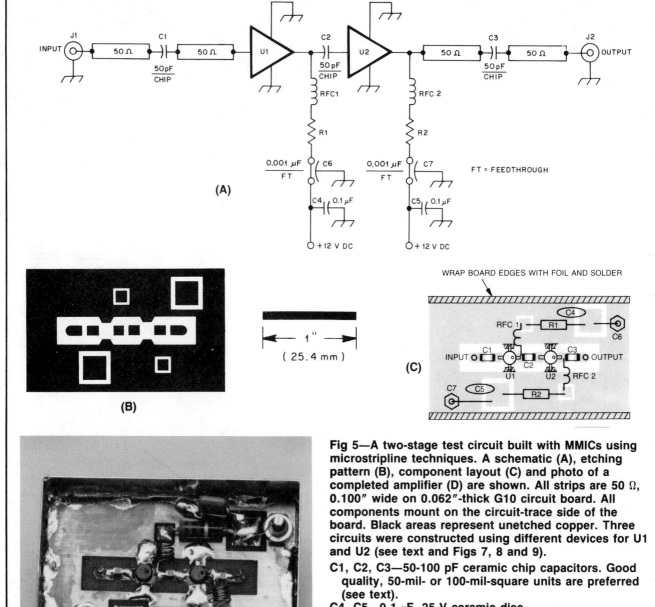

Fig 5—A two-stage test circuit built with MMICs using microstripline techniques. A schematic (A), etching pattern (B), component layout (C) and photo of a completed amplifier (D) are shown. All strips are 50 Ω, 0.100″ wide on 0.062″-thick G10 circuit board. All components mount on the circuit-trace side of the board. Black areas represent unetched copper. Three circuits were constructed using different devices for U1 and U2 (see text and Figs 7, 8 and 9).

C1, C2, C3—50-100 pF ceramic chip capacitors. Good quality, 50-mil- or 100-mil-square units are preferred (see text).
C4, C5—0.1-μF, 25-V ceramic disc.
C6, C7—470- to 1000-pF feed-through capacitor.
J1, J2—Female, flange-mount SMA connector.
R1, R2—Carbon bias resistors. See text and Table 4 for values.
RFC1, RFC2—4 turns no. 26 or 28 enameled wire, 0.125″ ID, spaced one wire diam.
U1, U2—Avantek 'xx04 series MMIC (see text).

transmitter strip, it may be better to use additional decoupling. Remember that MMICs, especially the '01xx and '08xx series, have significant gain at low frequencies (several megahertz). If the bias decoupling is not adequate, the amplifier may oscillate from feedback through the bias network. If you experience low-frequency oscillations, try adding a 1-μH RFC in series between V_{CC} terminals of each MMIC stage (see Fig 6).

Measured performance for three configurations: (1) '0104 driving '0104, (2) '0204 driving '0304, (3) '0404 driving '0404 is shown in Figs 7, 8 and 9. Notice the vastly improved

performance of the microstrip '0204-'0304 combination as compared to the VHF version shown in Fig 3. This results from good 50-Ω transmission lines that match the MMIC to its 50-Ω source and load. The actual gain was slightly less than advertised in the data sheets, but it is possible to enhance the performance above 2 GHz by using low-loss Rogers® 5880 or 3M circuit-board material (ϵ_r = 2.20). For 0.031″-thick material, 50-Ω lines would be 0.100″ wide; 0.200″ for 0.062″-thick material.

No low-frequency oscillations have been noticed in the bias/coupling networks of the microstrip MMIC amplifiers

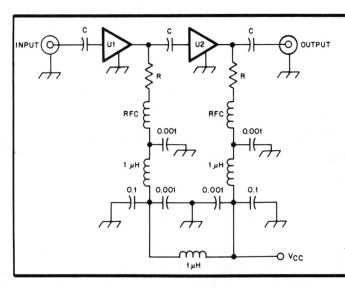

Fig 6—In some applications, additional bias decoupling may be necessary for completely stable operation. This is especially true when using the MSA-0835, which has tremendous gain (30 dB) at low frequencies. The network shown here will help to minimize low-frequency (HF/VHF) oscillations caused by feedback in the bias circuitry. The 0.001-μF and 0.1-μF capacitors, as well as the 1-μH chokes are the same for any cascaded MMIC circuit. The values of C, R and RFC should be chosen for proper MMIC operation at the desired frequency, as explained elsewhere in this article.

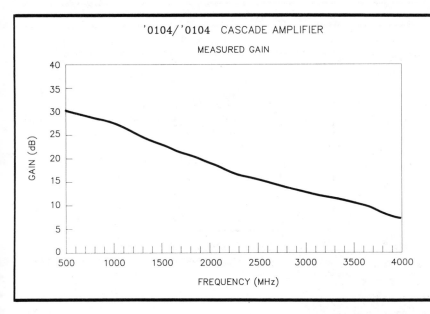

Fig 7—Gain versus frequency for the microstripline amplifier circuit of Fig 5 using an Avantek MSA-0104 driving an MSA-0104.

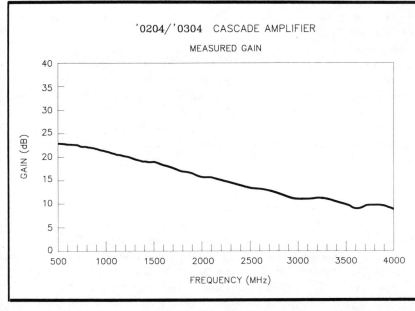

Fig 8—Gain versus frequency for the microstripline amplifier circuit of Fig 5 using an Avantek MSA-0204 driving an MSA-0304.

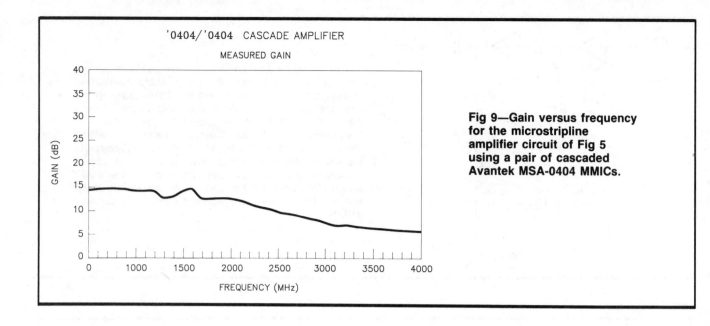

Fig 9—Gain versus frequency for the microstripline amplifier circuit of Fig 5 using a pair of cascaded Avantek MSA-0404 MMICs.

assembled to date. If you experience such problems, they can be controlled with 0.1-μF bypass capacitors at the cold end of the series resistor.

The noise figure for the '0104-'0104 series circuit was measured at 4.7 dB (1296 MHz) and 5.3 dB (2304 MHz). A 4.5-dB noise figure is typical below 1296 MHz. The 1-dB gain compression of the '0204-'0304 series combination measured + 10 dBm (1296 MHz) and + 5 dBm (2304 MHz). Similarly, for the '0404-'0404 series combination, the 1-dB gain compression point was + 13 dBm (1296 MHz) and + 12 dBm (2304 MHz).

A Conditionally Stable Amplifier

The MSA-0835 is similar to the '01xx- through '04xx-series MMICs except that it uses minimal series feedback. A higher-value internal feedback resistor allows greater gain and lower noise figure, but at the expense of "gain flatness." As a result, this particular MMIC is *not* unconditionally stable.

A simple microstripline test circuit was built to test the MSA-0835 in a similar fashion to the other MMICs. A 200-Ω 0.5-W carbon resistor was used to bias the '0835 at 25 mA, for the lowest possible noise figure. An RFC (2 turns no. 28 enameled wire, 0.125″ ID, turns spaced one wire diameter) was used in series with the bias resistor. When the two-turn RFC was added in series with the bias resistor, the amplifier exhibited a slight gain increase in the 500-2500 MHz frequency range without compromising stability. Experiments with RF chokes (up to 6 turns) yielded greater gain but marginal stability. Dependent on the inductance of the bias resistor, you may need to delete the series RFC to ensure stability under all circuit conditions. Actual measured gain response for two-turn and four-turn RFCs is shown in Fig 10. A gain of 24 dB is achieved at 500 MHz (for a single device!), while the gain at 3500 MHz dropped to 9 dB. The measured noise figure at 2304 MHz is about 4 dB with a gain of 13 dB—not bad for an untuned microwave amplifier using G-10 dielectric material!

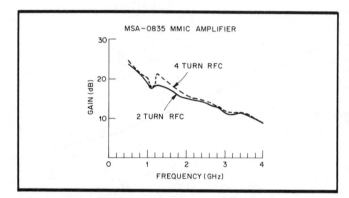

Fig 10—Gain versus frequency plots for microstripline test amplifiers using an Avantek MSA-0835 MMIC (see text).

Gain performance comparable to that in Table 2 could be achieved with a better dielectric material, such as Rogers 5880.

Parallel-Connected Amplifiers

MMICs can be cascaded easily for increased gain, but how can we increase the power output capability of these devices? Since the '01xx- through '04xx-series are unconditionally stable, they can be paralleled easily for increased power output. For two devices in parallel, the 1-dB compression point will approach + 3 dB over that of a single device. For four devices in parallel, it will improve almost + 6 dB. Of course, the gain will be no greater than that of a single device and may in fact decrease slightly from losses in the divider/combiner networks.

Four MMICs can be parallel connected as shown in Fig 11. The input and output impedances will be approxi-. mately 50/4 = 12.5 Ω. The input of each MMIC must be dc blocked from those of the other MMICs, but the outputs can be parallel connected and power applied through

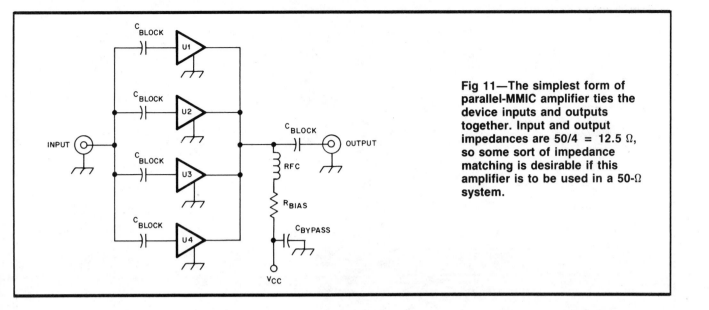

Fig 11—The simplest form of parallel-MMIC amplifier ties the device inputs and outputs together. Input and output impedances are 50/4 = 12.5 Ω, so some sort of impedance matching is desirable if this amplifier is to be used in a 50-Ω system.

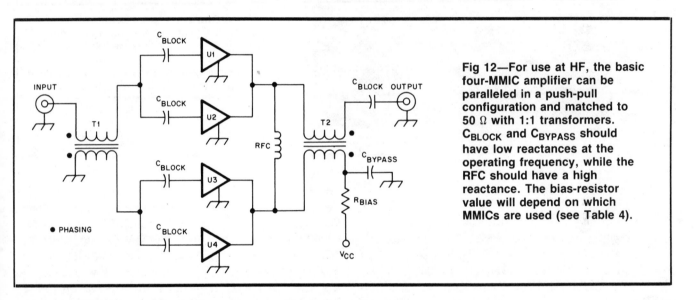

Fig 12—For use at HF, the basic four-MMIC amplifier can be paralleled in a push-pull configuration and matched to 50 Ω with 1:1 transformers. C_{BLOCK} and C_{BYPASS} should have low reactances at the operating frequency, while the RFC should have a high reactance. The bias-resistor value will depend on which MMICs are used (see Table 4).

a single RFC and series resistor of appropriate value and power rating. A single coupling capacitor is used on the output. Since it is normally desirable to retain 50-Ω input and output impedances, some sort of matching is required. For maximum bandwidth at HF, simple toroidal transformers may be used as shown in Fig 12. The transformers supply equal-amplitude signals that are 180° out of phase. These transformers, or baluns, lend themselves to push-pull operation rather easily. Amplifier bandwidth is mainly determined by the transformer response rather than that of the MMIC. An RF choke was included in the output network so that all four MMICs can be fed from a single bias resistor.

Parallel connection of MMICs at VHF can be accomplished with Wilkinson power-divider networks that use lumped elements to feed two or four MMICs. Fig 13 shows a suggested circuit for a pair of MMICs. Here are equations to calculate the element values for a single-section Wilkinson power divider in a 50-Ω system.

The values for L1-L4 are:

$$L = \frac{70.7}{2 \times \pi \times F_o} \qquad \text{(Eq 2)}$$

where
    L = inductance in henrys
    F_o = frequency of operation in hertz.

For C2, C3, C6 and C7:

$$C = \frac{1}{2 \times \pi \times F_o \times 70.7} \qquad \text{(Eq 3)}$$

where
    C = capacitance in farads
    F_o = frequency of operation in hertz.

For C1 and C8:

$$C = 2 \times C2 \qquad \text{(Eq 4)}$$

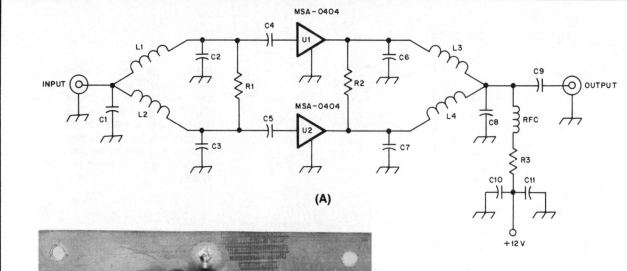

(A)

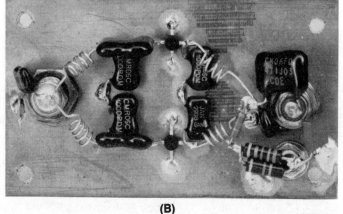

(B)

Fig 13—For VHF, MMICs in parallel
may be matched to 50 Ω with
Wilkinson divider/combiner networks
(A). This amplifier may be built for
220 or 432 MHz. See text and Table 6
for component values. A photo of the
220-MHz version, built on unetched
PC-board material is shown in (B).

For R1 and R2:

$$R = 2 \times Z_0 = 100 \ \Omega \qquad \text{(Eq 5)}$$

Since Z_0 will always be 50 Ω in MMIC circuits, R1 and R2 will always be 100 Ω. An in-depth description of Wilkinson power dividers is available elsewhere.[6]

C4, C5, C9, and C10 should have a low reactance (less than 1 or 2 Ω) at the operating frequency and RFC should have a reactance such that its impedance in combination with the series bias resistor value is approximately ten times the output impedance, or 500 Ω. C11 is a low-frequency bypass capacitor.

The Wilkinson power-divider approach works well with MMICs at amateur frequencies up to 225 MHz, but above that frequency performance may not be as expected for several reasons. First, the capacitor values are small (less than 10 pF); the exact value may be difficult to achieve with standard-value components. In addition, the values of dipped silver-mica capacitors are effected by significant parasitic components (such as lead inductance or shunt reactance) at UHF. Third, MMICs usually have nominal 50-Ω input and output impedances, but they may not be purely resistive. When an MMIC is designed to operate over a very wide bandwidth, the component values in the MMIC are chosen such that the gain (as measured in a 50-Ω system) is constant over a wide frequency range. As a result, the input and output match may not be optimum at the frequency of operation. If the input and output

impedance, or SWR, at each frequency was plotted on a Smith Chart, the plot would resemble a circle centered near 50 + j0 Ω. Since the devices are somewhat reactive, they change the resonate frequency of the Wilkinson networks. The Wilkinson network, however, is generally low pass by design, and it follows that if the network were designed for a slightly higher frequency than the actual operation, the MMIC amplifier may not require any further tuning.

To test MMICs with a Wilkinson divider, an amplifier was designed (Fig 13) for 220 MHz using the foregoing equations for the individual element values. Component values are shown in Table 6. Dipped silver-mica capacitors were used for the matching elements and the closest

Table 6

Component Values for the Circuit of Fig 13

Component	220 MHz	432 MHz
C1, C8	20 pF	1-10 pF (variable)
C2, C3, C6, C7	10 pF SM	5 pF SM
C4, C5, C9, C10	470 pF SM	100 pF SM
C11	0.1 μF	0.1 μF
L1-L4	50 nH	26 nH
	(see text)	(see text)
R1, R2	100 Ω	100 Ω
R3	62 Ω, 1 W	62 Ω, 1 W
RFC	0.47 μH	0.47 μH
U1, U2	MSA-0404	MSA-0404

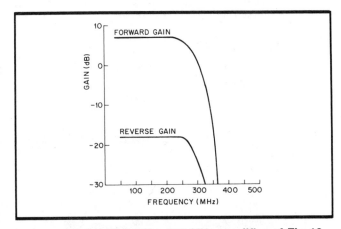

Fig 14—Gain plots for the 220-MHz amplifier of Fig 13. Both forward and reverse gain are shown to illustrate amplifier stability (see text).

standard values were used. L1 through L4 are each four turns of no. 24 enameled wire, 0.125″ ID, spaced one wire diameter apart, with 0.25″ leads.

Reverse gain (S_{12}) is indicative of amplifier stability. If $-S_{12}$ were no greater than forward gain (S_{21}), stability would be marginal. A swept-frequency plot of forward and reverse gain (Fig 14) shows that $-S_{12}$ is much greater than S_{21}, and the 220-MHz amplifier is quite stable.

As mentioned earlier, the circuit response is low pass in nature. Gain is similar to that of a single device, while the 1-dB compression point is +16 dBm (40 mW) and compressed output will be over +18 dBm (63 mW).

If greater gain is desired at the expense of power output capability, the '01xx-, '02xx- or '03xx-series devices can be parallel connected instead of the '04xx devices. This concept will work fine down to HF, as long as appropriate Wilkinson-element values are calculated and appropriate capacitors and RFC are chosen.

A similar amplifier was designed and built for 432 MHz using element values determined from the preceding equations. Component values are shown in Table 6. L1 through L4 are 1.5 turns no. 24 enameled wire, 0.125″ ID, spaced one wire diameter apart, with 0.25″ leads. I found

that gain could be peaked at 432 MHz and input and output SWR could be minimized if the shunt capacitors (C1 and C8) were made variable. The amplifier response is shown in Fig 15. Gain is "flat" down to 200 MHz (gain was not measured below 200 MHz), and input and output SWR are quite acceptable. By varying C1 and C8, the circuit can tune out the reactive components of the MMIC and produce additional gain over the untuned 220-MHz amplifier just described. The 432-MHz amplifier power output is similar to that of the 220-MHz amplifier.

Although parallel-connected MMICs work very well at HF and VHF, the real advantages don't show up until they are applied at 902 MHz and higher. At microwave frequencies, the transmission-line equivalent of a Wilkinson power divider is very easily constructed (two possible options are shown in Fig 16). The transmission line is $\lambda/4$ at the operating frequency, and its required characteristic impedance is determined from the following formula:

$$Z_0 = \sqrt{Z_{in} \times Z_{out}} \qquad \text{(Eq 6)}$$

where Z_{in} and Z_{out} are the impedances to be matched. For the two-MMIC approach shown at (A), the 50-Ω nominal impedance of the MMIC must be transformed to 100 Ω so that two of these networks can be parallel connected to yield 50 Ω. Therefore:

$$Z_0 = \sqrt{50 \times 100} = \sqrt{5000} = 70.7 \ \Omega$$

At (B), two MMICs are first parallel connected to yield 25 Ω and then transformed to 100 Ω so that when two of these networks are parallel connected the result is again 50 Ω. Therefore...

$$Z_0 = \sqrt{25 \times 100} = \sqrt{2500} = 50 \ \Omega$$

This approach is used for both input and output networks and requires no tuning. The 50-Ω and 70.7-Ω transmission lines can be constructed from coaxial cable or simulated in a microstripline configuration.

The (B) circuit is very attractive because low-loss, 50-Ω,

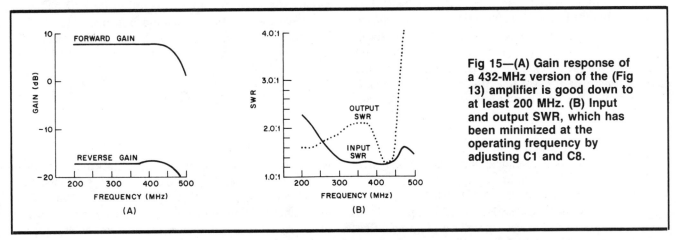

Fig 15—(A) Gain response of a 432-MHz version of the (Fig 13) amplifier is good down to at least 200 MHz. (B) Input and output SWR, which has been minimized at the operating frequency by adjusting C1 and C8.

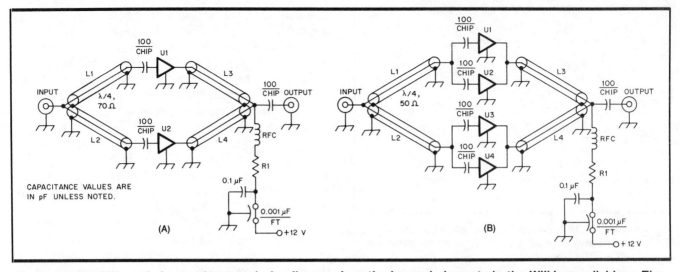

Fig 16—At 902 MHz and above, λ/4 transmission lines replace the lumped elements in the Wilkinson dividers. The circuit at A, for two MMICs, uses 70-Ω lines, while the four-MMIC amplifier at B uses 50-Ω lines. Line lengths for various frequencies are shown in Table 7. All 100-pF capacitors are 50-mil or 100-mil RF-type ceramic chips.

L1-L4—See text and Table 7.
R1—For the circuit in A: 62 Ω, 1 W. Set for 100-mA idling current. For the circuit in B: 40 Ω, 2 W. Set for 200-mA idling current.

RFC—6 turns no. 24 enameled wire, 0.125″ ID, spaced 1 wire diam.
U1-U4—Identical MMICs. MSA-0404 recommended for maximum power output.

Table 7

Lengths of λ/4 Lines for UT-141 Cable

Frequency (MHz)	Length (Inches)
902	2.3
1296	1.6
2050	0.9
2304	0.8

0.141″ semi-rigid cable is readily available, and it allows four MMICs to be easily connected in parallel. The 1-dB gain compression should be 5 to 6 dB greater than with a single MMIC. I recommend the MSA-0404 because it offers the highest 1-dB gain compression value of the inexpensive plastic devices. The measured 1-dB gain compression for an assembly of four '0404 devices is +19 dBm (1296 MHz) and +17 dBm (2304 MHz). At 902 MHz +19 dBm should be easily achieved. Saturated power output has been measured at over +20 dBm (100 mW) at 1296 MHz and over +18 dBm (60 mW) at 2304 MHz. Table 7 shows the physical length of the λ/4 lines for several frequencies. (Above 2 GHz the cable length was compensated for end effects and parasitics.) The cable dimensions are measured to the ends of the shield.

Complete construction information for 1296-MHz and 2304-MHz amplifiers is contained in my earlier *QST* article.[7,8] Gain at 1-dB gain compression measures 5 dB (1296 MHz) and 4 dB (2304 MHz). The usable bandwidth at 1296-MHz unit is 300 MHz. A microstrip amplifier using seven MMICs in a cascade/parallel arrangement that delivers over 17 dB gain and a 1-dB gain compression of +17 dBm at 2304 MHz is described in the same article.

PREDICTING MMIC AMPLIFIER PERFORMANCE

It's very easy to cascade and/or parallel MMICs for a wide variety of applications. When deciding which (and how many) devices are required to fill a given need, it is helpful to do a little homework first. In order to predict the performance of an amplifier made from a given combination of MMICs, one need merely understand a few basic parameters: gain, SWR, noise figure, 1-dB gain compression and intermodulation distortion (IMD) third-order intercept point.

When dealing with transmitter stages, all parameters except noise figure are considered important. (Since the noise figure for most MMICs is in the 5-6 dB range, the noise level is so low that other levels in the exciter, such as carrier suppression and phase noise, are dominant.) In a receiver, all parameters should be considered if good dynamic range is desired. Let's review these concepts and several examples. Actual system requirements will be left up to the builder.

Gain

Gain is a measurement of the difference in power available at the source and power available after the device under test (DUT) is inserted. A test setup to measure gain is shown in Fig 17. To get the most accurate gain measurements possible, the source and the power meter should exhibit a low SWR (less than 1.15:1) relative to the system impedance (50 Ω in this case). Occasionally the impedance of the signal source or power meter is not 50 Ω resistive.

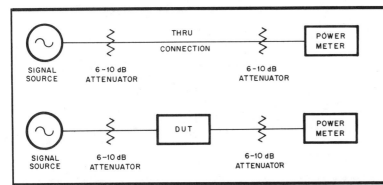

Fig 17—A test setup for measuring gain is first calibrated without the amplifier (DUT) in line. The 6-10 dB attenuators ensure adequate impedance matching of all components to 50 Ω.

50-Ω, 6- to 10-dB attenuators can then be used between the DUT and test equipment to obtain an adequate impedance match.

Since we are making a gain measurement with the "available power" method (which, by the way, is the standard accepted industry method), the effect of the DUT input and output SWR is automatically taken into account with the gain measurement. Included in the gain measurement of the DUT is the mismatch loss which is associated with the SWR of the DUT. Mismatch loss (ML) can be calculated from:

$$ML = -10 \log \left[1 - \left(\frac{SWR - 1}{SWR + 1}\right)^2\right] \qquad \text{(Eq 7)}$$

If the input and output SWR is 1.0:1, then the corresponding mismatch loss is 0 dB. Any improvement in the input and output SWR of an amplifier results in an increase in measured gain equal to the reduction in mismatch loss at each port.

When cascading MMICs, we would like to see the resultant measured gain equal to the sum of the individual MMIC gains. This would be possible if the input and output SWR of each MMIC were 1.0:1. However, this is rarely the case. Equation 8 can be used to calculate mismatch loss as a function of two SWRs beating against one another.

Multiple mismatch loss =

$$20 \log \left[1 \pm \left(\frac{SWR_1 - 1}{SWR_1 + 1} \times \frac{SWR_2 - 1}{SWR_2 + 1}\right)\right] \qquad \text{(Eq 8)}$$

The resultant mismatch loss will either add to or subtract from the sum of the individual MMIC gains. The " + " term in Equation 8 will give the maximum possible additional loss, while the " − " term will give the minimum possible additional loss (which is in reality gain). Maximum mismatch loss will occur at some electrical spacing, L, between the MMICs. Minimum loss will occur at a spacing λ/4 shorter or longer than L. It is possible for two SWRs (>1.0:1) to be a conjugate match (that is R + jX Ω and R − jX Ω). If this occurs, the cascaded MMICs will produce more gain than the sum of the gains of the individual MMICs would indicate is possible.

For example, two 1.5:1 SWRs could produce 0.34 dB additional loss, or 0.35 dB less loss (more gain) than the sum of the individual amplifier gains. Suppose an amplifier has two cascaded MMICs. The output SWR of MMIC no. 1 is 2.0:1, and the input SWR of MMIC no. 2 is 1.5:1. Assume the input SWR of MMIC no. 1 and output SWR of MMIC no. 2 to be 1.0:1. The mismatch loss could be + 0.56 dB maximum or − 0.6 dB minimum. If the gain of MMIC no. 1 is 6 dB and the gain of MMIC no. 2 is 7 dB, the possible resultant gain of the cascaded pair could be:

6 dB + 7 dB + 0.56 dB = 13.56 dB maximum gain

or

6 dB + 7 dB − 0.6 dB = 12.4 dB minimum gain.

The actual gain will be between 12.4 and 13.56 dB, depending on the electrical length between the two devices. Equation 8 gives an idea of the relative uncertainty of the cascaded gain. Keep this in mind as MMICs are cascaded.

Noise Figure

The noise of a cascaded series of devices is calculated readily from the following equation:

$$NF \text{ (total)} = NF_1 + \frac{NF_2 - 1}{G_1} + \frac{NF_3 - 1}{G_1 G_2} + \frac{NF_4 - 1}{G_1 G_2 G_3} \cdots$$

where noise figure (NF) and gain (G) are expressed in unitless ratios.[9]

As an example, let's analyze the noise figure of the 2304-MHz receiving converter shown in Fig 18. Two MSA-0835 MMICs are used as RF amplifiers, followed by a band-pass filter, doubly balanced mixer and IF amplifier.

To simplify the calculation, the loss of the filter and mixer can be added to the noise figure of the IF amplifier. This allows the receiver to be analyzed as only three stages: The two MSA-0835s, each having a 4-dB NF with 13-dB gain, and the filter/mixer/IF amplifier having a 10.5-dB NF and 10-dB gain.

$$NF \text{ (total)} = 2.5 + \frac{2.5 - 1}{20} + \frac{11.2 - 1}{20 \times 20}$$

$$= 2.5 + 0.075 + 0.255$$
$$= 2.60$$
$$= 4.15 \text{ dB}.$$

This calculation assumes no additional mismatch loss.

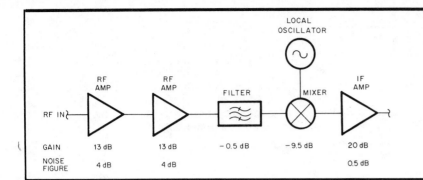

Fig 18—Block diagram of a 2.3-GHz receiving converter. To calculate the system noise figure of a cascaded series of components, the gain (or loss) and noise figure of each stage must be known (see text).

Mismatch loss can be factored in as additional loss, or as an increase in noise figure of the stage just following the mismatch.

Compression Point

It is considerably more difficult to calculate 1-dB gain compression, for a series of amplifiers, than gain or noise figure. The 1-dB gain-compression point typically occurs several decibels after the amplifier performance diverges from linearity, but it does vary with device characteristics. Unless this portion of the gain curve is accurately known, it may be hard to determine which stage is actually compressing. Further, it's possible for two or more stages to compress simultaneously.

The simplest solution is to ensure that the output stage is the only one driven to the 1-dB gain-compression point. To accomplish this, make sure that each driver stage is running at least 3 dB, and preferably 6 dB, lower than its 1-dB gain-compression point.

IMD Products

Of great concern to amateurs, who must share a band, is how "clean" an amplifier chain will be. Undesired close-in IMD products must be well below the level of the fundamental signal, or the result will be "splatter" for many kilohertz on both sides of the desired signal. MMICs are linear class-A devices, however, so they are relatively clean.

Typically when an MMIC amplifier is run up to 1-dB gain compression, the two-tone, third-order IMD products are at about 27 to 32 dB below the PEP output. For every 1-dB decrease in power output level, the third-order IMD power level will decrease by 3 dB. The IMD products relative to the desired signal decrease by $3 - 1 = 2$ dB. As power out approaches 1 dB gain compression, IMD becomes significantly worse than at lower power levels.

Measured IMD data is shown in Table 8 for several MMIC amplifiers at different frequencies. This data was taken with the amplifier power output at, or slightly greater than, the 1-dB compression point. IMD performance tends to be worse at higher frequencies.

IMD products for a cascaded series of amplifiers tend to be worse than for a single device. For example, in one test, third-order IMD products for a two-stage MSA-0404 amplifier were 2 dB worse than for a single device.

OTHER SOURCES OF INFORMATION

This article is a very broad overview of the many applications and uses of MMICs in the VHF and lower-microwave frequencies. You should be able to find many applications for these inexpensive, yet state of the art, microwave devices.

For additional information consult the following Avantek application notes:

AN-A001 Notes on Choke Network Design
AN-S001 Basic MODAMP MMIC Circuit Techniques
AN-S002 MODAMP MMIC Nomenclature
AN-S003 Biasing MODAMP MMICs
AN-S004 A Broadband IF Amplifier Using MSA-0235 and MSA-0335

I would like to thank my wife, Emily, for typing the

Table 8

Measured IMD Performance of MMIC Amplifiers

| Device (MSA-) | 1.3 GHz | | 2.3 GHz | | 3.4 GHz | |
	PEP Output (dBm)	3rd Order IMD Level (dB)	PEP Output (dBm)	3rd Order IMD Level (dB)	PEP Output (dBm)	3rd Order IMD Level (dB)
0485	+12	−32	+12	−28	+12	−28
0835	+15	−28	+15	−27	+12	−29
0404/0404	+12	−31	+12	−28	Not Tested	
7 × 0404	+17	−32	+17	−27	Not Tested	
	+18	−29	Not Tested		Not Tested	

manuscript, W5UC for reviewing the manuscript, and also K5DOI and N5GEJ for additional help in testing the modules. Thanks to Avantek for supplying test samples.

Notes

[1]Avantek, 3175 Bowers Ave, Santa Clara, CA 95054-3294, tel 408-727-0700.

[2]J. Fisk, "Simple Formulas for Microstrip Impedance," *Ham Radio*, Dec 1977, p 72.

[3]J. Fisk, "Microwave Transmission Line," *Ham Radio*, Jan 1978, p 28.

[4]D. Mitchell, "Microstrip Impedance Program," *Ham Radio*, Dec 1984, p 84.

[5]B. Olson, ">50: Chip Capacitors," *QEX*, Sep 1986, p 14.

[6]E. Franke, "Wilkinson Hybrids," *Ham Radio*, Jan 1982, p 12.

[7]A. Ward, "Monolithic Microwave Integrated Circuits, Part 1" *QST*, Feb 1987, p 23.

[8]A. Ward, "Monolithic Microwave Integrated Circuits, Part 2" *QST*, Mar 1987, p 22.

[9]Editor's Note: To convert a power relationship expressed in dB (which is logarithmic) to a simple ratio, divide the dB value by 10 and take the inverse base-10 log of the result (that is, raise 10 to that power). For example, 6 dB is a power ratio of 3.9811:1.

$$\frac{6}{10} = 0.6$$

$$10^{0.6} = 3.9811$$

Coaxial Switches and Their Application to UHF/Microwave Systems

By Carl Lodstrom, W6/SM6MOM
c/o Pressebo Electronics
7261 Coolidge St
Ventura, CA 93003

COAXIAL SWITCHES FOR UHF AND MICROWAVE USE

For this discussion, let us consider coaxial switches (relays) in two main categories: "RF" switches and "microwave" switches. We could group them by performance at frequencies over 1 GHz, but performance that is adequate for one application may be disastrous for another. Let us instead group them by their construction. Each may or may not work well at frequencies above 1 GHz—as we will see.

The RF Switch

In the RF switch, a single blade is moved to select between two output connectors. This design is almost always revealed by the physical appearance of the switch. A typical example is the Dow Key "60 series" switch in Fig 1 (all photos courtesy of Dow-Key Microwave).

Inside the switch, the blade rests just a millimeter or two from the center pin of the inactive output connector. Let's look at the isolation available from this kind of switch: with 1 kW of 145-MHz RF flowing in the blade, a well-matched 50-Ω system and coupling capacitance of 1 pF feeding the inactive line (which is terminated with 50 Ω), 2 W is passed to the *inactive* line—enough to deafen an LNA (low-noise amplifier)! Isolation lessens as

frequency increases; Fig 2(B) shows this trend for 1 pF of coupling capacitance. When coupling capacitance is reduced to 0.1 pF, the situation improves almost 20 dB, but still the isolation is only about 24 dB at 2.4 GHz; a 1-kW system would place 3.6 W at the LNA input.

In order to increase isolation, we need to reduce coupling capacitance (either by reducing contact size or increasing contact spacing). At the same time, however, there is the conflicting demand that the connectors carry high power. (At 1 kW, there is 4.5 A floating down the river, and the heating effects are more severe than in the dc case because of skin effect.) Hence, the connectors cannot be made very small. Obviously, we have a difficult case on hand!

There is one more trick we can try, however. By shorting the center pin of the inactive connector to ground, we can reduce the potential across the inactive load [although the system power lost through coupling will increase slightly—Ed.]. This can be done two ways: by an extra blade (which is grounded at its other end), or a special connector with movable center pin. The first case belongs to what I call "in between" switches (more about those later). The latter is something we call "G option" and it is available on 60-series switches for type BNC, TNC, C and N-connectors. (Fig 2 shows a BNC-G connector and a plot of its isolation.)

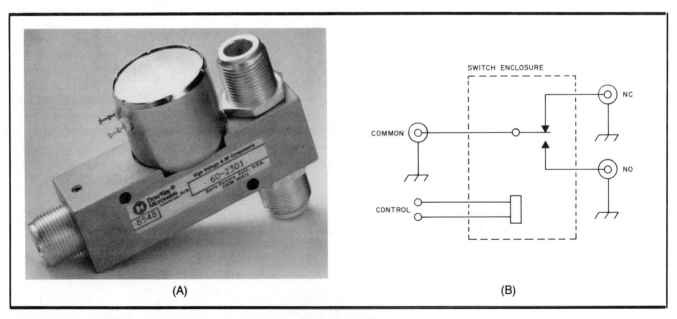

(A)   (B)

Fig 1—A Dow-Key "60 series" RF relay (A), with a schematic (B).

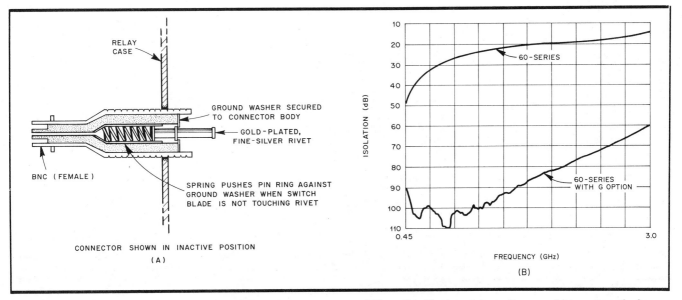

Fig 2—(A) A cross-section view of a BNC-G switch connector ("G option") shows how its movable center pin is grounded when the port is inactive. (B) shows plots of isolation versus frequency for a standard 60-series switch (upper trace) and one that uses the G-option connectors (lower trace).

The Microwave Switch

A microwave switch has two blades, which are moved so that each bridges between the common (center) connector and one of the output (outer) connectors. Further, only one of the two blades can make contact at any given time.

Isolation of the inactive port is greatly improved by using this arrangement (and a more complicated mechanism) rather than a single moving blade. Electrically, all the inactive center pin "sees" is a cavity, with the hot connector at the far end. The cavity is operating far below its cutoff frequency, and the center pin does not present much of a pickup, so isolation of the inactive port is great.

The Dow-Key 402-series is an example of this kind of switch (see Fig 3).

Microwave switches are not easily recognized from their appearance. There are ways to get the same line-of-three connector arrangement with an RF switch. In the RF switch, however, the coil is usually located off the axis of the connectors; while the coil is on-axis and space required for two push rods reveals that there are two blades to be moved inside the microwave switch.

The dimensions of the blades in microwave switches are chosen to create a 50-Ω transmission line within the cavity. This design works up to about 20-30 GHz, where two problems arise: First, push rods disturb the transmis-

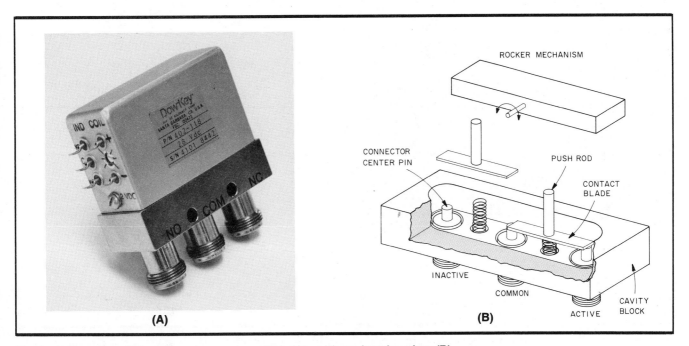

Fig 3—A Dow-Key 402-series microwave switch (A), with an interior view (B).

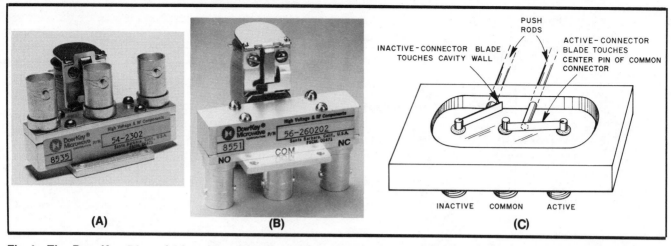

Fig 4—The Dow-Key 54- and 56-series relays (A and B, respectively) are in between those classed as RF and those classed as microwave switches. These relays have a pair of moving blades that are arranged so that the center conductor of the inactive line is grounded (C).

sion line impedance. Second, the transition from circular transmission line (in the cables) to rectangular transmission line (inside the switch) is not elementary anymore.

Let me give one word of warning here: If the *ends* of the inactive blade do not make good ground with the cavity "ceiling," considerable leakage will take place when the blade length is nearly $\lambda/2$—I have seen as little as 12 dB of isolation at about 12 GHz! When the blade makes adequate contact, it is more like 80 or 90 dB. It takes very little imagination to visualize what 12 dB down from, say, 25 W will do to a LNA! Even a barely visible glitch between blade and cavity cover will create problems. On the other hand, the blade must not be bent while making contact! This creates a mismatch and return loss that may be unacceptable. For proper operation, the blades must be *strong* and *flat!*

The "In-Between" Switch

"In-between" switches use two blades as well, but in different arrangement than in the microwave switch (see Fig 4). One blade is permanently fixed to each outer connector, and when one touches the common-connector center pin, the other one touches the cavity sidewall (or a termination resistor). The terminated in-between switch offers no better isolation than a 60-series switch with termination because it has the same problem with coupling capacitance. Nonetheless, it is much more difficult to excite a signal in something that is "almost grounded," and where the "less grounded" parts are farther away, down the cavity. The Dow-Key 56- and 54-series are examples of in-between switches. This kind of switch is probably the optimum compromise for the ham who does not want to spend a fortune on a switch.

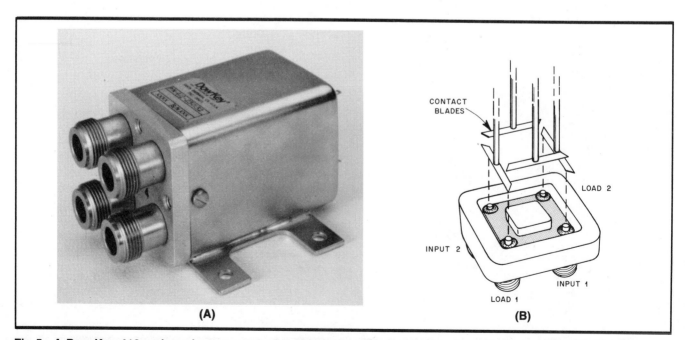

Fig 5—A Dow-Key 412-series microwave transfer switch (A), with an interior view (B). The parallel blade pairs move simultaneously (see text).

The Transfer Switch

This switch is a bit peculiar: It allows you to simply connect a load and termination to both transmitter and receiver so that neither is left open, or shorted, except during the instant of switch over. You can visualize the action by thinking of the switch as a bridge rectifier. Actuation of the blade pairs forms conduction paths in similar manner to the conduction states of a bridge during one cycle of ac. Fig 5 shows the Dow-Key 412-series as an example of this switch.

The isolation in a transfer switch is, by necessity, 6 dB less than in the corresponding 402-series switch, since there are two leakage paths rather than one. But, you would have to use solid-shield cable to even notice the leak in the switch! Fig 6 shows some typical applications of a transfer switch.

RELATED TOPICS

Hot Switching

This is not popular! That should explain it all! Okay, how much is hot? I must admit that I do not know. In one experiment a 860-MHz transmitter was switched, at gradually increasing power levels, into a matched load. The transmitter had a circulator and a dummy load on its output. Beginning with 5 W, 10,000 switching cycles were done; increased to 10 W, and another 10,000 cycles; 20 W and still no burns were visible under the microscope! After the 40-W run there were some burns. Very small, but they had penetrated the gold plating. Two more cycles were run, at 60 W and 90 W, before I tested the switch for insertion loss. There was no performance difference between the "burnt" and the "virgin" sides of the switch. Dc contact resistance was also as good as ever.

So, what does it matter then? Well, the gold was gone, and the material of the pin and the berylium-copper (BeCu) blade exposed. It is my private assumption that it does not matter very much at all, as long as the switch is used frequently. BeCu is naturally bound to oxidize sooner or later, but frequent use will keep the surfaces clean anyway.

There are, of course, limits to hot switching too. If the blade has recently been carrying power near its rated maximum, it is very hot, and the push rods are soft. Performing a hot switch then will add the extra temperature needed to soften up the push rod so that the normal contact pressure cannot be maintained, the contact points heat up even more, the push rods soften even more, and our switch signals its position by sending up black smoke!

Actuator Coils

There are problems associated with switch coils too— most related to temperature. If you have one on a mast outdoors (and it has been idle for a while), you have a good outdoor temperature gauge! Coil resistance varies with temperature according to:

$$R_t = R_{ref} (1 + 0.00395 \times (t - 20)) \qquad \text{(Eq 1)}$$

where

R_t = coil resistance, as affected by temperature

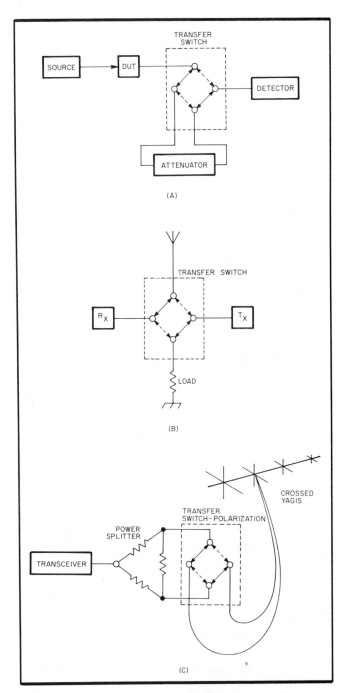

Fig 6—Three circuits for application of 412-series switches: Circuit A inserts or bypasses an attenuator. Circuit B grounds the receiver input during transmission and the transmitter output during reception for weak-signal work. In circuit C, the switch selects the sense of a circularly polarized antenna. One of the transmission lines from the power splitter to the transfer switch should be λ/4 longer than the other.

R_{ref} = coil resistance at 20 °C
t = coil temperature, in degrees Celsius.

This means that if it gets very hot up there in the sun and you saved a buck on the copper in the control cable, you must be sure that the coil gets the proper drive! For example, a coil in the sun might easily reach 200 °F (93.3 °C). A 160-Ω 12-V coil requires 75 mA for activation, the increase in temperature would raise the coil resistance

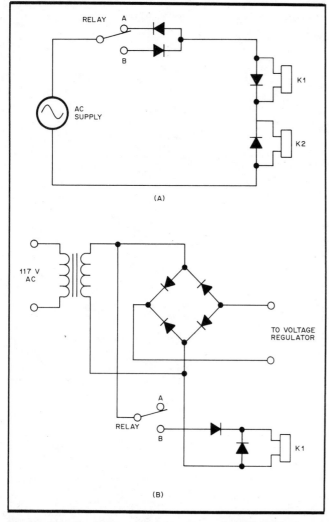

Fig 7—Circuits for energizing relay coils (all diodes are 1N4005 or equivalent). Circuit A can exclusively select one of two coils with only two control wires. Circuit B taps the transformer output of an existing dc supply to actuate a relay coil. [Be sure the transformer can stand the extra load.—Ed.]

to 206 Ω and require 15.5 V, rather than 12 V, *at the coil* to accomplish the task. The best way to check this is to measure the current, at nominal voltage, before you install the switch, and then check it, in place, on a hot day. You may be surprised what you find. Do not attempt to operate the switch coil with less than 80% of the nominal current! Two generic control schematics appear in Fig 7—use 1N4005 diodes, or the like (600 V, 1 A).

Latching Relays

Besides the "normal" relays we all know so well, there is another kind that may make life easier in certain applications. They are called latching relays. As the name suggests, they latch in a selected position without a continuous control current.

This end can be achieved in various ways, either by mechanical or magnetic means. Sometimes one adds the means to the part description, as in "magnetic latching relay," thus making it clear by what means the function is achieved. Since it is far simpler to achieve the end with a magnet, that is the prevailing method of construction.

A latching relay can be controlled with a magnet and one coil, if the current through the coil can be reversed. In many systems this is not convenient, so most latching relays have two coils. Sometimes the coils are not separated electrically, and there are three coil terminals on the switch case (see Fig 8). It is then important to know whether the coil polarity (common plus or common minus) is appropriate to your use. (Two-coil relays with four coil terminals have no such polarity to concern you.) If you want to "sink" either coil with a transistor, a common-plus relay makes the most sense. Instead of "pulling" in the right side, some relays may also work if you "repel" the other side. This can be worth trying if you are using junk-box parts, and have a three-terminal relay with the wrong polarity. Otherwise, use a circuit like Fig 9 to switch a latching relay with a TTL signal.

Fig 8—Coil wiring arrangements for magnetic latching relays. A two-coil circuit with a common terminal appears at A. B shows two completely independent switching coils.

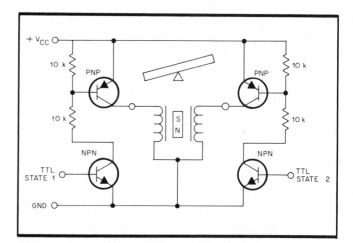

Fig 9—Schematic of a circuit to energize relay coils from TTL (a magnetic, latching relay is shown). Specific transistors should be selected by the constructor based on the requirements of the relay coils. General information about using transistors as switches appears in *The ARRL Handbook*.

Switching Speed and Contact Resistance

There are quite a few ways to measure these qualities. The simplest way to measure resistance is with a meter. I have, however, found that method to be quite insufficient. It is far more revealing to measure contact resistance while the relay is cycling. This measures not only the resistance at one instance, but also the stability and the consistency of the contact resistance. Effects of small contamination particles and friction in the mechanism are clearly revealed.

To perform the measurement, we need an oscilloscope. (One with two timebases is great!) Next, let's look at the circuitry to cycle the relay: We need a current chopper and a power supply.

For the chopper, we can use either a timer circuit, such as the dual timer '4538, letting them bite each other's tail (Fig 10), or pick off the timebase-B gate on the oscilloscope (Fig 11). One of these sources controls a transistor, such as a rugged MOSFET, IRF 520 by International Rectifier (100 V/8 A/0.3 Ω) to switch the coil current.

Actual resistance measurement presents a few problems: A large current, from a high voltage, will burn through possible layers of contamination on the contacts, making them look good, whatever their state when the test began. I have found that 1 mA at 0.4 V will not burn through anything. To make this constant current, all you need do is connect a reasonably stable resistor from a dc supply to the test fixture. Let's say the supply is 15 Vdc; you then need a 15-kΩ resistor.

Next we must limit the open-circuit voltage across the relay contacts to a value as low as possible, but larger than a few mV. We can connect a diode across the contacts to do that. Germanium will drop 0.1 V, Schottky 0.4 V and silicon 0.6 V. Any of these will do as long as the diode does not leak badly at a few mV, where the measurement will be carried out.

Running 1 mA through the contacts will produce 1 mV per Ω of contact resistance. Wait a moment! A normal contact may be 5 mΩ [that's *milliohms*—Ed.], that means we need to measure down to 5-μV! My oscilloscope must have 200 times as much to give a discernible display—we need an amplifier! This is a very useful piece of test gear anyway. (You can also use it to pick up minute voltage drops on a printed-circuit-board trace, to see where all the current is going, if the latest project does not work.) Let us use one of the best there is: AD524 by Analog Devices. It is an instrumentation amplifier—sort of an op amp, but the gain can be set without feedback to the input, leaving both inputs with very high impedance. Furthermore, the common-mode rejection (at gain 1000, which we will use) is 120 dB, meaning that it is one-million times as sensitive to signals across the inputs as to signals appearing on both of them. That is exactly what we need.

Now, let us put the pieces together! If a dual-timebase oscilloscope is used, then just set the B sweep to last for about half the screen, beginning at left or right end; this represents the time that the relay is energized. The amplifier output gives the resistance, at 1 V/mΩ. The amplifier noise

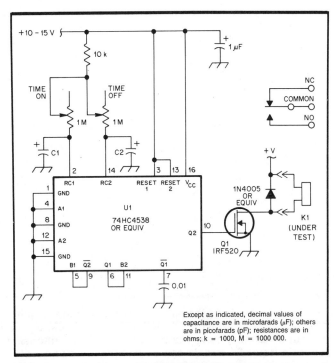

Fig 10—A chopper circuit that uses a '4538 dual, retriggerable, monostable multivibrator driving an IRF 520 power MOSFET to energize relay coils when measuring relay contact resistance. V+ is a positive supply as needed to actuate K1. (The IRF 520, from International Rectifier, can switch up to 100 V at 8 A. ECG 2382 is a possible substitute. The '4538 and '520 are available from Digi-Key Corporation, 701 Brooks Ave South, POB 677, Thief River Falls, MN 56701-0677, tel 1-800-344-4539.)

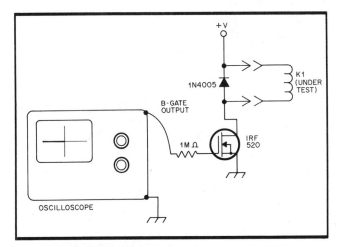

Fig 11—This circuit uses one timebase of a dual-timebase oscilloscope to control relay switching for contact-resistance tests.

is down in the region of a few mV, making it easy to see, say, 5 mΩ. Low-pass filtering with a cutoff frequency of 1000 Hz or so, will extend this to below 1 mΩ. Switching time will be obvious, since the sweep is intensity modulated by timebase B, and so will contact bounce—if it is present. If you use a '4538 or similar device to cycle the relay, then all you have to do is to synchronize the sweep

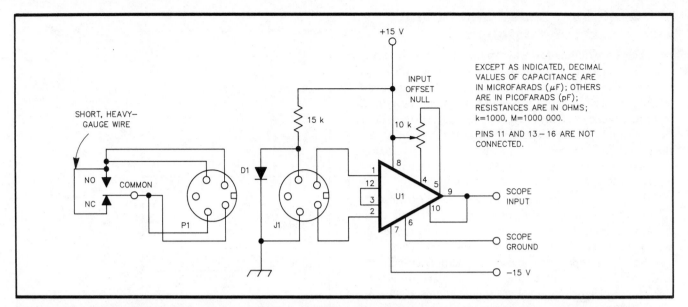

Fig 12—Schematic of the AD524 instrumentation amplifier and test fixture for measuring the contact resistance of a cycling RF switch with an oscilloscope. This circuit tests both switch contacts (normally open and normally closed) simultaneously. The constructor should choose an appropriate diode, based on information in the text. [Editor's Note: P1 and J1 can be any matched connectors with at least two pins, although four pins are required for a Kelvin connection. Analog Devices ICs are available in single-unit quantities from their direct-sales offices. Their worldwide headquarters is at POB 9106, Norwood, MA 02062-9106, tel 617-329-4700.]

of the oscilloscope somehow, and you can still see the baseline coming down when the contacts close. It may be a good idea to test both sides of the relay at the same time (Fig 12). If one side looks bad on the display, just unhook one side of the relay to identify it. With the dual-timebase approach, the sides are identified already. There seems to be a strong positive correlation between contact bounce and bad contact resistance. A relay with these tendencies may not even stand its rated power, much less survive any hot switching. Furthermore, it may have enough resistance to affect the insertion loss, and thereby degrade the noise factor of your "super duper" LNA.

Estimating Microwave System Performance

By Bob Atkins, KA1GT
103 Division Ave
Millington, NJ 07946

The nature of the signal paths involved in work on the higher microwave bands often enables us to make a fairly good estimate of signal-to-noise ratio (S/N) expected using given equipment over a predetermined path. When the path is optical, as is usually the case with 10-GHz portable work for example, then the path loss can be fairly accurately estimated. An estimate of signal strength over a given path is often referred to as a "link budget."

As an example of the utility of such a link-budget calculation, WA1VUW and KA1GT planned to make a contact over a 50-mile path on 10.368-GHz SSB. Before driving the 100+ miles required to set up stations at the ends of this path, we wanted to know whether or not there was a reasonable chance of success. The estimated equipment parameters were: (1) 0.5-mW PEP transmitter power, (2) 8-dB receiver noise figure, and (3) 17-dB horn antenna at one end of the path and a 2-ft dish at the other. So, given this information, how do we make an estimate of received signal strength?

PATH LOSS

First we must calculate the attenuation (dB) that a signal at 10.368 GHz will suffer over a 50-mile, line-of-sight path. This is known as the free-space path loss (FSPL) and is given by:

$$\text{FSPL} = 32.45 + 20 \log(f) + 20 \log(d) \qquad \text{(Eq 1)}$$

where

FSPL = free-space path loss in dB
f = frequency in MHz
d = distance in km.

$$\text{FSPL} = 36.6 + 20 \log(f) + 20 \log(d) \qquad \text{(Eq 2)}$$

when d is expressed in miles. The loss over a 50-mile path at 10.368 GHz is:

$$\text{FSPL} = 36.6 + 20 \log(10368) + 20 \log(50) = 150.9 \text{ dB}$$

Thus, we now know that a signal traveling 50 miles through free space at a frequency of 10.368 GHz will suffer 150.9 dB of attenuation.

TRANSMITTER EFFECTIVE ISOTROPIC RADIATED POWER

Next, we must calculate the EIRP of the transmitter. This is the amount of transmitter power, feeding an isotropic radiator, which would be required to give the same signal strength at a distant point as the actual transmitter and antenna in use. It is determined by the use of the expression:

$$\text{EIRP} = P_T + G_A - L_F \qquad \text{(Eq 3)}$$

where

EIRP = effective isotropic radiated power in dBm
P_T = transmitter power in dBm
G_A = antenna gain in dBi
L_F = feed loss in dB

In our case, P_T is 0.5 mW PEP, or -3 dBm. The antenna is a 2-ft dish. Its gain can be estimated using the relationship:

$$G_A = 7 + 20 \log(D) + 20 \log(f) \qquad \text{(Eq 4)}$$

where

G_A = antenna gain in dBi
D = dish diameter in feet
f = frequency in GHz

A feed efficiency of 50% is assumed. In our case, a gain of approximately 33 dBi is indicated. Since the dish will be mounted directly on the transmitter, there will be no feed-line losses, and the EIRP may be calculated as:

$$\text{EIRP} = -3 + 33 - 0 = +30 \text{ dBm}$$

Since we now know the EIRP of the transmitter and the free-space path loss we can calculate the signal level (P_R) at the receiving site. This is simply:

$$P_R = \text{EIRP} - \text{FSPL} = +30 - 150.9 = -120.9 \text{ dBm}$$

That is, the signal at the receiving site will be 120.9 dB below 1 mW (as received on an isotropic antenna).

RECEIVER SENSITIVITY

Now, we need to know whether the receiving system will be capable of detecting a -120.9 dBm signal. Calculation of receiving-system sensitivity requires knowledge of several factors. We need to know the receiver noise temperature (or noise figure, NF), the feed-line loss between the antenna and receiver, the antenna noise temperature, the receiver bandwidth and the antenna gain. Noise temperature is a measure of the noise contribution of any particular component, such as an antenna or preamplifier, to receiving system. It is related to noise figure (which is more commonly used) by the following expression:

$$\text{NF} = 10 \log \left(\frac{T}{290} + 1 \right) \qquad \text{(Eq 5)}$$

where

NF = noise figure in dB
T = noise temperature in kelvins

or this can be arranged to read:

$$T = 290 \left[10^{\frac{\text{NF}}{10}} - 1 \right] \qquad \text{(Eq 6)}$$

Thus, for an 8-dB-noise-figure receiver used here, the noise temperature calculates to be:

$$T = 290 \, [10^{(0.8)} - 1]$$
$$= 290 \, (6.3 - 1) = 1537 \text{ K}$$

The antenna temperature of a tropospheric antenna (one that looks at the ground, as opposed to an EME antenna, which looks at the sky) may be taken as about 290 K. It may be lower, but the factors involved are too complex to consider here, and affect the total system noise temperature very little in this case.

The total system noise temperature can now be determined by the use of the relationship:

$$T_S = T_A + (L_R - 1)290 + L_R T_R \qquad \text{(Eq 7)}$$

where

T_S = system noise temperature (K)
T_A = antenna noise temperature (K)
L_R = feed-line loss expressed as a ratio
T_R = receiver noise temperature (K)

For the system under consideration this gives:
$$T_S = 290 + (1 - 1)290 + 1 \times 1537$$
$$= 290 + 1537 = 1827 \text{ K}$$

We can now calculate the total receiving-system sensitivity, including the noise contributions from all components which are incorporated in the system noise temperature.

$$\text{sens} = 10 \, \log(k T_S B) \qquad \text{(Eq 8)}$$

where

sens = receive-system sensitivity, in dBm
k = 1.38×10^{-20} mW/Hz
T_S = system noise temperature in kelvins
B = receiver bandwidth in hertz.

This can be rewritten:

$$\text{sens} = 10 \, \log(B) + 10 \, \log(T) - 198.6 \qquad \text{(Eq 9)}$$

For the receiver in question, the bandwidth is 2.4 kHz (2400 Hz) and therefore:

$$\text{sens} = 10 \, \log(2400) + 10 \, \log(1827) - 198.6$$
$$= 33.8 + 32.6 - 198.6$$
$$= -132.2 \text{ dBm}$$

This means that a signal 132.2 dB below 1 mW will be as strong as the noise generated in the system, that is, an S/N of 0 dB at the final detector stage of the receiver. Since this receiver is being used with a 17-dB-gain horn antenna, however, signals 17 dB weaker will be able to be detected with this same 0 dB S/N, making the effective receiver sensitivity −149.2 dBm.

We know from our previous calculations that the signal at the receiver site is expected to be −120.9 dBm. This is 28.3 dB stronger than the signal required to give 0 dB S/N, and therefore should give an S/N of 28.3 dB. We have now done what we initially set out to do: estimate how strong the 10.368 GHz SSB signals should be over a 50-mile path.

The important question now is, "Do theory and practice agree?" The answer is, "surprisingly well." The measured S/N over the path from Mount Tom, Massachusetts, to West Peak, Connecticut, was +20 dB, only 8 dB below the calculated level. This difference can be written off to the effects of intermediate ground reflections and, perhaps, optimistic estimates of equipment performance.

These calculations become routine with a little practice and can be performed using an inexpensive calculator. They can save much time and effort, if used to plan DX contacts on the higher microwave bands.

If a link budget is calculated for the same task as above using Gunnplexers (20 mW, 12 dB NF and 200-kHz IF bandwidth) with 17-dB horns, the calculated S/N is 5.1 dB, much too small for intelligibility considering FM threshold and the usually optimistic nature of the calculations. A 2-ft dish at one end of the path should improve the S/N to 21.1 dB, which should allow the path to work on FM.

Receiver sensitivity calculations can also be used to predict the improvement in system performance when better preamplifiers, lower-loss feed lines or higher-gain antennas are used.

Readers wishing to learn more about receiver sensitivity and NF calculations might like to read an article by Jim Fisk, W1HR (October 1975 *Ham Radio*, p 8), and the extensive list of references cited in that article.

Calculating System Noise Temperatures

By Bob Atkins, KA1GT
103 Division Ave
Millington, NJ 07946

From time to time, we all try to make improvements in our equipment in the hope of working weaker and more distant stations. Keeping in mind the old adage that "If you can't hear 'em you can't work 'em," improvements in receiving systems are always desirable. In real systems the components (antenna, preamplifiers and so on) are connected by feed lines that have loss. The information here should enable you to determine the effects of this loss, in conjuction with the other system parameters, on the overall noise temperature of a receiving system.

Fig 1 shows the formula used to calculate system noise temperature in a receiving system consisting of two amplifier stages ahead of a receiver (or mixer). When you use this formula, if there is no loss between two components, set the feed-line loss between them (L1, L2 or L3) to 0 dB. If only one preamp is used in the system that you want to analyze, set the gain of the unused one to 0 dB and its noise temperature to 0 K.

Table 1 shows the results of a series of calculations for an EME system and a tropo' system using typical (of a good system) values. As can be seen in Table 1(A) placing a good preamp at the antenna yields a 2.45-dB improvement in received signal-to-noise ratio over the same system with the preamp in the shack. Adding a second preamp at the antenna yields another 0.5-dB improvement, which is probably worth having for EME operation. Table 1(B) shows what happens with a tropo' system where the antenna temperature (273 K) is much higher than in the EME system (50 K). Improvements are not so dramatic, but you can clearly see that adding preamps at the antenna generally gives a good improvement.

Before you go out and buy that expensive GaAsFET preamp to put in the shack, it might be instructive to cal-

culate just how much improvement it is going to give you! Note that:

$$\Delta = 10 \log \frac{N1}{N2}$$

where

    Δ = performance change in dB
    N1 = total system noise temperature after the change
    N2 = total system noise temperature before the change.

Table 1
Typical System Performance

(A) EME Antenna Temperature = 50 K

Configuration	Noise Temp	Improvement
1—GaAsFET in shack	180 K	—
2—GaAsFET at antenna	102.4 K	2.45 dB
3—GaAsFET at antenna, 2nd preamp in shack	94.4 K	0.35 dB
4—both preamps at antenna	91.3 K	0.15 dB

(B) Tropo Antenna Temperature = 273 K

Configuration	Noise Temp	Improvement
1—2nd preamp in shack	541.5 K	—
2—2nd preamp at antenna	446.3 K	0.84 dB
3—GaAsFET in shack	403.1 K	0.44 dB
4—GaAsFET at antenna,	325.4 K	0.93 dB
5—GaAsFET at antenna, 2nd preamp in shack	317.2 K	0.11 dB
6—both preamps at antenna	314.2 K	0.04 dB

GaAsFET—0.5-dB noise figure, 15-dB gain
Second preamp—1.5-dB noise figure, 10-dB gain
Antenna feed line—1-dB loss, 273 K
Receiver/mixer—3.5-dB noise figure

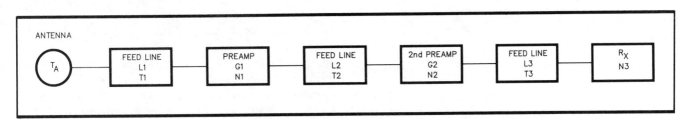

Fig 1—Calculation of overall noise temperature of a multicomponent system.

System noise temperature, N_S =

$$T_A + T1(L1 - 1) + (N1 \times L1) + T_2 \times \frac{L1}{G1}$$
$$\times (L2 - 1) + N2 \left(\frac{L1 \times L2}{G1} \right)$$
$$+ T(L3 - 1) + N3 \left(\frac{L1 \times L2 \times L3}{G1 \times G2} \right)$$

where
    T_A = antenna noise temperature in kelvins
    L = loss as a ratio (that is, 0 dB = 1; 1.3 dB = 2, and so on)
    T = physical temperature in kelvins (20° C = 293 K)
    G = gain as a ratio (that is, 10 dB = 10, 20 dB = 100, and so on)
    N = noise temperature in kelvins.

Note that: $N = 293 \left(10^{\frac{NF}{10}} - 1 \right)$, where NF is noise figure in dB.

Noise Temperature, Antenna Temperature and Sun Noise

By Bob Atkins, KA1GT

103 Division Ave
Millington, NJ 07946

Despite the fact that we can amplify a weak signal by virtually any desired amount, it is impossible to detect an arbitrarily weak signal because of the presence of random electrical fluctuations known as noise. This noise can be generated in the receiver itself or external to the receiver by such sources as the sun, the galaxy or the earth. One scale used to measure this noise is noise temperature (T).

In a device such as a resistor, electrons move in a random manner because of thermal agitation. This random motion generates electrical noise, known as thermal noise (or Johnson noise). This noise increases with increasing temperature. The total noise power generated in a given bandwidth is given by the relationship:

$$P = k\,T\,B \qquad \text{(Eq 1)}$$

where

    P = noise power in watts
    k = Boltzmann's constant (1.38×10^{-23} joule/K)
    B = bandwidth in hertz
    T = temperature in kelvins.

In this case, T would be the noise temperature of the resistor, and also its physical temperature. In other cases—for example, a GaAsFET amplifier—the device noise temperature, T, and physical temperature need not be the same. If the device generates a certain amount of noise power, P, in a bandwidth, B, its noise temperature, T, is given by:

$$T = \frac{P}{kB} \qquad \text{(Eq 2)}$$

Noise temperature bears a fixed relationship to noise figure (NF), since they both are a measure of the noise generated by a device (see Fig 1). The relationship is:

$$T = 290 \left(10^{\frac{NF}{10}} - 1 \right) \qquad \text{(Eq 3)}$$

or

$$NF = 10 \log \left(1 + \frac{T}{290} \right) \qquad \text{(Eq 4)}$$

where NF = noise figure in dB, and 290 is a standard temperature of 290 K (17 °C).

NOISE TEMPERATURE OF ANTENNAS

The noise temperature, T_A, of a perfect antenna is determined by the noise temperature of the object at which the antenna is aimed. This includes the noise temperature of objects in the antenna minor lobes. If the antenna is pointed at the ground, which has a physical temperature of around 290 K (17° C), it will have a noise temperature of 290 K. If the antenna is pointed at the sky, its T_A will depend on the noise temperature of that region of the sky the antenna "sees." At frequencies above 1 GHz, most of the sky is quite cold (at 3-cm wavelength, the background radiation from the sky is 2.7 K).

An average T_A value when pointed at the coldest part of the sky will be around 30-40 K (this includes some contribution from earth-bound minor lobes). If the antenna aperture includes the sun, T_A depends on its gain (what portion of the antenna main lobe does the sun fill?) and the frequency of operation (the sun exhibits different noise temperatures at different frequencies since its noise output is not purely thermal in nature). The solar noise output is also dependent to some extent on its relative activity (sunspot number). An approximate antenna temperature is given by:

$$T_A = \frac{FGL^2}{3.468} \qquad \text{(Eq 5)}$$

where

    T_A = antenna temperature looking at the sun
    F = solar flux (see Table 1)
    G = antenna gain as a ratio (that is, 13 dB = 20)
    L = wavelength in meters.

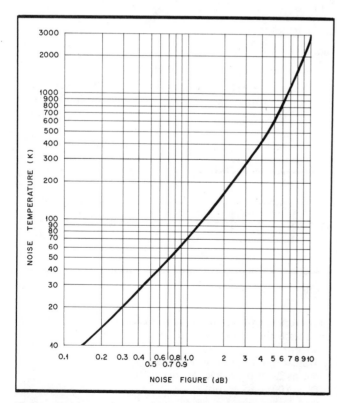

Fig 1—There is a logarithmic relationship between noise figure and noise temperature.

CHECKING RECEIVER PERFORMANCE WITH SKY, GROUND AND SUN NOISE

Since we can change antenna noise temperature by aiming the antenna at different objects, we can use an antenna as a variable noise generator. This, in turn, can be used to obtain a measure of receiver performance in the following way.

The noise temperature of a receiving system is the sum of the receiver noise temperature, antenna noise temperature and the feed-line noise temperature. Feed-line noise temperature is related to its attenuation by the relationship:

$$T_F = (L - 1) T_p \qquad \text{(Eq 6)}$$

where

T_F = feed-line noise temperature in kelvins
L = line loss as a ratio (that is, 3 dB = 2)
T_p = physical temperature of the feeder in kelvins.

Since noise power output is directly proportional to noise temperature (Equation 1), the noise output of the receiving system will be proportional to its noise temperature which, all else being fixed, will be dependent on antenna noise temperature.

Consider the following system, a 10.368-GHz receiver with a 10-dB noise figure and a 1-meter-diameter dish. A 10-dB noise figure corresponds to a noise temperature of 2611 K (from Equation 3). The antenna temperature when pointed at the coldest part of the sky will be around 30 K. The antenna temperature when pointing at the sun can be calculated from Equation 5. A 1-meter dish has a gain of about 5900 (37 dB), and thus will have a noise temperature of 460 K with a solar-flux value of 300 at 10.368 GHz. Thus, when the receiver is pointed at the cold sky, the noise power output will be proportional to 2641 K (2611 + 30 = receiver noise + sky noise). When it is pointed at the sun, the noise power output will be proportional to 3101 K (2611 + 30 + 460 = receiver + sky noise + solar noise). The ratio of these two power levels is:

$$3101:2641 = 1.174:1 = 0.70 \text{ dB}$$

Note that these numbers assume no image response in the receiver. If the receiver does have an equal image response, antenna temperatures will appear to be twice as great (since equal amounts of noise will be received simultaneously on both the signal and image frequencies).

With the same system, the ratio of cold sky to ground noise will be 2901:2641 (2611 + 290 = receiver noise + ground noise; 2611 + 30 = receiver noise + sky noise):

$$2901:2641 = 1.098:1 = 0.41 \text{ dB}$$

Receiver noise power output can be measured with an audio (ac) voltmeter. The measured power relationship for sun noise to sky noise is then:

$$20 \log \left(\frac{E1}{E2}\right) \text{ dB} \qquad \text{(Eq 7)}$$

where

E1 = noise voltage with antenna on sun
E2 = noise voltage with antenna on cold sky.

Table 1
Solar Flux (10^{-22} W m^{-2} Hz^{-1})

Frequency (GHz)	F (Min)	F (Max)
1.3	36	120
2.3	53	210
3.4	76	270
5.6	129	290
10	269	460
24	1046	1070

Note: F (min) represents the noise level of a quiet sun; F (max) represents the level of an active sun. Both values are approximate. [Editor's Note: Get timely values from the *SOLAR-GEOPHYSICAL DATA Prompt Reports* by the National Geophysical Data Center, NOAA/NESDIS, E/GC2, 325 Broadway, Boulder, CO 80303, or from the *Preliminary Report and Forecast of SOLAR GEOPHYSICAL DATA* published by the Space Environment Services Center, R/E/SE2, 325 Broadway, Boulder, CO 80303. Also see Fig 2.]

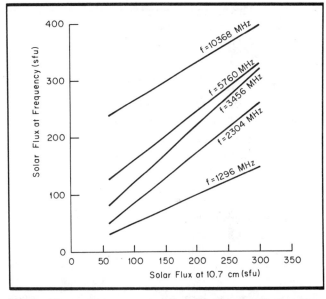

Fig 2—Flux values vary greatly with the sunspot cycle and other solar events (compare Table 1 to Table 1 of W8MIF's following section about system calibration). The sources noted in Table 1 contain the best available data, but this chart will help you make timely estimates. It shows probable relationships between solar flux at various frequencies and that at 10 cm, which is measured daily at Ottawa, Ontario. The daily 10-cm flux reading is broadcast over WWV and WWVH at 18 and 45 minutes after each hour, respectively. Even so, flux will vary greatly during a single day when there is a significant solar event.—*Ed.*

Note that the receiver must be operating under linear conditions; that is, the AGC must be off in AM modes (CW or SSB) or an FM receiver must be operating well below limiting.

Changes in equipment can be assessed by measuring sun/sky and ground/sky noise. Improvements in the system noise figure will give rise to higher values. The sun output varies, however, and you should consider that when sun/sky measurements are made over a long period of time.

Microwave System Calibration Using the Sun and Moon

By David B. Shaffer, W8MIF
1742 Saddleback Ct
Henderson, NV 89014

Once your microwave receiving system (meaning antenna, feed line and receiver) is assembled, how do you find out how well it is working? What you need is a test signal of known power. By comparing the received power from that test signal with the noise generated within the system, you'll have a good feel for the signal-to-noise (S/N) ratios expected in actual operation.

Fortunately, a pair of test "transmitters" exist for free. The sun and moon emit broadband radio noise at substantial power levels that are well defined through regular monitoring. This section discusses how to use these objects to verify the performance of microwave receiving systems.

SOLAR AND LUNAR RADIO RADIATION

The sun and moon emit radio waves, as do all objects with any warmth. [Zero kelvins (K) is the temperature where all molecular motion stops.—Ed.] All warm objects emit this "black-body" thermal radiation—even you! Your hand, for example, emits a substantial signal, which can be heard by a low-noise receiving system. [For safety reasons, NEVER attempt this with a microwave transceiver system that emits significant local-oscillator power.—Ed.]

Solar thermal radiation is augmented by non-thermal emissions from highly charged particles moving in the solar magnetic field. That part of the solar radiation varies with time, often spectacularly so. Solar bursts may increase radio emissions by a factor of 100 or more!

Lunar radio emissions are purely thermal in nature, and therefore very stable. Thus if your receiving system is sensitive enough to detect its radiation, the moon provides the most accurate reference—without any need for external calibration information.

Depending on frequency, radio waves from the sun come from different levels in the solar corona (the hot "atmosphere"), with longer wavelengths emanating from the higher levels. Corona temperature also varies with height (higher is hotter). Thus the radio-apparent size and temperature of the sun depend greatly on frequency. Solar radio emissions also vary considerably with the sunspot cycle. (See Kundu for a more detailed discussion of solar radio emission.[1]) Table 1 shows typical solar signal strengths for the amateur UHF/microwave bands. The units in this table are solar flux units (SFUs). One SFU equals 10^{-22} watts per square meter per hertz of bandwidth.

Since the solar output is variable, the values in Table 1 should be used only for rough evaluations. More accurate, up-to-date values of solar flux density (simply called "flux" from here on) are published monthly by the US Department of Commerce.[2]

Unlike the sun, the moon has an almost constant noise temperature, especially at the lower microwave frequencies. Above 5 GHz, the emissions are influenced by the phase of the moon as the lunar surface is heated by the sun. This phase-amplitude effect is about $\pm 6\text{-}8\%$ at 10 GHz and $\pm 10\text{-}15\%$ at 24 GHz. The variable component has an almost sinusoidal time behavior, with peak radio emissions lagging the full moon by about $45°$, or 3.5 days. Since the lunar orbit is elliptical, its distance from the earth varies, causing apparent strength variations of $\pm 14\%$ during a lunar cycle. (Experimenters can learn more about the moon from articles by Hagfors and Muhleman.[3,4]) An observer's earthly location can cause a 3% variation in addition to these other factors. A distance correction factor for the lunar values in Table 1 is calculated by the BASIC SUNMOON program on the ARRL Microwave Software Anthology Disk, which is described in the Appendix.

For a constant-temperature, disk-like source the radio flux at a specific frequency is given by:

$$S = 7.35\ T\ D^2\ f^2 \qquad \text{(Eq 1)}$$

where

S = flux 10^{-26} watts per square meter per hertz
T = effective temperature in kelvins
D = angular diameter in degrees
f = frequency in GHz.

For the moon, T is 225 K and D is $0.52°$ (mean).

Table 1

Typical Flux Densities of the Sun and Moon

Frequency	Typical Solar Flux Density (SFUs)[†]	Mean Lunar Flux Density (SFUs)[††]
440 MHz	30	
900 MHz	90	
1.3 GHz	100	0.076
2.3 GHz	110	0.24
3.4 GHz	120	0.52
5.6 GHz	150	1.4
10.0 GHz	300	4.5
24.0 GHz	1200	26.0

[†]1 solar flux unit (SFU) = 10^{-22} W m^{-2} Hz^{-1}. See Note 8.
[††]For an earth-to-moon distance of 383,100 km. The SUN-MOON program calculates a correction factor to be applied to these values.

Equation 1 gives flux, S, in units called "Janskys" by radio astronomers. A Jansky is 10,000 times smaller than the SFU discussed earlier. Table 1 shows the mean lunar flux in SFUs.

POINTING THE ANTENNA AT THE SUN AND MOON

How do you know where to find the sun and moon? Perhaps the easiest way is to buy an *Astronomical Almanac* from the US Government Printing Office.[5] This book gives the astronomical coordinates of the sun and moon, which must then be converted to azimuth and elevation for your time and location. The SUNMOON program will give the azimuth and elevation of the sun and moon for any date and UTC (for the next 50 years or so). The program first converts a standard calendar date to the corresponding Julian date (the astronomical date, where midnight occurs at 1200 UTC!) and then calculates the right ascension and declination (astronomical "longitude" and "latitude") from appropriate formulas. These values, plus the station location, allow determination of local azimuth and elevation.

The azimuth and elevation of the sun and moon change continuously as the earth rotates. Most amateur antenna systems can't easily follow these motions. If it is a clear day and the antenna can be driven in azimuth and elevation, alignment with the sun can be achieved by watching the shadow of the antenna elements or feed. [Align a dish antenna so that the feed shadow falls at dish center. Align a Yagi so that the elements cast a single shadow, with the boom shadow minimized and centered on the element shadow.—*Ed*.] Otherwise, it is far more practical to set the antenna to a position where the source will cross the main lobe at a later time. As the earth rotates (patience!), the progress of the source through the antenna beam should be seen. The precision of this setting should be better than about one tenth of the antenna beamwidth for best accuracy. Conversely, the antenna can be "wagged" back and forth (in either azimuth or elevation) across the expected path of the source and the peak response noted.

For example, an antenna movable only in azimuth can be swept back and forth across the path of the rising or setting sun or moon. (The time and azimuth of the event can be found by experimenting with the SUNMOON program.)

Antenna side lobes, of a high-sensitivity system, can be measured this way as well. These techniques have been used to measure the gain and side lobes (to 30-dB below peak) on 6- and 11-ft dishes at 4, 6, 11 and 14 GHz. Receiver noise temperatures were between 100 and 600 K (through the use of GaAsFET low-noise amplifiers).

WHAT QUANTITIES TO MEASURE

What parameter is most critical for best receiver performance? Clearly, signal-to-noise ratio (S/N) counts most for weak-signal work. Commercial microwave systems are generally characterized by the ratio of antenna gain (G) to system temperature (T), which communication engineers constantly strive to optimize. This ratio, G/T, is called the "figure of merit," and it is the single most important parameter for evaluating overall system performance. S/N ratio is directly proportional to G/T, since received signal power depends on antenna gain, and system noise is proportional to system temperature. Ideally, we would measure G and T separately. However, that requires a fair amount of effort, whereas G/T can be simply derived from signal-level ratios measured with a source of known signal strength.

The gain of an antenna at a given frequency is:

$$G = \frac{4 \pi f^2 A_E}{c^2} \qquad \text{(Eq 2)}$$

where

f = frequency in hertz
A_E = effective antenna collecting area
c = the speed of light (2.998×10^8 m/second).

For an antenna of effective area A_E, observing a source of flux S, the received power is equivalent to that generated by a matched resistor of temperature T_A (called the antenna temperature). The powers are:

$$k \, T_A \, B = \frac{S \, A_E \, B}{2} \qquad \text{(Eq 3)}$$

where

k = Boltzmann's constant (1.38×10^{-23} watts/K/Hz)
B = system bandwidth in hertz
S = flux.

By combining Equations 2 and 3 (eliminating A_E), we find:

$$G = \frac{8 \pi k f^2 T_A}{S c^2} \qquad \text{(Eq 4)}$$

Now, assume we can measure the ratio between receiver system output power levels when the antenna is pointed towards, and then away from, a source of strength, S. These power levels will be proportional to the system temperature plus source antenna temperature over the system temperature alone. This ratio is conventionally called the Y-factor and is often expressed in dB. Therefore:

$$Y = \frac{T + T_A}{T}$$

or

$$T_A = T(Y - 1) \qquad \text{(Eq 5)}$$

We have implicitly assumed that system gain did not change during the time required to make the measurement, otherwise the output levels could have changed independently of input power. Combining Equations 4 and 5, we have:

$$\frac{G}{T} = \frac{8 \pi k f^2 (Y - 1)}{S c^2} \qquad \text{(Eq 6)}$$

Thus, in order to determine G/T, all we need do is observe a source of known strength, S, and measure the Y-factor. If either G or T is known from other data (antenna manufacturer's specifications for G, hot/cold loads for T), the other factor can be immediately determined.

MEASURING Y-FACTORS

The problem of determining system performance has been reduced to measuring Y. To do this, we need to monitor receiver system output power, which should be proportional to input power if no stages are driven into saturation and limiter stages are bypassed or operated well below threshold levels. Output power can be measured at numerous places in the receiver. An ac voltmeter can be used to measure the audio output (don't forget that you have to square the voltage reading to obtain power level). This scheme limits the effective bandwidth to that of the audio output, generally a few kilohertz. As explained below, wider bandwidths are desired. Thus, it is better to tap into one of the IF stages with an RF voltmeter.

An even better method is to use a crystal detector in the IF stage. Such a device, when properly calibrated, can detect a very broad bandwidth with high accuracy. A crystal-detector probe for a high-impedance voltmeter is shown in Fig 1. A dedicated meter patterned after one Doug DeMaw, W1FB, described in QST[6] would be quite satisfactory (see Fig 2). As described in that article and another by Bry[7], careful calibration of detector output

with respect to input power is required to measure relative power accurately.

The relation between input power and output must be kept in mind when using the circuits shown in Figs 1 and 2. At moderate power levels (greater than about 10 mW input), these circuits produce output voltages (Fig 1) or output currents (Fig 2) that are proportional to the input RF voltage. Their readings must be squared to give results proportional to power. Crystal detectors working at very low power levels (less than about 0.1 mW input) operate in the "square law" region. Their output voltage is very nearly proportional to input power. The output voltages are quite small, however—a fraction of a millivolt per microwatt—so several stages of dc amplification may be needed to measure signals detected with a square-law device.

It is desirable to measure system performance through a wide bandwidth. Total power output depends on the product of bandwidth, gain and noise temperature. Therefore, a larger and thus easier-to-measure output exists in a broader bandwidth. In addition, there is less intrinsic noise in the measurement process. For a perfectly stable system, the expected measurement error, expressed as a fraction of the total power level, is

$$\frac{\delta P}{P} = \frac{1}{\sqrt{Bt}} \qquad \text{(Eq 7)}$$

where

B = pre-detection bandwidth in hertz
t = measurement integration time.

Hence, broad bandwidths and long integration times increase the potential precision of the measurement. A simple RC filter is a perfectly adequate means of achieving longer integration times. Time constants (R, in ohms, times C, in farads) in the range of 0.1 to a few seconds can produce dramatic improvements in measurement precision. Fig 3 shows an adaptation of Fig 2, with an RC filter added. The RC filter integrates voltage, not current, so the current amplifier of Fig 2 has been converted to a voltage amplifier in Fig 3.

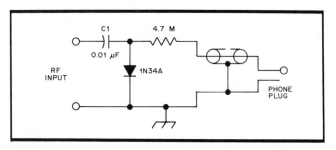

Fig 1—An RF probe for a high-impedance voltmeter to measure noise voltage. (This one is from the ARRL Handbook.)

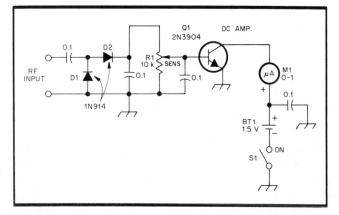

Fig 2—A simple RF meter based on Doug DeMaw, W1FB's 1985 QST article[6].

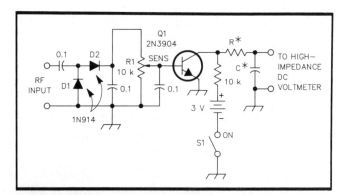

Fig 3—A simple RF meter with an integrator circuit. Choose values of R and C to yield your desired time constant (see text). R* should be 100 kΩ or larger to avoid loading. Note that this is an inverting system: higher powers will give lower voltmeter readings.

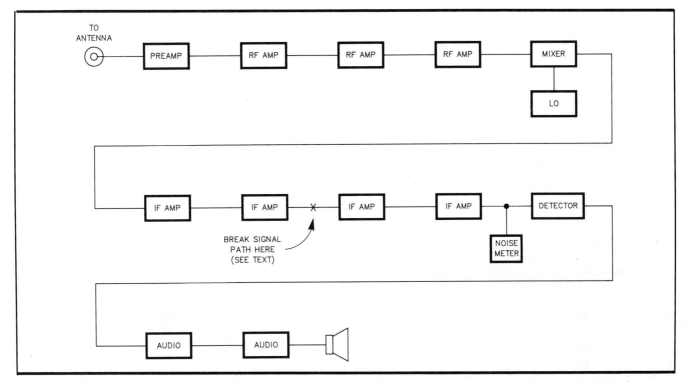

Fig 4—Before making noise measurements, record a base (no input signal) measurement for the circuit and test equipment. Break the signal path at some convenient point and note the voltage reading; subtract this voltage from later noise measurements.

Suppose we make audio (5 kHz, say) and RF/IF bandwidth (1 MHz, say) measurements. We can expect fractional error limits of 0.014 and 0.001, respectively, for 1-second integrations. Clearly, a good three-digit voltmeter would be desirable for reading the detector output voltage in the second case, in order to achieve the available precision. Y-factors that correspond to level changes of more than about 10 times the expected measurement error are desirable in order to obtain meaningful results. Thus, Y-factors greater than about 1.14 or 1.01 are rule-of-thumb limits for audio and RF/IF measurements.

Precautions

Many diode detectors/integrators have a residual dc offset voltage that must be subtracted from all readings. Measure any offset level in the output before noise measurements begin. Do this by reading the output level with the signal path broken at a point after the noise-determining stages (typically after one or two stages of IF amplification—see Fig 4).

Be careful to avoid errors caused by gain variations during a measurement. Such variations will probably set the precision limit. The incident solar RF power on a 10-ft dish is much less than a picowatt (10^{-12} W), so a lot of RF and/or IF gain is needed to raise the signal to a measurable level. (This gain is needed for communication signals too!) Even a small gain variation can cause changes in output power level that appear to be changes in noise level of the system, sun or moon. Physical-temperature and supply-voltage changes are likely causes of such gain vari-

Table 2
Beam-Size Corrections for Sun/Moon Observations

3-dB Beamwidth°	G/T Correction Factor
2.0	1.02
1.5	1.04
1.0	1.10
0.8	1.16
0.5	1.42

ations. Make several repeated measurements and average them (perhaps neglecting any wildly deviant values) to minimize the effects of gain variations.

Since the sun and moon have considerable angular size, they may be partially resolved by antennas with small 3-dB beamwidths. [That is, the solar or lunar disk fills a non-negligible fraction of the beam main lobe.—*Ed.*] The received signal will then be smaller than the total flux expected from the source; the exact value will depend on how the sun or moon fills the antenna radiation pattern. Table 2 shows the factors (by which measurements should be multiplied) for several beam widths. This correction factor should be applied to the value of Y − 1, thus changing the value of G/*T* calculated in Equation 6. Notice that a 28-ft dish at 1.3 GHz (beamwidth of about 1.6°) requires only a small correction factor, but that very modest antennas have the problem as frequency increases. For example, a 6-ft parabolic antenna has a beamwidth of only 1° at 10 GHz.

Notes

[1]M. Kundu, *Solar Radio Astronomy*, New York: Interscience Publishers, 1965.

[2]Each month (with a publishing delay of a few months) the Ottawa 10.7-cm flux values, as well as solar radio fluxes over a range of other wavelengths, are published in the *SOLAR-GEOPHYSICAL DATA Prompt Reports* by the National Geophysical Data Center, NOAA/NESDIS, E/GC2, 325 Broadway, Boulder, CO 80303. Hence, for the highest calibration accuracy you must wait a bit for the correct values. The price is quite reasonable, however, and I encourage you to have your club buy a subscription. The weekly publication *Preliminary Report and Forecast of SOLAR GEOPHYSICAL DATA* contains additional information about solar radio emissions at a variety of frequencies. This is published by the Space Environment Services Center, R/E/SE2, 325 Broadway, Boulder, CO 80303.

These journals may also be available in the research library of a nearby technical university.

[3]T. Hagfors, *Radio Science*, Vol 5, Feb 1970, pp 189-227.

[4]D. Muhleman, in "Thermal Characteristics of the Moon," from *Progress in Astronautics and Aeronautics*, Vol 28, ed. J. W. Lucas (Cambridge: The MIT Press, 1972), pp 51-81.

[5]You can write to the US Government Printing Office at: North Capitol and "H" St, NW, Washington, DC 20401 (tel 202-275-2051).

[6]D. DeMaw, "Learning to Use Field-Strength Meters," *QST*, Mar 1985, p 26.

[7]A. Bry, "Beam-Antenna Pattern Measurement," *QST*, Mar 1985, p 31.

[8]Editor's Note: Flux values vary greatly with the sunspot cycle and other solar events (compare Table 1 to Table 1 of KA1GT's earlier section about sun noise). The sources in note 2 contain the best available data, but Fig 5 is a chart to help you make timely estimates. The daily 10-cm flux reading is broadcast over WWV and WWVH at 18 and 45 minutes after each hour, respectively. Even so, flux will vary greatly during a single day when there is a significant solar event.

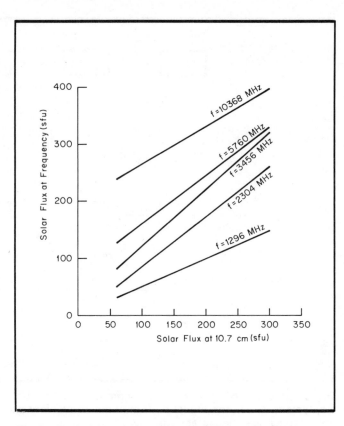

Fig 5—Probable relationships between solar flux at various frequencies and that at 10 cm, which is measured daily at Ottawa, Ontario (see note 8).

Chapter 8

Microwave Fabrication Techniques

By Maurice P. Johnson, W3TRR
768 Trenton Ave
Severna Park, MD 21146

INTRODUCTION

Microwave equipment design and fabrication as practiced commercially is an impressive endeavor. A professional microwave circuit designer generally has access to CAD programs such as COMPACT™ or TOUCHSTONE™ that can be used to quickly calculate S-parameters, stability factors, gain, noise figure, bandpass characteristics and even the effects of component variations on overall circuit performance. Many final circuits are the result of letting a computer grind away to "fine tune" and optimize what started out as a quick and dirty paper design.

Translation of an electrical design into hardware may also involve computer interaction in artwork layout. At the fabrication stage, advanced assembly techniques involve working with devices in "chip" form and bonding leads under a microscope, keeping in mind the overall concept that smaller is usually better when working at microwave frequencies.

At the test and alignment phase, fascinating (and costly) network analyzer test sets permit sweep alignment and measurement of circuit parameters, along with noise-figure measurements to confirm optimum performance of the circuits. Equally important, spectrum analyzers allow scanning over broad bandwidths to verify that no in-band or out-of-band parasitics or undesired responses exist (conditions which often plague initial designs). In many cases, the test equipment is computer controlled. See Fig 1.

The luxury of such elaborate and expensive equipment is seldom available to the hobby constructor, unless he also works in the microwave field. Thus, an obvious constraint on amateur microwave activities is the need to develop methods that can be pursued within the framework of amateur resources. To this end, projects must be scaled to practical amateur facilities and assembly methods. Most importantly, the hobby constructor must have a good understanding of microwave principles in order to better appreciate the practical trade-offs that can be made in adapting circuits and methods to a hobby level. Particularly

in the fabrication or "realization" phase of project development, creative use of available materials and construction methods can sometimes result in an amateur project providing performance rivaling that of a professional effort.

At one time, much microwave hardware was produced in waveguide or coaxial form. These construction techniques often required complex precision machining to a degree intimidating to most home constructors. These construction techniques may still be the preferred methods where RF losses must be reduced to an absolute minimum, or where power levels are high enough that heat transfer is a factor. However, the development of stripline, and then microstrip, has provided a construction medium very adaptable to many amateur projects.

The tools for microstrip consist essentially of artwork and subsequent photographic procedures; with these tools it becomes feasible to reproduce circuit boards in quantity, at low cost, with accuracy difficult to exceed even with more laborious methods. Fabrication of such microstrip boards and the attendant assembly of associated discrete parts is well within the capabilities of most amateur builders.

With an understanding of device parameters and appropriate matching concepts, much practical design can be accomplished at the Smith Chart level (Fig 2). Further, MMIC methods can be sacrificed in favor of more practical microstrip assemblies with encapsulated parts. As an aid to simplifying test and alignment, circuits can be divided into "building blocks" so that the performance of each rudimentary section can be individually evaluated. By matching the input and output of each block to the system impedance (usually 50 ohms) blocks can be tested and then cascaded to produce an overall system.

In view of the above, the following discussion of practical solid-state construction techniques will concentrate on the use of microstrip combined with encapsulated discrete components and active devices, attached by soldering to

(A)

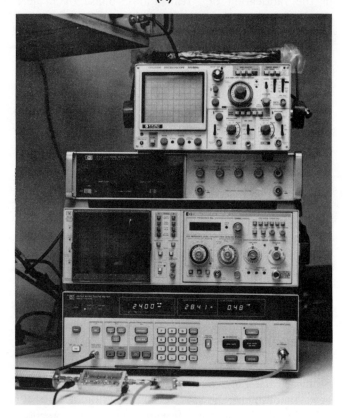

(B)

Fig 1—Commercial microwave designers have access to equipment usually beyond the reach of the amateur. The test setup at A is used for sweep-aligning microwave amplifiers. Noise figures are measured with the setup at B. *(photos courtesy of Chesapeake Microwave Technologies)*

Fig 2—Practical design work can be done with Smith Charts.

to the substrate tracks. No attention will be directed toward wire bonding or MMIC methods. Some cautions and assembly hints that have proven valuable will be mentioned. Throughout, only construction methods that are feasible with amateur facilities will be considered.

REALIZATION

Realization is the term used to designate the activity between conceiving a project and actually producing it as hardware. This is often the time when the experimenter realizes that a lot of effort and know-how are required to translate an idea into a final product.

A typical microwave project is undertaken by first considering the electrical design. The overall scope of the project can be evaluated, perhaps with the help of a block diagram where the gain and gain distribution, signal levels, frequency conversions, power levels, bias voltages and such parameters are determined. From this it becomes possible to select suitable transistors for various circuit functions. Most microwave projects can be defined as solid-state, small-signal circuits that can be built with bipolar transistors. At the higher microwave frequencies, or where very low noise figures are required, GaAsFETs may be utilized for front-end circuits. For detectors and mixers, microwave diodes will of course be called for. If the project is to be a transmitter or RF power generator, the heat sinking may be a consideration, and this may influence layout and packaging of the circuits. In the majority of cases, however, microstrip substrates will be convenient and adequate elements for creating the design in hardware form.

One of the very first tasks to be confronted when constructing a microwave project is the selection of suitable active devices. While there are many suitable devices available, they are generally characterized at both input and output ports with "complex" impedances. This means that they present reactive as well as resistive components to the "outside world." Even more interesting is the fact that the magnitudes of both components will generally change with frequency. If either input or output parameters are plotted on a Smith Chart, a spiraling orbit will result. See Fig 3. The plot may be inductive over part of its frequency range and appear capacitive at other frequencies. The resistive part may also change over the path. Further, this orbit will seldom cross the center of a 50-ohm chart. Thus, the resistive component will usually differ from the microwave system impedance of 50 ohms.

The presence of these complex impedances makes it necessary to match the input and output of the active device to the impedance of the circuit. Usually this dictates a power match for maximum energy transfer, which requires that the resistive component be translated to the system impedance and the reactive component be "tuned out" in keeping with the concept of conjugate matching. For optimum noise figure, the matching circuit may not be built to exactly tune out the device reactance, since specific mismatching may give the best noise figure. Fortunately, many device manufacturers furnish data and curves for the important parameters as functions of frequency, including noise match parameters. This makes life a bit easier for the experimenter, as measuring and determining the optimum noise match network "from scratch" may require some extensive laboratory equipment.

One satisfactory approach to matching active devices in a microwave circuit is to use a transformer to translate the resistive component of the device impedance to the system resistance (usually 50 ohms, unless another active device forms the source or load). A conjugate reactance is then used to cancel the reactive component of the device. It may be practical to use the series or parallel equivalents of the device impedances as convenient. At microwave frequencies, these matching networks can be produced as distributed elements, formed in microstrip.

For example, suppose that we wish to design a pre-amplifier to be mounted at an antenna location to supply some gain before feeding a long cable to a downconverter which is located indoors. See Fig 4. Typically, a gain of 20 dB or so will be required, helping to establish the system noise figure by providing gain ahead of the cable loss. Electrical design will then commence with the selection of suitable transistors for this small-signal application. For an amplifier to operate at 2300 MHz, bipolar devices can be found with inherent noise figures below 2.0 dB and about 12 dB gain. Such transistors as the NEC NE-64535 or Avantek AT-41435 would make good choices, especially since these manufacturers can also furnish detailed data for noise match, and complete S-parameters. With two stages, a gain of over 20 dB can be expected, so the first stage could be noise matched and the second stage matched for maximum gain.

At the design frequency, such active devices offer a capacitive input with a resistive component less than 50 ohms. A simple matching concept uses the series equivalent, with a transformer to step down the system resistance to that of the device and a series inductor to cancel the

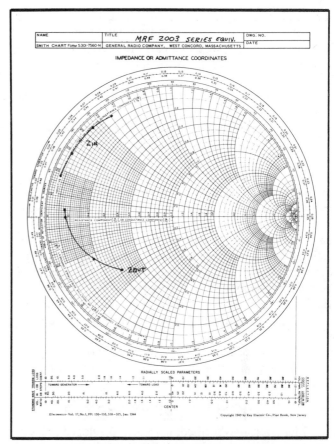

Fig 3—If input and output parameters are plotted for a typical microwave active device, spiraling orbits result.

Fig 4—A two-stage amplifier mounted in a die-cast box. The amplifier is secured to the box lid with the coaxial connector mounting hardware.

device reactance. This network may then be developed with microstrip elements.

Once suitable transistors are selected for the amplifier, the electrical design effort continues to define the input, interstage and output matching networks and translate them into suitable microstrip transmission lines. These lines are usually conceived in terms of impedances and wavelengths, and are then converted to line widths and lengths for the physical microstrip layout. The dc bias voltages to be applied to the transistors require a suitable bias circuit, and this may be included as a part of the etched substrate layout even though much of the bias circuit is not truly microstrip.

Outside world interconnections for signal and power supplies must be considered, as well as eventual packaging in a weatherproof enclosure, since the preamplifier will be located at the outdoor antenna site.

Next, the circuit must be translated into microstrip by laying out the microstrip networks in artwork form, providing for chip components where required, as well as transistors, conventional parts and connectors. This artwork is then photographically copied to furnish a working negative for use in etching the microstrip substrate. After etching, any cutting and drilling is done, and then the discrete components, transistors, and connectors attached before the assembly is mounted in a suitable enclosure. Any final debugging or "tweaking" required to render the circuits operational will then determine if the project is a success.

With the above procedures in mind, various facets of the construction techniques applicable to such a typical microwave project can be discussed.

MICROWAVE SUBSTRATES

Many assembly methods have been developed to interconnect and house components in finished electronic equipment. At one time in the early history of radio, open layouts of parts secured to a bakelite or wooden board (a true breadboard) served for amateur station equipment. Gradually this evolved into metal chassis bases to support sockets and parts that were fitted with solder lugs to permit interconnection with hookup wire. In the 1930s and 40s, most receivers and transmitters operating in the HF bands were constructed in this way. With the advent of TV and concern for TVI, shielding the equipment became important, so cabinets with RFI integrity were developed.

Gradually, printed circuit boards, which combined component support with associated wiring, appeared in ham gear. Many functions previously performed by vacuum tubes were then taken over by transistors and integrated circuits. These devices, much smaller than tubes, are housed in packages intended for PC board applications. Both digital and analog devices now coexist in modern transceivers and amateur equipment. In these applications, transistors and ICs are classed as discrete lumped components; they are small in size when compared to the operating wavelength.

At VHF and UHF frequencies, lumped components with hookup wire interconnections have served adequately for some projects. Usually, however, it is necessary to introduce a ground plane into the design to ensure stable operation of the circuit. At these frequencies, wiring may be done without undue concern for the length and corresponding impedance of the leads. PC-board assemblies are often adapted for use at these frequencies. Again, parts are relatively small in size compared to wavelengths.

At microwave frequencies, physical sizes of components often become large fractions of wavelengths at the frequencies involved. This factor becomes very influential in dictating the construction of microwave gear. It becomes necessary to know and control circuit impedances all along the RF paths; this rules out most methods of wiring with hookup wire. More suitable circuits and interconnections have resulted from refining PC-board concepts.

So-called "no-etch" PC boards will have very little application for microwave assemblies; also unacceptable are perf board, wire-wrap, dead-bug, cordwood and similar modules that are described as suitable for lower-frequency hardware in recent editions of the *ARRL Handbook*. Much better circuit accuracy and precision are generally needed to create microwave circuits, especially if more than one unit is to be built.

Moreover, construction techniques for microwave equipment bear very little resemblance to the methods that are encountered at lower frequencies. This is largely because lead lengths, circuit discontinuities and transmission losses become important parameters to be reckoned with. One satisfactory design approach is to carefully match impedances throughout passive and active portions of a microwave circuit to ensure that the RF signals can "flow smoothly" (with least loss) when traveling from input to output. This is most readily accomplished by interconnecting circuits and components with transmission-line networks. Because wavelengths at operating frequencies approach the physical size of circuit elements, many lumped elements can be replaced by distributed circuits. Specialized techniques have evolved to simplify the creation of such networks.

It is possible, of course, to fabricate transmission lines from pieces of coaxial cable. Transmission lines can also be made from open-wire line created by supporting pieces of conductor in air over a ground plane, using insulated posts or bits of dielectric material for support. The effective dielectric constant for open-wire line approaches that of air (1.0). In addition, with open-wire line, wave propagation occurs at essentially the same speed as through free space, and transmission-line elements will then be physically full size, as large as in free space.

The practical approach for most microwave construction depends on the use of microstrip substrates as the essential building blocks. This is the mechanism by which passive and active components are interconnected using transmission networks and lines of defined impedance. The microstrip also provides a mechanical support for these components. In microstrip, such transmission lines are created by using a continuous dielectric material to support conductors over a ground plane. The circuit conductor pattern is etched into copper-clad board, much like a printed-circuit board. Unlike a regular PC board, however, the microstrip provides etched transmission lines and matching circuits as well as simply interconnecting the components. The impedance of these transmission lines depends on the width of the conductors and the type and thickness of dielectric material appearing between the conductors and the ground plane. The dielectric material also affects losses; much of the RF loss encountered in a circuit constructed in microstrip form is due to the type and thickness of dielectric material used, although many secondary factors also have influence.

Microstrip

Microstrip has evolved as a result of the desire (or need) to have access to the center conductor of coaxial structures. Refer to Fig 5. With standard coaxial feed line, the center conductor is concentrically surrounded by an outer shell or braid, and thus is inaccessible without "breaking into" the structure. With antenna feed lines, this restriction is unimportant, but when active or passive components must be introduced to the center conductor path, accessibility may become very important.

Stripline is an attempt to convert the coaxial structure into a rectangular shape, where flat ground planes entrap the center conductor and dielectric in a "sandwich" form. The ground plane may or may not be contiguous, depend-

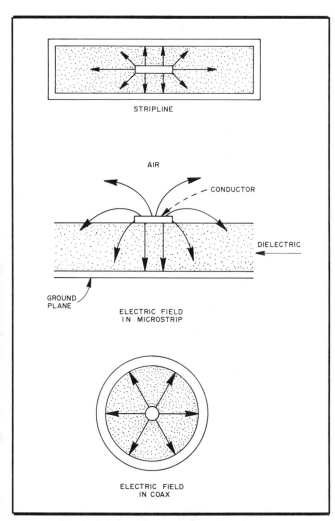

Fig 5—Microstrip can be considered as feed line with half the dielectric removed and replaced with air. See text for details.

ing on the particular design. Sometimes screws or soldered metal foil are used to complete the ground surround. When assembled, stripline completely encases the center conductor and circuits with a similar dielectric material in all directions.

Microstrip can be considered as stripline with half of the dielectric removed and replaced with air. It can be thought of as "one-sided" stripline. The dielectric is no longer the same in all directions.

With the upper dielectric and ground plane removed, much of the electric field exists in the dielectric material of the board (substrate), concentrated between center conductor and ground plane, as shown in Fig 5. There is flux leakage into the air above the board as well. For this reason, wave propagation is by means of a composite dielectric, and the effective dielectric constant value will lie between that of air and that of the actual dielectric constant of the board. Calculation of the effective dielectric constant becomes a bit involved, because the sharing of field between air and board dielectric depends to some extent on the width of the center conductor.

With the upper half of the dielectric and ground plane removed (as compared to stripline) the center conductor now lies out in the open, making it very convenient to introduce circuits and components into the center conductor path. Of course, the microstrip assembly will eventually be housed in a shield or enclosure, but the advantages of simple access to the center conductor during construction are obvious.

Microstrip has become one of the most practical construction techniques applicable to amateur microwave projects. It permits creating circuits and components in the form of transmission-line sections etched on circuit boards. These elements are termed "distributed" to distinguish them from more conventional "lumped" components.

To utilize microstrip, a designer must be able to determine line widths in terms of impedance, and line lengths in terms of wavelength. To a first order of accuracy, line widths are functions of dielectric type and thickness, independent of frequency. Line *lengths*, however, are frequency dependent, so wavelength on microstrip will change with frequency as well as with the type of dielectric.

The impedance of transmission lines on microstrip boards will depend on the dielectric constant and thickness of the board, as well as the width of the conductor lines. Since line width is not a function of frequency, a 50-ohm line will be the same width for 2 GHz as for 4 GHz. The board thickness does effect line width, however, so that a 50-ohm line will be twice as wide on 1/16th-inch board as it would be on 1/32nd-inch board. An inverse relation exists between line width and the dielectric material of the board. For a given line impedance, lines will be wider on low dielectric materials, and narrower on high dielectric materials. Finally, low-impedance lines will be wide while high-impedance lines will be narrow. The exact mathematics of these relationships is involved, but for practical purposes the math can be simplified greatly without unduly compromising the accuracy of the results. Line widths and lengths for useful impedances and wavelength fractions as functions of board materials and frequencies have been tabulated, so most calculations may be avoided. Some of these charts even correct for second-order effects (such as fringing) for improved accuracy. See Table 1.

All of this means that point-to-point hookup wire run in air to interconnect components is seldom encountered in microwave equipment. Instead, circuits are connected together with lengths of line of definite, controlled impedances. These may appear as the microstrip tracks etched on microwave substrates. Microstrip transmission lines, transformers, stubs, chokes and capacitors are all formed from sections of line of definite impedance. In turn, the substrate material, acting as a dielectric, deter-mines the physical size and the range of impedance of lines which can be etched on the substrate. This makes it obvious that the selection of substrate material is one of the essential choices to be made when contemplating a microwave project.

Substrate Materials

When selecting a suitable substrate material, factors to be considered are cost and availability, ease of machining and etching and electrical properties. To produce microstrip circuits, boards should be metal-clad on both sides, since one metal surface will be retained essentially intact as the ground plane while the opposite metal side will carry the microstrip circuit tracks (see Fig 6). The intervening insulation functions as the dielectric. For microstrip work, a low-loss dielectric should be used.

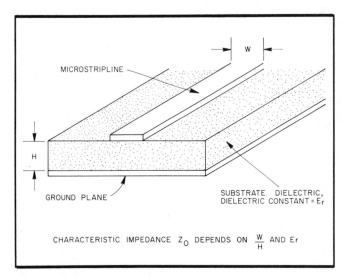

Fig 6—Dielectric material clad with metal on both sides is used to form microstrip circuits.

Table 1

Line Lengths and Widths for Glass Epoxy Substrate

4.80	Dielectric constant
0.00009 in.	Copper thickness
0.062 in.	Dielectric thickness

f = 1000 MHz

Line Impedance (ohms)	Line Width (inches)	Full Wavelength (inches)	Quarter Wavelength (inches)
150	0.005	6.82	1.70
125	0.011	6.72	1.68
100	0.023	6.61	1.65
90	0.031	6.55	1.64
80	0.047	6.50	1.63
70	0.056	6.44	1.61
60	0.077	6.37	1.59
50	0.105	6.29	1.57
40	0.155	6.18	1.54
30	0.230	6.06	1.51
25	0.300	5.98	1.49
20	0.400	5.89	1.47
15	0.550	5.80	1.45
10	0.900	5.67	1.42

f = 2000 MHz

Line Impedance (ohms)	Line Width (inches)	Full Wavelength (inches)	Quarter Wavelength (inches)
150	0.005	3.41	0.852
125	0.011	3.36	0.839
100	0.023	3.30	0.826
90	0.031	3.27	0.819
80	0.047	3.25	0.812
70	0.056	3.22	0.805
60	0.077	3.18	0.795
50	0.105	3.14	0.785
40	0.155	3.08	0.770
30	0.230	3.02	0.755
25	0.300	2.98	0.744
20	0.400	2.93	0.732
15	0.550	2.89	0.720
10	0.900	2.81	0.702

The materials commonly used for microwave substrates will have dielectric constants typically ranging from 2.0 to 10.0 (see Fig 7). The dielectric constant influences the speed of wave propagation along transmission lines etched on the board, with materials with high dielectric constants producing the slowest wave propagation. This means that physical wavelengths are shortened on dielectric-loaded transmission lines when compared to free space. This in turn means that microstrip circuits will be slightly smaller when created on substrates with high dielectric constants.

Some materials used as dielectrics in MMICs have exceptionally high dielectric constants (30.0 or more). For more conventional microstrip substrates, alumina and ceramic have dielectric constants near 10.0. Substrates are produced by plating a ground plane on these materials with metal, often gold, and applying conductor patterns with

Fig 7—Materials with different dielectric constants can be used for microstrip construction.

screening techniques, usually on small 2-inch × 2-inch dielectric plates. These materials are brittle and difficult to machine with amateur methods, however, so they are seldom applied to hobby projects.

Other high dielectric-constant materials have been developed by such companies as Keene, Rogers and 3-M by mixing ceramic powders with Teflon™ (the actual process is much more complicated; this is a simplistic description). This can result in a very high-quality (low RF loss) material, extremely uniform and homogeneous, with a dielectric constant near 10.0. It is often used as an alternative to alumina, and can be supplied in larger sizes than ceramics.

This dielectric material tends to be somewhat soft, and consequently is usually coated on a thick metal carrier, which then becomes the ground plane of the resultant substrate. The dielectric is typically coated in a thickness less than 1/16th inch and a thin copper layer applied over the top, where the microstrip circuit tracks can be etched. Because the carrier (plate) is usually aluminum, of 1/8-inch or 1/4th-inch thickness, any cutting, drilling, or machining is more involved than for ordinary PC boards, so the machining is generally done before the etching. Commercial products of this type also tend to be somewhat expensive. Nevertheless, at the higher microwave frequencies, or where uniformity is important and microstrip losses must be minimized (such as where low noise figure is of concern), these materials may still be the best choices even for hobby projects.

Microstrip circuits designed to be fabricated on such high dielectric-constant materials will be most compact or compressed because of the wave-slowing action of the dielectric. Usually, this is an advantage, but there may be instances where such small size makes it difficult to fit any conventional discrete parts into a microstrip layout. There are Teflon/ceramic mixtures with dielectric constants somewhat lower, such as 6.0, which will produce physically larger microstrip layouts; this helps to alleviate the component-mounting problem.

At one time, Paul Shuch (N6TX) expounded the use of conventional glass-epoxy PC boards as a suitable vehicle for many amateur microstrip projects. At the lower microwave frequencies and for less-critical applications, this may well be the material of choice, since the cost is low and the material is readily available. Mixtures of fiberglass with epoxy result in dielectric constants of about 4.8, and double-clad boards are typically 0.032 or 0.062 inch thick, with sufficient mechanical stiffness to support the discrete components that are usually added to a microstrip assembly. Even with connectors and low-frequency bypass capacitors soldered to such boards, most small-signal projects will also be mechanically complete. With 0.062-inch board, with one side solidly copper clad to form a ground plane, a 50-ohm transmission line will be 0.104 inch wide (typically etched as 0.100 inch). This is a very convenient dimension for etching without difficulty. This width also conveniently agrees with the width of many chip components that are used in microstrip assemblies.

In the case of power amplifiers where heat dissipation may be a concern, it is often practical to attach such a PC-board substrate to a heat sink, and secure the transistors directly to the sink. This form of construction has long been used for VHF RF power amplifiers.

There are penalties for using PC-board materials for microwave circuits, and the builder should be aware of this. There may be variations in the exact dielectric constant of the board material from sample to sample, or from vendor to vendor. (For "normal" PC-board uses, the dielectric constant is not such a critical factor). Also, depending on the operating frequency, transport loss will be encountered by a signal passing along the board. This can amount to 0.1 dB per inch to as much as 1.0 dB per inch in low-grade materials. Some of this loss occurs as dielectric heating, some as loss in conductors and some from actual radiation from the microstrip elements. The effects of such loss must be evaluated in terms of the particular circuit application.

For example, a ½-dB loss may not upset the designer of a high-level amplifier with 25-dB overall gain, provided power levels are not so high that the loss results in heating the board! Another designer striving to make an amplifier exhibit a noise figure of 1.0 dB would be very disturbed if a ½-dB loss appeared ahead of the first gain stage. Yet, experience has shown that it is very possible to use glass-epoxy board to make a 2-GHz amplifier with transistors rated at 2.0 dB noise figure, using two gain stages to produce 23 dB gain with an overall noise figure measured as 2.3 dB. The point is that low-cost board materials may be entirely satisfactory in many applications, but for lowest noise figure, or at the higher microwave frequencies, even the amateur builder should resort to quality substrate materials.

There are also materials based on Teflon combined with glass either in the form of small fibers or as woven fabric embedded in the dielectric. Such materials have dielectric constants in the range 2.0 to 2.6, and exhibit quite low RF losses. When used in the form of double-copper-clad PC boards, these materials may tend to warp or bend after etching, and may require a carrier or support, especially if the surface area involved is extensive. Still, these materials are very useful at the higher microwave frequencies or for circuits with critical performance parameters. They are commonly used in commercial equipment.

Dielectric Influences

By now, it should be obvious that the dielectric material of the substrate will have an influence on the physical size of the microstrip elements. Consequently, artwork which has been developed for a microstrip circuit on glass epoxy board cannot be directly used for a board with a different dielectric constant. Further, artwork intended for board material with a particular thickness cannot be used with boards of other thicknesses. Finally, a microstrip layout intended for one frequency cannot be used to make a substrate for some different frequency. Artwork must be used with the intended board material and thickness, and at the frequency for which it was designed.

As already mentioned, for many hobby projects at frequencies below around 3 GHz, the most practical materials for microstrip work will undoubtedly be those intended for printed-circuit boards. Dielectric materials such as epoxy, fiberglass (and mixtures of these materials), as well as Teflon/glass combinations, clad on both sides with one ounce or thinner copper will have adequately low loss for most substrate applications. Boards 0.062 inch thick are popular and readily available. On boards of this thickness, line impedances ranging from 10 to 100 ohms may be conveniently etched; this is a convenient range of values adequate for almost all microstrip circuits.

An advantage of such material is the ease with which it may be worked and etched when making substrates. It may be sheared or cut to size with a hacksaw, filed or sanded, drilled with conventional metalworking drill bits and etched with PC-board etchants. The finished substrate usually has sufficient strength and rigidity to support components without additional bracing. Small wonder then that this is a favored material for amateur use (and many professional applications as well).

The higher the dielectric constant of the board material used for a substrate, the slower will be propagation along its microstrip circuits. This means that the physical circuit layout will be compressed, occupying less area than it would if the dielectric was air. Also, as the dielectric material between conductors and ground plane is made thinner, the microstrip conductors for a given impedance become narrower.

Dielectric material acts to constrain the electric field between conductor and ground plane. The more this field is confined and constrained, the less it will radiate, and the less it will be influenced by nearby conductors or metal. This is an important factor to bear in mind when evaluating the effects of a metal enclosure on the operation of the enclosed microstrip circuit. In this regard, it would seem almost obvious that a metal enclosure can be brought intimately close to the ground-plane side of the substrate without modifying the field patterns. Above the conductor side of the microstrip circuit, however, some leakage field exists, and metal brought close to this surface will modify the field patterns, thus changing line impedances, coupling and the like. As a rule of thumb, metal covers or enclosures should ideally stay five to ten times the board thickness away from the microstrip circuit side of the circuit board. Also, conductors running side by side on the circuit side of the microstrip board should be separated by about three line widths, or run at angles instead of parallel to one another, in order to minimize mutual coupling. Fortuitous location of grounds between conductors can sometimes serve to reduce coupling. Compounding the above, it should be evident that substrates made from materials with higher dielectric constants will be less disturbed by nearby metal enclosures; substrates made with low-dielectric materials will be more affected by nearby metal. Thus it is easier to package a microstrip circuit made on ceramic than a circuit made with pure Teflon as the dielectric.

The overall size of the intended enclosure should be considered for potential "waveguide" effect, which can radically modify the behavior of a microstrip circuit between its open air performance and operation within the enclosure. Coupling effects will be evident if circuit performance is substantially different with the enclosure cover installed than it is with cover removed. It may be necessary to add lossy absorber materials within the enclosure, located above the circuit side of the microstrip board.

Substrate Circuits

When building hardware, microstrip circuit elements will form many of the circuit components, and this dictates the physical layout of the substrate board. While microstrip may also be used for many of the bias feeds and signal paths, it is entirely practical to include more-conventional PC-board layouts for other parts of the circuit that are not in the RF paths. Often it makes good sense to combine conventional printed circuits on the same substrate with the microstrip layouts. For example, an audio amplifier or an IF strip could be included with a microwave mixer, filter or local oscillator as a common assembly. The low-frequency circuitry can be arranged according to the rules for PC layout, while microstrip is used for the microwave portions of the design. It is easiest to combine the two types of circuitry if top surface-mount components are used throughout.

Several down-converter designs and image-rejecting doubly balanced mixers with associated quadrature-combining IF strips have been very successfully combined and fabricated as one-sided layouts with surface-mounted components. These circuits clearly show that this concept is feasible (see Fig 8). Obviously, a combined circuit of this type permits the use of a single artwork template as well as the etching of a single substrate, instead of requiring the fabrication of several independent units. In many cases this is a decided convenience, while in others it may limit the ability to test, change or rework one portion of a circuit without redoing the entire circuit. There may be times when it is actually preferable to work with a number of small interconnected modules rather than a large common unit. This is especially true in early developmental phases of a project when portions of circuits may be subject to modification. Good judgment will obviously guide and determine the best approach.

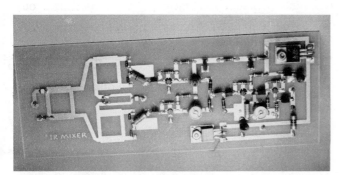

Fig 8—This image-rejecting mixer circuit combines surface-mounted components with microstrip circuitry.

COMPONENTS FROM MICROSTRIP

One of the advantages of microstrip is that it can be used to create components as well as interconnections. Throughout a substrate layout, sections of transmission line are used to tie various active and passive discrete components together. In addition, sections of transmission line are used to form capacitors, inductors, chokes, stubs and even transformers. All of these are etched simultaneously with the interconnecting lines to produce large portions of many circuits without requiring any additional discrete parts. Often, such circuit elements as couplers, power dividers, combiners and even filters can be produced in microstrip form without adding a single discrete part. Single-ended, doubly balanced or image-rejecting mixers, and up or down converters only require the addition of a few diodes. Even active amplifiers, which obviously do require discrete transistors or FETs, require a minimum of additional parts added to the substrate.

The electrical design of a microwave project will define the active devices and the associated matching elements required to produce an overall circuit. Generally the external interfaces (the input and output ports) will be matched to a system impedance (usually 50 ohms). Active elements must be furnished with suitable dc bias from the system power supply, usually through a voltage divider. In addition to any added discrete resistors and capacitors, microstrip circuit elements will be used to create chokes, matching networks, stubs, inductors and capacitors and similar circuit elements in distributed form.

A suitable substrate must be selected, since its dielectric material and thickness influence the line widths and lengths required on the microstrip. Equations or charts are available for determining the proper dimensions of microstrip circuit elements once dielectric parameters and operating frequencies have been established.

The dielectric material is a major factor determining RF loss for a microstrip circuit, but circuit layout can also contribute to the loss, so layout should be carefully considered. The signal path should follow a straight line, and the line should be no longer than necessary. Abrupt changes in direction can cause loss by radiation at the corners. Miter any corners that must be used (Fig 9); this keeps the impedance constant around the bend. Another option is to make direction changes gradually with a radius.

Generally, an input connector feeds into a 50-ohm microstrip line, with a gap to accommodate a blocking

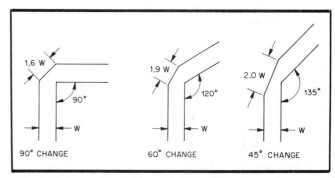

Fig 9—Microstrip circuits should follow a straight line if possible. Any corners should be mitered to keep the impedance constant around the corner.

Fig 10—This amplifier circuit shows a straight-line signal path from input to output. Bias voltages are supplied by high-impedance quarter-wave lines run at right angles to the signal path.

capacitor in chip form. Any transformation from this impedance to another value to match the resistive component of the input device can be made with a series quarter-wave line section. Reactance can be canceled by tying a stub in shunt with the signal path, orienting the stub at right angles to the signal path. Likewise, microstrip chokes used to supply bias voltages to the active devices are provided by high impedance quarter-wave lines, also run at right angles to the signal path. See Fig 10.

In keeping with transmission-line theory, half-wave lines repeat their terminating impedance, while quarter-wave lines act as impedance inverters. Thus a grounded stub that is an odd number of quarter wavelengths in length will appear as an open circuit at its input. To keep losses down, however, elements should be kept as short as possible when creating a circuit function. Open lines shorter than a quarter wave will act as capacitors, and this effect is enhanced if the capacitors are made from low-impedance lines. High-impedance quarter-wave lines act efficiently as chokes. Line widths that provide an impedance of 100 ohms are commonly used for such chokes. Grounded stubs can be used as elementary filters. If an input is shunted with a grounded stub, a quarter wavelength long at the design frequency, it will appear more and more as a short circuit as the frequency lowers. Thus the stub can act to reduce low-frequency response in a microwave amplifier, where microwave transistors inherently have lots of gain.

Stubs can be tuned, or their reactance varied, by changing their length or width. An open-ended stub can be tuned by cutting and peeling off a bit of the length, or conversely adding a bit to the length with tuning foil. When stub tuning is anticipated during initial circuit layout, small pads can be added adjacent to the stub end, as shown in Fig 11. These pads can then be added by soldering or bridging with foil. Grounded stubs can be tuned with chip

capacitors that bridge the stub edge to ground. The tuning capacitors can be slid along the stub edge to effectively alter the ground point. Stubs grounded at RF need not always be dc grounded, since a capacitor can serve to bypass RF to ground. Of course it is also possible to solder a true variable capacitor onto a microstrip circuit and tune with a "diddle stick" in the usual way (see Fig 12). Vendors can supply small variable capacitors (and inductors) fitted with ribbon leads or other mounting means so that they are compatible with microstrip. Surface-mount types are more convenient than kinds which must mount through the substrate. The experimenter usually will try to stick to pure microstrip stubs to create capacitors and inductors, if not for the convenience, then certainly for the low cost.

Microstrip transformers are usually incorporated as series connected quarter-wave line segments with an impedance equal to the mean of the impedances encountered at their two ports, as shown in Fig 13. These

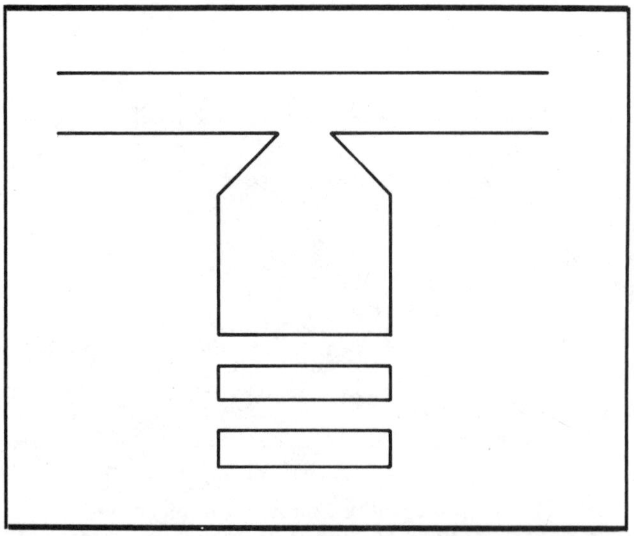

Fig 12—Close-up view of an oscillator tank circuit showing a series-tuned variable piston capacitor used to set the oscillator frequency. A ceramic pad is used to increase output coupling between the oscillator tank and the input line.

Fig 11—Stub tuning can be accomplished by adding small pads adjacent to the end of the stub. These pads can then be added as required by bridging the gaps with solder.

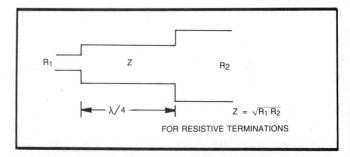

Fig 13—Series impedance transformers can be easily constructed in microstrip circuits by using a quarter-wave line segment with an impedance equal to the mean of the impedances to be transformed.

line segments are readily configured in microstrip. Minor adjustments with tuning foil will permit a change of length or width to correct wavelength or impedance variations.

Signal and bias circuits are laid out on the top surface with a solid ground plane confined to the back side of the board. This will minimize the number of "via" holes that must be used to return circuits to the true ground plane on the back. Remember that grounds are not "returned" until they reach the true ground plane. Series inductance introduced by elongated ground leads cannot be ignored, particularly in the grounding of stubs and bypass capacitors, or in the common return lead of active devices. Nanohenrys of inductance contributed by an extra 0.1 inch of lead length may not seem significant, but this amount can radically modify the S-parameters (and thus the performance) of a transistor or FET in an amplifier stage.

Typical Layout Procedure

A microstrip circuit layout can be plotted using a straightforward procedure. Such simple methods as drawing the circuit on graph paper, a few times larger than life size, will efficiently develop a layout arrangement to fit the available enclosure with minimum fuss. A good scaling factor will increase the accuracy of the layout. This layout can then be converted to microstrip art by blocking in conductor outlines with a black wick pen (see Fig 14). This can then be converted to camera-ready art by photocopying if the contrast needs to be enhanced. Such basic techniques have been used for many projects with excellent results. It is also practical to use more professional methods, such as Rubylith or taped mylar if desired.

As an example, consider the layout of the microstrip for a typical small-signal single-stage amplifier designed to operate at 1.0 GHz. A paper layout plot should first be made at some convenient scaling factor to develop a feasible circuit arrangement for the microstrip together with bias feeds and any other associated items. The layout should progress toward an overall rectangular outline for convenient eventual packaging of the substrate. Layout on paper could begin by locating a spot for an input coax connector at one end of the sheet, providing for right-angle launch into the microstrip. A short run of 50-ohm microstrip transmission line would then lead away from the connector center pin, followed by a quarter wavelength of 35-ohm line to serve as a step-down transformer to match the bipolar transistor.

Assuming that 0.062-inch glass/epoxy board is to be used for the substrate, dimensions for the lines to be used can be determined. The input 50-ohm line will be 0.104 inch wide, of a convenient length to include room for mounting a blocking capacitor (chip) before reaching the transformer. A gap in the 50-ohm line must be provided, typically 0.060 inch for a 0.100-inch chip. The 35-ohm transformer is 0.190 inch wide by 1.53 inches long (a quarter wave at 1.0 GHz on this PC board). These are finished dimensions, so the layout scaling factor must be incorporated in the drawing.

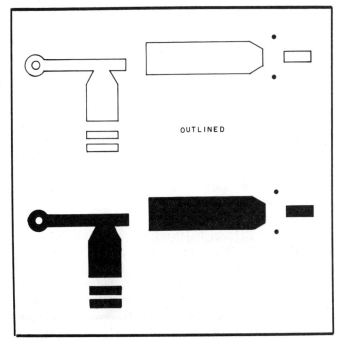

OUTLINED

Fig 14—A line drawing can be easily converted to camera-ready artwork by coloring with a wick pen.

The next series element will be an inductor, leading into the transistor base. This is used in series to "tune out" the internal capacitance of the transistor input at 1.0 GHz. The inductive reactance of the series inductor must equal the capacitive reactance of the transistor at the design frequency. The inductor line width must be small compared to a 50-ohm line, so a 100-ohm line (0.023 inch wide) would be a suitable choice. An eighth wavelength of such line would offer 100 ohms of inductive reactance, but the transistor reactance is somewhat less than this, so a shorter line length will suffice. Since the device impedance is actually 20-ohms reactive, the required line length is readily calculated. The tangent of the required line length will be X_L/Z_L, which is 20/100 or 0.2. Taking the arctangent we find that the line length is just a bit under 12 degrees. Since a quarter wave (90 degrees) of 100-ohm line is 1.65 inches long, a 12-degree length would be 12/90 × 1.65 inches, or 0.220 inch long. Instead of drawing this length of 100-ohm line leading into the transistor base, it may be just as convenient to let the actual transistor base lead furnish this required inductance (after first ensuring that the selected transistor comes with a base lead at least this long!). A similar technique can be used at the transistor output port if series inductance is required in the output network.

Circuits for supplying base bias can now be arranged. Working from the transistor toward the dc source, it is first necessary to bridge a quarter-wave choke across the signal path to the base. This can be a 100-ohm line 90 degrees long, so it will measure 0.023 inch wide by 1.65 inches in length. An open-ended capacitive stub is tied to the cold end of the choke, to serve as a microwave decoupling bypass. For maximum bypassing action, a low-impedance quarter-wave stub is used, measuring 0.400 inch wide and 1.47 inches long. The circuit is now decoupled at microwave frequencies, so it is possible to use conventional components from this point on to the power source. Carbon resistors and lumped low-frequency bypass capacitors will now suffice. It is only required that low-frequency decoupling be accomplished, so small solder pads can be arranged for securing these conventional components. Leads can be bent and cut very short to permit them to be surface mounted to the circuit board without drilling holes.

It is good practice to bring the bias choke away from the RF path at right angles, to minimize coupling between the two circuits. The size and shape of the circuit may sometimes be improved if the choke is folded to compress the area it occupies. Unless the selected transistor is unconditionally stable (K greater than unity) at all frequencies (not just at the design frequency), provision should be made for top loading the bias choke. This is done by leaving a gap between the choke and the RF line to accommodate a 50-ohm chip resistor added in series with the choke at the "hot" end of the choke. Top loading places the resistor at the most effective location.

Similar layouts are developed for the output of the transistor, arranging a microstrip output network, blocking capacitor in a 50-ohm line, and similar bias choke and decoupling stub to feed bias to the collector circuit.

Finally, a resistive voltage divider is included to divide the supply voltage to suitable values for the transistor. A typical small-signal bipolar device may only draw 10-20 mA of collector current, so a bleeder current through the voltage divider of 1-3 mA should suffice. Because the voltage divider is decoupled by the quarter-wave chokes and stubs, it is isolated from the RF circuits and is invisible to the signal path. No RF feedback or degeneration is created by this bias circuit arrangement. Other techniques may be used to reduce low-frequency gain, such as by shunt feedback, where resistors are directly shunted across the transistor base-collector path. These techniques are not considered here.

All of this RF-circuit layout in microstrip, together with bias feeds and dc circuits included on the same substrate, can be sketched on graph paper with a pencil until a satisfactory layout has been developed. A final paper sketch then should be made, as accurately as possible. Microstrip lines should be outlined with a sharp black "wick" pen, precisely to scale, and then these outlines can be filled in as required to produce opaque transmission-line silhouettes of the required distributed components.

Similar methods are used to draw the bias and dc portions of the layout, but here it is not as important to preserve line lengths and impedances, since these lines are only used for interconnection. This portion of the layout can follow conventional PC-board concepts, except that it is generally advisable to stick to surface-mounted components rather than the "through the board" lead dress typically used for PC layouts. This simplifies the etching and drilling of the substrate. Components that are not grounded but are mounted in "through" holes require clearance or additional conductor tracks on the ground-plane surface, necessitating two-sided art work and etching; this is best avoided if possible.

DISCRETE PARTS FOR MICROSTRIP

As operating frequencies are raised to the microwave region, it becomes necessary to keep component lead lengths to a minimum. Also, it is important to make components as "pure" as possible; for example, a capacitor should display minimal resistance and inductance. To this end, components and active devices, even assemblies, tend to shrink in size while much of the interconnection is done with microstrip.

As a general approach, microwave circuit layouts attempt to create as much of the circuit as practical in the form of distributed microstrip components. In addition to the usual 50-ohm interconnecting lines, such circuit elements as matching networks, bias feeds, stubs and pads for tuning, couplers, splitters and combiners, inductors and capacitors may all be produced in microstrip form. A few components will always remain that must be included as discrete parts. Such items as coupling and blocking capacitors, decoupling and bypass capacitors and resistors and terminations may be added as discrete parts on a microstrip layout. While it is possible to fabricate resistors as thick-film depositions onto a microstrip substrate, such methods will hardly be used by an amateur builder.

Resistors and capacitors used for power-supply or low-frequency bias-feed decoupling are usually out of the circuit areas that carry RF signals, so these components do not function at microwave frequencies. More conventional components may be used for these circuit applications. Coupling capacitors and terminating resistors that appear directly in the RF signal paths must function at microwave, however, and specialized components should be used for these circuit regions.

A few adjustable or tunable components are also available for substrate use. Premium-quality (and premium price!) variable capacitors have been developed by companies such as Johanson. The styles with ribbon leads designed for surface mounting are most useful on microstrip. Some very small circular trimmer capacitors by MuRata-Erie can sometimes be adapted to microstrip. Other specialized components are available, including variable inductors.

Components that appear in the RF paths should be selected for microwave compatibility. This means that lead lengths for component connection have been reduced to a minimum, and component volume has been reduced to a minimum as well. Carrying this concept to a limit has resulted in the development of special "chip" components designed for microwave use.

Chip Components

An obvious characteristic of the chip components shown in Fig 15 is that they have been considerably reduced in physical size. Capacitors and resistors have shrunk to small cubes, typically 0.1 inch or smaller on each dimension. Some packages are rectangular to accommodate larger capacitor values, or to permit higher power-handling capabilities (in the case of resistors).

In addition to this size reduction, chip components have been stripped of connecting leads. Instead, opposite faces of the part are provided with solder pads as a terminus for a solder "fillet," to mechanically secure the part as well as provide electrical connection to a microstrip circuit. This minimizes the amount of lead required to go from microstrip to component and back again, and reduces to an absolute minimum the added inductance attributable to lead length. The combination of miniaturized component and reduced interconnecting lead length results in much less parasitic inductance, making for more "pure" capacitors and resistors.

Since these components have equivalent circuits more closely approaching "pure" parts, design is simplified; resistors can be considered to be resistors instead of complex RLC networks, and capacitors can be treated as true capacitors over much of the microwave frequency range. Because of their internal structure, even chip capacitors have a series-resonant frequency, and above this frequency they display some inductance. This series resonance can sometimes be used to advantage since the series impedance has a minimum value (resistive) at

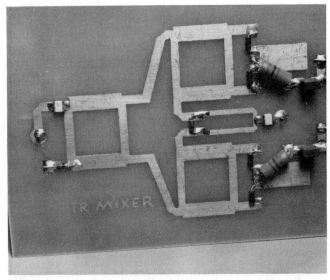

Fig 16—It is possible to surface mount regular leaded components on microstrip circuits. The leads should be cut very short and dressed for mounting.

resonance. This can be utilized effectively in some coupling or bypassing applications. Otherwise, care should be used to select capacitance values which permit the capacitor to function at frequencies below resonance, where the component appears as a true capacitor. Very useful charts of resonant frequencies for various chip capacitors in both A and B sizes are available from such suppliers as ATC.

Chip resistors should be used in RF portions of a microwave circuit. Good candidates are RF feedback paths, terminations on hybrids, couplers, splitters and combiners, loss pads or parasitic suppressors or any place where a resistive element is needed with a minimum of parasitic inductance or capacitance. With care, in some applications, it is sometimes possible to use small carbon tubular resistors of 1/8 or 1/10-W size in place of chips, but the leads must be cut extremely short if these parts are to serve as pure resistance. Leads should be formed and

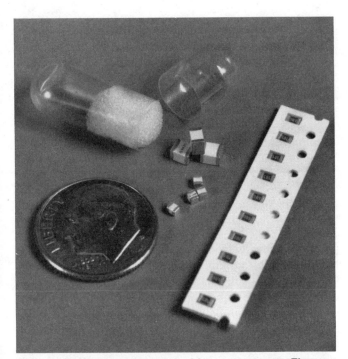

Fig 15—Some representative chip components. Figures 6 and 8, in Chapter 4, show the internal structure of some chip capacitors and resistors.

Fig 17—Chip components are 0.1 inch wide, the same width as a typical 50-ohm microstrip line.

dressed so the resistor can be surface mounted on the circuit side of the substrate board, as shown in Fig 16.

There is a definite advantage in using chip components in the RF paths of microstrip circuits. The physical size of the component corresponds nicely with the microstrip line width. A typical 50-ohm line width of 0.1 inch is essentially the same width as the chip component. Such a chip can be soldered directly to the microstrip line with minimum discontinuity in width, and the solder fillet is used to smooth the transition in height from line to component (Fig 17). All of this contributes to keeping SWR low over the transmission paths of the microstrip circuit, even when discrete parts must be introduced into these paths.

Surface-Mounted Parts

Since microwave substrate layouts go to great lengths to reduce component lead lengths, a technique of "surface-mounting" components has been developed. Digital and low-frequency printed-circuit boards generally insert discrete components from the side of the board opposite the etched circuit tracks, running the component leads through drilled holes in the board. Components are then secured by soldering on the copper side of the board, often by dip or wave soldering methods. This technique means that all component lead lengths are extended by the thickness of the PC board, as leads must extend through the board before they can reach the circuit tracks. Even this amount of lead extension may be undesirable in a microwave circuit assembly.

Surface-mounting techniques are used to minimize component lead lengths. The components are attached to the circuit board on the etched-circuit side (the "bottom" of a conventional board, but it now becomes the "top"). No holes need be drilled through the board for lead passage, and the parts are soldered directly to the circuit traces with small solder fillets, as shown in Fig 18.

Chip components have been configured for this mounting method, and more and more parts are appearing in packages intended for this application. Even integrated circuit devices are now available in new smaller packages for surface mounting. Recently, large-value electrolytic capacitors and power resistors have been encased in rectangular cases fitted with solder flanges or ribbon leads to facilitate their use in this manner. Chip components and many other microwave components (including small-signal transistors and diodes), are so small and lightweight that no additional support is needed beyond the support provided by soldering the part to the circuit traces.

Active Devices

Small-signal transistor packages are often suited for surface mounting. In particular, devices designed for microwave use usually appear in "macro-X" or "micro-X" cases, (or something similar; see Chapter 4, Fig 1), and these are very convenient for surface mounting. See Fig 19. Some device packages have no projections below the

Fig 18—Another example of surface-mounting of regular leaded components.

Fig 19—A surface-mounted "Micro-X" transistor. Note the clearance hole drilled in the substrate to accommodate the "pill." At higher frequencies, the ground pads above and below the dielectric would be connected by a rivet, a "Z" wire or copper foil wrapped through the hole.

plane of the leads, and these can be soldered directly to the circuit without requiring a hole in the circuit board. Other packages will surface mount if a clearance hole is drilled under the transistor body.

Of course, stud-mounted and high-power device packages may require heat sinks or specialized mounting methods which may not be compatible with surface-mounting techniques. Beam-lead diodes can be attached by surface-mounting methods, and even conventional glass-encapsulated diodes can have their leads bent slightly to enable them to be surface mounted. Again, some diodes may be more readily attached to the circuit board if a suitable clearance hole or groove is first drilled or cut into the board under the diode package.

GROUNDS ON MICROSTRIP SUBSTRATES

"Daisy chain" grounds which loop from place to place and then eventually are tied to the chassis or ground plane are often encountered in audio and digital hardware, but this grounding method must be avoided in microwave circuits. The paramount rule for successful microwave work is to make each and every grounded circuit or component go as directly to the ground plane as possible. Any unintentionally added lead length in a ground return adds inductance that could cause circuit instability, loss of gain, even oscillation in a microstrip amplifier.

The common lead (usually the source or emitter) of an FET or bipolar transistor can be particularly prone to cause trouble if any excess lead length is introduced in this path to ground. As a rule of thumb, one millimeter of lead length creates one nanohenry of inductance. Even this slight amount of inductance added in a device common lead can cause extreme changes in effective S-parameters at microwave frequencies.

For this and other similar reasons, circuit layout must provide very short paths to ground in each and every ground return. The object is to provide a solid ground plane on the back of the substrate, and then to ensure that all ground returns go back to this surface as directly as possible. Each device or component should be grounded independently, rather than having several devices share common paths to ground.

In the case of microwave transistors and FETs, multiple leads are usually provided for the common connection so that multiple paralleled ground returns can be used to reduce the lead inductance when grounding this critical element. Mounting methods for these active devices then must concentrate on keeping the ground paths short. One method for devices in packages such as the micro-X case is to drill a clearance hole in the substrate and mount the active part from the ground-plane side. This may shorten the emitter (or source) leads, but requires that input and output leads be bent up through the clearance hole to reach the circuit tracks on the microstrip side of the board (Fig 20). Conversely, the device may be inserted into the hole from the top, with the common leads bent to reach down to the ground plane below, while the input and output device leads lie flat on the top (Fig 21). These methods may be electrically acceptable, but bending the leads can cause strains on the device and complicate its removal because it is soldered on both the top and bottom of the substrate. It is usually better to mount the device from the top of the substrate, but avoid bending any of the device leads.

Some builders insert small copper straps through the clearance hole to bond pads on the top to the ground plane below, (Fig 22), and then solder all device leads at the top surface of the substrate. This makes parts much easier to remove.

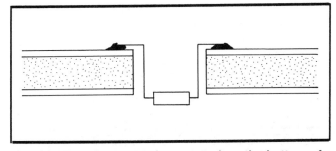

Fig 20— **Transistors can be mounted on the bottom of the microstrip board. This minimizes ground lead length, but requires that the input and output leads be bent up through the board to the microstrip circuitry.**

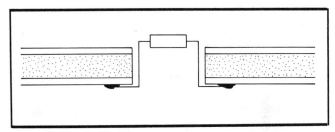

Fig 21—**With the device mounted on top of the microstrip board, the ground leads must be bent down through the board to reach the ground plane.**

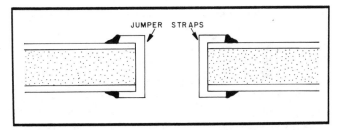

Fig 22—**Ground pads on top of the microstrip board can be bonded to the ground plane with small copper straps.**

In another method, (somewhat easier to implement), no circuit pads are needed on the top side for the emitter (or source), and no clearance hole is required for the micro-X package. Instead, small eyelets or rivets are inserted through the substrate where the device common leads will be located, spaced as close as possible to the body of the device. Input and output conductors are etched on the top of the substrate in the usual manner. The device is then soldered from the top, soldering the common device leads directly to the eyelets which have first been soldered to the ground plane below (Fig 23). This technique results in very satisfactory grounds on double-clad circuit-board substrates.

In the rare case where a builder is using soft substrate

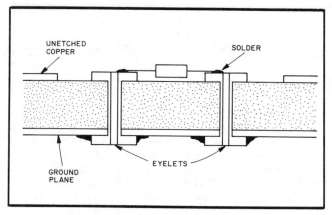

Fig 23—Active devices can also be grounded by soldering their leads to eyelets which have first been soldered to the ground plane.

Fig 24—If a ground plane is added to the top of the microstrip board, it must be bonded to the bottom-side ground plane at intervals of less than a quarter wavelength at the operating frequency.

with a thick carrier or heat sink as the ground plane, it may be impractical to insert rivets or eyelets into the thick carrier. Some builders have successfully used small screws which are tapped into the heavy metal, with the device soldered to the screw heads. Higher-power devices are usually fitted with heat-dissipating common leads which have low-inductance flanges that are large enough to be mounted to the carrier with screws.

Another approach to grounding to thick metal carriers is the use of roll pins that are inserted under compression into holes drilled into the metal carrier. These pins must be properly plated so they may be soldered to the microstrip conductors after insertion. When working on substrates with massive metal ground-plane structures or carriers, it may be helpful to use a temperature-controlled hot plate to heat the heat sink or metal backplate to slightly below soldering temperature. Otherwise the heat flow away from the area being soldered and into the heat sink may prevent any reasonable soldering iron from ever doing a satisfactory soldering job. These methods are a bit difficult or specialized, so it is often easier to use double-clad PC board with eyelets for ground returns, and then laminate or otherwise attach the assembled board to the heat sink or carrier if required.

Some experimenters like to introduce a ground plane on the top side of the microstrip circuit, in addition to the usual underside ground plane. This may sometimes aid in isolating or shielding various portions of the circuit, but it may also introduce losses from coupling between conductors and adjacent grounds. If ground plane is added to the top side, it must be carefully bonded to the true ground plane below. This calls for bonding ties from top to bottom at intervals less than a quarter wave at the microwave frequency of the circuit. See Fig 24. Rivets or eyelets may be inserted at such intervals and soldered on top and bottom.

If the added ground plane is near the outer edges of the board, "edgewrap" may be used to bond top to bottom. This edgewrap consists of thin copper foil which

can be folded around the edges and soldered to both top and bottom ground planes. In effect it serves to extend the ground plane up and over the board edge to extend onto the top surface. Even with the edges wrapped, however, it may still be necessary to also add ties through the board if the extension of the ground plane projects more than a small part of a wavelength onto the top.

Although eyelets and rivets make for a neat appearance, it is also possible to use short pins of bare wire to bridge or tie top and bottom ground plane surfaces together. Snug clearance holes are simply drilled where required and the bare wire jumper inserted through the hole and soldered top and bottom, as shown in Fig 25. Once the wire is soldered, the projections of wire beyond the board surface are clipped off.

It is often possible to eliminate the need for ties through the board (called *vias*) by avoiding the use of top-side ground runs. Only circuit conductors are etched on

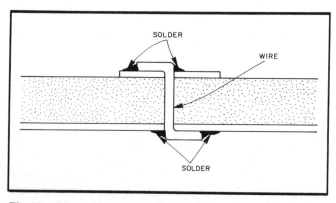

Fig 25—Short pieces of bare wire (sometimes called "Z wires") can be used to bond ground pads on top of the microstrip board to the ground plane.

the top side, and all grounds are carried to the back side. This will probably result in the circuit layout with the lowest loss, besides minimizing the number of holes that must be drilled in the substrate. Common leads for active devices are then carried to the ground plane with feed-through eyelets, as previously mentioned. Some low-frequency decoupling will usually be required, and this can be done with discrete bypass capacitors. Moreover, it is desirable to keep the back side of the board free of parts to permit easy mounting within an enclosure. In this case, surface-mount components are required (or standard components modified for surface mounting, as discussed above), and assembly must be restricted to the circuit side of the substrate.

The bias feeds to the device are decoupled at microwave with microstrip chokes and stubs. Grounded stubs, chip capacitors and resistors and any low-frequency decoupling capacitors all must also be returned to the ground plane. In the case of conventional decoupling capacitors (with wire leads) hollow eyelets are a convenient way to bring the lead to ground. Alternately, a simple clearance hole for the lead may suffice to bring the wire through to the ground plane for soldering (Fig 26).

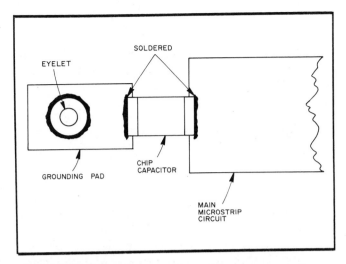

Fig 27—Chip capacitors can be soldered to a small pad; this pad is then connected to the ground plane with an eyelet.

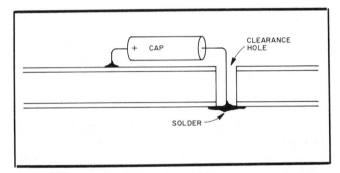

Fig 26—Hollow eyelets or simple clearance holes can be used to bring the leads of bypass capacitors to the ground plane.

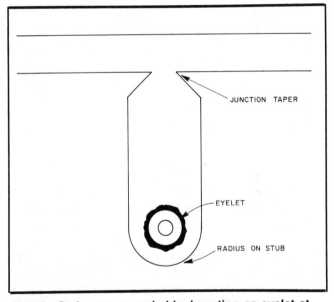

Fig 28—Stubs are grounded by inserting an eyelet at the location that produces the desired wavelength factor.

To ground chip parts, it is usually necessary to etch a small top-side island to provide sufficient surface area for soldering the ground side of the component and a feed-through eyelet to connect to the ground plane, as shown in Fig 27. Stubs are grounded by inserting an eyelet at the location that produces the wavelength factor required for desired electrical function of the stub, as shown in Fig 28. It is often desirable to cut a radius on the conductor forming the stub, adjacent to the grounding eyelet, to minimize the discontinuity at the feedthrough. The effective electrical length of a stub with such a radius is found by measuring to the eyelet center.

BIAS

Most circuit construction involves two basic concerns: provision for an RF path and dc bias on the active devices involved. In vacuum-tube work, bias generally refers to the voltage (usually negative) applied to the grid; in solid-state work, bias has become a generic term applying to any and all dc voltages supplied to the active devices. Thus transistors are supplied with both base and collector bias from the dc power supply (or supplies).

Both bipolar and FET devices are common in microwave designs, but each device requires different dc bias. Bipolar transistors require forward bias on the base-emitter junction in order to initiate current flow, while the collector is reverse biased as an output circuit. A bipolar transistor may be considered as two back-to-back diodes; from this it can be seen that a single power source can supply both the forward and reverse bias required by the device. It is common to find a single dc power source in many bipolar transistor circuits.

The operation of an FET is similar to that of a vacuum tube in that negative bias is required on the gate, while a positive potential is needed on the drain. Without gate bias, full drain current will flow in the FET channel. Insulated gate FETs (IGFETs or MOSFETs) permit the gate potential to swing both negative and positive without damage (within limits) but GaAsFETs used at microwave cannot tolerate much forward gate current without damage. Consequently, GaAsFET gates are biased negatively to establish the dc drain current and then not driven with signal levels that could cause gate conduction (or destruction!).

Supplying the gate with a negative potential while the drain is biased positive requires a dual power supply, if the common return (source) is to be directly grounded. If a resistor is inserted into the common source lead, in the manner of a cathode resistor in a vacuum tube, negative bias will be developed across it, so a single dc supply will suffice to bias the FET. This bias technique is not without problems, however, because instabilities in device operation can be readily introduced if the source is not tied directly to ground.

With the dc bias requirements in mind, methods of supplying the required voltages can be considered. The bias voltages must be supplied in parallel with the RF paths, but with a minimum of interaction or loading of the RF system. For the most part, RF paths function at fairly low impedances, so the dc bias may be introduced in the RF paths with high-impedance bridges. A common technique is the use of RF chokes to tie dc bias into the signal circuits.

Refer to Fig 29. Microstrip RF chokes are made with quarter-wave lengths of line which have an impedance considerably higher than the system impedance (Z_0, usually 50 ohms). It is common to use 100-ohm lines for chokes. Even higher impedances are useful, but may be difficult to etch since line widths become very small as impedances increase above 100 ohms. Another way to produce an RF choke is to wind a quarter wavelength of fine wire into a solenoid form using a small drill or nail as a form. This air-core coil can then be soldered into place on the microstrip substrate.

These RF chokes will appear as open circuits (or very high impedances) at one end if they are connected to RF ground at the other end a quarter wave away. In some circuits this can be a "hard" ground for both RF and dc, while in others it is only an RF ground produced by attaching a bypass capacitor at that point. Quarter-wave chokes are of course frequency sensitive since they are only a true

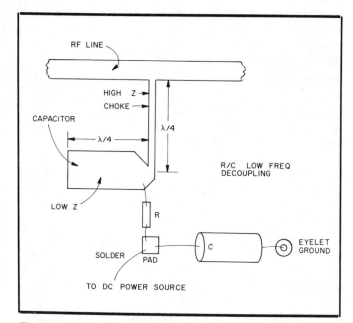

Fig 29—Microstrip RF chokes are made with quarter wavelengths of high-impedance line.

quarter wave long at one specific frequency. Degradation over narrow bandwidths will be slight, however, and can be largely ignored for amateur purposes.

Stability Considerations

RF chokes can be effectively used to inject dc voltages into the RF paths without loading the signal circuits. The chokes are connected to the bias supplies, with series resistors added (if needed) for voltage dropping or for decoupling. Additional bypassing is often required to decouple the bias lines at lower frequencies. Although the reactance of the quarter-wave chokes drops with lower frequency and the chokes degenerate toward short circuits at very low frequencies, the transistors supplying the microwave gain have considerably more inherent gain at lower frequencies than at the design frequency. For this reason, it is generally a more difficult problem to suppress the low-frequency gain of an amplifier than to develop gain in the desired passband. Many amplifier designs have produced satisfactory response in the desired passband, but they oscillate at some lower UHF or VHF frequency. It is extremely important to check the wideband stability of the circuit if unconditional stability is to be assured. Care in configuring the bias feeds can make or break an amplifier circuit in this respect.

One important fact to bear in mind when building active microwave circuits (those with gain) is that most microwave devices are inherently stable *when they are working in a 50-ohm circuit*. Without this stability it would be impossible to measure the S-parameters that characterize the device. This means that the device will operate without oscillation or stability problems if both input and output ports are supplied with 50-ohm loads at *all* frequencies, not only at the design frequency.

Resistors will satisfy this requirement, but RF chokes, filters and antennas will not! Obviously, open or short circuits do not serve as satisfactory 50-ohm loads. If matching networks or transmission lines and such circuitry form the RF interstage loads, it is important to make sure that the networks degenerate toward 50-ohm resistive loads at out-of-band frequencies, especially at the lower frequencies where troublesome parasitics usually lurk to catch the unwary.

One neat way to ensure this condition of degeneration is to top load the bias chokes with 50-ohm chip resistors where they attach to the RF paths, as shown in Fig 30. This makes the associated circuit see the 50-ohm resistor become more and more the total device load as the frequency lowers and the choke becomes more and more like a short circuit. This simple concept has salvaged many designs that suffered from out-of-band instability problems.

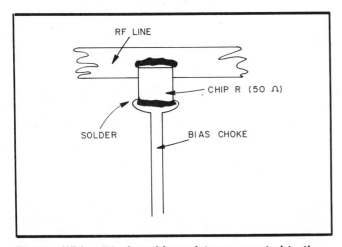

Fig 30—With a 50-ohm chip resistor connected to the RF path at the top of a choke, the circuit sees the load get closer and closer to 50 ohms at lower frequencies where the choke becomes a short circuit.

Other techniques used to ensure amplifier stability make use of shunt resistive loading at the input or output ports (or both ports) of the transistor. Sometimes small series "stopper" resistors are beneficial. Shunt feedback is also effective; this involves feeding back from the output to the input with a resistive feedback circuit (a blocking capacitor must be included to keep output bias isolated from the input). All of these techniques function by lowering the gain of the circuit at frequencies below the design frequency of the amplifier. Series feedback can be accomplished by adding a feedback element in the common lead of the device, but this may be a bit trickier to control—instability may actually be introduced instead of corrected.

The object, of course, is to reduce gain at out-of-band frequencies, or at frequencies where the device may tend to "take off" with parasitics. Suppressive measures should not influence operation within the desired passband, however. Lowering in-band gain may worsen noise figure as well, depending on the suppressive measures taken. All of this means that some insight and care is necessary when stabilizing an inherently troublesome design. It becomes obvious that there are advantages to using unconditionally stable active devices whenever possible.

Biasing Diodes

It should be mentioned that the operation of such "gainless" devices as the microwave diodes used in mixers and detectors can sometimes profit from dc bias. The detection threshold of both mixers and detectors can be improved to give better sensitivity by applying enough forward bias to overcome contact potential in the device. This means that the diode is biased almost to the point of current flow with no signal applied. Forward bias can also lower the amount of power required from the local oscillator in mixer applications, because without dc bias a portion of the LO power is used to overcome the diode contact potential. Bias may be supplied from a voltage source through series resistance to limit current flow with the usual decoupling and bypassing at microwave.

Typical Bias Circuit

It may now be helpful to review the dc bias circuit for a typical two-stage small-signal RF amplifier (Fig 31). Assuming the amplifier is to operate at 2 GHz, bipolar transistors such as the NEC64535 or Avantek AT41435 would be good choices for the active devices. The data sheet lists 8 volts at 10 mA as a suitable dc collector bias for small-signal operation. If the amplifier is to operate from a 12-V dc power source, a simple resistive voltage divider can be connected across the power supply to furnish collector voltage and base bias. Note that it is good practice to keep the power-supply voltage lower than the breakdown voltage of the transistor!

With the emitter tied directly to ground, a base voltage slightly greater than 0.7 volt will be required to turn the transistor on. This can also be supplied by the voltage divider, which then consists of three series-connected resistors across the power supply. It now is necessary to connect the two bias voltages to the transistor in the RF circuit.

The first step is to bridge the RF-input network to the transistor base with a feed from the dc-base-bias source. Since the RF circuit should not be upset or loaded, a quarter-wave choke will be used as an isolator between dc and RF, at the microwave design frequency. In microstrip, this is implemented with a 100-ohm line, a quarter wavelength long at 2 GHz. The top end of this choke (where it attaches to the RF path) must appear as a high impedance at 2 GHz, which means that the opposite end of the choke (a quarter wave away) must appear as an RF

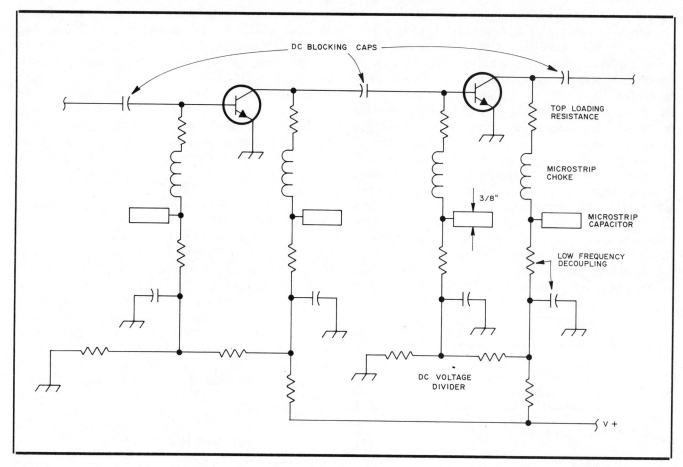

Fig 31—Two-stage small-signal RF amplifier used to illustrate dc biasing considerations. See text for details.

ground at 2 GHz. This calls for an RF bypass at the low end of the choke. A chip capacitor can be used for this bypass, but a microstrip capacitor can serve the same function. A low-impedance line can be used to form a capacitor, but a low-impedance quarter-wave line (stub) can be even more effective. This stub is left open-circuited so that it appears as a short circuit at its opposite end. This end becomes the point of attachment to the "cold" end of the bias feed choke, so an effective decoupling has been accomplished at 2 GHz. If we did not need to worry about out-of-band decoupling, the bypassed low end of the bias choke could now be connected to the source of the base bias voltage, and a similar decoupling network arranged for the collector circuit to finish the design. If nothing is done to suppress the inherently high gain of the transistor at low frequencies, however, the circuit will probably oscillate at frequency lower than the intended design frequency.

To solve this problem, an additional decoupling network can be added in the bias feed path, consisting of a series resistor and low-frequency bypass capacitor, so that the microwave decoupling is augmented by low-frequency decoupling. A similar circuit can be used to feed the collector, accounting for the voltage drop across the decoupling resistor passing the collector current. If this voltage drop is a problem, a ferrite bead can be used

instead of the resistor. In principle, of course, the low-frequency decoupling could be implemented in microstrip, but the physical size of quarter-wave lines at low frequencies makes such an approach impractical.

The complete two-stage amplifier shown in Fig 31 uses the above bias arrangement. Individual voltage dividers are used for each stage, so that collector and base voltages may be scaled for each stage if desired. This is especially useful if different transistor types are used in the two stages. Microwave decoupling by means of microstrip lines appears closest to the RF circuit, with low-frequency decoupling at the cold end of the microwave network. Remember that the microwave decoupling is completely ineffective at low frequencies.

One additional element is added for enhanced stability: the 50-ohm top-loading resistors where the microwave chokes attach to the signal path. These resistors steer the networks toward the center of the Smith Chart as the eventual degenerative condition at low frequencies.

INTERCONNECTIONS

Although considerable circuitry can be arranged on a microstrip substrate or carrier, sooner or later this circuit must be interfaced with the outside world. Circuit inputs and outputs and power interconnections must be extended beyond the confines of the substrate. In the case of power leads, decoupling is the main element of concern, so that signals or "trash" do not enter or leave through the power leads. Feed-through filters, series chokes and shunt-bypass capacitors or coaxial-cable power feeds may be used, depending on the situation, to bring bias voltages to a microstrip circuit. It is important to be sure that adequate decoupling is included on bias feeds to filter on a broadband basis, not just at the design frequency of the RF circuit involved.

RF inputs and outputs (and any IF or sampling outputs) will usually be connected to a microstrip board using coaxial connectors. Here it is important to select connectors that exhibit a constant impedance within all parts of the connector. Unfortunately, connectors in the so-called "UHF" series (PL-259 and SO-239) are not very satisfactory in this regard. Better results are obtained from the SMA series; these connectors are very suitable for general microwave use unless power levels are high enough to require type N connectors. Bayonet-type connectors should be avoided at microwave; screw-on types are mandatory for reliable connection with low SWR. In a few cases, waveguide-to-microstrip transitions may be involved, requiring specialized hardware.

Circuits at lower frequencies will often have a coax connector attached to the wall of a cabinet or enclosure and then a length of wire or coax cable run to the circuit board or other input hardware, which may even be some

distance away. This is a common arrangement for antenna inputs on HF communications receivers. At microwave, this technique introduces too many discontinuities and too much loss at circuit inputs, and should be avoided. A much better approach is to mount the RF connector directly to the substrate without introducing any unwarranted feed-line length between connector and input device.

When interfacing microstrip to coaxial cables with RF connectors, the object is to make as smooth and gentle a transition as possible. No impedance bump should be created, and insertion loss caused by the connector should be minimized. Internal dimensions of the SMA connector are carefully controlled so that a constant impedance is retained through the connector. At the connector/microstrip interface, the connector center conductor must "flow" onto the microstrip line. This is enhanced by a smooth solder fillet at the joint. Connectors with tab center conductor exits are most adaptable to edge connection to microstrip, while round center conductors mate well with microstrip lines when using right-angle connection techniques. SMA connectors are available in both versions.

In addition to maintaining a smooth center-conductor path through the connector and onto the microstrip, it is important to carry the connector outer shell ground onto the microstrip ground plane if low SWR is to be maintained. This is easier to accomplish with right-angle connectors than with edge connectors. Refer to Fig 32. The

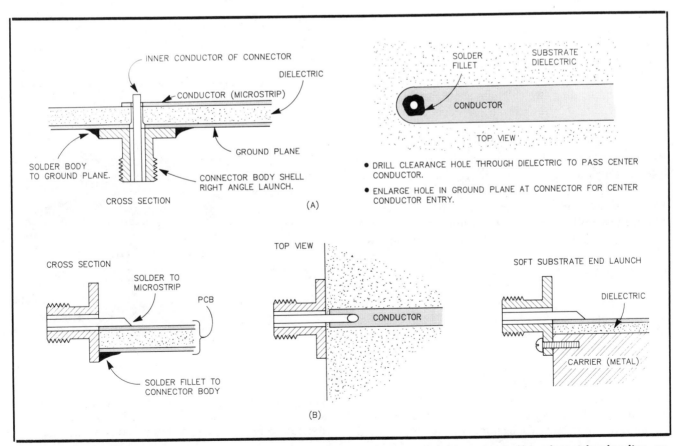

Fig 32—SMA connectors can be mounted with their center conductors at right angles to the microstrip circuitry, as shown at A, or in line, as shown at B.

connector is attached from the ground-plane side, with the body shell soldered around its perimeter to the ground plane. The center conductor pin extends through the board dielectric to reach the microstrip circuit conductor on top. Removing a small circular area of ground plane at the point of entry of the center conductor will serve to maintain a constant impedance into and through the board.

Right-angle connectors also make it easy to combine the circuit connection with a simple method of mounting the microstrip assembly into an enclosure. Since the SMA connector flange is soldered to the microstrip ground plane, the flange provides an efficient way of assuring a good interface between connector shell and microstrip ground, while the connector body nuts can be used to secure the the assembly into an enclosure. This is effective even with plastic enclosures, because the important system ground is from connector shell to microstrip ground plane, and this ground should be firmly connected at both input and output. A metal enclosure does provide the advantage of shielding the open face of the microstrip assembly, but ground continuity should be established independent of the enclosure.

If all RF connectors are introduced at right angles to the ground plane, the board is easy to fit into an enclosure, as shown in Fig 33. There may be occasions, however, where edge-mounted connectors must be used, as shown in Fig 34. These connectors are mounted by soldering the connector center conductor to the microstrip line; the microstrip must be brought to the edge of the board. The connector ground flange must be soldered to the edge of the ground plane. A solder bead may then be used to support the connector shell at the ground plane. It may be desirable to use a metal angle bracket for added support, giving more surface to solder the connector to the ground plane. The ground plane on most board stock is only a thin copper cladding, which limits connector support. A better mechanical arrangement for edge connectors is possible where soft-substrate is being used, since here the carrier/ground plane may be 1/8 or 1/4 inch thick. In this case, the connector shell can be attached with small screws, at least along one edge. The carrier is usually aluminum, so soldering is ruled out and a pressure-contact ground may deteriorate with time. In general, it is more difficult to obtain a low SWR with edge-connection launch methods. Also, if connectors are attached on more than one edge of the board (Fig 35), the task of mounting the board in an enclosure can become very complicated.

In some cases coaxial cable may be soldered directly to the microstrip circuit, without intervening connectors. Unless the outer shell or braid of the cable can be maintained as a cylinder intersecting the ground plane, and soldered all around, an impedance bump will be created which will affect SWR. Thus, laying the cable flat (parallel to the ground plane at the point of entry to the microstrip) should be avoided, as it is almost impossible to retain a constant impedance with the outer conductor ground. Combing the braid and twisting it into a lead to be soldered

Fig 33—If the RF connectors are mounted through the circuit board, the assembly can be attached to its enclosure with the connector mounting hardware.

Fig 34—There may be occasions when edge-mounted connectors are most convenient.

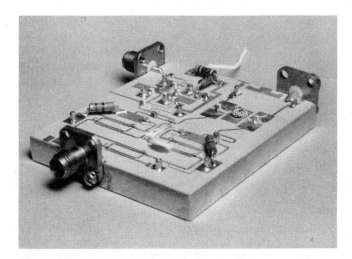

Fig 35—If connectors are attached to more than one edge of the microstrip circuit board it can be very difficult to mount the board in an enclosure.

to the ground plane or to a solder lug is very unsatisfactory. With care, it may be possible to interface semi-rigid cable by approaching at a right angle to the ground plane while retaining the outer shell concentricity to simulate a right-angle connector, but interfacing with RF connectors is much easier and more satisfactory.

Bias voltage (dc power) is usually fed to a microstrip circuit from a separate power supply. A single voltage is often all that is required to bias bipolar devices, since voltage dividers can be provided on the microwave substrate. The requirements for bringing dc bias into the enclosure are less stringent than for the RF connectors, so connector requirements are less critical. For convenience, however, it is often possible to bring a supply voltage to the substrate with another coaxial connector. With the "hot" side fed on the center conductor and the ground carrying the return, a degree of built-in power-supply shielding is obtained when the bias voltage is fed over coaxial cable. Coaxial multipin connectors can be used if more than one bias voltage may be needed.

MICROSTRIP ARTWORK

The process used for making microstrip substrates is very similar to making printed-circuit boards. Graphic arts materials and processes are used to produce templates that permit mass duplication of microstrip circuits. The electrical circuit must first be designed and translated into a planar layout in artwork form. This is usually produced at a scale larger than the final etched circuit so that the artwork can be photographically reduced to make a negative (or positive) that becomes the working tool for exposing and etching the copper-clad circuit boards. Creating the artwork at large scale serves to reduce any inaccuracies in layout by the reduction factor when the working negative is produced (a 0.1-inch error on a $4\times$ layout becomes a 0.025-inch error on the $1\times$ finished product). The same concept is applied when art is produced for integrated circuits; the original IC artwork is many feet wide, and this original is tremendously reduced before fabrication. The accuracy required for microstrip is seldom that extreme, and a reduction of 4 to 10 times is more than adequate. This in turn says something about the size of the artwork and also about the size of the working negative.

Very few hobbyists have copy cameras capable of producing negatives larger than 4×5 inches, and this can restrict microstrip substrate size. Fortunately, commercial graphics-arts photographers can make larger working negatives at reasonable cost, so the negative size need not be a major factor in determining the microstrip circuit area. Alternatively, projects may be designed as a series of small substrates which can be individually assembled and tested, then interconnected, thereby keeping substrate areas within practical bounds.

In addition to improving the accuracy of a layout by working with a scaling factor for the artwork, it is usually more comfortable to draw or cut silhouettes that are an inch or two in size than to try working with minuscule life-size layouts. This is particularly true at frequencies above 3 or 4 GHz or with high-dielectric substrate materials where the finished life-size circuit can be quite small indeed.

Coloring Book Art

Creating the artwork itself is a task where ingenuity can pay off. When the electrical design is complete, input and output matching circuits for the active devices, interconnections and bias feeds will have been determined. These must now be created in the form of microstrip art. One way to do this is to simply draw the circuit on paper, first outlining the conductors and then filling them in with a wick pen (Fig 36). The density and uniformity of such artwork silhouettes can often be improved by making a copy on a recent vintage photocopy machine.

While this may seem as a very rudimentary technique for creating artwork, its very simplicity makes it valuable. Many complex circuit substrates have been developed with this method, and the accuracy is limited only by the attention and care given to the process. Even complex circuits can be made from individual paper layouts by merely photocopying, cutting and pasting.

Fig 36—Layouts for microstrip circuits can be drawn by hand with a wick pen.

Tape Layouts

Another very suitable technique for layout is to use opaque tape, either plastic or paper, with an adhesive backing that will adhere to a transparent plastic sheet (Fig 37). The tape may be cut to size with knife or scissors before sticking it to the layout sheet. Many graphics-arts vendors furnish such tape in various widths suitable for lines of common impedances. For example, 0.10-inch-wide tape is correct for 50-ohm lines on 1/16-inch-thick glass-epoxy circuit board. Some vendors also provide cutouts such as "bull's-eyes" of various diameters—these are useful for spotting holes to be drilled or locating eyelets.

Fig 37—Microstrip layouts can also be made with opaque tape.

Fig 38—A professional method for producing microstrip layouts is to use Rubylith. After the Rubylith is cut with a sharp knife, the unused sections are simply peeled off.

Other precut forms include radiused corners, IC pinouts and similar useful objects. These materials markedly reduce the amount of cutting and trimming and are very useful for anyone planning to do more than a casual microstrip layout.

Rubylith

Another professional method for producing artwork is to use Rubylith, which is a clear plastic sheet with an adhesive-backed translucent plastic layer (the layer is usually red). The circuit is outlined on this material and then the red layer is cut with a sharp knife. See Fig 38. After the layer is cut, the unused portions are simply peeled off. Companion red plastic tape is also available for patching, correcting mistakes or supplementing the layout.

Since commercial process photographic films are blind to red, the portions of the layout where the red layer remains will photograph as black in the copy. Thus either black or red tape will show up as black on the working template. Also, since the process film is extremely sensitive to blue, anything appearing on the artwork in blue color will vanish in the copy negative.

Cue Marks

It is a good idea to include a dimension reference directly on the template to indicate the reduction scaling factor being used. This reference should be placed somewhere beyond the boundaries of the microstrip circuit. This may be as simple as drawing a line which will be 1 inch long on the final template. This simple indicator will give a quick check that the artwork has been correctly reduced when copied.

Another indicator that should be included in the artwork is an alignment reference. Since the artwork template must be carefully positioned onto the substrate board when exposing the photo resist during successive steps of fabrication, registration marks or corner outlines should be added to the layout art to define the intended board edges (Fig 39). These then serve as trim lines when the board is cut to final size. Alternatively, the board may be cut to the exact finished size of the substrate before exposing and etching—in this case the artwork outline cue marks will allow exact positioning of the template on the unexposed board.

With conventional glass/epoxy board materials used as microstrip, drilling and shearing is done after etching, so registration of the template to a drilling plan is usually not required. Bull's-eyes and other hole-plan indicators included on the artwork become the template for drilling and cutting. In the (rare) case where a soft substrate material is used on a carrier, machining is done before etching and exact registration of the template is mandatory. This can be implemented with registration holes in the template which fit over registration pins in the substrate. Well-made artwork is essential for successful microstrip board fabrication (Fig 40).

Experimenters who create a large number of substrates are advised to name or otherwise identify the artwork so that the identification appears in the negative. Revision letters are also advisable so that final circuits are readily identified. This makes it easy to identify or locate the correct templates for a given substrate at some future time.

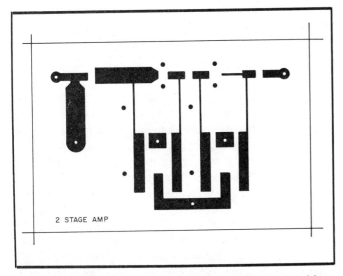

Fig 39—Registration marks or corner outlines should be included in the board layout to facilitate the correct positioning of the layout on the substrate.

Fig 40—A good microstrip board starts with well-made artwork.

ETCHING MICROSTRIP CIRCUITS

Once the electrical design for a microstrip circuit is done and the design has been translated into artwork form (usually resulting in artwork that is scaled several times larger than the finished substrate), the artwork must be photographically reduced to make working templates for the actual production of circuit boards. The reduction should result in templates which are accurate and dimensionally correct. The circuit must then be transferred to the substrate—with microstrip, this is best done by photographic methods.

Essentially, the PC-board copper surface is photosensitized, so that an exposure and development process can transfer the artwork to the copper. This is followed by an etching step which removes copper in regions where it is unwanted and (ideally) retains copper in areas representing the desired microstrip circuit.

Many methods have evolved for etching home-brew PC boards. Some of these methods are quite primitive and some are quite exotic. At one extreme are the professional spray etching methods used to process high-dielectric soft substrate materials; these techniques are hardly economically feasible for hobby use. At the other extreme are techniques of painting resist traces directly on the board copper to make a one-of-a-kind crude circuit to be etched. Some attempts even avoid the etching step by carving and peeling the copper with knife or router, but this is a difficult task that usually meets with only limited success.

Certainly, for microstrip work, it is obvious that a photographic template (negative or positive, as required) should be used to transfer the circuit to the substrate, and that the board copper should be etched (not peeled) to produce the microstrip tracks. The required precision rules out simplistic methods of painting or taping directly on the copper-clad board. This circuit transfer through the etching phase is not particularly difficult, but it does entail a series of steps which must be followed with a degree of fastidiousness if success is to be ensured.

Cleaning

The first step in the transfer sequence involves cleaning the copper board surfaces to remove oxides and grease. Household kitchen scouring cleansers work well for this. The copper should not be scratched or abraded, so a nonabrasive cleaner must be used. The board should then be carefully washed and dried (baking at low heat will remove all traces of moisture). Etching failures can often be traced to insufficient cleaning, and the copper surface should not be touched once it has been cleaned. The board should be cleaned just before it is coated with etch resist, so that no oxidation occurs between cleansing and resist application.

Coating

The photosensitive resist is a coating material that becomes resistant to an etching solution after the coating is exposed to ultraviolet light. Photo resists, developers and suitable etchants (and other related materials) are available from such firms as Kodak, Kepro and others. Both negative and positive forms of resist exist; after exposure to ultraviolet light, one becomes soluble in the developer, the other insoluble. This makes it possible to work with either negative or positive artwork templates, depending on the type of resist used. Negative artwork films will have clear areas for regions to be retained in the copper and opaque areas where copper is to be removed. Conversely, positive artwork templates will be transparent in regions where copper is to be removed and opaque where copper will be retained.

The cleansed substrate board can be coated by dipping or immersing the board into the resist solution, then letting the board drain dry vertically. An additional dip followed by draining with the board rotated 90 degrees vertically can help produce an even coating. Another way to coat is by spray painting the resist onto the board. Both sides of the board must be coated, since the copper on the ground-plane side must not be removed in the etching solution. To conserve resist material, the ground-plane surface may be completely covered with masking tape or adhesive plastic to prevent the etchant from affecting it. The resist coating should be as uniform as possible, of equal thickness throughout. Commercial enterprises often use a "spincoating" technique, where a coated board is rotated on a turntable; this may give a more uniform coat. When coating both sides, it may be convenient to spray and dry one side at a time, rather than to attempt to coat both surfaces simultaneously. Finally, the coated board should be completely dried by baking for a few minutes at about 90 degrees.

Another type of resist is available as a photosensitive plastic film that can be pressed or laminated onto the board copper. Some vendors can supply PC board materials already coated with resist. This might appeal to those who feel that the above coating procedure is a bit over-ambitious.

Photographically Copying Artwork

The choice of negative or positive resist and template is affected by a few factors. The resist and artwork must of course be matched, because the desired end result is to retain copper as the microstrip circuit and etch away the copper in non-circuit areas. There are advantages and disadvantages to either type of resist, so it may be wise to have both negative and positive photo templates made when photographically copying the artwork.

Some experimenters will be able to handle the photographic work of copying, since the process is not complicated, but it does require the use of camera equipment. High-contrast films must be used, and the reduction factor must be carefully established so that the copy negative will be exactly the correct size.

If a commercial service is used, specify that templates be made with "emulsion down" so that the most intimate contact may be ensured between template and copper at the time of resist exposure. Commercial copy films are rather thick, and introducing this film thickness into the exposure path may serve to diminish accuracy by dispersing some of the light that passes through the artwork when exposing the resist. This can be avoided by placing the film with emulsion side closest to the copper when making the ultraviolet exposure. This is the same concept applied to contact printing conventional photographs.

Exposure

Coated boards are photosensitive and should be protected from light (especially sunlight or ultraviolet sources) until ready for the desired exposure. At this stage, the film template is placed, emulsion down, onto the sensitized board and the two are carefully pressed or sand-wiched together (Fig 41). This is best done in a vacuum printing frame, but can be accomplished with a photographic printing frame salvaged from darkroom use. The artwork must be aligned to the substrate if any registration is critical before exposure.

Actual exposures may run several seconds, even minutes, depending on the light source and intensity. It may even be possible to use sunlight (outdoors, not passed through window glass) for the exposure, especially if other forms of ultraviolet-rich light are unavailable. Experience will be the best teacher in judging exposures, so a few trial runs may be appropriate before attempting the "real thing" in earnest.

To ensure that the ground-plane copper surface will not be removed during etching, it is necessary to expose this side of the board to ultraviolet light (without masking) after the microstrip circuit side has been exposed through the template. (This step is avoided if the ground plane has been covered with plastic or tape.) Since the changes in the resist coating become visible only after it is developed (the coating does not visibly change after exposure), a mark or other way of identifying circuit and ground plane sides of the board should be added when the board is exposed.

Fig 41—Good contact between the board and the template can be assured by using a contact printing frame.

Developing

The resist must be developed before the board can be etched. During the developing process, unexposed resist is removed by a solvent and washed away. Toluene can be used as a developer for most resist products; alternately, a product sold by the manufacturer of the resist can be used. After the resist is developed, the board must be dried and then inspected to see that the microstrip (and other) patterns are satisfactory and undamaged. The inspection is easier if the remaining resist is dyed to make it more visible for inspection. Vendors such as Kodak and Kepro can supply suitable developers and rinses for associated photo resists. Be sure to heed any safety and health precautions when handling developers and etchants. [Editor's Note: As with any chemical solvent, avoid skin contact and ensure adequate ventilation of the work area. Obtain more detailed handling instructions from a ''material safety data sheet,'' which should be available from the substance manufacturer.]

After the unwanted resist is removed, the next step is to remove the unwanted copper from the board. This is done with an etching solution that dissolves the copper where there is no resist. Remember that copper is to be retained intact on the entire back side of the board, as this forms the necessary ground plane!

Etching

Suitable etchants are ferric chloride or ammonium persulfate which can be obtained in liquid form and then mixed with water according to the supplier's instructions. The etchant is poured into a suitable tray and heated to approximately 100°F to speed up its activity. The circuit board is then immersed into the solution (often using a support frame) and inspected every few minutes to observe

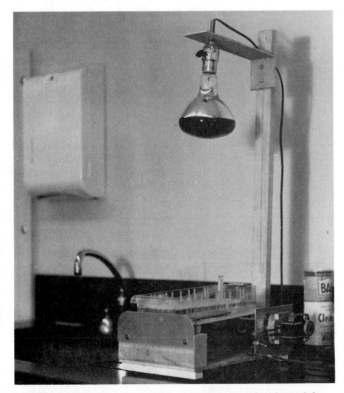

Fig 42—The etchant should be heated and agitated for best results. Here, a heat lamp keeps the etchant bath between 90 and 115°F, and the tray for the bath is rocked at one end by a motor driving an eccentric disc.

the etching process (Fig 42). As with photographic processing, agitating the solution will help ensure a uniform etch. Etching must remove copper from unwanted regions without being allowed to continue to the point of undercutting the circuit edges. Excess etching can narrow transmission lines and thereby raise their impedance.

When etching is complete, the board should be washed and dried. The resist remaining on the copper can be left until the board is to be used (to protect the copper) or washed off with solvent. Finally, machining can now be done, such as shearing the board to size, drilling holes and inserting eyelets and generally getting the board ready for component assembly.

Accuracy

If the preceding techniques of coating, exposing and etching a copper-clad substrate are applied with reasonable care, circuit tracks can be repeatedly etched with accuracies approaching a thousandth of an inch. This is more than sufficient to make a planned 50-ohm line etch out to be a 50-ohm line on the substrate. A 150-ohm line might etch out as slightly higher or lower by a few percent, but this is not too important for creating an RF choke. Restricting the electrical design to impedance values in the range of 10 to 100 ohms will ensure that etched lines are adequately accurate.

Using these methods at the higher microwave frequencies it may be impractical to attempt to make very complicated circuits, (such as a multi-section Lange interdigitated coupler, for example), but then such a broadband device should seldom be chosen for a hobby microwave project anyway. A little common sense and foresight in the electrical design phase will result in microstrip circuits that can be readily translated into hardware using amateur methods.

ASSEMBLY OF MICROSTRIP SUBSTRATES

After etching has been completed, the next step is to assemble the substrate. See Fig 43. For the most part, this is done by soldering grounds, feed-throughs, connectors and components onto the microstrip traces. A light hand is required for all this soldering activity, and it is wise to do the soldering in a defined sequence.

Connectors, such as the preferred SMA coaxial fittings, should be soldered rather than bolted to the substrate. This means running a solder bead completely around the connector shell to mechanically as well as electrically attach the connector shell to the ground plane. Right-angle connection makes this an easy operation, since the entire connector shell sits on the ground plane. Edge connection permits only part of the shell to be soldered to the ground, unless a bracket or mounting lip is added.

Because the connector represents a sizable heat sink, soldering should be done with a fairly large soldering iron, not a small pencil iron. This means that it is a good idea to attach the connectors early in the assembly sequence when high heat levels will not effect other board com-

Fig 43—Assembly can begin after the microstrip board is etched.

It is helpful to tack solder one end of a chip while holding the chip in place on the microstrip with the probe. The other end of the chip part is then more carefully soldered to form the desired fillet, without applying heat long enough to melt the opposite end. If a satisfactory fillet is not quickly formed, it is best to remove the iron, let the joint cool a bit, then reapply the iron to reform the fillet. This intermittent soldering helps prevent the opposite "holding" joint from softening so the chip slides from its desired position on the microstrip circuit. Once the fillet is satisfactorily formed, the original end may be resoldered to produce a smooth joint at that end also. The technique is easier to master than to describe, and with care the mortality rate in soldering chip parts will be minimal. Some commercial houses use special low melting-temperature solders, but ordinary tin/lead radio solders are generally suitable (and more readily available).

Active components, such as diodes and transistors, should not be attached to the substrate until all passive parts have been soldered. This will minimize the amount of heat to which the active devices are exposed. Excess lead lengths should be carefully trimmed and the parts should be held in place with tweezers or a similar tool that will help heat sink the part while soldering. Allow the part to cool between soldering operations, especially if more than one pass is required to secure a given lead. Remember that active devices (especially FETs) can be damaged by static discharge, so keep the soldering iron, the operator and the work surface properly grounded (Fig 44). A bit of common sense and care when soldering parts to the substrate can avoid troubleshooting part failures and rework later in the project.

Sometimes special very low-temperature indium solders are suggested for microstrip work, but these can create problems of their own during the life cycle of the hardware. Conductive epoxies should be avoided wherever

ponents (since they are not on the board yet!).

Vias and other "pass through" connections to the ground plane (including the eyelets used to carry microstrip grounds and the emitter returns of transistors) should all be soldered in early phases of the assembly. On the circuit side of the board the amount of heat sink presented is usually minimal, but the ground-plane copper covers a large area and thus acts as a large heat sink which again calls for a reasonable iron wattage.

Once the connectors and other large bulk components have been soldered, smaller components should be attached with a pencil iron. Chip components in particular should be delicately soldered, with care taken to form smooth fillets without overheating the parts. It may be helpful to improvise a "holding tool" such as a wooden probe to help hold chip parts in position while soldering. It can help to first tin the microstrip copper at places where chip components are to be attached to improve solder flow when forming fillets.

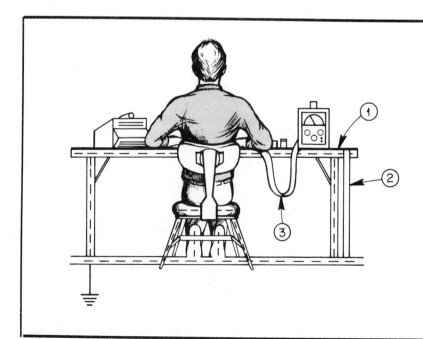

Fig 44—During circuit assembly, proper grounding is essential to avoid damaging active devices. Here is a typical static-safe work station. At 1, a conductive sheet covers the bench-top work area. At 2, a strap connects the work area to earth ground. At 3, is a grounded wrist strap in contact with skin.

it is at all practical to solder. An unsoldered, bolted-together junction should never be used for electrical RF continuity—a soldered joint is necessary for long-term reliability. Care at the assembly stage can prevent insidious corrosion problems or failures later in the life of the equipment.

Flux residue should be removed from the finished assembly. Sometimes a coating of clear acrylic is sprayed over a finished unit, but this can modify the electrical performance of some microwave circuits, so a trial test should be made before and after spraying to ensure that electrical parameters are not compromised. The acrylic can also make any future unsoldering or part removal at bit more messy.

The assembled substrate is now ready for testing or tuning (if required) before it is mounted in an enclosure. If the instructions given here are followed with care, a finished project should be produced to the complete satisfaction of the builder.

HINTS AND NOTES

Here are some miscellaneous construction ideas, notes and hints that are the results of working in the microwave field at the hobby level for many years. While these items did not seem to fit directly into the topics of previous discussion, they may be of value to experimenters.

Microstrip L/C

Transmission-line theory states that a transmission line can be represented as series inductance and shunt capacitance. The line impedance is then equal to the square root of the L/C ratio. A true transmission line is composed of distributed capacitance and inductance, but it is also possible to approximate a transmission line with lumped series inductors and shunt capacitors. Delay lines have been fabricated in this way, and the smaller the increment of L and C the more the line approximates a true transmission line.

If a transmission line is terminated in its characteristic

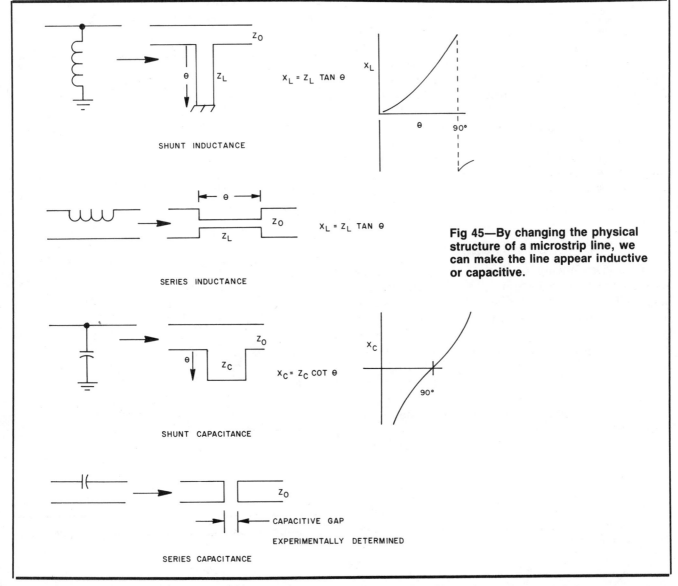

Fig 45—By changing the physical structure of a microstrip line, we can make the line appear inductive or capacitive.

impedance, no standing waves are created, and the line is "flat"; a signal propagating along the line is smoothly attenuated by the various losses in the line. By changing the L/C ratio in the line, we can make it look more like an inductor or a capacitor. Refer to Fig 45. To make the line appear inductive, we reduce the amount of shunt capacitance (this is easier than increasing its series inductance). This can be done by making the line width narrower, thereby reducing the area of the conductor appearing over the ground plane—just like making smaller plates on a capacitor. For a given series inductance, lowering the shunt capacitance makes the line look more inductive, and raises its impedance. Microstrip *inductors* are made with *high-impedance* lines. Conversely, since the series inductance is difficult to adjust, a line is made to appear capacitive by increasing the shunt capacitance for a given series inductance. This is done by making the line wider (increasing the size of the capacitor plate relative to the ground plane). This lowers the line impedance. Thus microstrip *capacitors* are made from *low-impedance* lines. A moment's reflection will reveal that it is easier to make a shunt microstrip capacitor than a series capacitor. However, inductors can be made in both series or shunt forms.

After much discussion about avoiding bumps and impedance changes along transmission lines, we should mention that the discontinuity encountered when a shunt capacitor is connected to a transmission line can be improved by balancing the capacitor across both sides of the line. Instead of one large capacitor hanging unbalanced on one side of the line, it is smoother to make two capacitors, each half the capacitance value, and attach them opposite one another to balance the line. Further, because capacitors are best made from low-impedance lines, they can be tapered at the point of attachment to the signal line. These are small points, but in microstrip, every little bit helps!

Device Impedances

Data sheets usually specify the four S-parameters as vectors with both magnitude and phase. In particular, the input and output values can be conveniently translated from vectors to impedances on a Smith Chart. These can be read as resistance components together with a reactance, which can be inductive or capacitive, depending on the frequency. Both components can vary over the frequency range of the device, so design usually first concentrates on the values at the operating frequency. The values read on the impedance Smith Chart represent series resistance and reactance.

If the device is inductive at the intended design frequency, conjugate capacitance is needed to tune out the inductance. Series capacitance is hard to make, so it is more convenient to use a shunt capacitance. This means that the series device parameters should be converted to equivalent parallel values; this then represents the shunt circuit of the device. If the series Smith Chart form is used, $R_s + jX_s$

has been determined; this is then changed to the equivalent $R_p + jX_p$. Once the parallel reactance is known, the reactive component can be tuned out with shunt $-X_p$ (see Fig 46).

In a similar manner, if the device is capacitive, series inductance can be used to tune out the series reactance. This can be created as series microstrip inductance, so the series device parameters can be used directly.

It is sometimes possible to series match into reactive devices with series line sections driven from a 50-ohm source, remembering that lines shorter than a quarter wave appear capacitive, longer lines appear inductive and quarter-wave lines appear resistive.

Both impedance and admittance versions of the Smith Chart are available, and a convenient version combines both on a single sheet, called an immittance chart. One form may be most convenient at a given time, depending on whether the series or the parallel circuits are being studied.

While the above discussion implies that matching to the device can be done with network L-sections, more flexibility is provided by pi-sections. In a pi network, three elements can be varied, and this flexibility has given the pi network the reputation of the network to use to match

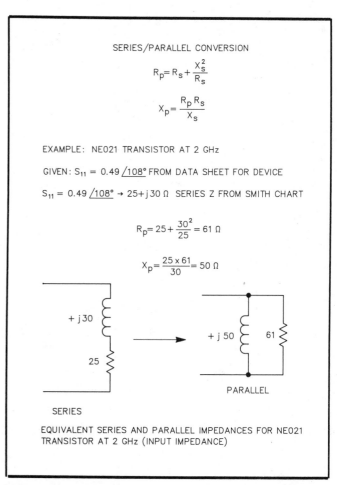

SERIES/PARALLEL CONVERSION

$$R_p = R_s + \frac{X_s^2}{R_s}$$

$$X_p = \frac{R_p R_s}{X_s}$$

EXAMPLE: NE021 TRANSISTOR AT 2 GHz

GIVEN: $S_{11} = 0.49 \underline{/108°}$ FROM DATA SHEET FOR DEVICE

$S_{11} = 0.49 \underline{/108°} \rightarrow 25 + j30\ \Omega$ SERIES Z FROM SMITH CHART

$$R_p = 25 + \frac{30^2}{25} = 61\ \Omega$$

$$X_p = \frac{25 \times 61}{30} = 50\ \Omega$$

SERIES

PARALLEL

EQUIVALENT SERIES AND PARALLEL IMPEDANCES FOR NE021 TRANSISTOR AT 2 GHz (INPUT IMPEDANCE)

Fig 46—Converting a series impedance to its parallel equivalent.

"anything to anything." However, if pi sections are used to tune both input and output of a transistor, the capacitance values must be selected carefully. It is possible to adjust an improperly designed pi network to the point where the device will break into oscillation.

Microstrip Filters

Many microwave experimenters fabricate RF band-pass filters using cavity or helical resonators, but it is also possible to make very satisfactory filters on microstrip. Low-impedance line sections with lengths less than a quarter wave are used as capacitive stubs. Lengths of one-eighth wave are very useful; at that length, the stub reactance is equal to its line impedance. Thus, a 1/8th-wavelength of 30-ohm stub will have a reactance of $-j30$ ohms.

Refer to Fig 47. If quarter-wave grounded lines are used, they act as parallel tuned circuits or resonators. The Q of the circuit will be limited by the microstrip dielectric losses, but it can approach 100. Ungrounded half-wave lines appear as resonators; quarter-wave and half-wave lines can be coupled together to function as band-pass filters. A half-wave line can be connected between two grounded quarter-wave lines to make a three-pole filter. The quarter-wave grounded lines are tapped at the 50-ohm point along their sides to provide input and output ports. Another microstrip filter uses only quarter-wave sections, with the center line inverted to facilitate coupling. The coupling factor ("K") is largely determined by the space between the edges of the coupled lines, so the resonators are made of closely spaced low-impedance lines.

As an experiment, a three-pole 2-GHz filter was made with three quarter-wave resonators on a 1.5×2-inch glass epoxy board. The 25-ohm resonators were less than 1 inch long, and they were grounded with eyelets. Low loss SMA connectors were attached to the input and output taps. The center frequency of the filter was adjusted by cutting equal amounts off each resonator at the open end. All three resonators were trimmed so that they all had the same resonant frequency.

The measured 1-dB bandwidth was 100 MHz, the 3-dB bandwidth was 200 MHz and the 10-dB width was less than 500 MHz. The skirts continued down to -30 dB about 800 MHz from center. The insertion loss was less than 3 dB.

This filter was used between a preamplifier and a

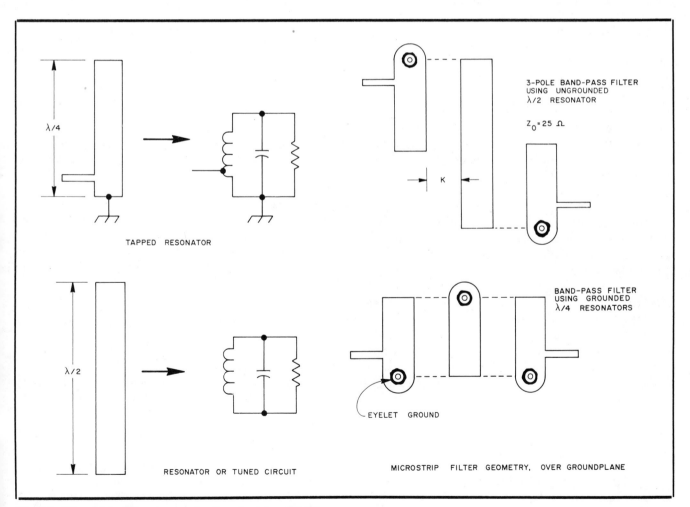

Fig 47—Microstrip filter concepts. See text for details.

down-converter to minimize UHF pickup caused by the wide inherent bandwidth of the preamplifier. Filtering reduced the level of the UHF signals that reached the down-converter mixer section. Inserting this filter between the antenna and the input to the preamplifier was undesirable because of the 3-dB loss; this would kill the system noise figure. Locating the filter between the preamplifier and the down-converter made a very satisfactory system.

Drilling Substrates

During the substrate layout phase, it is a good idea to spot the locations where holes will be drilled after etching. The etched substrate can serve as a drilling template as well. Holes can be spotted on the artwork with bull's-eye patterns or tape. After etching these will appear as copper "donuts"—metal rings with empty centers. These rings work very effectively to steer the drill into the desired center spot, much as centerpunching functions to center a drill bit. These donuts are particularly useful for spotting holes for the grounding eyelets under the common leads of transistors. For large copper areas such as the ground plane or stubs, the same result is secured by leaving small round clear spots in the layouts. The donut locator need not be the same size as the drilled hole, since it merely serves to locate the center of the hole to be drilled, but it is best to have the hole in the donut (after etching) a bit smaller than the drill size if it is to properly steer the drill bit. Otherwise the bit can wobble around when seeking a center.

Spotting hole locations with an opaque dot on the artwork will result in a copper "pimple" on the substrate after etching. While this may define the hole location correctly, the copper bump will make the drill bit walk away from the intended center rather than steering it to the center.

Conventional high-speed steel drill bits will drill holes in glass/epoxy substrate materials, and have some degree of flexibility or "bendability" which often prevents breakage. The abrasive aspects of the substrate will dull such bits quite rapidly, however. Harder carbide bits are available; these survive the abrasive action of the glass/epoxy better, but they are brittle and less forgiving of any sideward pressure when drilling. The substrate should be held firmly while drilling until the drill has gone completely through the board and has been lifted back up out of the hole. Use care not to bump the drill with the substrate.

Eyelets and pins used as vias to connect between the top and bottom of the substrate should be easy to solder. Clean copper is satisfactory, but with time copper tends to oxidize or corrode. Having to polish or clean a copper surface just prior to soldering can be a nuisance. Tinned surfaces are preferred. This applies also to the copper surface of the microstrip itself. A bare copper substrate should be buffed or polished clean just before assembly and soldering.

Bibliography

J. R. Fisk, "Simple Formula for Microstrip Impedance," *Ham Radio*, Dec 1977, p 72.

J. R. Fisk, "Microstrip Transmission Line," *Ham Radio*, Jan 1978, p 28.

I. J. Bahl and D. K. Trivedi, "A Designer's Guide to Microstrip Line," *Microwaves*, May 1977, p 174.

M. Wilson, ed, *The ARRL Handbook for the Radio Amateur* (Newington: ARRL, 1986), pp 32-17 to 32-21.

"S Parameter Design," HP Application Note 154 (Palo Alto, CA: Hewlett Packard, May 1973).

P. Shuch, "Microstrip Preamplifier for 1296 MHz," *Ham Radio*, Apr 1975, p 13.

P. Shuch, "Low-Cost 1296-MHz Preamplifier," *Ham Radio*, Oct 1975, p 42.

P. Shuch, "Solid State Microwave Amplifier Design," *Ham Radio*, Oct 1976, p 40.

J. Grimm, "Two-Stage Low-Noise Preamplifier for Amateur Bands from 24 cm to 12 cm," *VHF Communications*, 1/1980, p 2.

G. H. Krauss, "Low-Noise Preamplifier for 1296 MHz," *QST*, Jun 1982, p 36.

T. Laverghett, *Microwave Materials and Fabrication Techniques* (Dedham, MA: Artech House, 1984).

C. Bowick, *RF Circuit Design* (Indianapolis, IN: Howard W. Sams, 1982).

J. N. Gannaway and S. J. Davies, *The Microwave Newsletter Technical Collection* (Potters Bar, Herts, UK: RSGB, 1983)

Microwave Update 1987 (Newington: ARRL, 1987).

Diode and Transistor Designer's Catalog (Palo Alto, CA: Hewlett Packard).

H. Fukui, *Low-Noise Microwave Transistors and Amplifiers* (New York: IEEE Press, 1981).

"Application of Microwave GaAsFETs," *NEC Application Manual AN82901* (Santa Clara, CA: California Eastern Labs).

"S Parameters . . . Circuit Analysis and Design," *HP Application Note 95* (Palo Alto, CA: Hewlett Packard, 1968).

"Transistor Parameter Measurements," *HP Application Note 77-1* (Palo Alto, CA: Hewlett Packard).

PIN Diode Designers Guide (Burlington, MA: Microwave Associates, 1980).

Transistor Designers Guide (Burlington, MA: Microwave Associates, 1978).

Microwave Semiconductors (Woburn, MA: Alpha Industries).

J. Hardy, *High-Frequency Circuit Design* (Reston, VA: Reston Publishing Co, 1979).

H. Howe, Jr, *Stripline Circuit Design* (Dedham, MA: Artech House, 1974).

G. Gonzalez, *Microwave Transistor Amplifiers* (Englewood Cliffs, NJ: Prentice-Hall, 1984).

T. C. Edwards, *Foundations for Microstrip Circuit Design* (New York: John Wiley and Sons, 1981).

G. Vendelin, *Design of Amplifiers and Oscillators by the S-Parameter Method* (New York: Wiley Interscience, 1982).

T. Uwamo, H. Kitamura and A. Hashima, "An MDS Down-Converter of Thick-Film MIC for 2-GHz Pay TV," *IEEE Transactions on Consumer Electronics*, Aug 1981, pp 410-415.

G. H. Krauss, "A Low-Noise Preamplifier for 2304 MHz," *Ham Radio*, Feb 1983, pp 12-15.

J. Franke, "Stripline Bandpass Filters for 2304 MHz," *Ham Radio*, Apr 1977, p 50.

The Microwave Workshop

By William H. Sayer, WA6BAN
25219 W Posey Dr
Hemet, CA 92344

This section presents some useful techniques for working with the materials used to build VHF, UHF and microwave equipment.

WORKING WITH SHEET AND HEAVY-GAUGE METALS

When considering metals for construction of cavities to be used with vacuum tube amplifiers, the properties of each metal are a determining factor (see Table 1). For instance, copper has the best electrical and thermal properties for cavities, and it is easy to solder with all types of solder. However, copper is very hard to work; drills and taps have a tendency to grab.

Aluminum is the next best metal electrically and thermally, but good electrical contact is hard to make if the aluminum is oxidized. Brass is commonly used because it is easy to machine and solder. Brass sheet stock is usually available in 0.064, 0.090 and 0.125-inch sheets, and thin brass shim stock is very useful for making small boxes. Most suppliers have a cutting charge and will shear this metal to size if you figure out in advance the actual measurements needed.

Bronze is available only occasionally. It machines well, but is not quite as easy to use as brass. Phosphor bronze and beryllium copper are used for springs and fingerstock, but these metals require heat treatment before they can be used to make satisfactory finger stock and springs. Several suppliers make most kinds of finger stock already heat treated.

Invar rod is used mainly for temperature compensation in high-Q cavities. Copper-clad Invar was available a few years ago but does not seem to be available today. This was fabricated in sheets about 0.064 inch thick.

Tools for Cutting, Drilling, Machining, Forming and Filing

To do an accurate layout of the amplifier the following tools are required:
4-inch and 12-inch machinist's dividers
12-inch machinist's square
Machinist's scribes
Mechanical centerpunch
Plain centerpunch
Machinist's bluing
Small hammer
Vernier calipers

Table 1
Common Metal Characteristics

Metal	Electrical Resistivity ohms/cm^3 × 10^{-6}	Heat Conductivity cal/cm^3 °C	Coefficient of Thermal Expansion at 20°C
Copper	1.7	0.9	16 × 10^{-6}
Aluminum	2.8	0.5	24 × 10^{-6}
Brass	6.4-8.4	0.2-0.26	19 × 10^{-6}
Phosphor-bronze	10.5		17 × 10^{-6}
Beryllium copper	7.7		
Invar	8.5	0.025	0.9 × 10^{-6}
Steel			10 × 10^{-6}

If your eyesight is not the best, a dial indicator on the caliper is a great help. If more than one amplifier is to be built, a template, of steel or aluminum sheet, is a good investment.

To drill the round holes, centerpunch and then use a small drill to make it easy to start the larger hole in the drill press. Clamp the work securely to the table with C clamps. A small round file can be used to shift the holes a little if necessary in case of a "goof."

Unfortunately, access to a lathe and a good drill press is a must for most UHF cavities. With a lot of patience, however, some designs can be fabricated with simple tools. Some of the smaller machine shops will do good work if you can wait for their slack times. Some shops are very expensive, however, so be sure to get an estimate before they start.

To use finger stock properly, it is necessary to machine a metal ring (collet) of 1/8-inch or 1/4-inch material to which the thin finger stock is soldered. Brass or copper cylindrical stock can be used for these rings, or rectangular stock can be used if a four-jaw chuck is available for the lathe. In making collets for the various vacuum tubes, it is generally easier to use round stock with a three-jaw chuck to machine the inside diameter for the finger-stock mounting.

Refer to Fig 1. For a 2C39 tube, the plate and grid fingers are made of 97-135 stock and have 0.03-inch compression when the tube is inserted. The cathode connector is made from collet; use 97-74 with one finger

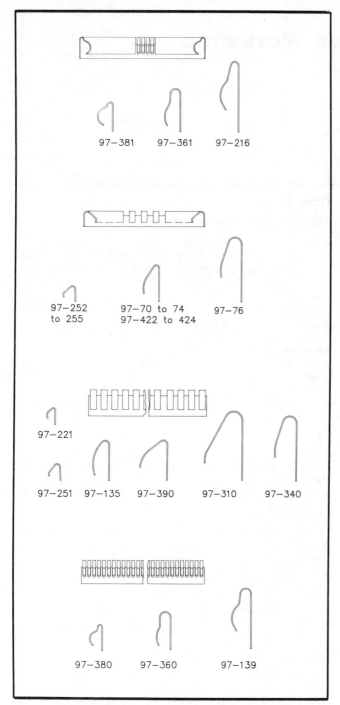

Fig 1—Finger stock is available in many different shapes and sizes from Instrument Specialties Co, Inc (tel 714-579-7100—west or 717-424-8510—east).

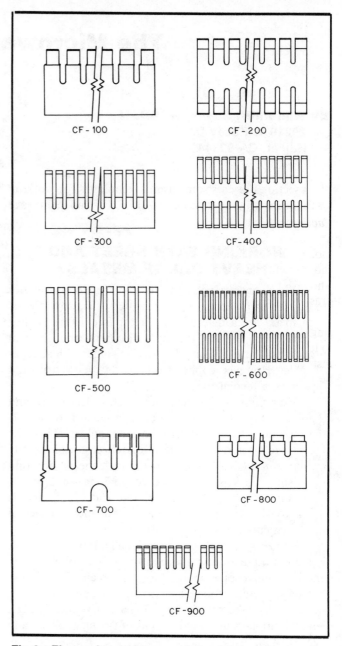

Fig 2—Eimac also makes a variety of finger stock. Eimac products are distributed by Richardson Electronics, Tel 800-323-1770.

cut off. The grid diameter is 0.590 inch and requires a hole size of 0.790 inch. It usually pays to bore the hole for the finger stock smaller than the calculated size and then try the fit on the tube. Too much force is not good, but a loose fit is not acceptable either. The screen collets can be made from 97-135 stock. The screen diameter is 1.425 inches so the hole should be about 1.625 inches. With 38 contacting fingers, a fair amount of force is required to insert the tube with 0.03-inch compression.

Eimac makes contact collets for their UHF tubes.

Eimac also makes a variety of finger stock (Fig 2). CF800 can be used to make sliding shorts in waveguide cavities. A good example of a commercial cavity for 900 MHz is shown in the 3CX400U7 data sheet.

SOLDERING

One of the most important rules for a good soldering job is that the metals must be clean. Some of the cleaning methods are:
1) use fine steel wool
2) use carborundum paper
3) use Scotch Brite®
4) use chemical cleaning with acid

Steel wool leaves steel residue which must be removed, and chemical cleaning is not safe in a home environment.

Once the metals are cleaned, avoid getting finger prints on the cleaned surface.

Soft solders are made from tin and lead of varying amounts. Fig 3 shows various solder melting temperatures and compositions.

Eutectic soft solder (64% tin, 36% lead) is the only one with the same liquidus and solidus temperature. The flow temperatures and melting points of the other alloys are not the same. One other tin solder is used for plumbing in West Germany made of 96% tin and 4% silver. Its melting point is 440°F. A new type of solder consists of 95% tin and 5% antimony. A complete list of various solders including hard solders and fluxes can be found in the *MIT Vacuum Tube Laboratory Manual*.[1]

After soldering, be sure to wash all flux away thoroughly. The fumes of some fluxes are toxic, so these should not be used in a closed room. Most "hard" solders (those with high melting points) will anneal copper and brass so allow work to cool before cleaning with water.

When soft-soldering the finger stock to the machined rings, do not use a torch—this can cause the finger stock to lose its temper. Use a gas burner or an electric hot plate instead. The finger stock from Instrument Specialties can be finished to a bright clean by specifying the part with an "A" after the stock number. Eimac division of Varian Associates makes rings with the finger stock soldered in place and then silver plated.

For home construction, in general, it is better to use low-temperature solders; the hard solders require that you use a torch, and this can cause the parts to warp from uneven heating. However, hard solder is much stronger than the soft solder. In soldering three pieces together, the first solder should be a hard solder and the second solder a soft solder. This method is effective because the lower temperature of the second solder will not cause the first piece soldered to fall off.

INSULATORS

Table 2 shows the properties of some of the insulating materials that are suitable for use in microwave construction projects. Copper-coated Kapton sheet can be cut to size with a pair of Wiss® compound shears. Any air space between the insulation and the metal is prone to electrical breakdown. The copper-coated Kapton does not have this problem because there is no air space. After deciding on the area of the copper of the Kapton to be used, the rest of the copper can be etched away with ferric chloride, similar to the printed-circuit board fabrication process.

If copper-coated Kapton is not available, use a very thin layer of Dow Corning No. 4 silicon grease on both surfaces. Silver-coated mica is used commercially. If mica is available you can make your own silver coat by using DuPont conductive coating materials[2]. Teflon® is quite soft and will puncture quite easily by high voltage if any

Table 2
Properties of Insulating Materials

Material	Dielectric Constant	Mechanical	Loss at UHF
Teflon	2.1	soft	very low
Kapton	4.0	hard	low
Mylar		very hard	lossy
Bakelite	3.7-5	good machining	medium
Epoxy fiberglass	5	good machining	medium
Mica	5.4	foliates	low
Ceramic	5.75	brittle	low
Nylon		machines easily	lossy
Polyethylene	2.26	soft	low loss
ULTEM	3.15	good machining	low

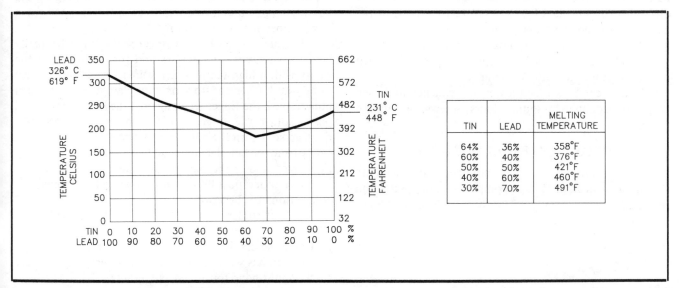

TIN	LEAD	MELTING TEMPERATURE
64%	36%	358°F
60%	40%	376°F
50%	50%	421°F
40%	60%	460°F
30%	70%	491°F

Fig 3—Solder melting temperature as a function of composition. Notice that 64/36% tin/lead solder has the lowest melting point.

metal chips are left on the surface of the Teflon. Sears also makes compound shears in three models: (1) cuts left; (2) cuts straight; (3) cuts right. A leather hole punch does a great job for small holes in most of the thin sheets of insulators. Copper-coated epoxy-fiberglass board can be hack sawed, drilled and filed, but be careful to avoid breathing the fiberglass dust.

Sources of metallized Kapton are DuPont Co, Fairfield, CT, phone 203-259-3351, and Oak Materials, Hoosic Falls, NY, phone 518-686-4374. Ultem can be obtained from Westlake Plastics, Lenni, PA 19052.

Power Amplifier Cavities

Cavity resonators using vacuum tubes are used from 70 cm to 13 cm wavelengths because they are efficient and easy to construct. The best cavity design is one which approximates a square toroidal section, as shown in Fig 4.

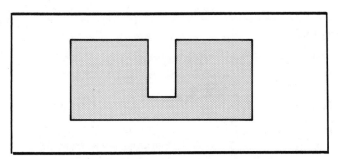

Fig 4—The best cavity design is one approaching a square toroidal shape.

In practice, however, the ceramic insulator and internal geometry of the vacuum tube makes the theoretical determination of the resonant frequency of the cavity quite difficult. The so-called "goodness" factor (R/Q) of the design is beyond the scope of this discussion.

Two types of cavity tuning are used:

1) The cavity is tuned to a higher frequency and then tuned to resonance with capacitance.

2) The cavity is tuned lower in frequency and then tuned to resonance by sliding doors, screws, or rotating paddles.

STRIP-LINE AMPLIFIERS

A strip-line cavity is a modified coaxial-cavity resonator. Instead of circular components, flat plates and rectangular boxes are used. The characteristic impedance of strip-lines in a rectangular cavity is:

$$Z_0 \approx \frac{377S}{w}$$

where
S = spacing
w = width of the strip

The width of the strip must be greater than the spacing S. The physical length of the strip line and tube for ¼ wavelength can be calculated from:

$$Z = Z_0 \tan \beta\ell$$

$$\beta = \frac{360}{\lambda}$$

where
ℓ = line length in cm
λ = wavelength in cm
Z = output impedance of the tube at the operating frequency
Z_0 = characteristic impedance of the strip line

At the higher frequencies, the output capacitance of the tube is relatively large. When this is the case, the strip line becomes undesirably short and power output coupling becomes too difficult. There are two ways to increase the physical length of the strip line:

1) Add another ¼ wavelength of strip line on the original strip line to make the overall electrical length ½ wavelength with the tube at one end.

2) Add another ¼ wavelength of strip line on the other side of the vacuum tube. This puts the tube in the center of the cavity and equalizes the RF currents.

COAXIAL TUBE SOCKET CONSTRUCTION

The 2C39, the 4X150G series and the 3CX400U7 series are suited for using finger-stock connections for the plate and the grids. Any capacitive reactance in the grid or screen circuits is fatal at UHF. The best procedure is to physically ground the grid on the 2C39 and the 3CX400U7 with many low-inductance contacts. Likewise, the screen of the 4X150G should have about 38 low-inductance contacts and no bypass. This, of course, means a change in power-supply configuration when using the tetrode. The hole in the metal plate used for the finger-stock mounting should be only large enough to compress the finger stock for a firm connection when the tube is inserted.

The metal plate for the finger stock is mechanically held to the cavity with screws and then soldered to the cavity with a high-temperature solder (96/4% tin/silver) using your kitchen gas stove or a hot plate. Using a wooden plug to push the finger stock against the hole in the metal plate, solder the finger stock in place using 60/40% tin/lead solder on the gas stove or hot plate. Remove the cavity from the hot plate immediately after the 60/40 solder flows freely since the plate retains heat a long time.

The other possibilities for making low-inductance connections to the grid are:

1) Soft solder a soft copper plate to the grid.

2) Use a machined hole only slightly larger than the grid and use conductive silver paste for the connection. This design has worked on 13-cm amplifiers where finger stock would have too much inductance.

3) Use silver-plated springs in a machined groove, as shown in Fig 5.

If both the plate and grid contacts are made with

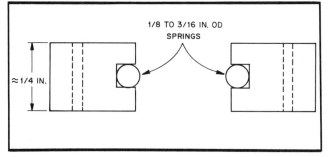

Fig 5—Silver-plated springs in a machined groove provide a low-inductance contact for a tube grid. Not to scale.

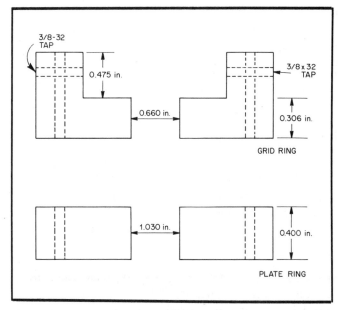

Fig 6—A means of providing low-impedance contact for the grid and plate of a 2C39 tube.

springs, be sure the springs are inserted the same way, as a twisting motion is necessary to insert the tube. Trial and error is necessary to determine the depths of the grooves for the springs.

CAVITY CONSTRUCTION

Cavities for 70 cm (432 MHz) can be made from a section of heavy-wall copper, brass or aluminum pipe with a top and bottom of heavy-wall copper or brass sheet stock. Depending on the size of the lathe available, the pipe can be faced to the required dimension by using the lathe jaws inside or outside the pipe. After facing both ends to the required dimensions, it is useful to scribe a light cut where the holes are to be drilled to hold the top and bottom plates on the pipe. After the hole positions are scribed and center punched, the ring is drilled. Be sure to clamp the ring securely to the drill press table. Be careful, go slowly and use plenty of lubricant on the drill.

Cavities can also be constructed using ¼-inch thick strips to make a square box configuration. These strips are drilled using a machinist's vise on the drill press for making the holes to fasten the top and bottom plates. Again, be sure to clamp the vise down on the table and go slowly.

Finally, if a box brake is available, a 70-cm cavity can be bent up with just the top plate removable.

In contrast, most 23-cm cavities are built using the first two designs, and 13-cm cavities are usually machined from solid stock. For 13 cm it is imperative to use low-inductance contacts for the grid and plate. The use of silver-plated springs in grooves is one way to provide these low-inductance contacts.

Another way to provide low-inductance contacts is shown in Fig 6. The grid hole is machined to approximately 0.660 inch, slightly larger than the 2C39 grid. The grid contact is then coated with a conductive silver paste and fitted quite snugly. Likewise, the top plate of the cavity is machined larger than the measured diameter of the tube's plate contact by two times the thickness of the insulation used (5 mil Kapton). The insulation is cut slightly longer so that the overlapping seam will fit in a filed notch in the machined hole for the plate of the 2C39. The capacitance of this bypass (5 mil Kapton) is about 290 pF. This cavity's

internal diameter is machined to resonance in small steps. Two BNC connectors with small loops were used as a transmission cavity to determine the resonant frequency after each machining. BNC connectors have 3/8 by 32 threads. The nut from a common potentiometer can be used as a jam nut on the BNC connector.

BYPASSING

Try to eliminate the need for bypassing using design techniques. For example, tie the screen grid of a tetrode directly to ground. The power supply must be then changed to provide correct screen and grid voltages. Likewise, when using 2C39 tubes, fasten the grid to ground physically and then use cathode bias with a normal bypass for the cathode circuit.

An open ¼-wavelength of coax can be an effective short if the coax has a solid outer conductor. The actual physical length is found by multiplying the velocity factor times the electrical ¼ wavelength. The velocity factor is equal to $\sqrt{E}$ where E is the dielectric constant of the insulating material. For example:

for Teflon E = 2.1

$$VF = \frac{1}{\sqrt{2.1}} = \frac{1}{1.449} = 0.69$$

The same idea can be used in the plate and cathode bypass at the higher frequencies by making ℓ in Fig 7 an electrical ¼ wavelength at the operating frequency.

Home built feed-through bypasses can be made from discs of copper-coated Kapton with metal washers on both sides, as shown in Fig 8.

Ferrite beads on both sides of the bypass are recom-

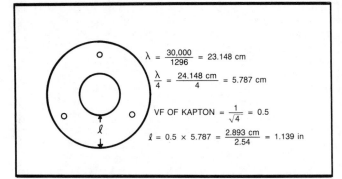

Fig 7—Making ℓ = ¼ wavelength at the operating frequency provides an effective RF bypass.

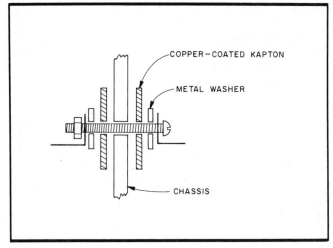

Fig 8—A home-built feedthrough bypass.

mended. Some commercial feed-through capacitors, although expensive, do a good job. Small pieces of double-sided PC board make effective bypasses where there is room.

AIR AND WATER-COOLING METHODS

Since no vacuum tube is 100% efficient, heat is generated which must be removed. The relative flows required for one kilowatt heat removal for air at sea level and for water at any level, are:

air = 90 cubic feet/min at 30°C inlet for each 20°C rise in temperature

water = 0.189 gal/min for each 20°C rise in temperature

Examples of Air Cooling

4CX250 and 2C39 family tubes have external anodes. The basic formula for temperature rise for air cooling is:

$$\Delta T = \frac{TK \times W}{164 \times Q}$$

where

TK = inlet temperature in kelvins
W = watts
Q = air flow in cubic feet per minute
T = temperature rise in °C

The air flow required for each type is usually given at sea level conditions and with an incoming temperature of 40°C to 50°C. For example, Eimac requires 18 cubic feet/minute at 0.23-inch of water column pressure for a 4CX1500B. Solving for ΔT:

$$\Delta T = \frac{323 \times 1000}{164 \times 18} = 109.4\,°C$$

The average temperature rise is not the only factor involved, however. We must also consider the ceramic-to-metal seals, which may be affected by RF heating. A crack

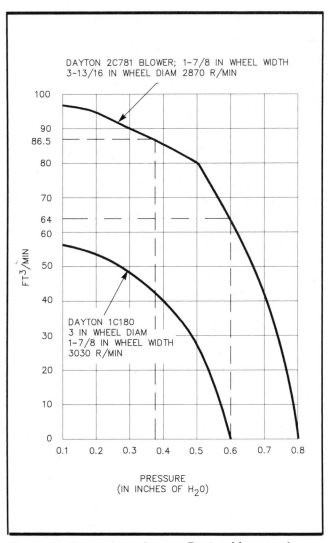

Fig 9—Air-flow volume for two Dayton blowers at different pressure levels.

may develop in the ceramic due to differential heat past a certain point. Cavities designed to produce symmetrical RF currents will reduce the possibility of this occurring.

At higher altitudes, the air density decreases. The density of dry air can be calculated as follows:

$$\rho \text{ (g/cm}^3) = \frac{0.001293 \times H}{1 + (0.00367 \times T) \times 760}$$

where

H = air pressure in mm of mercury
T = °C

Using the 4CX1500B at a height of 3 km (1.8 miles), H = 528 mm Hg, T = 40°C:

$$\rho = \frac{0.001293 \times 528}{1 + (0.00367 \times 40) \times 760}$$

$$= 0.007833 \text{ g/cm}^3$$

Using the 4CX1500B at sea level, H = 760 mm Hg, T = 40°C:

$$\rho = \frac{0.001293 \times 760}{1 + (0.00367 \times 40) \times 760}$$

$$= 0.0011274 \text{ g/cm}^3$$

To get the same cooling as at sea level, the air flow has to be increased by the ratio:

$$\frac{1.1274}{0.7833} = 1.4392 \times 18 \text{ ft}^3/\text{min} = 25.9 \text{ ft}^3/\text{min}$$

The pressure will be increased by the square of the volume ratio:

$$(1.4392)^2 = 2.07 \times 0.23 \text{ in water column}$$
$$= 0.476 \text{ in H}_2\text{O}$$

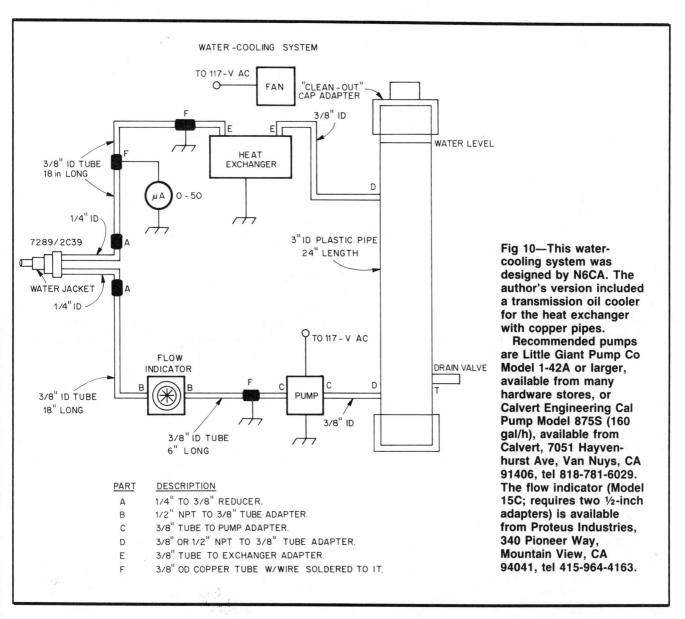

PART	DESCRIPTION
A	1/4" TO 3/8" REDUCER.
B	1/2" NPT TO 3/8" TUBE ADAPTER.
C	3/8" TUBE TO PUMP ADAPTER.
D	3/8" OR 1/2" NPT TO 3/8" TUBE ADAPTER.
E	3/8" TUBE TO EXCHANGER ADAPTER.
F	3/8" OD COPPER TUBE W/WIRE SOLDERED TO IT.

Fig 10—This water-cooling system was designed by N6CA. The author's version included a transmission oil cooler for the heat exchanger with copper pipes.

Recommended pumps are Little Giant Pump Co Model 1-42A or larger, available from many hardware stores, or Calvert Engineering Cal Pump Model 875S (160 gal/h), available from Calvert, 7051 Hayvenhurst Ave, Van Nuys, CA 91406, tel 818-781-6029. The flow indicator (Model 15C; requires two ½-inch adapters) is available from Proteus Industries, 340 Pioneer Way, Mountain View, CA 94041, tel 415-964-4163.

Refer to Fig 9. The Dayton 2C781 blower will be more than sufficient. However, the Dayton 1X180 would not produce enough pressure to allow for any turbulent effects caused by ducting angles.

Instead of blowing air on the tube's radiator, the heat can be removed by suction in an exhaust system. Here the incoming air to the blower is much hotter. In order to keep the ΔT at 109.4 °C:

$$Q = \frac{432.4 \times 1000}{164 \times 109.4} = 24 \text{ ft}^3/\text{min}$$

As you can see, a Q of 24 cubic feet/minute required at 50 °C inlet temperature is quite a bit more than the 18 cubic feet/minute using a blower. However, this does bring more cool air around the rest of the transmitter components. Whereas the blowing system fills the cabinet with hot air.

Examples of Water Cooling

Water cooling is a natural for cooling vacuum tubes in cavities. It is quiet and has few components which are simple and reliable. Distilled water has a resistivity of 40,000 ohms/cubic inch. Thus, with a water column of 1 to 2 feet of small plastic tubing (approximately 3/8 inch ID), the DC loss at 1.4 kV is quite small. (There is no RF on the cavity type of anode if the RF bypass is doing its job.) This is not true for strip-line amplifiers. For example, using N6CA's 2C39 amplifier design, we can calculate the temperature rise as follows. It is necessary to dissipate a peak plate power of 520 watts for a pair of 2C39s operating at 1400 volts at 0.35 A per tube:

$$\Delta T = \frac{\text{watts}}{264 \times \text{gal/min}} = \frac{520}{264 \times 1} = 1.96 \text{°C}$$

The Little Giant Pump Model 1-42A is capable of 2.66 gal/min with no head. Therefore, with some pressure drop in the 2C39 water jackets, we still have a flow of 1.0 gal/min.

This explains why the power output is more stable with water cooling; with air cooling there can be large changes in temperature and subsequent large variation in power output. Try to use only copper tubing, plastic hose, plastic

Table 3
Electropotentials of Various Metals

Metal	Electropotential
aluminum	− 1.66
duraluminum	− 0.83
zinc	− 0.763
cadmium	− 0.403
iron	− 0.44
tin	− 0.136
lead	− 0.126
nickel	− 0.25
copper	+ 0.344
silver	+ 0.8

pumps and a copper heat exchanger. Dissimilar metals must be used with care in a water system. Each metal has its own electropotential, and when wet this difference will cause corrosion and drastically increase the leakage current as well as eating the metal away.

Distilled water should be used if possible. The next best is so-called "deionized" water. Change the water if the leakage current increases. The water schematic shown in Fig 10 was originated by N6CA. If two tubes are used, two flow indicators should be used with two water "Ts."

Electropotentials of various metals are shown in Table 3. Use metals as close together as possible. For instance, use cadmium-plated screws in aluminum rather than brass screws.

CONCLUSION

Construction of microwave equipment is not difficult if a few common-sense steps are followed. Granted, microwave design and construction is a bit more difficult than construction at HF, but amateurs can still build equipment that works well.

Notes
[1]MIT Vacuum Tube Laboratory Manual, pp 111-112.
[2]MIT Vacuum Tube Laboratory Manual, pp 101-102.

Chapter 9

Antennas and Feed Lines

Yagi Antennas for UHF/SHF

By Günter Hoch, DL6WU
Gersprenzweg 24
D-6100 Darmstadt-Eberstadt
Federal Rep of Germany

YAGI VERSUS APERTURE ANTENNAS

While at VHF there is hardly an alternative to Yagi antennas, it is just as clear that aperture antennas are a must at microwave frequencies. But where is the "transition zone"? What are the arguments for or against either design in a given application?

A look at the familiar "beam-transmission equation" may provide some insight. Received power P_2 depends on transmitter power P_1, transmitter antenna area A_1, receiver antenna area A_2, distance d, and wavelength (λ) as follows:

$$P_2 = k \; \frac{P_1 \; A_1 \; A_2}{d^2 \; \lambda^2} \qquad \text{(Eq 1)}$$

where k is a propagation constant.

Thanks to modern semiconductors, receivers can detect approximately the same minimum power, regardless of frequency; therefore, let us assume P_2 to be constant. The distance between stations, d, can also be considered constant, regardless of frequency. Assuming that the difficulty of generating power increases as the square of the frequency (P_1 / λ^2 is constant), we may conclude that to communicate over a certain distance, the same effective antenna areas will be required, regardless of frequency. This is not an implausible thesis.

For all practical purposes, effective area equates to physical dimensions. This is obvious for aperture antennas, such as horns or parabolic dishes, but it is equally true for antennas made up of discrete elements, such as phased arrays and Yagis. For illustrative purposes, the relationship between isotropic gain (G_i) and effective area is helpful:

$$G_i = \frac{4 \; \pi \; A}{\lambda^2} \qquad \text{(Eq 2)}$$

The amount of gain or area required depends on the type and grade of communication desired.

To start with one extreme, let us look at EME communications. Practice shows that a 6-meter dish antenna will suffice on all UHF/SHF bands. Assuming 60% efficiency, this equates to an effective area of about 10 m². From Eq 2 we can calculate the associated gain figures:

- 70-cm band: 27 dBi
- 23-cm band: 37 dBi
- 13-cm band: 42 dBi

As shown later, achieving these gains would take no more than eight long Yagis on 70 cm, while even 16 extremely long Yagis would be insufficient on 23 cm or higher frequency bands. Feed problems resulting from the loss in coaxial cables rule out yet larger arrays.

Things look a lot different for an array designed for local- or medium-distance tropo work, satellites, and the like. Sacrificing 20 dB of gain reduces the required area by a factor of 10, putting 23-cm and 13-cm requirements within the reach of one very long Yagi or a quad array of medium-length ones. A dish of comparable gain would still be nearly 2 meters in diameter and would certainly have more weight and wind load (Fig 1).

The data presented in the following sections will show that even "super long" Yagi antennas are neither hard nor critical to design or build. They should be considered a true alternative to small and medium size dishes at the longer centimeter wavelengths.

YAGI THEORY

A rigid mathematical treatment of Yagis would easily fill a book by itself. So, theory in this context shall mean no more than some help in understanding the principles.

Beam Formation

The function of a multi-element antenna is usually described by calculating the currents in all elements and adding up their influence at some distant point. This is a formidable task with a parasitic array, where currents are

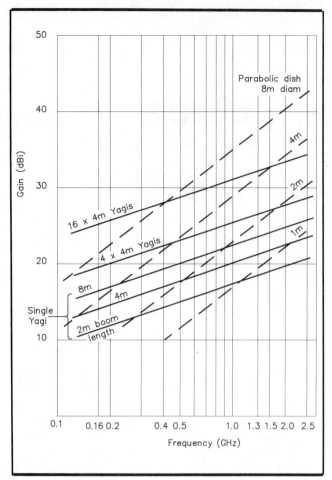

Fig 1—Gain of various Yagi and dish antennas as a function of frequency.

the RF energy together. What is needed is some sort of focusing. This can be done by the Yagi structure itself. We start with a section having high retardation and "confinement," consisting of long elements and close spacing. It makes the waves emanating from the radiator "stumble forward" into the next (radiating) section. With the right amount and proper distribution of retardation along the element string, waves leaking out will tend to be overtaken on the outside by those having taken off earlier (closer to the feed end). A more-or-less planar wave front is formed, equivalent to a beam leaving the antenna in the forward direction.

Gain Calculation

THEORETICAL GAIN

The term "antenna gain" is misleading. Total power leaving an antenna by radiation is, at most, the power fed in from the transmitter. So, power can only be "gained" through concentration—by not radiating it in all directions. Gain is defined as the ratio of power radiated in the desired direction divided by the power radiated by an *isotropic* (omnidirectional in all planes) antenna at the same power input. More gain usually means squeezing the energy into a sharper beam. Assuming no power is lost by dissipation, there is a proportional relationship between directivity (beam sharpness) and gain. Knowing the radiation pattern of an antenna is essentially knowing the gain.

In a typical Yagi, as we move away from the direction of maximum radiation, received power will drop quickly. The angle between the two headings where power is down exactly 50% (−3 dB) is called the half-power beamwidth or aperture angle. This need not be equal for both horizontal and vertical displacement, for the beam is usually not rotationally symmetrical around the boom axis. Still, knowing the two aperture angles in the E (plane of the elements) and H (perpendicular to the elements) planes has been shown by Kraus[1] to allow an approximate calculation of gain:

$$G_i \approx \frac{42,000}{\phi_E \, \phi_H} \qquad \text{(Eq 3)}$$

where

G_i = gain relative to an isotropic radiator
ϕ_E = aperture angle in the E plane
ϕ_H = aperture angle in the H plane

Since a dipole has a 1.53-fold (2.14 dB) gain over an isotropic radiator:

$$G_d \approx \frac{25,200}{\phi_E \, \phi_H} \qquad \text{(Eq 4)}$$

These approximations are based on several assumptions:
- No power is being dissipated.
- The pattern has only one lobe—no sidelobes or backward radiation.
- The aperture angles are small, about 50° or less.

induced by radiation coupling. Advanced mathematical and computer models allow a fair prediction of the most sought-after features like front lobe width and gain, but hardly help us in getting an idea of "how the thing works."

Rather than look at discrete elements, let us regard the Yagi structure as a waveguide. A ladder structure of elements electrically shorter than one-half wavelength, spaced less than one-half wavelength apart will conduct RF energy. Similar to other waveguides, the Yagi structure has a passband characteristic. Toward the high-frequency edge, losses are low and the speed of propagation decreases quickly. Toward the low-frequency end, propagation speed approaches that of free space and losses increase; in other words, the line becomes "leaky." Operation as an antenna is best in a transition zone towards the low-frequency end. We want the energy to radiate instead of being reflected back and forth between the waveguide ends, as would be the case near the upper cutoff. (There are applications for this reflection type mode in short, resonant Yagis and backfire antennas.)

Unfortunately, it becomes harder to couple energy into the line as the propagation speed approaches the speed of light. Behaving almost like free space, it will not hold

PRACTICAL GAIN

Real antennas radiate part of the energy into directions other than the desired one, which, in Yagi antennas, is called the *boresight* axis. Some of the power applied to the driven element is not captured by the director chain, but radiates in other directions. Some energy leaves via the rear end, or after it is reflected back from the end of the director chain. These lesser amounts of energy interfere with each other and the desired beam, forming a multitude of minor beams or *lobes*.

Each type of antenna has characteristic features in the radiation pattern, which link the physical dimensions with the number and strength of the minor lobes. The power ratio of the main lobe to the strongest sidelobe is called *sidelobe* suppression, or, if the rear lobe is concerned, *front-to-back ratio*. When these figures are known, it is often possible to estimate the total power "wasted" in unwanted radiation. (An exact calculation would call for an integration of the complete spatial radiation pattern.) This amount must be subtracted from the power available to the desired front lobe, reducing the gain accordingly. Thus, the Kraus formula could be corrected for each particular case.

ESTIMATING GAIN FROM E-PLANE PATTERNS

Fortunately, all Yagi antennas have common features that allow a good estimate of gain—even if only parts of the complete spatial pattern are known. By comparing measured gain to readily available E-plane patterns a graph was derived (Fig 2). The only assumption is that the front-to-back ratio is at least 2 dB higher than the estimated forward gain.

For example, a Yagi with a 30° half-power beamwidth in the E plane, having first sidelobes 15 dB down, would

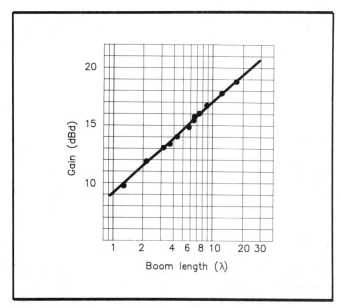

Fig 3—Measured gain of long Yagi antennas versus boom length.

yield a forward gain of approximately 13 dBd. This, by the way, does not imply that simply reducing the sidelobes to −19 dB would increase gain to 14 dBd. Reducing sidelobe radiation usually increases the beamwidth. In well-designed Yagis there is a trade-off between beamwidth and sidelobe level, with the maximum available gain limited by the boom length. Fig 3 shows this relationship, taken from countless measurements. For reasons to be discussed, a high value of sidelobe attenuation is always desirable, nevertheless.

Yagi Profiles

It has been pointed out that for best performance, a certain distribution of delay must exist on the Yagi structure. There are endless combinations of element length, diameter and spacing that yield the same results. This fact, combined with the difficulty of determining optimum performance by experimentation, has led to the seemingly innumerable "optimum" designs published. A majority of this variety is eliminated if all the designs are converted to a common center frequency and all elements to a common diameter. This can be done with the aid of the constant-reactance graph found in the following section. When treated in this way, all designs become comparable and it turns out that good, proven antennas show a striking resemblance. This is true not only for a given boom length. If an element number versus element length plot is drawn for the "normalized" Yagi, all designs group very closely around one common profile. A simple averaging technique can then be applied to derive the "Yagi to end all Yagis." The same goes for the spacing sequence, which shows a gradual increase from a starting value of about 0.15 λ, remaining constant at 0.4 λ beyond a point about 3 λ from

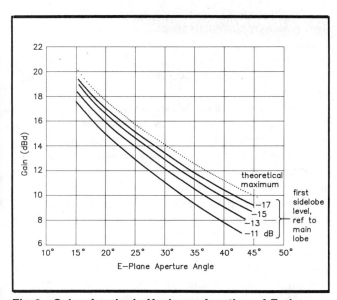

Fig 2—Gain of a single Yagi as a function of E-plane beamwidth and first sidelobe level.

the driven element. Spacing of the first few elements shows some variation, probably due to the strong influence on feed point impedance, which is obviously influenced by the type of driven element.

Many experiments were performed to validate these somewhat surprising findings. It turned out that the gain values measured for the "averaged" designs were up to the best individually optimized ones. (A byproduct of these measurements is a boom length versus gain plot of long Yagi antennas, shown in Fig 3.) The averaging process resulted in a logarithmic taper profile, with optimum slope depending on element diameter. A shallower slope will result in increased sidelobe radiation, and element lengths will no longer be independent of chosen boom length (gain will remain approximately the same). Steeper slopes will result in decreased sidelobe radiation, but a loss of gain. Here again, optimum element lengths will depend on boom length.[2]

The antennas patterned after the logarithmic profile have a sidelobe suppression of about 16 dB. If this is insufficient, additional tapering of the last few directors can be tried, with only a minimal reduction in gain.

Further Improvement

It has been shown that by slight departure from the logarithmic profile and use of a lower-impedance feed, a further reduction of sidelobes is possible without broadening the main lobe; up to 0.5 dB additional gain is achievable with respect to Fig 3 (see contribution by K1FO).

So far such improvements have been reported only for singular designs. It appears, however, that on very long arrays ($\geq 10\,\lambda$) a general gain bonus of about 0.3 dB can be obtained by making the first director up to 3% longer than indicated by Fig 4 and steepening the taper profile of the next five or six directors accordingly. This lowers the feed impedance to around 30 Ω and necessitates a transforming feeder element.

In low-noise applications such as EME it can be dangerous to overdo the tweaking because pattern and noise performance may be degraded. When the frequency of maximum gain is exceeded, element currents rise sharply, causing extra noise through skin-effect loss, and additional ground noise may be picked up by stronger sidelobes. For the sake of radiation efficiency and pattern purity (and to allow for construction tolerances) Fig 4 has about a 1% safety margin built in of which a part should always be kept. Of two equal-gain antennas the one with lower intrinsic loss will perform better in a low-noise environment.

By the way, computer models with lossless elements will always predict a frequency of maximum gain slightly higher than measured in practice, for the reason just discussed.

Rod or Loop Elements?

The first SHF Yagis to gain widespread acceptance

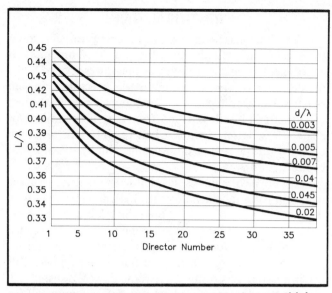

Fig 4—Optimum director length versus element thickness. (Data valid only for antennas with eight or more directors.)

were G3JVL's loop Yagis.[3] In their later, tapered version, performance matched rod-element Yagis of equal boom length. So, from a performance standpoint, the choice of element style is more or less a matter of personal preference. The advantages of loop antennas are the self-centering feature, the cleverly designed feed/balun element and the ease of fine tuning by bending the elements. Rod-element Yagis have lower wind load, are less sensitive to deformation, and are more easily constructed from square boom material. These features clearly favor rod elements on 432 MHz, while on 1296 MHz and above there seems to be a tie between the two systems.

Short or Long Booms?

As shown in Fig 3, the gain of a Yagi increases at the slightly sub-proportional rate of 2.35 dB per octave (length doubling). Stacking two antennas results in 2.5 to 2.8 dB of additional gain; there seems to be a case for stacking medium-sized antennas instead of building "super long" ones.

The apparent gain advantage in stacking must be weighed against the difficulties encountered in bringing power to several feed points. To keep losses low, heavy cable must be used above 450 MHz. Even with the finest of cables, distribution loss is likely to become excessive if more than four or six antennas are grouped together. These considerations speak for making individual Yagis as long as possible before increasing their number. For the same reasons, the design principles described in this paper have been restricted to a family of antennas ranging from medium length to extremely long. If short Yagis are desired, the scaling methods presented in the next section are recommended to adapt proven designs.

DESIGN OF YAGI ANTENNAS

Anyone setting out to construct an antenna would, of course, like to have a building plan specifying all the antenna dimensions. There is, however, such an endless variety in the choice of boom and element materials, operating frequencies, and desired antenna length or gain that it is impossible to provide more than a few examples of hard data. Considering the sizable time and effort consumed by the necessary handwork, it is a reasonable expectation to perform simple calculations before sawing aluminum. Furthermore, a general recipe has the advantage of allowing adaptation to any frequency.[1]

Design Procedure[4]

First, the required boom length for a desired gain is determined by looking at Fig 3. As all remaining calculations are done on the basis of operating wavelength, λ_o, this value must be derived from the operating frequency, f_o, with sufficient accuracy.

$$\lambda_o = \frac{c}{f_o} \qquad \text{(Eq 5)}$$

where c (the speed of light) is 3.0×10^8 meters per second, or 1.1811×10^{10} inches per second. Therefore, if $f_o = 432$ MHz, $\lambda_o = 0.6944$ meter or 27.34 inches.

Element placement can now be determined from Table 1. Since director length is a function of element diameter, Eq 5 should be used to convert rod thickness to the equivalent fraction of a wavelength. Once this value is in hand, Fig 4 will provide the necessary director lengths (the driven element and reflector will be treated later). Interpolation between two curves is usually necessary, but is accurate enough if done with care. For example, the third director of a 432-MHz Yagi made from 3/16-inch (4.76 mm) diameter rod must be 0.420 λ or 11.48 inches (292 mm) long.

Keep a record of the required dimensions, but don't cut the directors yet. The boom has an influence on director length, which must be taken into account.

Table 1

Yagi Element Spacings (Center-to-Center) for Antennas with Eight or More Directors

Element	Spacing (λ)	Total Distance from Reflector (λ)
REF	—	—
DE	0.185	0.185
D1	0.079	0.264
D2	0.180	0.444
D3	0.216	0.660
D4	0.252	0.912
D5	0.281	1.193
D6	0.302	1.495
D7	0.317	1.812
D8	0.331	2.143
D9	0.346	2.489
D10	0.360	2.849
D11	0.374	3.223
D12	0.382	3.605
D13	0.389	3.994
D14	0.396	4.390
D15	0.402	4.792
D16	0.402	5.194
⋮	⋮	⋮

Spacing remains 0.402 λ for additional directors.

Boom Correction

A metallic boom near the current loop of an antenna element will make it appear shorter. The effect is strongest for elements passing through the boom with electrical contact upon entering and leaving. Some effect remains, however, for elements mounted above the boom or passing through it via insulators.

On HF, these boom effects are negligible. They remain insignificant on VHF, but they become prominent when the boom diameter reaches several percent of the wavelength. Fig 5 shows the shortening effect for cylindrical elements passing through a metallic boom, assuming full

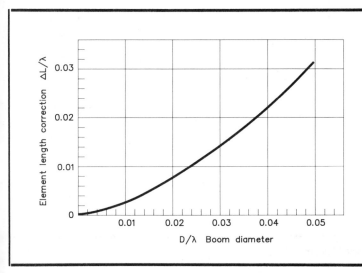

Fig 5—"Shortening" effect for cylindrical elements passing through and making full electrical contact with a metallic boom.

electrical contact on both sides. The shape of the boom (round, square or rectangular) is of minimal importance.

If, for instance, the free-space length of a 432-MHz director element was calculated to be 11.5 inches (292 mm), what would be the effect of a 1-inch (25.4-mm) metal boom? The boom thickness as a decimal fraction of wavelength is 1 / 27.34 (or 25.4 / 694.4) = 0.0366. From Fig 5, the corresponding correction is determined: 0.023 λ = 0.63 inch (16 mm). So, the element must be made 12-1/8 inches (308 mm) long. This means that the element must be lengthened by 63% of the boom diameter, a typical value which, however, was not found to remain constant with varying boom diameters.

What about the effects of other mounting methods? Elements passing through the boom, but electrically insulated, suffer about one half the shortening effect of Fig 5, as do elements mounted directly on top of round booms, insulated or not. With increasing separation the effect vanishes, and it can be neglected when the distance is greater than one boom radius. It is very hard to predict the influence of clamps or other metallic holders, except that they will all make elements appear shorter.

If you want to determine the influence of a non-standard element mount, here is a method: Build a simple 3-element Yagi using "free-space" element lengths, mounting the director on a cardboard cylinder that telescopes into the boom, as shown in Fig 6. Use an adjustable matching section (such as a gamma match) and tune it for zero reflected power. Replace the cardboard section with a piece of the actual boom and desired element mount, making sure the spacing is exactly as it was before. Trim the director until reflected power is again at zero. The same length correction will have to be applied to all elements.

Scaling of Element Dimensions

If all physical dimensions of an antenna are multiplied by a factor, S, performance will be exactly the same at S times the original wavelength (under the assumption that loss is negligible because conductivity does not scale). We have made use of this rule when normalizing our basic Yagi design. Any antenna that is known to work well on one frequency can thus be modeled for another. While this is hardly a problem for spacing, it can lead to some uncommon element diameters. The dimensions found by scaling can easily be adapted for the available material by use of Fig 7. The curves of this graph are lines of constant reactance. As the function of parasitic elements is determined by their reactance, elements on one line can replace each other.

The length of an equivalent element with diameter d_2, to a given one of length l_1, and diameter d_1, can be found where the curve passing through l_1, d_1 intersects the vertical line corresponding to d_2. If there is no curve directly passing through l_1, d_1, a curve must be drawn through this point, parallel to the existing ones.

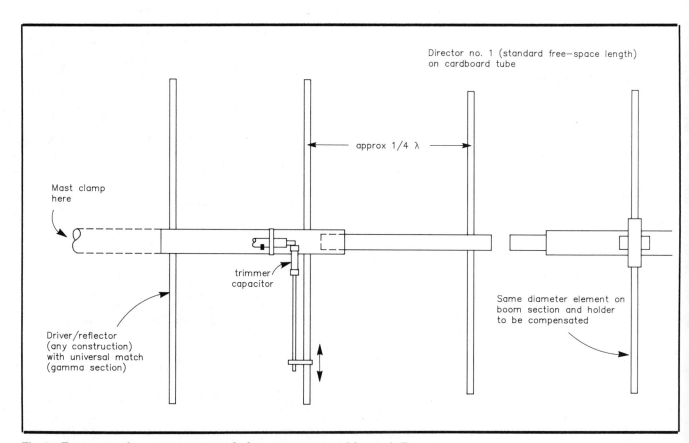

Fig 6—Test setup for measurement of element mount and boom influence.

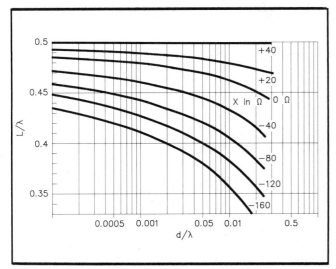

Fig 7—Parasitic element length versus diameter for a constant reactance.

Choice of Element Material

The author's experiments were carried out mainly on 70 cm, where the typical range of element thickness is about 0.003 to 0.01 λ. This is where the data presented is most accurate. Additional tests were run on 2 meters and 23 cm, extending the range to about 0.001 and 0.015 λ, respectively.

Thicker elements are slightly ''flatter'' than a pure, constant-reactance transformation from thin elements would predict—there remain a few unsettled questions as to this behavior.

Very thin elements are ruled out by stability considerations and because they suffer from excessive rain detuning. On 70 cm, 4-mm (5/32 to 3/16 in) elements look like an optimum choice, while 3 mm (1/8 in) seems fine for the 23-cm and 13-cm bands.

Any metal with low specific resistance will work well; conductivity demands increase with frequency. On 23 cm, no difference could be measured between copper, aluminum and silver elements. Thick (4 mm) brass elements performed well, while thinner (2 mm) brass and steel elements showed degraded performance (approximately −0.3 and −1.1 dB, respectively). Regardless of acceptable electrical performance, brass is not recommended because of corrosion and the tendency of some alloys to crack when weathered. A good, low-corrosion aluminum alloy is still the best choice, and performance will not degrade even with some tarnish on the surface.

Feed Methods

As many tests have shown, even the longest logarithmically tapered Yagis have a gain bandwidth of several percent between the −1 dB points. To make full use of this feature, care must be taken to provide a reasonable match over the entire operating frequency range.

The driver section, usually consisting of a dipole and

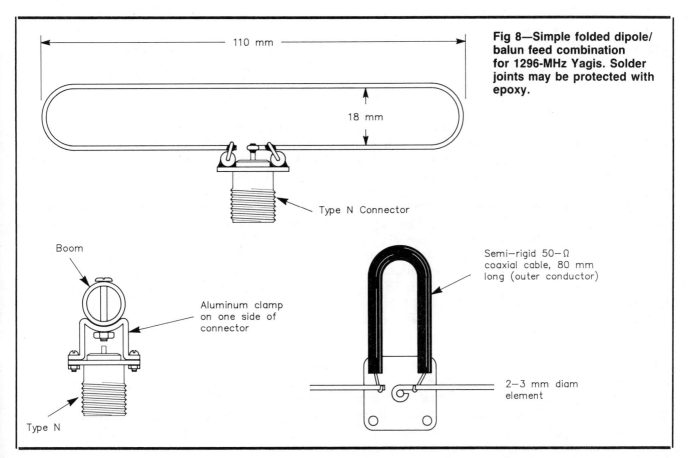

Fig 8—Simple folded dipole/balun feed combination for 1296-MHz Yagis. Solder joints may be protected with epoxy.

110 mm

18 mm

Type N Connector

Boom

Aluminum clamp on one side of connector

Type N

Semi−rigid 50−Ω coaxial cable, 80 mm long (outer conductor)

2−3 mm diam element

reflector, has considerable influence on the antenna impedance. Perhaps the worst possible choice is a thin dipole, matched by a narrowband device like a gamma section, plus a single rod reflector. This combination may work fine over a narrow bandwidth, but SWR will rise quickly on either side and "eat up" the gain. As the dipole diameter increases, so does the matching bandwidth; 0.015 λ will usually be sufficient. The length should be chosen from Fig 7 to provide X = 0 Ω at the *lowest* desired operating frequency for the radiator and X = −35 Ω for the reflector. A 1:1 balun should be used for direct connection of 50-Ω coaxial cable; otherwise, pattern asymmetry and sheath radiation might result.

Satisfactory results were always obtained with folded dipoles and 4:1 coaxial baluns. A very simple, but quite efficient solution for 23 cm is shown in Fig 8. Conductor diameter is not critical, neither is limb separation, which can be anything from 0.02 to 0.1 λ. The overall folded dipole length must always be 0.473 λ, favoring a slight detuning toward lower frequencies. The use of Hardline for the balun is strongly recommended. In some cases, grounding the middle upper limb of the folded dipole has caused asymmetric excitation of the first directors. Letting it "float" does no harm if the receiver input provides a solid ground. Insulated directors are less sensitive to excitation asymmetry.

Fig 9 shows the gain and SWR curves for a Yagi fed in the manner described above (DL7YC). An improvement was noted by slightly displacing the dipole perpendicular to the element plane. A further smoothing of the impedance curve and a widening of the matching bandwidth (along with other advantages) can be obtained by the use of multiple or screen reflectors, as explained in the following section.

Reflectors

A reflector on a Yagi antenna serves two basic purposes—to suppress backward radiation and to help focus energy on the director chain. The effect on gain is often overestimated. Y23RD has experimented in this area and found that rarely is more than 1 dB lost when the reflector is removed. Conversely, reports of significantly higher gain resulting from exotic reflector arrangements must be treated with utmost skepticism. Additional forward gain can only result from suppression of unwanted radiation. If there are no major rear lobes with one reflector, little or nothing is to be gained by adding more!

There are, however, good reasons for recommending the use of multiple or grid reflectors on UHF/SHF Yagis. As more and more directors are added, the rear radiation "panorama" undergoes some changes. Lobes appear, move, and disappear, causing the F/B ratio and feed impedance to fluctuate. A planar, multiple-rod or "sheet" reflector tends to reduce these effects significantly, necessitating less experimentation by the builder.

The outer dimensions of a grid or sheet reflector should be 0.6 λ in height and width, spaced about 0.2 λ

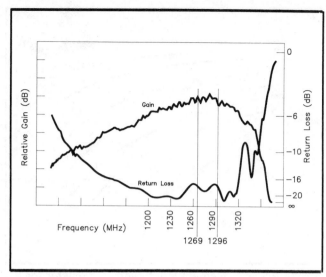

Fig 9—Gain and return loss curves of a long (13-λ) 23-cm Yagi.

behind the driver. Four 0.6 λ rods spaced 0.2 λ from each other will do the same job. Spacing may be varied slightly for an optimum match.

Do not expect more than 0.2 dB of extra gain from this or any other "enlarged" reflector on a long Yagi. However, F/B ratio improvements of up to 6 dB are common. Remember that a 26 dBd array with a 20 dB F/B ratio still has 6 dB of "backward gain" over a dipole! At high output power levels, this extraneous radiation can be quite a nuisance.

PRACTICAL CONSTRUCTION

Required Precision

Well-designed Yagis have bandwidths of several percent, so it would seem adequate to maintain 1% or about 0.005-λ precision for element lengths. When directly copying a tested design this should be sufficient. However, if scaling is necessary, or dimensions have to be determined from graphs, additional sources of error come into play. Therefore, the precision of 0.003 λ called for in the *National Bureau of Standards Technical Note 688* is quite realistic.[5] This means cutting elements to about 1 mm (1/32 in) on 23 cm, which is a manageable amount. Gain drops off much more rapidly on the high-frequency side, so the effect of overly long elements is most severe. On the other hand, it is easier to trim the elements shorter than to cut new, longer ones.

Element spacing strongly affects the value of feed impedance. This is important if groups of identical antennas are to be built. Slight deviations from the recommended spacing sequence have little or no effect on gain, but all antennas in an array must have the same impedance, or feed imbalance and pattern distortion will result. All booms should be marked off together to ensure accuracy.

Element Mounting

From the electrical point of view the best way of mounting elements is above the boom, on insulators. Excitation symmetry is not a problem, and boom influence is minimal. Unfortunately, ready-made insulators are hard to find, and mass fabrication at home can become quite tedious. Almost any material that can withstand weather and ultraviolet radiation will do, because elements are held at the voltage node. Rectangular plastic blocks with two holes for "pop" rivets and a transverse hole for the element have been used successfully. If lots are big enough (club project, large arrays), small machine shops might be interested in making them. For elements mounted through or on top of the boom, in direct contact, a lasting electrical connection must be assured or performance will quickly deteriorate. Soldering or welding the connection would be fine, but is usually impractical because of the materials used. With fairly elastic metals a lasting press-fit should be obtainable. Make sure it is tight on both sides of the boom!

Plastic shoulder washers have been used with good results to insulate elements passing through the boom. Retaining rings or a couple of dabs of silicone rubber can be used to secure the elements. Also, there is a type of hollow nylon rivet used for fastening metal plates that expands by driving in a nylon peg. These make excellent insulators by forcing the elements through instead of the pegs.

There might be problems with insulated elements running through thick booms because of shielding effects. One-inch (25 mm) booms used on 70 cm and 3/8-inch (10 mm) on 23 cm have not produced any negative effects.

Dipole Mounting

A weatherproof and mechanically stable connection of the (usually heavy) feed line to the dipole is one of the major problems in home construction of Yagis. In most cases the use of a rigidly mounted type-N connector provides the best solution. Well-designed commercial antennas use this arrangement. In many areas, the advent of CATV is making UHF TV antennas obsolete, yielding dipole units that can often be salvaged from discarded antennas and adapted for amateur use.

Open-wire feeders are well suited for use with folded dipoles—no baluns are needed. Although it is an attractive proposition on 70 cm, precision requirements might be hard to meet on the higher bands.

Field Distortion by Structural Parts

The potential of a metal part to obstruct the field of an antenna is determined by its size, orientation and proximity. Energy in a Yagi propagates within a narrow cross section before it starts to expand near the open end. Therefore, the area of highest (near) field strength has the approximate shape of a funnel. The cylindrical part of the "funnel" has a diameter roughly equivalent to one optimum stacking distance (see the later section on stacking), while the conical part extends several wavelengths out past the front. This space should be kept free of sizable metallic objects running parallel to the elements.

Of course, field strength is highest between the directors, near the boom. This is why even small objects, like screws protruding from a mast clamp, can severely distort the field. The mast itself will cause pattern asymmetry if it is thicker than about $1/10 \lambda$. This also holds true for masts passing on one side of the boom, through the plane of the elements.

Masts thicker than 3 inches (75 mm) on 70 cm or 1 inch (25 mm) on 23 cm should be avoided if they must pass through the antenna. Needless to say, a mast running through the antenna, parallel to the elements, will ruin the pattern completely. Even a "one-sided" mount of this type causes severe distortion—some people forget that mounting a vertically polarized Yagi on an insulated pole and running the feed line down this pole has the same effect.

It is difficult to predict the influence of small parts, feed lines, other antennas, and so forth, on the radiation pattern. A reasonable check is to measure SWR before and after mounting the antenna or nearby obstruction in question. If a change is evident, you can be sure of interaction; however, *the reverse isn't always true!*

Practical Design Examples

For those who do not wish to calculate their own antenna dimensions, Tables 2 through 5 and Figs 10 through 13 contain ready-to-use information for a number of antennas. Represented are 14- and 27-element designs for 432 MHz, and 26- and 48-element versions for

Table 2

Dimensions of a 14-Element 432-MHz Yagi

Element	Length (mm)	Spacing (mm)
REF	345	130
DE	328	—
D1	308	55
D2	304	125
D3	300	150
D4	296	175
D5	293	195
D6	293	210
D7	289	220
D8	289	230
D9	289	240
D10	285	250
D11	285	260
D12	281	260

Note: Boom is 20 mm square. Elements are 4 mm diameter and mounted through the boom but insulated by shoulder washers. Feed system is a folded dipole.

Table 3
Dimensions of a 27-Element 432-MHz Yagi

Element	Length (mm)	Spacing (mm)
REF1-4	345	130
DE	328	—
D1	309	55
D2	305	125
D3	300	150
D4	296	175
D5	294	195
D6	292	210
D7	290	220
D8	290	230
D9	285	240
D10	285	250
D11	285	260
D12	280	265
D13	280	270
D14	280	275
D15-17	280	280
D18-23	275	280
D24,25	270	280

Note: Boom is 20 mm square. Elements are 4 mm diameter and mounted through the boom but insulated by shoulder washers. Feed system is a folded dipole. There are four reflectors.

Table 5
Dimensions of a 48-Element 1296-MHz Yagi

Element	Length (mm)	Spacing (mm)
REF	124	50
DE	110	—
D1	110	18
D2	109	42
D3	108	50
D4	107	58
D5	106	65
D6	105	70
D7	104	73
D8	103	76
D9	102	80
D10	102	83
D11	101	86
D12	101	90
D13	101	92
D14-16	100	92
D17-20	99	92
D21-25	98	92
D26-31	97	92
D32-39	96	92
D40-46	95	92

Note: Boom is 15 mm. Elements are 2 mm diameter and mounted through the boom with full electrical contact (not insulated). Feed system is a folded dipole.

Table 4
Dimensions of a 26-Element 1296-MHz Yagi

Element	Length (mm)	Spacing (mm)
REF	118.0	50
DE	110.0	—
D1	104.0	18
D2	102.5	42
D3	101.0	50
D4	99.5	58
D5	98.0	65
D6	97.0	70
D7	96.0	73
D8	95.0	76
D9	94.0	80
D10	94.0	83
D11	93.0	86
D12	93.0	90
D13	92.0	92
D14	92.0	92
D15	92.0	92
D16-18	91.0	92
D19-21	90.0	92
D22-24	89.0	92

Note: Boom is 0.5 inch (12.7 mm) square. Elements are 4 mm diameter and mounted through the boom with full electrical contact (not insulated). Feed system is a folded dipole.

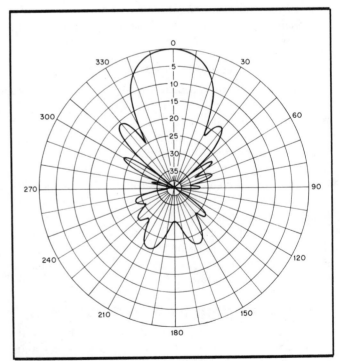

Fig 10—Measured E-plane pattern of the 14-element, 70-cm Yagi in Table 2.

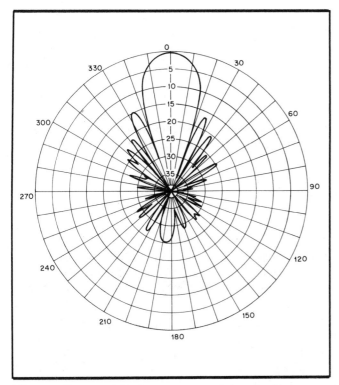

Fig 11—Measured E-plane pattern of the 27-element, 70-cm Yagi in Table 3.

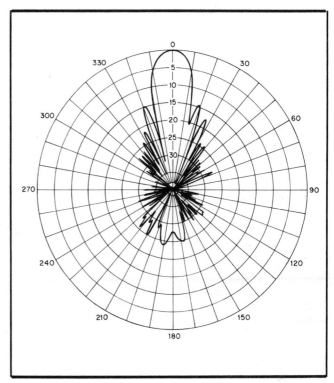

Fig 13—Measured E-plane pattern of the 48-element, 23-cm Yagi in Table 5.

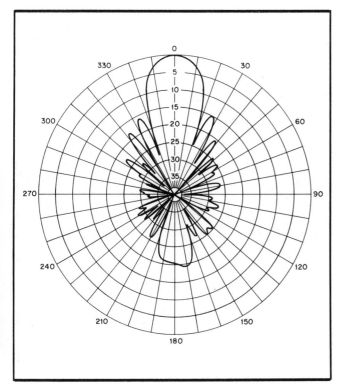

Fig 12—Measured E-plane pattern of the 26-element, 23-cm Yagi in Table 4.

1296 MHz. If minor differences appear between calculated and stated dimensions, they are of no consequence to performance.

STACKING AND POWER DIVISION

Stacking Gain

Perhaps the easiest way of explaining stacking gain is through the concept of effective areas. If two antennas are separated far enough in a field (so the effective areas do not overlap), they will capture twice the power of one. Since antennas function the same way on reception and transmission, the power is doubled (+ 3 dB) in both cases. The necessary stacking distance is determined by the size and shape of the effective areas (treated later in the *Optimum Spacing* section).

Stacking Pattern Formation

In contrast to gain, radiation pattern formation is more easily understood in the transmitting mode. If power from one source is coherently radiated by two antennas, there will be regions of power addition and cancellation, depending on phase relationship. The power emanating from point sources P_1 and P_2 in Fig 14 (equal power, equal phase) will add up at all points that are equidistant from both sources; these points all lie on the horizontal

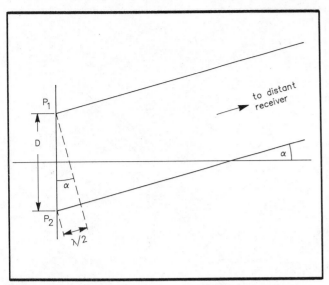

Fig 14—Condition for phase cancellation of radiation from two point sources, P_1 and P_2, separated by distance, D.

axis. Power will also add in all points where the difference in distance to both sources is a multiple of 1 λ (phase difference = 360°, 720°, and so on).

Cancellation will occur where the path difference is λ/2 or odd multiples thereof (phase difference = 180°, 540°, and so on). The associated directions indicated by the angle α can be calculated from Fig 14 with simple geometry. For the mth lobe (field maximum):

$$\alpha_m = \frac{m \lambda}{D} \qquad \text{(Eq 6)}$$

For the nth null (field cancellation):

$$\alpha_n = \frac{(n - 0.5) \lambda}{D} \qquad \text{(Eq 7)}$$

where D is the distance between the two point sources. Depending on the ratio of D to λ, there will be a sequence of nulls and lobes when α is altered, forming a radiation pattern. If there are more than two sources field relationships become more complicated. Numerous minor lobes are formed by partial phase addition and cancellation.

The Superimposition Principle

Thus far only point sources (isotropic radiators) have been considered. The previously described procedure can also be used to calculate the H-plane patterns of dipoles stacked in a row, since they look like point sources when viewed from the end. For the corresponding E-plane pattern we must consider the patterns of each individual dipole. There is no radiation off the ends of a dipole; even if a like arrangement of point sources produced a lobe in this direction, it would be suppressed. Therefore, the E-plane pattern of a row of dipoles looks like that of a row

of point sources superimposed on the pattern of a single dipole. This principle holds true for groups of any type of antenna, even for groups of groups.

If, for example, two Yagis are stacked and we want to know the pattern in the stacking plane, we must superimpose the pattern of two imaginary point sources at the same spacing with a Yagi pattern in the same plane. Where radiation from the point sources would cancel, there will be no radiation from the Yagi array. Obviously, if the individual Yagi patterns have strong minor lobes, chances are they will coincide with lobes from the imaginary point sources and produce "grating lobes" of considerable strength, far off the desired beam heading.

Optimum Spacing

The simplest case of stacking involves just two antennas. Theoretically, the best spacing occurs when the effective apertures just meet. At smaller spacings there would be a loss of capture area; at larger spacings there would be no sacrifice in gain, but an unnecessary splitting up of the pattern (and additional loss in the phasing lines). The optimum distance (D_{opt}), based on the assumption of a circular capture area determined from real gain, turns out to be

$$D_{opt} = \frac{\lambda}{2 \sin\left(\frac{\phi}{2}\right)} \qquad \text{(Eq 8)}$$

where ϕ = the half power beamwidth. For long Yagis (ϕ < 30°), D_{opt} is equal to 57 λ/ϕ. Computer simulation and practical measurements have confirmed this to be the distance beyond which there is no noticeable gain increase.

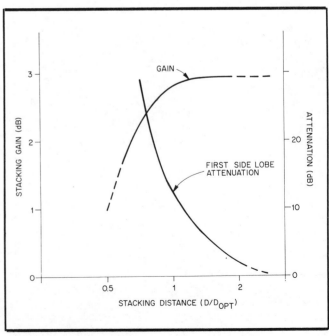

Fig 15—Stacking gain and sidelobe level versus normalized stacking distance (two antennas).

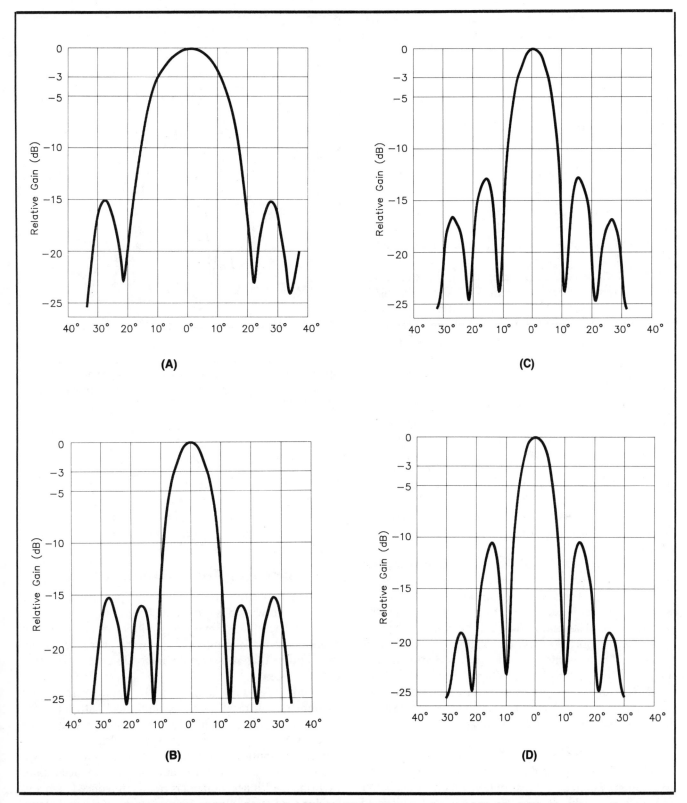

Fig 16—Computer-generated H-plane pattern of a single, 22° half-power beamwidth Yagi (A). H-plane patterns are given for pairs of similar Yagis stacked at 0.9 D_{opt} (B), D_{opt} (C) and 1.1 D_{opt} (D).

For example, the H-plane aperture angle of a 1296-MHz loop Yagi was measured to be 20°. From Eq 8, the optimum stacking distance (in wavelengths) is determined:

$$D_{opt} = \frac{\lambda}{2 \sin 10°} = 2.88 \, \lambda$$

(The approximate formula $57 \, \lambda \, / \, \phi$ would yield 2.85 λ.) The wavelength, λ, is

$$\frac{3 \times 10^8}{1.296 \times 10^9} = 0.2315 \text{ m}$$

So, D_{opt} would be about 0.666 meter, or 26.25 inches. Fig 15 shows stacking gain and first sidelobe level as a function of normalized stacking distance (with D_{opt} taken from Eq 8).

DJ9BV's calculated patterns for a single and two stacked Yagis at different spacings are shown in Fig 16 (A-D). One can see that significantly better sidelobe suppression can be obtained at a very small gain sacrifice by slightly understacking. For two antennas, a spacing of 0.9 to 0.95 D_{opt} looks like an excellent compromise in both the E and H planes—the benefits are independent of polarization.

Similar calculations were carried out for rows of three and four Yagis. They led to interesting findings:
• D_{opt} remains the same, regardless of the number of antennas stacked.
• The first sidelobe (and the second, in the case of 4 antennas) remains almost unchanged for large departures from D_{opt}.
• The best overall sidelobe suppression occurs at or slightly beyond D_{opt}; hence there is no case for understacking.

Practice has confirmed the above findings in most cases. Where larger differences were reported, they could usually be traced to the constituent Yagis—if they possess high sidelobe radiation, interaction can lead to grossly unequal power distribution. The best stacking results have always been reported with Yagis exhibiting low sidelobe radiation. This is particularly true for EME arrays where sidelobe noise pickup is a problem. Fig 17 shows the measured E-plane pattern of such an array, six K2RIW 19-element Yagis stacked two high and three wide, spaced in accordance with the above findings.

Power Distribution

All that has been said about stacking is based on the assumption of even power distribution, that is, equal power and phase at each antenna. This distribution will yield maximum array gain, usually of prime interest to amateur designers. To achieve this, the feed system must be laid out accordingly. Before proceeding, a word of caution is in order: *leave transforming-type feed lines to the "specialists."* Amateurs should use matched, low-SWR coaxial sections and high grade λ/4 transformers or combiners. At UHF and SHF, coaxial cable has enough loss

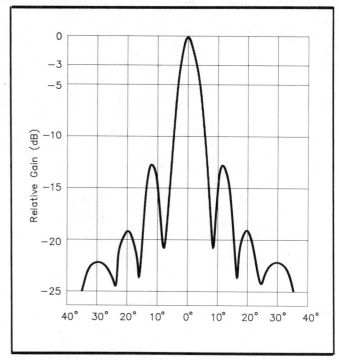

Fig 17—Measured E-plane pattern of six 25° half-power beamwidth Yagis stacked two high and three wide, spaced 2.23 λ.

without putting standing waves on it. Cascading transformers means cascading lossy distribution sections, so try to obtain your gain with four or six *long* Yagis before extending to eight or sixteen, which cannot be fed from one distribution point.

Uneven Power Distribution

Any departure from an evenly spaced and excited array design will cause marked changes in the radiation pattern. There are so many possibilities of changing (on purpose or inadvertently) the power, phase or spatial distribution that it is next to impossible to catalog the consequences.

Only a few typical cases can be named here: power asymmetry will result in an asymmetrical pattern; phase asymmetry will cause squint (that is, a shifting of the main lobe away from boresight). A symmetrical, but uneven power distribution favoring the "outer" antennas will produce increased sidelobe radiation and reduced gain; favoring the "inner" antennas results in reduced gain and sidelobe radiation, along with a widening of the main lobe. The latter can be desirable if low noise is the prime goal. The distortion arising from symmetrical, but uneven power distribution can be caused by coupling between adjacent antennas, which is stronger on the inner sections of an array. As a remedy for the distortion, a slight relocation of the inner Yagis could be tried. Interaction seems to be strongest with Yagis having insufficient sidelobe suppression.

Open-Wire Feeders

In contrast to what has been said about transforming coaxial cable sections, there is a case for open-wire feed lines in 70-cm EME arrays. Open-wire losses are primarily caused by resistance ($N = I^2 R$), and in high-impedance lines current is low even with standing waves present. Only a few hints can be given here. Use one characteristic impedance throughout the system (400 Ω is a good value), and try to limit SWR to 2:1. Provide a variable balun section at the point of transformation to coaxial cable, because you never end up with exactly 200 Ω. See Figs 18 and 19.

Design your Yagis to fit the feed harness, for you have no way of changing the spacing. The characteristic impedance of a two-wire feeder is

$$Z \approx 276 \log \frac{2D}{d} \qquad \text{(Eq 9)}$$

where

    d = the wire diameter
    D = the center-to-center spacing

Construction of Power Dividers

Probably the best material to build dividers from is 1-inch-OD square tubing. Type N sockets fit on the outside perfectly. Brass or aluminum are good for the sleeve, but copper should be used for the center conductor. Silver coating the center conductor isn't really necessary, perhaps saving 0.1 dB on 23 cm. Plastic plugs can be used for the open ends of the divider, but a ventilation hole should be provided to keep water from condensation from accumulating.

The characteristic impedance of a coaxial line with a square outer conductor is

$$Z \approx 138 \log 1.08 \frac{D}{d} \qquad \text{(Eq 10)}$$

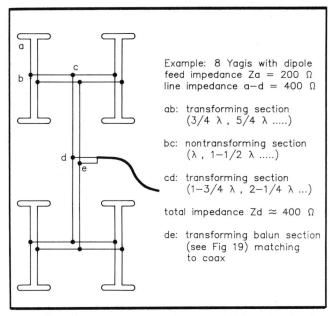

Fig 18—Feed harness for eight Yagis with 200-Ω feed impedances.

where
    D = the inner width of the outer sleeve
    d = the OD of the inner conductor

Assuming D is 7/8 inch, a 35.4-Ω section transforming 50 Ω to 25 Ω would have a ½-inch-OD inner conductor.

For higher transformation ratios (4, 6 and 8-way dividers), λ/2 T sections should be used because of the greater bandwidth (and because one cannot put six connectors around a four-sided coaxial line!). The six-way transformer uses a 40.8-Ω line to match three 50-Ω ports in parallel to 100 Ω on either side of the center connector. If D is again 7/8 inch, the center conductor for the six-way unit is 7/16-inch OD.

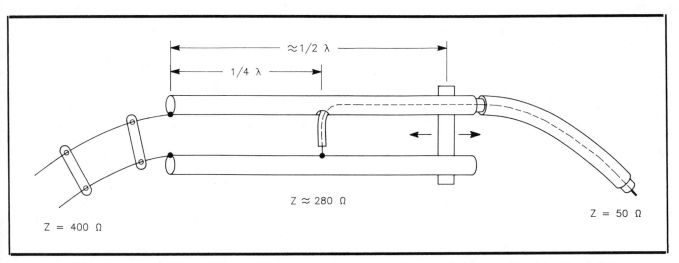

Fig 19—Transformer/balun. The position of the short and exact spacing are determined by experimentation.

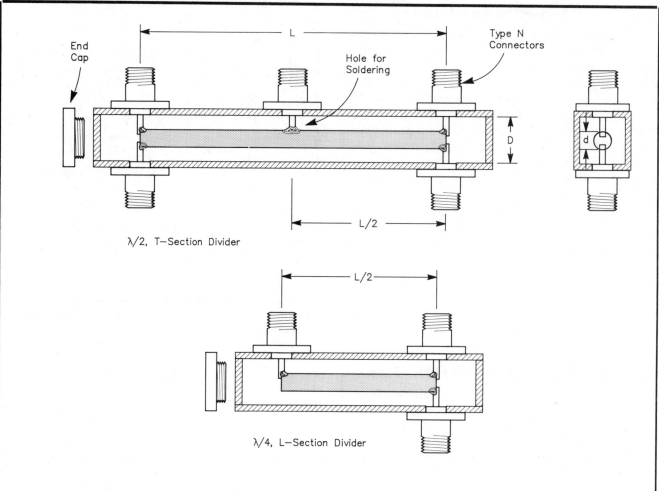

(Length of λ/2, T—Section dividers; divide by 2 for λ/4, L—Section type)

f (MHz)	L (mm)	L (inches)
432	347	13–13/16
1296	116	4–9/16
2304	65	2–9/16

Division ratio	λ/4 L Section		λ/2 L Section	
	Z	D/d	Z	D/d
2:1	35.4 Ω	1.67	70.7 Ω	2.98
3:1	28.9 Ω	1.50		
4:1	25.0 Ω	1.40	50.0 Ω	2.13
6:1			40.8 Ω	1.83
8:1			35.4 Ω	1.67

Above table is only valid for 50–Ω systems

Fig 20—Construction details of coaxial power dividers (see text).

For other configurations, see Fig 20. The length of the inner conductor must be exactly λ/4 or λ/2 end-to-end; the same goes for the center-to-center spacing of the connectors. Make the sleeve long enough to receive the end plugs. It should be noted that if wideband performance is not a must, dividers can be used in the third-harmonic mode. A 70-cm T divider, suspended in the radiator plane of four or six 23-cm Yagis will make an excellent feed with very short coaxial lines.

ANTENNA TESTING

Because of the precision involved, building antennas for the UHF and SHF bands isn't exactly for the novice. Unless you assemble a kit (and sometimes even then!), you are likely to make something a little different, resulting in a change in performance. The curves and dimensions presented in the preceding sections are meant to be an experimenter's guide, rather than a cookbook. Antennas patterned after them will work, but most builders want optimum performance. So, before putting up or even building, say, 16 long Yagis, a prototype should be made and tested.

For a solid background in antenna testing procedures, study of Fred Brown's *QST* article is recommended.[6] Once these principles are in hand, simple equipment and minimal proficiency are all that one needs to perform sufficiently accurate antenna tests.

Test Range Requirements

For really precise measurements, the antenna under test must be placed in a homogeneous field. Throughout the capture area, there should be no change of field strength nor any deviation from a plane phase distribution. Yagi antennas have considerable length, so the source must be far enough away to avoid excessive dropoff of the field strength between both antenna ends.

The "natural enemies" of antenna measurement are reflections. Ground and objects within the beam of the illuminating source antenna can cause standing waves, and thus field inhomogeneities. If you have ever witnessed how hard it is to remove these even from so-called anechoic chambers, you won't be surprised by the inaccuracy of amateur gain and pattern measurements.

For checking the performance of a Yagi, an undistorted field is required, the size of which is roughly determined by rotating the antenna about its center, in all axes. IEC Standard 136 calls for less than 0.5 dB of field strength ripple within this volume—amateurs can settle for about twice this value.

Evaluating the Test Range

A handy tool, not only for checking a test site, is a dipole-reflector assembly, or better yet, a multiple reflector assembly. The reflector(s) shields the dipole from reflections off your body when holding it from behind, probing the field. You'll get nowhere with a bare dipole! If it is your back yard where you want to do the testing, set up a source antenna close to the ground, radiating away from buildings. Use a beam no wider than necessary to illuminate the required volume evenly. Fix your probe where the test antennas will go and raise the source until you find the first maximum reading. (There will be higher peak readings as the source is raised further, but the resulting homogeneous field volumes will be smaller.) Then probe the "test volume" for homogeneity.

After some experimenting you will probably find a combination of positions that will bestow you with a fairly evenly illuminated volume 60 to 80 feet away from the source antenna. (The distance should be great enough so the antenna under test cannot distinguish between the source and the image below ground.) Since these combinations will differ from band to band, it pays to note them for future use. Now that a suitable test site has been established, what can be achieved with it?

• A backyard range will *not* allow precision pattern measurements.

• It will allow a fairly good gain comparison between similar antennas.

• The main lobe and others can be analyzed with sufficient accuracy to draw conclusions about design changes (with the aid of the earlier *Yagi Theory* section).

Beamwidth Measurement

If a calibrated detector is at hand, it is quite easy to measure the half-power beamwidth. Even a simple beam aiming setup, such as a garden umbrella footing, a piece of tubing with a wire pointer attached to it, and a large protractor will fulfill the requirements. The antenna is simply rotated on both sides of the boresight axis, noting the angular displacement at the −3 dB points. This is the half-power beamwidth of the antenna.

Checking the plausibility of this measurement is easily done, too. After the indicated power has passed the −3 dB points, it will quickly drop further as the antenna is rotated, pass through a pronounced null and rise to the peak of the first sidelobe. The angle between the two nulls on either side of the boresight is at most equal to twice the half-power beamwidth. For long antennas, about 6 λ or more, the front lobe is practically circular in cross section. Half-power beamwidth is the same in both polarization planes and the beamwidth/nullwidth ratio is 0.50. Shorter Yagis have slightly wider beamwidths in the H plane, and the E plane half-power beamwidth is less than one-half the nullwidth by a few percent. At 3 λ, the overall ratio is about 0.475. The null angles are usually easier to measure than the −3 dB angles—in many cases this is sufficient information.

Sidelobe Attenuation

After passing through the null, the indicated power rises to a value representing the first sidelobe. The difference between this value and that of the main lobe is the sidelobe attenuation. Further off the boresight, more sidelobe peaks may be detectable, but anything lower than 20 dB below the main lobe can hardly be trusted on a simple outdoor range. Large sidelobe asymmetries are either due to range deficiencies or a feed imbalance. The latter can be detected by flipping the test antenna over.

Front-to-Back Ratio

The F/B ratio of a long Yagi should always be higher than the gain over a dipole. Unfortunately, F/B ratio can rarely be measured to any degree of accuracy on backyard ranges. An excessively strong rear lobe should always arouse suspicion, however.

SWR Measurement

SWR is not as important as some people think. Of course, even an exceptionally good antenna will not work well when it is totally mismatched. Fortunately, correcting this problem is easier than turning an "air-cooled dummy load" into a good antenna! Regardless, checking the SWR over the expected operating frequency range can reveal a lot about performance. Besides, it might tell why your

GaAsFET preamplifier oscillates at 415 MHz, despite a perfect match at 432 MHz.

Unlike Yagis with only a few elements, long, stagger-tuned UHF/SHF Yagis do not have just one or two resonances. The SWR curve will be more of the "bathtub" type, especially when the recommended multiple reflectors are used (Fig 9). On the high-frequency side of resonance the curve will show pronounced ripple, followed by a sharp rise associated with the upper limit of the gain passband. Beyond this edge there usually are two or three deep and narrow dips in SWR, corresponding to self-resonant modes of the antenna operating as a disrupted waveguide. These dips are most pronounced in homogeneous (equally spaced, uniform-element-length) Yagis. A little pruning, as described in the *Feed Methods* section, will help move one of the small SWR "valleys" to your favorite operating frequency, or provide improved overall SWR.

Performance Analysis

Data gathered from the simple measurements described in the preceding subsections can be used for performance analysis. Gain can be estimated from Fig 2 when beamwidth and sidelobe attenuation are known.

With Yagis of any type, the first null is a good indicator of correct performance. If there is no more than a shallow "shoulder" instead of a pronounced dip of about −20 dB, you can be sure that you are operating above the optimum frequency. First E-plane sidelobes less than 13 dB below the main lobe (10 dB in the H plane) also indicate improper dimensions.

Gain Measurement

Although gain is usually referenced to a dipole, never attempt to measure this power ratio directly! Aside from the difficulty of measuring large power ratios with amateur means, stray pickup by the dipole will, in most cases, render the results useless. Comparison to a reference antenna with known gain, preferably of the same order, is much easier. For medium-gain antennas the EIA standard is fine. This standard antenna—two λ/2 dipoles fed in phase, spaced λ/2 and mounted λ/4 in front of a 1-λ × 1-λ ground plane—has a gain of 7.7 dBd. For high-gain antennas, especially above 1300 MHz, a standard gain horn is recommended as a reference.

Fig 21 shows the various methods of measuring gain on a test range. Direct comparison by a ratiometer (A) is optimum.[7] It eliminates source and range instabilities, but calls for a large homogeneous test field volume (the antennas must not couple, even when turned!). The apparatus is quite expensive, too. Sequential comparison by exchanging test and reference antennas (B) must be done with great care. Any change of source power and other parameters will enter into the measurement. Sufficient accuracy can be obtained, however, if the test is repeated often enough. An acceptable compromise is the setup in (C), which cross references all readings to an auxiliary antenna, whose gain need not be known. It may be positioned at the edge of the usable field.

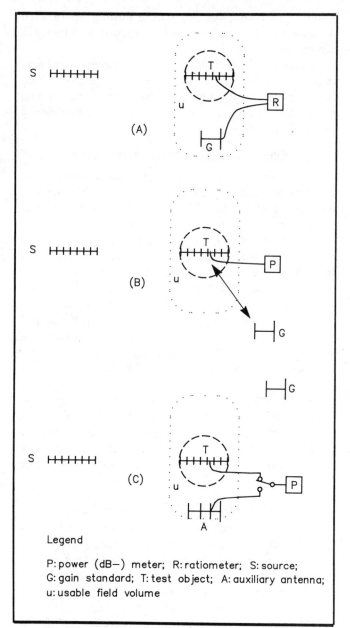

Fig 21—Gain measurement methods: ratiometry (A), sequential comparison (B) and cross referencing (C).

Regardless of the measurement method used, all results should be compared to the beamwidth/gain graph in Fig 2. It will reveal gross errors immediately.

Gain-Bandwidth Measurement

This topic is somewhat beyond the scope of this discussion, but a few hints might be welcome. When testing for gain bandwidth, use two *identical* antennas—one for transmitting and one for receiving. Sweep the frequency range at constant power. Use a feed line of typical loss and a matched detector to simulate SWR effects—this is what happens in practice. Be sure to divide all gain deviations by 2, as they enter twice—once for each antenna.

Some of the test methods treated previously can be

roughly performed by using no more than a beacon signal and an S meter. They were presented in more detail to encourage more meaningful and accurate experimentation. Amateur Radio is, first of all, an experimental service! The relatively small dimensions of UHF/SHF antennas make them ideal for toying with in the backyard. In our world of digitalized electronics, there is hardly a better way of getting the "feel" of RF.

Computer-based Yagi Optimization

The Yagi design procedure presented in the preceding sections was derived experimentally in the late '70s when computer analysis of antennas was still in the development stage.

Around 1980 a series of publications, namely by the late James Lawson, W2PV, called the attention of a large public to this matter. At about the same time moderately priced Personal Computers became available and an explosion of amateur and semi-professional work on Yagi optimization set in. Doubts of the accuracy of simplified models of idealized antennas were washed away by the sheer beauty of 5-digit gain figures. Obvious discrepancies were blamed on the experimenters who, as in the NBS case, often could not protest anymore.

Meanwhile, much of the smoke has cleared away and a first evaluation can be attempted. As of 1988 there are three classes of antenna analysis programs available:

A) The "NEC" class characterized by segmentation of elements and the "method of moments" for current computation. It employs multiple precision matrix algebra and allows the consideration of lossy ground and skin effect loss. "NEC" stands for Numerical Electromagnetics Code; it was developed by the US Naval Ocean Systems Center and runs on mainframe computers only.

B) The "MININEC" class. Programs of this class also employ element segmentation and the method of moments. Simpler algebra is used and infinite conductivity of ground and elements assumed to permit running on mini computers and larger personal computers.

C) The so-called "Lawson" programs. These are based on W2PV's rather crude element self-impedance function and use half-wave dipoles only for computation of mutual impedance. Element currents are assumed sinusoidal and ohmic loss is neglected.

At the time this is written, there appear to be only a handful of hams, worldwide, who have occasional access to type-A programs. The author is greatly indebted to Rainer Bertelsmeier, DJ9BV, who spent many hours repeating test-range experiments on the computer and discussing the results.

For multi-element Yagi antennas, the precision of highest-grade computer simulation approaches that of good open-air test-range measurements. If loss is taken into account, gain figures match within 0.2 dB. Dimensions and frequency data are modeled to 0.5%, patterns to about 1° of angle and about 1 dB for the first sidelobe; the accuracy diminishes toward the higher-order lobes, which are equally uncertain on all but good anechoic chamber test sites. Type-C programs are typically one-half order of magnitude less accurate, which is not so bad if one considers the enormous difference in required computer power. MININEC-type programs are in between, accuracy depending on the number of segments per element and on the precision of the approximation algorithms used. The most serious drawback of the latter two program classes is the neglecting of loss, that is, radiation efficiency. Extensive experimentation with MININEC showed that introducing a load of 0.3...0.5 Ω at the center of each element can be a reasonable substitute for skin-effect calculations.

Automatic (self-searching) optimization of multi-element Yagi structures is still beyond the capability even of large main-frame computers. If segmentation is chosen fine enough for meaningful results, run times for a 10-λ array are in the minute range per optimization step. This rules out random perturbation of all element lengths and spacings, and allows only systematic probing around a good basic design. Ohmic loss must be considered, to avoid running into high-current "super gain" modes which usually cannot be produced with finite-conductivity real-world elements. This is why some optimization attempts have produced nonsense results, although the programs used model existing designs quite satisfactorily. By and large it can be stated that computer modeling has become a most valuable instrument in antenna design, not by making experiments superfluous but by greatly reducing their necessary number.

Foreseeable advances in matrix algebra and computer architecture will put automatic optimization of large arrays within reach of main frame computers in the coming decade. At least until then a standard design procedure like the one presented here will remain an indispensable tool.

Notes

[1]Kraus, *Antennas* (New York: McGraw-Hill, 1950).

[2]G. Hoch, "Extremely Long Yagi Antennas," *VHF Communications*, 1982 no. 3, pp 130-138.

[3]Jessop, Ed., *VHF/UHF Manual*, 4th Ed (Potters Bar, England: RSGB, 1983).

[4]Available as a PC program by Bob Stein, KY4Z. An updated version (DL6WU-G.BAS) was released by Ian F. White, G3SEK, in 1987.

[5]P. Viezbicke, "Yagi Antenna Design," *NBS Technical Note 688*, US Department of Commerce, Washington, DC, Dec 1976 (out of print).

[6]F. Brown, "Antenna Gain Measurements" (Parts 1 and 2), *QST*, Nov 1982, pp 35-37, and Dec 1982, pp 27-31.

[7]R. Knadle, "UHF Antenna Ratiometry," *QST*, Feb 1976, pp 22-25. See also "Feedback," *QST*, Apr 1976, p 57.

An Optimum Design for 432-MHz Yagis

By Steve Powlishen, K1FO
816 Summer Hill Rd
Madison, CT 06443

The latest rage in 432-MHz Yagi design seems to be extremely long antennas—more than 10 wavelengths. I spent nearly two years perfecting two different 10.5-wavelength designs (24-foot boom length) and presented the results of those efforts in 1986 at the major VHF/UHF conferences. Frank Potts, NC1I, successfully used one of the 10.5-wavelength designs in a 16-Yagi earth-moon-earth (EME) array. Frank's success encouraged me to plan a 26.0-dBd-gain array using eight of those Yagis. The antennas would be stacked two wide by four high and located 80 feet high for tropo and EME use. After thoroughly researching this planned array, however, I came up with a different solution. This article describes my efforts.

WILL IT STAY UP?

An often overlooked antenna design consideration is windload. Windload is the force put on a structure by wind blowing against it. I live in an area where ice loading combined with moderate winds can quickly destroy a poorly engineered antenna system. With this in mind, I analyzed possible antenna configurations for gain versus windload.

Calculations showed that the eight-Yagi array would cause the collapse of my present Rohn 25 tower the first time winds exceeded 40 mi/h! The eight long Yagis, stacking frame and cables exhibit a total windload area of nearly 40 sq ft. Since the Yagis were to be elevated for EME, the array had to be centered more than 14 feet above the top guy wires. I calculated the bending moment for this configuration in an 80 mi/h wind. The resultant force of almost 17,000 foot-pounds is nearly the level that would collapse a Rohn 55 tower and three times that which would destroy a Rohn 25 tower. These sobering figures encouraged me to find another way to construct a high-gain 432-MHz array.

Next, I examined a plan that used 16 moderately sized Yagis. Using low-windload, lightweight antennas (similar in size and mechanical construction to the popular K2RIW 19-element design), a 16-Yagi array has a windload area of 32 sq ft. The antenna booms are much shorter, so this array has to be mounted only nine feet above the top tower guys. The resultant bending moment on the tower for the array of 16 shorter Yagis is a manageable 8600 foot-pounds—half that of the array of eight long Yagis. I anticipated that the 16-Yagi array would have 27.0 dBd gain. In terms of gain versus windload, the array of shorter antennas seemed to be a better approach. The only penalty would be a more complicated feed system.

As an interim step, I decided on a 25.7-dBd-gain array of 12 shorter Yagis. The 12-Yagi array has a windload area of 24 sq ft and a bending moment of 6500 foot pounds. My over-guyed Rohn 25 tower could handle this antenna.

YAGI DEVELOPMENT

Once I decided on the array configuration, the next step was to choose an antenna design. The 19-element K2RIW Yagi (RIW 19) is enormously popular in North America because of its

- light weight
- low windload
- clean pattern (except for rear lobe)
- self-supporting boom (no braces required)
- good wet and dry weather performance.

I had been using arrays of RIW 19s for several years with good success. I had learned enough from working with Yagis extensively over the past few years, however, to convince me that a much better design could be had within the same approximate windload as the RIW Yagi. In March 1986, I started work on a new moderate sized Yagi, one that I hoped would become a replacement for the RIW design. The design criteria included

- low windload (<1 sq ft)
- light weight (<4 lb)
- no boom support
- gain about 1 dB better than the RIW 19
- improved pattern compared to the RIW 19:
  E-plane sidelobes −17 dB or better
  H-plane sidelobes −16 dB or better
  H-plane minor lobes substantially better
  rear lobe −20 dB or better (5 dB improvement)
  lobes on either side of rear lobe −25 dB

Much of the design and analysis work was done using MININEC, a microcomputer-based antenna analysis program. Modeling antennas on the computer makes it possible to try many designs without drilling a single boom. I do not have sufficient computer power, or a sophisticated enough Yagi analysis program, to simultaneously optimize element spacing and element lengths. I started with a spacing pattern based upon knowledge and experience and used the computer to optimize element lengths. Several possibilities came to mind.

Modifying the RIW 19. Much computer time was spent on this approach because I had a significant investment in RIW 19 Yagis (12 of them to be exact). Although I found I could get more gain out of an RIW 19 by making a longer center boom section and using a single reflector, the RIW design was compromised by change. The target gain could not be reached with a reasonable boom length while keeping a clean pattern.

Using the DL6WU design. The DL6WU antenna is an excellent performer. Its flexible design (it can be made 2 to 14 wavelengths long) requires a trade-off, though: The Yagi will not be optimized for any given boom length. Using the DL6WU element spacing yielded a 20-element Yagi on a 13-ft, 8-in boom. Computer analysis indicated that this antenna would not meet my gain target. If an additional director was added, the boom would be 14 ft, 7 in long. I don't feel comfortable using a self-supporting small-diameter boom of this length. I had previously optimized the DL6WU director lengths for a 31-element, 24-ft Yagi. Reducing this antenna to a 20-element, 13-ft, 8-in Yagi did not give good results; that optimization had negated the variable-length design feature.

Starting from scratch. In this day and age, starting from scratch is almost like reinventing the wheel, and it soon became apparent that it would take a major effort to design from scratch an antenna that would outperform the modified DL6WU design. My objective was to create a better EME array; it was not merely a theoretical exercise.

THE W1EJ DESIGNS

Fortunately, I found someone who had already reinvented the wheel! Tom Kirby, W1EJ, had spent several years working on computer-optimized Yagi designs. Tom found that each Yagi size needs its own set of spacings to achieve the best combination of gain and pattern. He had worked out two geometries that might be suitable for my use. One was a 33-element, 10.6-wavelength (24-ft) model, and the other was a 17-element, 4.5-wavelength (10-ft) version.

I modeled two different approaches on the computer. The first cut the 33-element Yagi to a 22-element version; the second extended the 17-element model to 21 elements. Both the 21- and 22-element models (which use different element spacings) would be about 14 ft long. This is the maximum boom length I felt safe with, considering that my antenna criteria called for a lightweight, low-windload and no-boom-support design.

I built examples of Tom's 33- and 17-element Yagis, but found they performed considerably worse than expected. Careful pattern measurements and further computer analysis indicated that the antennas were tuned too low in frequency. Revised versions of the 33-element Yagi (with shorter elements) gave measured performance near what the computer predicted. This indicated that the W1EJ designs were worth pursuing. It also showed how a computer-created design must go through post-computation measurement and adjustment to verify its performance.

Examination of adjusted computer models of the 21- and 22-element Yagis showed that, as with any engineering design problem, there were trade-offs between both designs —and no clear-cut winner. The 21-element model could be computer tweaked for more gain (15.9 dBd theoretical

versus 15.8 dBd for the 22-element Yagi). The pattern on the 22-element design was easier to control, and it had a significantly smaller rear lobe. When test antennas were constructed, the 22-element version won because of its better pattern (important for EME work). Note that the 21- and 22-element designs are not the ultimate in gain, as their spacings were not specifically optimized for a 14-ft boom length. Optimization of spacings for such a Yagi of this specific length could take several months and produce no more than an additional tenth of a decibel in forward gain!

Tom's computer design work provided antenna dimensions given in tenths of millimeters. I spent the several weeks adjusting the Yagi's geometry on the computer to create an easy-to-build version with dimensions given in US customary units that would retain the theoretical performance of the computer model in real life. In addition, I worked on the "tuned too low" problem. It took only two tries to build a real Yagi with acceptable performance from the computer model.

The finished 22-element antenna was presented at the New England and Central States VHF conferences in 1986. On my home antenna range, I measured an antenna gain of 15.7 dBd—0.8 dB better than an RIW 19. The front-to-back ratio (F/B) measured 20 dB (5 dB better than the RIW). At the New England conference, the measured gain was 0.6 dB better than the RIW; at the Central States conference, it measured 1.0 dB better. Overall pattern measurements showed the 22-element antenna to have a better pattern than the RIW 19.

Computer modeling calculates the 22-element antenna gain to be 0.9 dB more than the RIW 19 with the pattern improvements confirmed on the test range. When you use a computer program to optimize a design, you can never be sure that the design will work as expected. This is because all models have some errors caused by calculation assumptions, algorithm errors or just plain "multiple-calculation build-up" errors. If a design is optimized with an even slightly erroneous calculation, the resultant dimensions will incorporate those errors.

FURTHER OPTIMIZATION

I still wanted to try for a better pattern and more gain before building the new EME array. Another two months were spent further optimizing the design and reworking the dimensions for metric units. I felt that metric units were appropriate if this was to be an antenna design of the 1980s and beyond. The final design has the same gain at 432 MHz (15.7 dBd) and an improved pattern. The peak gain of this Yagi is 1 MHz higher than the previous version (437 MHz). This was done to improve the pattern, assure excellent operation in large arrays and retain that performance in wet weather.

In its final form, no two element length or spacing dimensions are the same. This seems to be characteristic of Yagis with maximum all-around performance. By maximum all-around performance, I mean a combination of a very clean pattern, excellent gain bandwidth and high gain for the boom length.

Resistive Losses

You may wonder where the missing 0.1 dB is between the calculated and measured Yagi gain. Such a small difference (3%) could easily be attributed to calculation error. After several years of building and measuring Yagis and comparing them to computer models, however, I have added correction factors to account for most of the differences.

Resistive losses account for most of the gain difference. Aluminum has an electrical resistance. Because current flows in all elements of a properly designed Yagi, losses will accumulate in the elements. Günter Hoch, DL6WU, has shown that resistive losses are distributed fairly evenly throughout all elements. For maximum performance, the Yagi must be built from material with good conductive characteristics that will perform well in the weather.

Rainer Bertelsmeier, DJ9BV, has analyzed the K1FO 22-element Yagi with the sophisticated NEC3 program and calculated its resistive losses to be about 0.06 dB. Changing to copper elements would reduce these losses to 0.04 dB. My antenna is among the better designs in terms of resistive

loss. Although lower losses are possible (0.04 dB is the lowest calculated by DJ9BV for a Yagi with similar gain using aluminum elements), lower-loss designs require greater boomlength to achieve the same gain. There is no perfect solution. Part of the design problem is determining a tolerable resistive loss versus gain per boomlength. The resistive-loss problem demonstrates another trap in computer analysis: It's possible to come up with a great theoretical design that may be a poor real-world performer because of resistive losses—this has occurred!

The other 0.04 dB difference between calculated and measured gain is caused by losses in the UT-141 balun. The use of an air-dielectric quarter-wave sleeve balun could reduce these losses to about 0.02 dB.

As a practical matter, of course, element and balun losses are not detectable in an antenna system used for terrestrial work. Even in an EME array, it will require the best of receiving systems to detect any improvement made from the reduction of these losses.

Pattern Measurements

Both the calculated and measured results demonstrate the value of the time spent in cleaning up the pattern. Fig 1 shows the calculated E- and H-plane patterns, and Fig 2 shows the measured E-plane pattern. The front-to-back

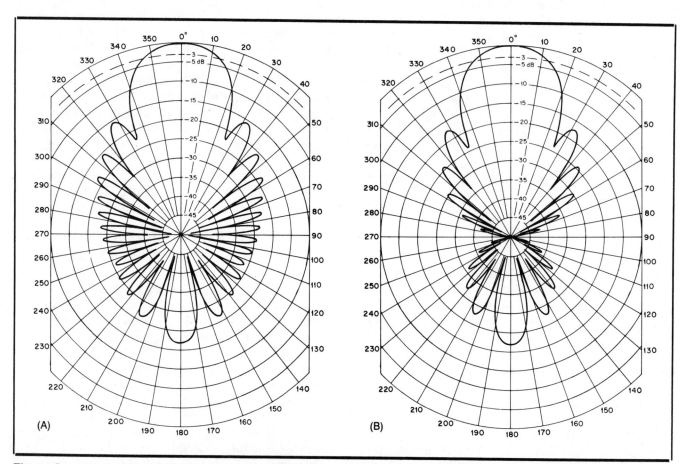

Fig 1—Computer-predicted H-plane (A) and E-plane (B) patterns for the K1FO 22-element, 432-MHz Yagi. Note: These antenna patterns are drawn on a linear dB grid, rather than the standard ARRL log-periodic grid. The linear dB grid shows sidelobes in greater detail and allows close comparison of sidelobes among different patterns. Sidelobe performance is important when stacking antennas in arrays for EME work.

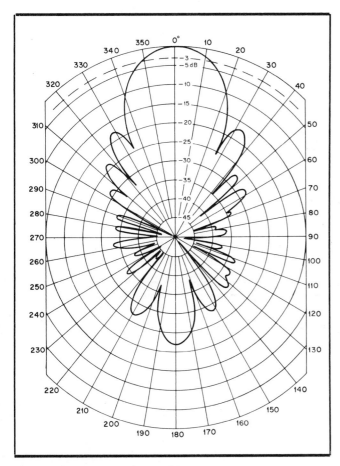

Fig 2—Measured E-plane pattern for the K1FO 22-element Yagi. Note: This antenna pattern is drawn on a linear dB grid, identical to the grids in Fig 1, rather than the standard ARRL log-periodic grid.

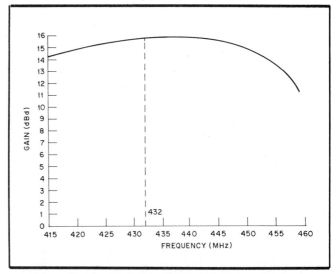

Fig 3—Gain versus frequency for the K1FO 22-element Yagi. Note that the 1-dB gain bandwidth is 31 MHz and that the gain peak occurs at 437 MHz.

ratio is 22 dB, and the first E-plane sidelobe is down about 17.5 dB.

Gain Bandwidth

Fig 3, a plot of calculated gain versus frequency, demonstrates the extremely wide gain bandwidth of the K1FO 22-element Yagi. With an absolute gain peak at 437 MHz, the gain is less than 1.0 dB down between 420 and 450 MHz. The persistent myth that Yagis have very narrow bandwidths should be discredited forever.

Gain bandwidth (a measure of forward gain versus frequency) should not be confused with SWR bandwidth (SWR versus frequency). SWR bandwidth is a measure of the feed-point impedance and is not necessarily indicative of gain or pattern performance.

A wide gain bandwidth is important, even if operation will be on only a narrow band of frequencies. This is true for the following reasons:

1) *Construction tolerances.* The wider the bandwidth, the less critical the tolerances when building the Yagi. This makes it easier to retain excellent performance when duplicating antennas.

2) *Minimum shift of phase center.* A Yagi with smooth gain rolloff characteristics usually has less of a phase difference at the driven element as frequency changes. This is important in large arrays where the center Yagis will be operating at different points on their frequency response (this is caused by unequal mutual-impedance effects). Large phase shifts are characteristic of Yagis with many element spacings and lengths that are the same. It is also one of the major reasons why early amateur long Yagi designs were poor performers when used in large arrays.

3) *Array center frequency.* The value of wide gain bandwidth is related also to mutual-impedance effects. At 432 MHz, most of us are using arrays of Yagis (two or more antennas). Mutual-impedance effects tend to lower the center frequency of an array of Yagis relative to the center frequency of an individual Yagi. I have measured the drop in center frequency for an array of four RIW 19s to be about 400 kHz. Based on this experience, an array of 16 RIW Yagis might exhibit a center frequency drop of more than 1 MHz. An array made from wide-gain-band-width Yagis is a better choice than an array made from Yagis that exhibit a sharp gain drop on the high side of the peak gain frequency.

If the gain of a Yagi drops off rapidly just above the desired frequency of operation, lowering the array center frequency causes the stacking gain to be substantially lower than the theoretical 3.0 dB for doubling the array size. In addition, the pattern deteriorates rapidly above the maximum gain frequency for most Yagis (and especially for narrow bandwidth designs). For EME operation at 432 MHz, such poor Yagi pattern characteristics also create poor array patterns. This results in inferior receive performance because of unwanted earth-noise pickup.

SWR Bandwidth

A lot of time was spent designing a driven element that would have excellent dry weather and good wet weather SWR. I decided on a T match and optimized it at 432 MHz using a Hewlett-Packard 8753A network analyzer. A sweep of SWR versus frequency is shown in Fig 4. In dry weather, the SWR measured less than 1.10:1 from 431.2 MHz to 433.1 MHz.

The good SWR bandwidth results from the wide gain bandwidth of the Yagi and from tuning the director string above the center operating frequency. For this Yagi design (as well as for other designs that were built and tested), the driven element impedance changes less with frequency on the low-frequency side of the gain peak than at or above the gain peak.

I used a garden hose to wet the Yagi for simulated heavy rain conditions. A plot of SWR versus frequency under these wet conditions (Fig 5) demonstrates how the match center frequency shifts when the Yagi is wet. The network analyzer showed that when wet, the driven element impedance becomes more inductively reactive. The SWR at 432 MHz is still an excellent 1.18:1 when the Yagi is wet. My present array of twelve 22-element Yagis measures (in the shack) well under 1.2:1 when dry, and about 1.3:1 in heavy rain. Icing is a different story. As with all other 432-MHz Yagis I have tested, performance is seriously degraded under icing conditions.

I have been asked if a quad-loop driven element could be used with this Yagi. I do not favor the use of a quad-loop driven element on a long Yagi. The only advantage of a quad loop is a slightly greater driven-element match bandwidth. All the old myths about lower noise pickup, higher gain and better pattern are exactly that: old myths. The quad-loop driven element also adds weight and wind-load area to the antenna without improving its gain. (I modeled this design on the computer with a quad-loop driven element and found that to make it work at all would require extensive changes to the first three or four director lengths and positions. If you want to try a quad-loop driven element or a driven-element feed system other than a T match, you have quite a job ahead of you, and you're on your own.)

CONCLUSIONS

The excellent pattern and gain of the 22-element Yagi are confirmed by the stacking spacings that give best array gain versus noise temperature. Optimum stacking distances are 65 inches in the E-plane and 62 inches in the H-plane. At those distances, stacking gain is almost 2.9 dB in both planes. (Phasing-line losses and gain loss caused by mechanical errors such as frame sag and misalignment are not included). The beamwidth of the Yagi at 432 MHz is 23 degrees in the E plane and 24 degrees in the H plane.

In examining the stacking characteristics of several popular 432-MHz commercial Yagis, I found it to be impossible to obtain more than 2.5 dB stacking gain (excluding phasing-line losses).[1] This phenomenon was not a function of the physics of stacking Yagis. It was caused by the design limitations of the Yagis under test. By

[1]Powlishen, S., "Stacking Yagis is a Science," *Ham Radio,* May 1985, pp 18-33.

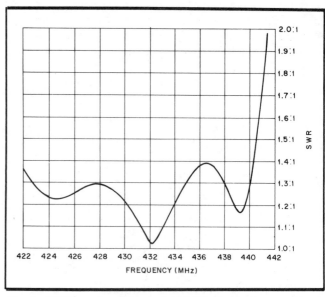

Fig 4—SWR performance of the K1FO 22-element Yagi in dry weather.

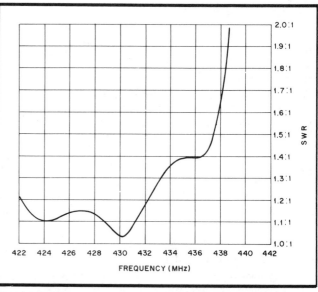

Fig 5—SWR performance of the K1FO 22-element Yagi in wet weather.

comparison, calculated and measured stacking gains of approximately 2.9 dB (in both the E and H planes) were obtained with the K1FO 22-element design. This figure excludes phasing-line losses.

At 15.7 dBd gain for a 6.1-wavelength boom, the gain of the K1FO 22-element Yagi approaches the theoretical maximum for its boom length. It may seem that I have done a lot of work perfecting the design—and that a gain variation of a few tenths of a dB one way or the other isn't worth worrying about for a single 14-foot long Yagi. For an EME array of 8, 12 or 16 Yagis, however, the array gain versus windload problem makes the effort required to tweak the antenna *very* worthwhile!

Tables 1 and 2 provide some construction details. More-complete construction information can be found in the Antenna Projects chapter of the *ARRL Handbook*. It will also be provided in the UHF/Microwave projects book that will be published by ARRL.

Table 1
Specifications for 432-MHz Yagi Family

No. of El	Boom length (λ)	Gain (dBi)*	FB ratio (dB)	DE impd (ohms)	Beamwidth E / H (°)	Stacking E / H (inches)
15	3.4	15.67	21	23	30 / 32	53 / 49
16	3.8	16.05	19	23	29 / 31	55 / 51
17	4.2	16.45	20	27	28 / 30	56 / 53
18	4.6	16.8	25	32	27 / 29	58 / 55
19	4.9	17.1	25	30	26 / 28	61 / 57
20	5.3	17.4	21	24	25.5 / 27	62 / 59
21	5.7	17.65	20	22	25 / 26.5	63 / 60
22	6.1	17.9	22	25	24 / 26	65 / 62
23	6.5	18.15	27	30	23.5 / 25	67 / 64
24	6.9	18.35	29	29	23 / 24	69 / 66
25	7.3	18.55	23	25	22.5 / 23.5	71 / 68
26	7.7	18.8	22	22	22 / 23	73 / 70
27	8.1	19.0	22	21	21.5 / 22.5	75 / 72
28	8.5	19.20	25	25	21 / 22	77 / 75
29	8.9	19.4	25	25	20.5 / 21.5	79 / 77
30	9.3	19.55	26	27	20 / 21	80 / 78
31	9.7	19.7	24	25	19.6 / 20.5	81 / 79
32	10.2	19.8	23	22	19.3 / 20	82 / 80
33	10.6	19.9	23	23	19 / 19.5	83 / 81
34	11.0	20.05	25	22	18.8 / 19.2	84 / 82
35	11.4	20.2	27	25	18.5 / 19.0	85 / 83
36	11.8	20.3	27	26	18.3 / 18.8	86 / 84
37	12.2	20.4	26	26	18.1 / 18.6	87 / 85
38	12.7	20.5	25	25	18.9 / 18.4	88 / 86
39	13.1	20.6	25	23	18.7 / 18.2	89 / 87
40	13.5	20.8	26	21	17.5 / 18	90 / 88

*Gain is approximate real gain based upon gain measurements made on six different-length Yagis.

Table 2
Free-Space Dimensions for 432-MHz Yagi Family

Element lengths are for 3/16-inch-diameter material.

El No.	Element Position (mm from rear of boom)	Element Length (mm)	Element Correction*
REF	0	340	
DE	104	334	
D1	146	315	
D2	224	306	
D3	332	299	
D4	466	295	
D5	622	291	
D6	798	289	
D7	990	287	
D8	1196	285	
D9	1414	283	
D10	1642	281	−2
D11	1879	279	−2
D12	2122	278	−2
D13	2373	277	−2
D14	2629	276	−2
D15	2890	275	−1
D16	3154	274	−1
D17	3422	273	−1
D18	3693	272	0
D19	3967	271	0
D20	4242	270	0
D21	4520	269	0
D22	4798	269	0
D23	5079	268	0
D24	5360	268	+1
D25	5642	267	+1
D26	5925	267	+1
D27	6209	266	+1
D28	6494	266	+1
D29	6779	265	+2
D30	7064	265	+2
D31	7350	264	+2
D32	7636	264	+2
D33	7922	263	+2
D34	8209	263	+2
D35	8496	262	+2
D36	8783	262	+2
D37	9070	261	+3
D38	9359	261	+3

*Element correction is the amount to shorten or lengthen all elements when building a Yagi of that length.

Parabolic Reflector Antennas and Feeds

By Dick Turrin, W2IMU
PO Box 65
Colts Neck, NJ 07722

The parabolic reflector is generally considered the most effective antenna for UHF and microwaves.[1] The most popular form is the front-fed, circular aperture type, dubbed a *dish* antenna from its appearance (Fig 1).

The most attractive feature of this antenna is the broadband reflector, which requires no adjustment when constructed accurately. Only feed changes are required when changing bands.

GAIN

For most Amateur Radio applications, high antenna gain is the single most important factor. Side and rear radiation are typically unimportant, since amateur UHF and microwave communications are not yet interference-limited.

Parabolic reflectors are in the class of antennas where the aperture is the projected area of the reflector in the direction of the main beam. The effective gain of an aperture antenna is given by

$$G_{eff} = \eta \, \frac{4\pi \, A_o}{\lambda_o^2} \qquad \text{(Eq 1)}$$

where A_o is the projected area in the same units as λ_o, the free space wavelength. The efficiency factor, η, is principally related to the method of illuminating the reflector surface. For paraboloidal reflector antennas, η will have a practical range of 50-70%.

Parabolic reflector antennas develop high gain through a focusing property, where energy collected by the aperture is redirected and concentrated at the focal point of the reflector. The effective gain of the antenna is the same for transmitting as it is for receiving.

BEAMWIDTH

The radiation pattern of a large, high-gain parabolic antenna has a main beam that is nearly circular. The -3 dB beamwidth is given by

$$\alpha = \frac{K}{D/\lambda} \qquad \text{(Eq 2)}$$

where D/λ is the diameter of the reflector in wavelengths, and K is related to the aperture illumination. For typical, high-gain dish antennas, K is about 64.

As antenna size and gain increase, beamwidth decreases. Large antennas with beamwidths of 1° or less make it increasingly difficult to properly aim the main beam with sufficient precision, and maintain this position under all environmental conditions.

Fig 1—An impressive 12-foot parabolic reflector or *dish* antenna set up for reception of Apollo or Skylab signals near 2280 MHz. Note the preamplifier taped below the feed horn. For more information about this antenna, see the article by K2RIW in August 1972 *QST*, or the 15th edition of *The ARRL Antenna Book*.

ILLUMINATION

Reflector illumination is usually accomplished with a small feed antenna positioned with its phase center at the focal point of the paraboloid. An ideal feed would have a conical radiation pattern, illuminating only the reflector. Such a feed antenna is impossible to achieve in practice, due to diffraction limitations of small antennas. Practical feeds are usually small horns or simple linear-element antennas, with a radiation pattern consisting of a single tear-drop shaped, circularly symmetric main lobe, exhibiting very low (< -20 dB) side and rear radiation (Fig 2). The portion of radiated feed energy that does not illuminate the paraboloid is called *spillover* and accounts for part of the loss in antenna efficiency.

Parabolic antenna gain is also related to the way energy from the feed is *distributed* over the reflector aperture area. For maximum gain, the energy should be distributed uniformly over the entire area, but due to feed radiation characteristics, there is a tapering of energy from the center of the reflector to the rim. The greater this taper is, the

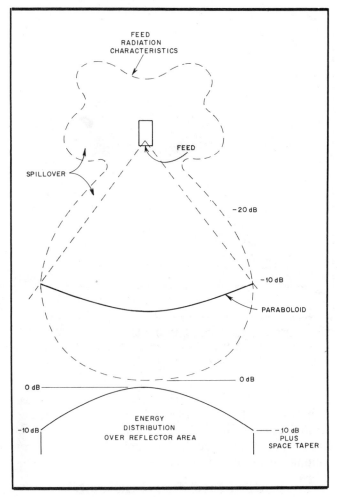

Fig 2—Feed illumination of parabolic reflector showing spillover and aperture energy distribution for a typical design.

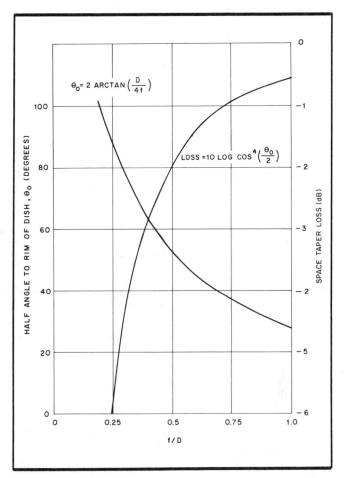

Fig 3—Curves relating space taper and angle to the rim of the dish v f/D.

lower the effective gain will be, and the broader the beamwidth.

There is also an intrinsic "space taper" due to the geometry of the paraboloid. The distance from the feed to the rim of the reflector is always greater than that to the vertex. This difference imposes an additional tapering of the feed energy, which is dependent on the focal length-to-diameter (f/D) ratio of the reflector. Fig 3 relates space taper (in dB) to the f/D ratio.

Optimum performance of a given feed is largely a trade-off between least illumination taper and minimum spillover. Evaluation of a specific feed requires careful numerical analysis; however, a useful rule-of-thumb is to choose an f/D ratio that provides a feed illumination taper of −10 dB around the rim of the reflector, including the effects of space taper.

BLOCKAGE

On a dish antenna, the feed is centrally located directly in front of the reflector, where RF fields are highest. The loss in effective antenna gain resulting from this blockage

is usually under 0.2 dB, but can increase to about 1 dB when the effective blockage area is 1/5 the aperture area. If this occurs, the dish is too small in diameter compared to the feed. Support struts for the feed can also cause blockage, which may be more than the feed itself if the struts are large in cross section and made of conductive material.

REFLECTOR GEOMETRY

Parabolic reflector surface geometry is shown in Fig 4 for both rectangular and cylindrical coordinates where the f/D ratio is the principal factor. A practical range of f/D ratios is 0.25-1.0. Reflectors with f/D ratios below 0.35 are considered to be "deep dishes." These are compact structures, but difficult to feed efficiently for maximum gain. Reflectors with f/D ratios above 0.75 have long focal lengths, making feed support difficult as well as requiring the use of large feeds. Long focal lengths have only one distinct advantage—the feed location is not as critical as with low f/D ratios. For most amateur applications, an f/D ratio in the range of 0.4-0.6 is recommended.

The f/D ratio of a paraboloidal reflector may be found by first measuring the depth of the dish from the plane of the rim to the vertex at the center of the dish.

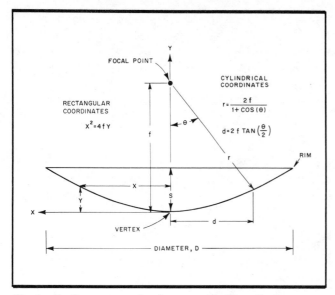

Fig 4—Surface geometry for a parabolic reflector.

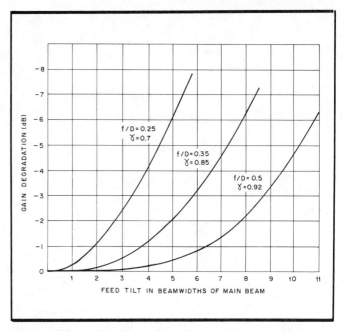

Fig 5—Off-axis feed steering of main beam vs gain degradation for 3 f/D ratios. γ is the beam deviation factor; beamtilt = γ × feed tilt.

Measure the diameter at the rim, and use the formula f/D = D/16s, where s is the depth.

Parabolic curve formulas are important because they permit laying out the shape of the curve when making ribs for large paraboloids, templates for checking surface accuracy and templates for forming reverse molds. Typically, only the curve from the vertex to the rim is required, since a parabola of revolution (paraboloid) consists of the same shape curve for all radial sections.

FEED STEERING

Although the feed antenna is normally placed at the reflector focal point for optimum performance, incremental steering of the main antenna beam may be obtained by moving the feed laterally away from the center of the reflector. Moving the feed an angular amount in one direction will shift the main beam in the diametrically opposite direction. (The angular shift of the antenna beam will be slightly smaller than that of the feed, because the reflector is not a planar mirror.)

Moving the feed off axis will also cause phase distortion in the aperture fields, which results in degradation of effective gain and also in radiation pattern distortion. However, useful main beam shifts of a number of beamwidths may be obtained before performance degrades noticeably. Fig 5 shows the relationship between gain degradation and main beam shift for several f/D ratios. The beam shift ratio, γ (beam shift divided by lateral feed displacement in angular units), is also indicated. As shown, deep dishes are not tolerant of off-axis feed steering, while flatter reflectors with larger f/D ratios and longer focal lengths are better suited.

Feed steering of the main beam can be useful with antenna mounts that have fixed, locked pointing intervals and with very large-diameter, long focal-length reflectors

primarily intended for limited-scan EME operation. The capability of feed steering also suggests that multiple feeds may be mounted around the focal point for multiband or multiple-beam operation.

FEEDS FOR PARABOLOIDS

Over the past 50 years, numerous feeds have been devised. Unfortunately, many of them are less than optimum. A simple dipole with a linear or plane reflector has radiation characteristics that are far from circularly symmetric, rendering it not well suited as a high-efficiency feed antenna. Similar characteristics prevail for open-end waveguides, either rectangular or circular. Feeds with asymmetric radiation characteristics can also have ill-defined phase centers.

An improvement in the radiation characteristics of a rectangular waveguide can be achieved by flaring it into a rectangular horn with an aperture size providing nearly equal E- and H-plane radiation characteristics out to the −10 dB points. In general, the waveguide aspect ratio is about 2:1, necessitating a greater flare in the E plane to achieve the desired results. The horn flare must also be as gradual as possible to keep the phase centers for both planes close together. Similar compensation for the radiation characteristics of a flared round waveguide can be obtained by deforming the circular cone into an elliptical one.

Owing to their asymmetry, rectangular and elliptic aperture feed antennas can only be used for linear polarization. Regardless, small aperture-flared feed horns were used quite extensively. Better feed designs are presently available and are recommended.[2]

Diagonal Horn

A form of symmetrical horn that can support both linear and circular polarization is the *diagonal horn*.[3] The smallest aperture diagonal horn is the basic diagonal waveguide (Fig 6). This form of waveguide may be excited for linear polarization by a diagonally oriented short dipole as shown.

Since the center of the dipole is at current maximum, it must be located near the waveguide end shorting plate to excite the dominant mode. The distance from the dipole to the end shorting plate, s, determines the resistive part of the impedance match, while the length of the dipole is adjusted to minimize the reactive part. Note the sleeve balun or "bazooka" section that should be included to reduce excitation of unwanted modes.

This method of excitation is useful to about 4 GHz. At higher frequencies a rectangular waveguide may be used through a series of transitions from rectangular to round and then round to square, as shown in Fig 7. The round section can also include a circular polarizer, which if rotated 90° will change the polarization sense from right to left.

The small-aperture diagonal horn is nearly circularly symmetric in radiation characteristics and has low sidelobe radiation.

Both diagonal horn feeds shown in Figs 6 and 7 are suitable for reflectors with an f/D ratio of 0.35. They can be used on longer focal length reflectors by simply flaring out the square aperture into a larger dimension. The yield is a pyramidal section with a flare angle not exceeding 7°. An approximate formula for the radiation angle in degrees to the −10 dB contour vs the aperture dimension d, for *larger* aperture feeds is $100 / (d/\lambda)$.

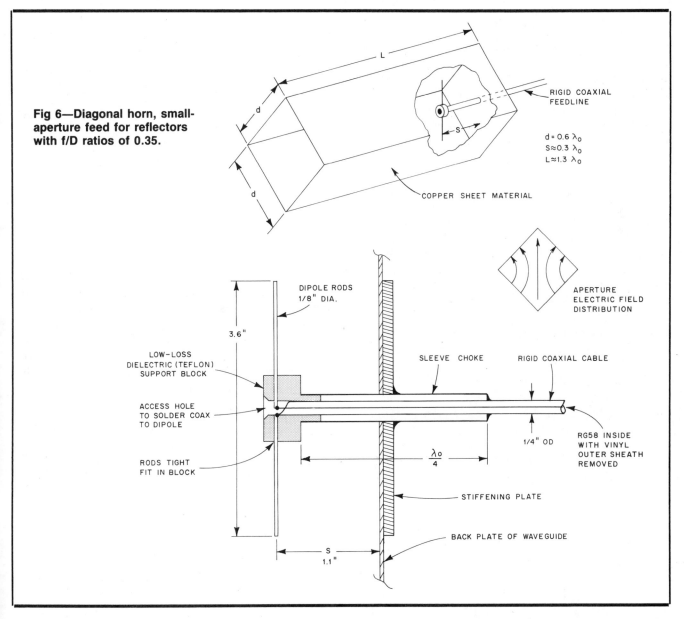

Fig 6—Diagonal horn, small-aperture feed for reflectors with f/D ratios of 0.35.

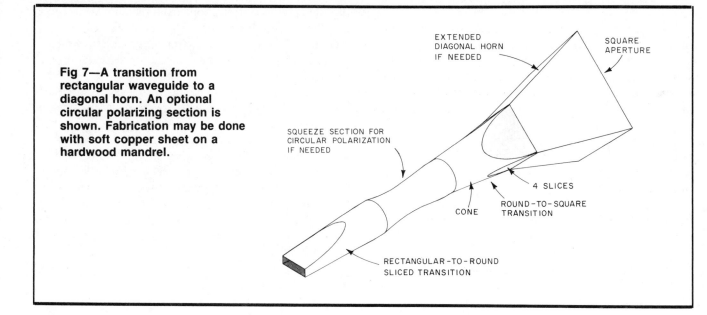

Fig 7—A transition from rectangular waveguide to a diagonal horn. An optional circular polarizing section is shown. Fabrication may be done with soft copper sheet on a hardwood mandrel.

EXTENDED DIAGONAL HORN IF NEEDED

SQUARE APERTURE

SQUEEZE SECTION FOR CIRCULAR POLARIZATION IF NEEDED

4 SLICES

ROUND-TO-SQUARE TRANSITION

CONE

RECTANGULAR-TO-ROUND SLICED TRANSITION

Scalar Feeds

The secret of a good, small-aperture feed horn is the minimizing of "edge currents." These currents result from the relatively high E-plane fields at the rim of the horn. Surface currents flow transverse to the edge of the horn, resulting in spurious radiation in the form of side and rear lobes from the feed. Quarter-wave slot traps may be placed around the aperture to minimize these currents, but it has been found that a single trap is not very effective and is also frequency sensitive.

A better solution is to use a multiplicity of low-Q traps surrounding the aperture.[4] Feeds of this kind are usually built with a circular aperture for simplicity and are called *scalar feeds* (Fig 8). This type of feed is somewhat aperture inefficient, since the basic aperture is only the round waveguide, and the traps occupy a much larger area. The result is higher aperture blockage in front-fed paraboloids, which is offset by better illumination characteristics. This feed is not recommended for paraboloids less than 10 λ in diameter because of aperture blockage. The principal feature of a scalar feed is its broad bandwidth, requiring no tuning.

The most popular form of scalar feed has been developed for the TVRO industry, and is known as the Chaparral™ feed, after the originator. In this design, the traps are on a flat circular collar surrounding the open waveguide (Fig 9). A unique advantage of the Chaparral feed is that the trap collar position affects the radiation characteristics, providing highest antenna gain for a range of f/D ratios from 0.3-0.45. Sliding the collar back from the aperture broadens the radiation pattern for lower f/D-ratio dishes. This same feature may be used to obtain highest gain and best noise performance for satellite or EME applications by simply sliding the collar.

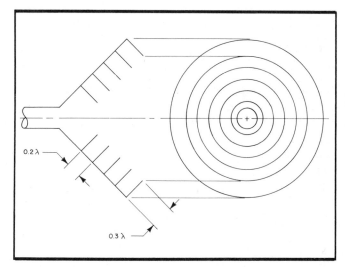

Fig 8—Scalar feed design in circular geometry. Side and rear radiation is greatly suppressed with no adjustments required.

0.2 λ

0.3 λ

Dual-Mode Feed

More aperture-efficient horns exist that control edge currents by introducing a modified aperture field distribution, forcing the field intensities at the rim of the horn to nearly zero. Two such types are the *dual-mode* and *hybrid-mode* designs. Each may be built with a round or square aperture, but round designs are easier to fabricate and have excellent circular symmetry. Of these two designs, the dual-mode, small-aperture feed is the easiest to fabricate, has excellent radiation characteristics and causes the least

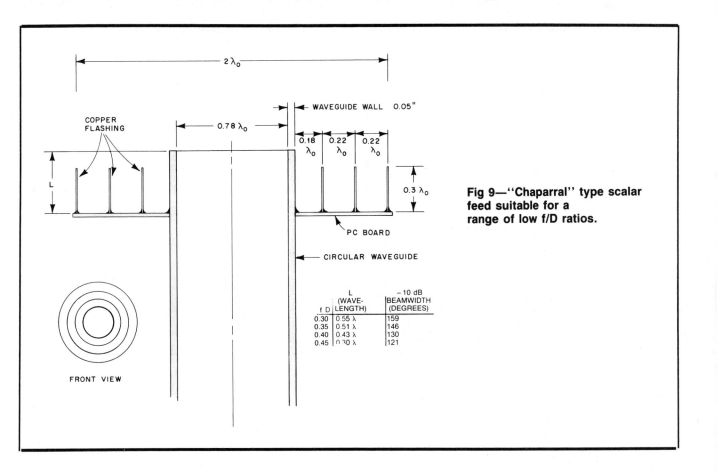

Fig 9—"Chaparral" type scalar feed suitable for a range of low f/D ratios.

f/D	L (WAVE-LENGTH)	−10 dB BEAMWIDTH (DEGREES)
0.30	0.55 λ	159
0.35	0.51 λ	146
0.40	0.43 λ	130
0.45	0.30 λ	121

aperture blockage.[5] Because of the introduction of a higher-order TM_{11} mode in the circular form, this design will not efficiently feed reflectors with an f/D ratio less than 0.5.

Fig 10 illustrates the dual-mode design, which may be scaled to any frequency (except for the flare angle, which remains constant at 30°). Bandwidth is about 8%, which is more than adequate for amateur applications and is limited almost entirely by the dispersion between the two modes in the drift section of the horn. The length of this section can be readily adjusted to provide optimum radiation characteristics at a desired frequency by measuring the intensity of radiation in the E-plane at right angles to the axis of the horn. There will be an optimum length where sidelobe radiation will be at a minimum.

Although the method of excitation as shown is an electric field probe, other methods may also be used. The dipole excitation described for the diagonal horn feed is a better choice for linear polarization. With a dipole feed, section l_1 may be reduced to λ/4 because of the higher mode purity obtained. The dual-mode horn may also be excited through a waveguide transition from rectangular to round, suggested by Fig 18.

Hybrid Mode Feed

The *hybrid-mode* design offers greater bandwidth than the dual-mode horn, but is much more difficult and expensive to fabricate. The radiation characteristics are

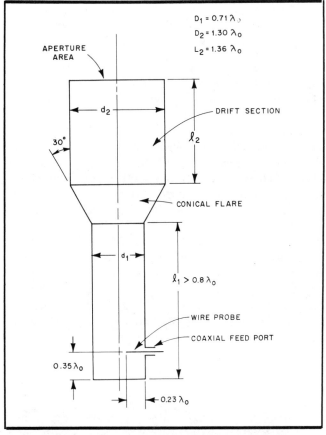

Fig 10—Dual-mode feed horn. See text for details.

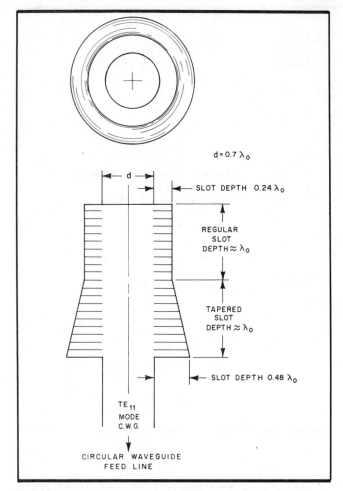

Fig 11—Smallest-aperture hybrid mode feed. A minimum of 10 slots per wavelength should be used.

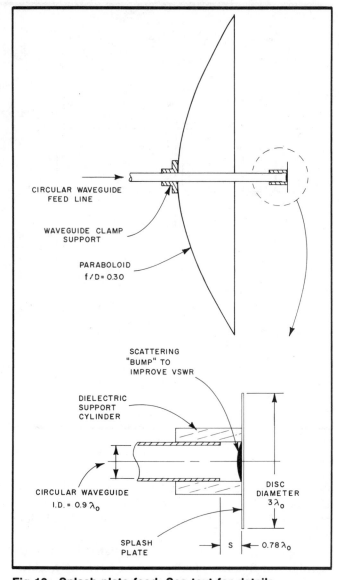

Fig 12—Splash-plate feed. See text for details.

nearly ideal for a small-aperture feed, but it cannot efficiently illuminate paraboloids with f/D ratios of less than 0.4.

Fig 11 illustrates this intricate structure, which may be scaled to any frequency band. The most important dimension is the depth of the radial slots, which is approximately $\lambda/4$ at one end and approximately $\lambda/2$ at the other. Operating bandwidth is in the region above where the slots are resonant, making the slot impedance capacitive.

Both the dual- and hybrid-mode designs may be gradually flared in a conical shape to achieve a larger aperture. Flaring must be done gradually to preserve the mode integrity, and in the case of the dual mode design, the length of the flare must be carefully adjusted to preserve the phase between the two modes. However, since most of the mode dispersion occurs in the small diameter throat, the bandwidth of that design will be little compromised when flared out to provide a large aperture horn.

Reverse Feeds

All of the feeds described so far require the transmission line to enter the horn from the rear. This is good practice because it eliminates feed aperture shadowing by any objects placed between the feed and the reflector surface. For this reason, feed strut supports should be attached to the rim of the reflector and extend to the rear of the feed. A *reverse feed* is one in which the feed line enters through the feed aperture itself, contrary to the best design principles.

"Splash Plate" Feed

One type of reverse feed, which may also be referred to as a degenerate Cassegrainian type, is the *splash plate* (Fig 12). It employs a rigid feed line entering the center rear of the paraboloid that extends out to near the focal point. A small horn directs the energy toward a reflecting plate directly in front of it. This is a very simple feed that requires no support struts for small antennas and only thin guy wires for large ones. It provides good efficiency, but suffers from higher sidelobes than most other feeds. A small bump at the center of the plate is used to improve SWR by scattering energy that would otherwise be directed back into the feed line. This bump may be in the form of

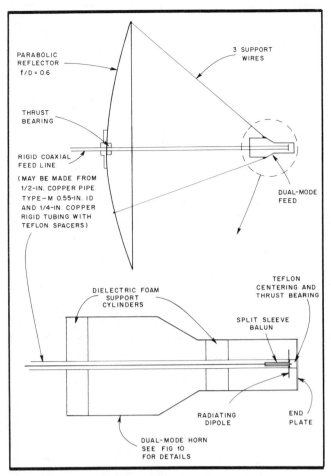

Fig 13—Reverse-fed dual-mode feed horn (K2RIW design). See text for details.

a shallow metallic cone about the same diameter as the waveguide and approximately 0.06 λ high.

Adjustment of the spacing, S, is relatively critical for best performance and should be done experimentally while observing the relative gain. Note that the splash plate is relatively large; therefore, to avoid aperture blockage this feed should not be used with small-diameter reflectors. Note also that this feed tends to illuminate the rim area more than the center, resulting in higher spillover losses, but improving aperture efficiency. Experimental results indicate efficiency factors as high as 60% can be achieved.

Reverse Dual-Mode Feed

Another type of reverse feed uses the dual-mode horn, and was introduced by K2RIW. In this arrangement, the feed line is a rigid coaxial section that extends through the paraboloid vertex into the mouth of the horn (Fig 13). The horn is supported on the coaxial line by low-loss plastic cylinders and is terminated in a dipole. Even though the feed line is located directly in the center of the feed horn, this arrangement provides good efficiency.

Impedance matching will require adjusting the length of the dipole as well as the spacing from the waveguide end plate. This may be done initially without the paraboloid in place. The dimensions given in Fig 10 apply to a dual-mode feed horn. The dipole excitation is similar to that shown by Fig 6, and is adjusted in a similar manner.

Circular Polarizer

Both the splash plate and reverse dual-mode feeds are

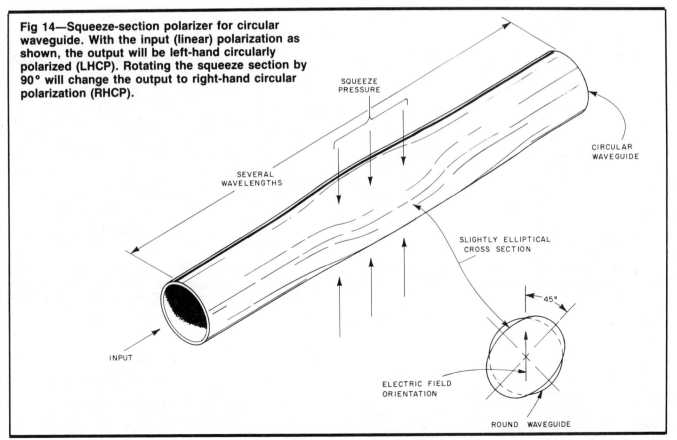

Fig 14—Squeeze-section polarizer for circular waveguide. With the input (linear) polarization as shown, the output will be left-hand circularly polarized (LHCP). Rotating the squeeze section by 90° will change the output to right-hand circular polarization (RHCP).

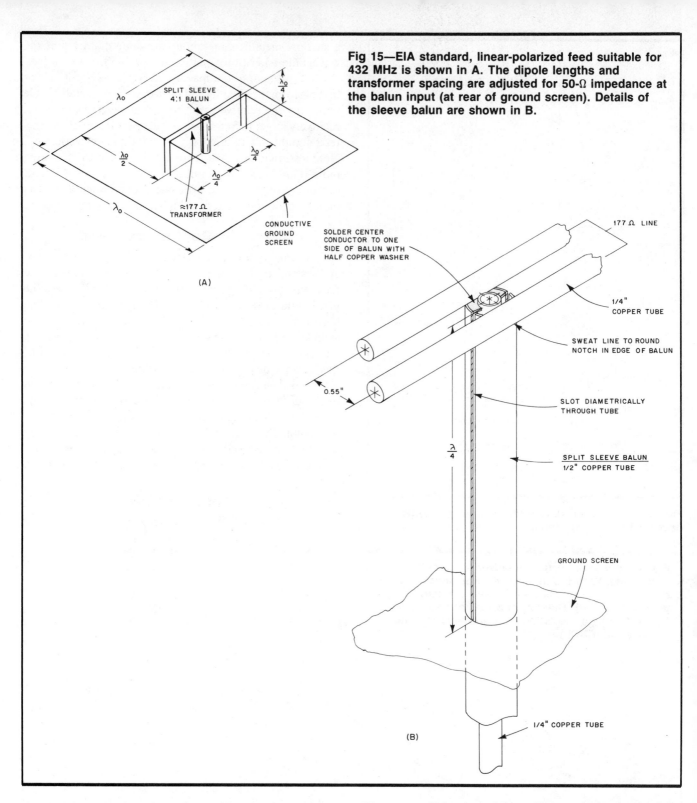

Fig 15—EIA standard, linear-polarized feed suitable for 432 MHz is shown in A. The dipole lengths and transformer spacing are adjusted for 50-Ω impedance at the balun input (at rear of ground screen). Details of the sleeve balun are shown in B.

circularly symmetric and may be used for circular polarization. All that is necessary is to introduce a phase-shift polarizer in the circular waveguide.

A simple and effective differential phase shifter at microwave is a "squeeze section." This can be made by simply squeezing a circular waveguide into a slightly elliptical cross section over several wavelengths. The elliptical section is then oriented with one of its axes at 45° to the linearly polarized electric field, as shown in Fig 14.

This method works because the squeeze section has different cutoff wavelengths for the major and minor axes.

The wave will be slowed down if the polarization is along the minor axis of the ellipse and sped up if along the major axis. By over squeezing the section a bit, the tube will take on a stable deformation and clamps will not be necessary to maintain the desired shape. This method allows easy fine tuning for excellent circularity. If the squeeze section is too short, excessive deformation will be required, resulting in impedance mismatch problems and impaired circularity.

Double-Dipole EIA Feed

A good feed at VHF and UHF using linear elements

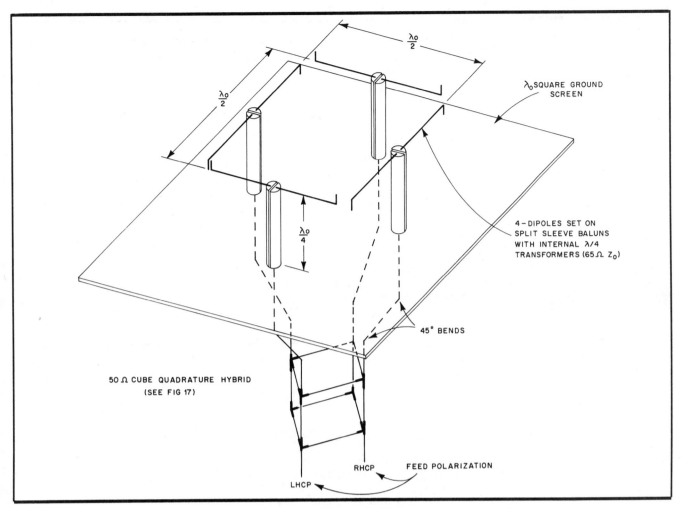

Fig 16—Circularly polarized EIA feed using a cube quadrature hybrid. See text for details.

is the *double-dipole with reflecting plane*. This feed was first used for VHF radio astronomy in Australia, and later the American Electronic Industries Association (EIA) proposed it as a reliable and reproducible gain standard for VHF and UHF. As such, it has an effective gain of 9.8 dBi ±0.2 dB.

This design is shown in Fig 15. Two dipoles are placed λ/2 apart and fed in phase to achieve a sharper radiation pattern in the plane transverse to the elements (H-plane). Both dipoles are mounted λ/4 in front of a ground plane to achieve unidirectional radiation that is circularly symmetric. The feed has suitable characteristics for illuminating a paraboloid with an f/D ratio of 0.5 for maximum gain.

A modified version for circular polarization uses four dipoles in a square configuration, with each fed individually from the rear of the ground plane through split-sleeve, impedance-matching baluns (Fig 16). The impedance of each dipole is close to 85 Ω (resistive) when the reactive component is tuned out by shortening the dipoles by a few percent. Pairs of parallel dipoles may be fed in quadrature to obtain circular polarization.

Cube Hybrid

A form of quadrature power divider, the *cube hybrid*,

allows direct implementation of left- and right-hand circular polarization through isolated feed ports (Fig 17). This is a matched four-way hybrid with quadrature-sequenced outputs, permitting direct connection to the four dipoles of the modified EIA feed antenna. A feature of this power divider is that all sections are an electrical λ/4 at the operating frequency and have the same characteristic impedance as the port terminations. For 50-Ω systems the divider may be constructed from sections of low-loss coaxial transmission line, or homemade air-dielectric coaxial sections, as shown in the figure. This hybrid may be unfolded into a simple planar hybrid for combining four power amplifiers.

The circularly polarized EIA feed has advantages in applications such as EME, where not only is Faraday fading eliminated, but the left- and right-hand ports are isolated between 20 and 30 dB. This means that the customary high-power T/R switch can be eliminated; the transmitter and receiver are connected to separate ports, with only a modest amount of additional protection necessary to prevent burnout of the receiver input stage.

FEED CONSTRUCTION MATERIALS

Since most of the preferred feed antennas are circular in geometry, it is convenient to use materials readily avail-

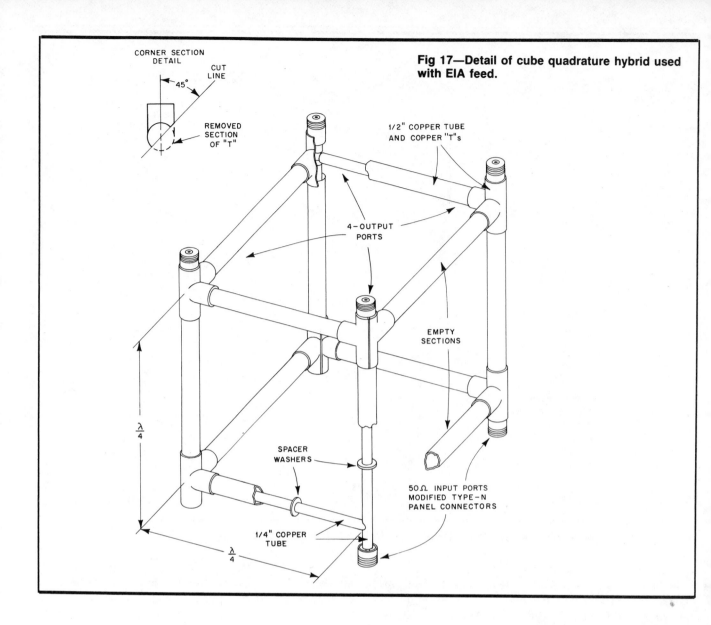

CORNER SECTION
DETAIL

CUT LINE
45°

REMOVED SECTION OF "T"

Fig 17—Detail of cube quadrature hybrid used with EIA feed.

1/2" COPPER TUBE AND COPPER "T"s

4-OUTPUT PORTS

EMPTY SECTIONS

$\frac{\lambda}{4}$

SPACER WASHERS

50 Ω INPUT PORTS MODIFIED TYPE-N PANEL CONNECTORS

1/4" COPPER TUBE

$\frac{\lambda}{4}$

Table 1
Copper Water Pipe Data

Pipe Size Nom ID (in.)	Cutoff Freq Circular Waveguide (GHz)	Useful Operating Range (GHz)
½	13.8	15.2-18.0
¾	9.2	10.1-12.05
1	6.9	7.6- 9.04
1¼	5.53	6.1- 7.23
1½	4.61	5.1- 6.03
2	3.46	3.8- 4.52
3	2.31	2.5- 3.01
4	1.73	1.9- 2.26

Useful operating range and cutoff frequencies are as defined in Table 2.

Copper water pipe is nonprecision round tubing and is available in four types:

M (coded red) thin wall, nominally 0.03 inch thick
L (coded blue) medium wall, nominally 0.05 inch thick
K (coded green) heavy wall, nominally 0.065 inch thick
DWV (drain, waste and vent tubing) thin wall, about 0.04 inch thick

able from plumbing supply houses. Round copper tubing up to 4 inches diameter is available as water or drain pipe. Also, various cans used to distribute food and other products should not be overlooked. An excellent source of small brass telescoping tubing is a hobby shop. These tubes are graduated in 1/32-inch steps from 1/16 to 5/8 inch OD, and are ideal for making impedance matching transformers, sliding tuners and dipole elements. Soft copper and aluminum sheet are available at building supply centers as roof flashing material. Special shapes, such as small horns, may be fabricated by shaping copper flashing material over a wooden mold.

Table 1 lists standard copper water pipe sizes along with the useful operating frequency ranges for use as circular waveguide. Some of the more commonly available can sizes are listed in Table 2. Although most cans are made of coated aluminum or iron, their use in feed antennas is satisfactory for all but the most stringent low-noise antenna requirements.

Since copper water pipe is not precision manufactured, there may be some cross-polarized coupling when

Table 2

Container Can Data

Can Designation	Diam (in.)	Length (in.)	Cutoff Freq (GHz)	Useful Operating Range (GHz)
Regular beer	2.6	4.75	2.66	2.9-3.47
Tennis ball	2.75	8.0/10.5	2.51	2.7-3.29
Brake fluid	3.25	7.0	2.13	2.3-2.78
B&M baked beans	3.25	5.5	2.13	2.3-2.78
Quart oil can	4.0	4.8	1.73	1.9-2.26
No. 10 juice can	4.0	6.75	1.73	1.9-2.26
Gallon paint can	6.5	7.5	1.06	1.2-1.39
Rectangular Cans				
Pint size	1.625 × 3.75	5.75	1.57	1.7-3.1
Half gallon	3.25 × 5.0	7.5	1.18	1.3-2.3
Gallon	4.0 × 6.25	9.4	0.95	1.05-1.89

The cutoff frequencies for the first two modes in the circular guide are:

f_{co} (GHz) = 6.92/diam inches f_{co} (GHz) = 9.04/diam inches
   TE_{11} mode TM_{01} mode

The useful operating range in circular waveguide is approximately:

$$1.1 \times f_{co} \quad <f \quad <f_{co}$$
$$TE_{11} \quad \text{oper} \quad TM_{01}$$
$$\text{range}$$

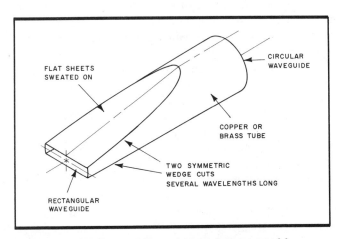

Fig 18—A simple round-to-rectangular waveguide transition made from copper or brass tubing with a diameter about equal to the broad dimension of the rectangular guide. A rectangular waveguide flange should be sweated on to complete the transition.

it is used as waveguide due to its slightly elliptic cross-section. Choose tubing with care, discarding pieces with bumps, dents and squashed areas—and by all means avoid seamed tubing. Circularity of the OD may be checked with a caliper by simply rotating the pipe in it. In long (>10 λ) sections, even slight deformations can result in severe cross-polarized coupling. If so, it may be alleviated by carefully squeezing small sections of the tubing until the desired polarization purity is obtained. As a general rule, rectangular waveguide should be used when a high degree of polarization purity is desired. Rectangular-to-circular waveguide transitions are easily fabricated when the OD of the circular guide is approximately equal to the wide dimension of the rectangular guide, as illustrated in Fig

18. The taper should be 6 to 10 λ long for a low VSWR transition.

It is good practice at UHF and microwaves to use materials with high conductivity, such as silver, copper, aluminum or brass, and to avoid materials with low conductivity, such as lead, iron, steel and solder. Regardless of the potential for loss, soldering is a most convenient method of securing brass or copper edges and joints. Use as little solder as possible in active RF regions and remove any excess by filing or scraping until the smooth, bright metal underneath is visible. Solder bridges in high-Q circuits can cause large losses if they occur where high current is flowing. Extra care with such details is worth the effort at UHF and microwaves.

REFLECTOR SURFACE CONSIDERATIONS

The reflector surface should conform as closely as possible to the geometry described in Fig 4. Any departure from an exact paraboloid will result in reduced effective gain. Surface bumps or dents which are less than 1 λ in size will cause little degradation. Larger variations, undulations and warpage will cause a decrease in gain, which is related to the extent of the deformation and variation from a true paraboloid. The loss is caused by misdirection of energy and by phase errors over the desired plane aperture wavefront. A poorly constructed reflector surface can also result in an ill-defined focal point.

A simple test for possible warpage of a dish is to sight along the plane of the rim. Gross warpage can be easily detected by this method, and deviations of greater than λ/10 should be corrected. Large reflectors should be checked for warpage by proper support in an almost upright position to maximize distortion due to gravity and aging.

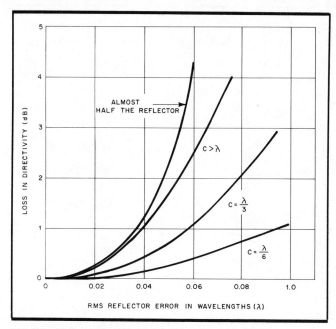

Fig 19—Theoretical loss of effective gain for a paraboloidal reflector antenna as a function of surface deformations. The RMS surface error is measured over the entire area, while the parameter C specifies the average deformation radius in wavelengths.

Assessment of a reflector surface to determine the extent of gain degradation is a very difficult task. It involves an accurate survey of the entire surface to determine a root mean squared (RMS) departure from an exact paraboloid. For small reflectors a well-made template will simplify the procedure, but for large reflectors, direct physical measurements may have to be made from a common datum point, such as the expected focal point. If a value for the RMS surface departure can be obtained, then an upper limit on the degradation in gain is given by

$$\text{Loss in gain (dB)} = 10 \log_{10} \epsilon^{-\left(4\pi \frac{\text{RMS}}{\lambda_o}\right)^2} \qquad \text{(Eq 3)}$$

Fig 19 plots the loss of gain in decibels vs surface RMS error. Curves are also included to show the variation in loss with size of deformations in wavelengths. The RMS error is the square root of the sum of the squares of all surface deviations measured at regular intervals no greater than a wavelength apart, divided by the total number of measurements.

For larger reflectors where a template becomes unmanageable, another method is suggested that uses a small, three-wheeled "mouse" that travels along radial paths on the reflector surface, which is in the stow position (beam pointed to the zenith). The mouse is drawn along the radial paths by means of a light string attached to a yoke at the single front wheel axle and extended over the rim of the reflector. A second string is secured to the expected focal point of the reflector and extended under the same pulling axle of the "mouse" as an idler, and then over the rim of the reflector at the same point as the first string. This second string is kept in constant tension to just keep it parallel with the first string. If both strings are light weight

and the mouse is relatively heavy, the required tension can be provided by free hanging weights.

If the reflector surface were a true paraboloid, the differential in string length would be zero as the mouse is pulled along a radial path. Differential string length can be directly related to surface deviations in the direction of the string from the focal point. Numerous paths must be measured in this way around the rim to obtain a good survey of the surface. An RMS error is then calculated and used in Eq 3 to get a worst-case estimate of antenna gain degradation.[7]

This method is particularly suited to the automatic processing of data by a small home computer. However, while geometrical measurements can give mathematical statistics, it is of greater practical interest to determine where and by how much to correct the surface errors.

It is evident that even small deviations from an exact paraboloid can result in reduction of effective gain. This is because reflector radiation is more sensitive to phase errors over the aperture than it is to amplitude errors. Any displacement of the surface from a true paraboloid almost doubles the phase error at the aperture due to that displacement. Because of the wavelength dependence on gain degradation, a reflector behaves somewhat like a low-pass filter. If the same reflector is used over a wide range of frequencies, there will be some upper limit on frequency where the loss in effective gain due to surface deformations will not be acceptable.

Since it is usually quite difficult to construct a large and accurate reflector, it may be prudent to build a well-constructed, smaller reflector for a given gain requirement. In general, reflectors up to 12-ft diameter can be constructed with good accuracy in "backyard" environments, while larger reflectors require much more effort and care. Reflectors over 20-ft diameter require extreme dedication and pose a real challenge to home construction methods. The cost of constructing a large reflector, in terms of manpower and materials, goes up at approximately the cube of the diameter.

Surface Material

A reflector surfaces does not have to have very high conductivity because it is a low-Q structure with surface currents spread over a wide area. Ordinary aluminum window fly screening, hardware cloth (a zinc-coated iron wire grid structure), and aluminum foil (kitchen wrap) are suitable. Recently, expanded aluminum sheet has become available because of its widespread use in TVRO antennas. This material is better suited for doubly curved surfaces because it will expand in two dimensions.

Since fly screening is available in widths up to 48 inches, it will be necessary to use multiple strips or-triangular-shaped sections for large reflectors. The smallest dimension of each section should be at least 1 λ or more in size. Electrical bonding between sections or crossover points in the grid is not needed. However, where neat butt joints are difficult to make, a tight overlap of material by about λ/4 or more is recommended to minimize leakage through the seams.

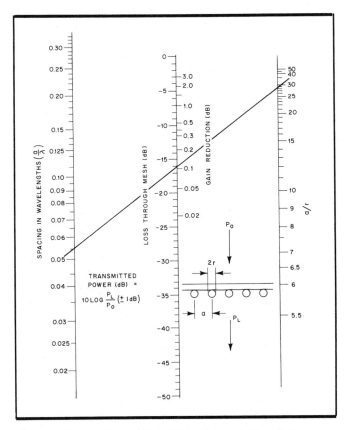

Fig 20—This nomograph relates transmission loss through a square mesh screen of conductive material, to the screen mesh and wire size. The resulting loss in antenna gain is also included.

For example, suppose galvanized iron hardware cloth is selected for the surface material. The square mesh size is ½ × ½ inch and the wire diameter is 0.0340 inch. Therefore, a = 0.5 inch, r = 0.0175 inch and λ = 9.13 inches. At 1296 MHz, a/λ = 0.055 and a/r = 28.5. Connecting these values on the appropriate scales with a straight line (as shown) gives a transmission loss of 16 dB. The corresponding loss in antenna gain for this material will be 0.1 dB, which adds about 8.5 K to the antenna noise temperature.

Any material which has a regular pattern of holes, such as a square or hexagonal grid, will leak RF through to the back side of the reflector. This leakage is related to the maximum dimension of the hole and to the size of the wire making up the grid (Fig 20). A general rule is that the maximum dimension of the holes should be less than λ/10 to keep leakage under 0.2 dB.

Another material suitable for reflector construction is semi-rigid building insulation, which is a sandwich of aluminum foil on both sides of a foam core. It is available in 4- × 8-foot sheets, ½- or ¾-inch thick. This material is lightweight and relatively fragile, but can be cut easily with a knife. It will sustain a moderate curve in one direction only. Attachment to parabolic ribs can be accomplished with channel strips or wide battens.

For small reflectors, typically used at high microwave frequencies, a conductive paint can be applied to most nonconductive, smooth surfaces to obtain an RF reflector. Conductive paint usually contains silver and is expensive.

Fortunately, only a thin coat will satisfy RF skin-depth requirements. A topcoat of weatherproof latex paint is recommended to seal off the conductive layer. Note that ordinary aluminum paint is *not* conductive; it is not recommended for reflector coating.

If sun noise measurements are anticipated as part of the antenna/receiving system evaluation, solid reflector surfaces should be coated with a dull, nonreflective paint to prevent possible heat damage to the feed. Painting of reflector surfaces does not result in degradation of performance. Since paint is a very thin dielectric layer, and the electric field on the reflector surface is essentially zero, no heat losses can occur. The coating material must be over λ/10 thick to interact with the electric field. For the same reason, a reflector surface that has corroded will show no degradation until the material has been completely eroded away, leaving no conductive path for surface currents to flow.

REFLECTOR CONSTRUCTION

The method of constructing a paraboloidal reflector will depend on the size. One method for reflectors larger than 8-ft diameter employs trussed, parabolically curved ribs extending radially from a central hub, with circular hoops attached to the ribs (Fig 21). Surface material is attached to the hoops to complete the reflector.[6]

Aluminum tubing is typically used to minimize weight and maintain longevity, although thin-wall electrical conduit can also be used. Gusset plates and pop rivets are extensively employed to join structural members. The number of ribs depends on the diameter of the reflector. A 30-foot reflector can have 48 or more ribs, while a 12-foot reflector can use as few as 6. The parabolic side of the rib should be made from a section of tubing that is preformed close to a parabolic curve. The hoops should also be preformed with a rolling mill in order that the circularity will be acceptable. An electrician's bending tool (called a "hickey") can also be used, if care is exercised. By attaching the circular hoops to the ribs with adjustable spacers, they can be adjusted to the exact parabolic curve.

In general, the hoops should be placed no more than 18 inches apart (radially) to obtain good surface conformity with heavy grid surface material. The largest hoop is the rim, which should be made of heavier tubing for maximum stiffness. It is mounted at the end of the rib and must maintain surface registration with the hoops. For large reflectors, the rim may need additional trussing to prevent warpage under wind loading and gravity.

Surface material can be secured to the frame with short pieces of wire looped through the mesh and twisted at the rear of the hoops, or with sheet-metal screws, preferably stainless steel. If aluminum fly screening with unbonded mesh is used, it should be applied with the grid wires at 45° to the hoops for ease in conformity to the doubly curved surface.

A modified construction method, which is more popular, eliminates the circular hoops and places the surface material directly on the more accurately formed

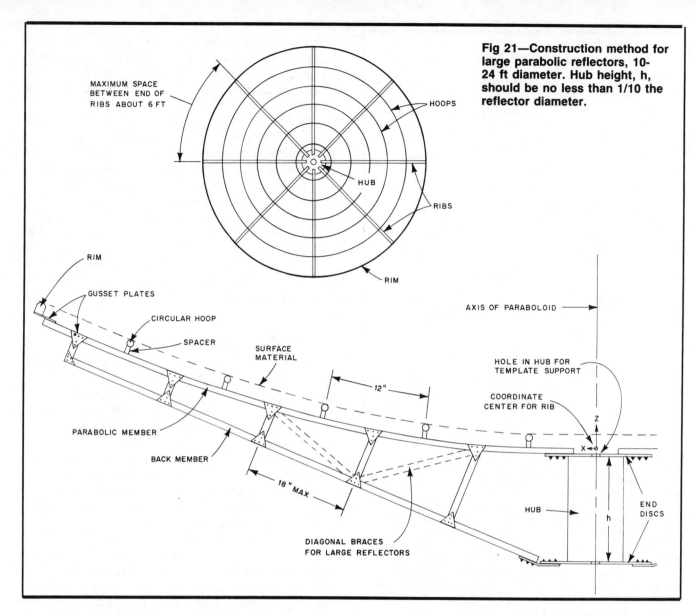

MAXIMUM SPACE
BETWEEN END OF
RIBS ABOUT 6 FT

HOOPS

HUB

RIBS

RIM

RIM

Fig 21—Construction method for
large parabolic reflectors, 10-
24 ft diameter. Hub height, h,
should be no less than 1/10 the
reflector diameter.

RIM

GUSSET PLATES

CIRCULAR HOOP

SPACER

SURFACE
MATERIAL

12"

PARABOLIC MEMBER

BACK MEMBER

18" MAX

DIAGONAL BRACES
FOR LARGE REFLECTORS

AXIS OF PARABOLOID

HOLE IN HUB FOR
TEMPLATE SUPPORT

COORDINATE
CENTER FOR RIB

Z

X

HUB

h

END
DISCS

ribs. If the number of ribs is increased, equal surface accuracy may be obtained. However, by using fewer ribs and allowing the surface material to be essentially curved in only one plane, good results can be obtained.

This "petal" arrangement of cylindrical parabolic sections is much easier to build using surface material that will only bend in one plane. The lack of conformity to an exact paraboloid will result in some loss of effective gain. Fig 22 shows this type of construction and gives an equation relating the geometry of the petals to gain degradation.[7]

STRESSED CONSTRUCTION

A different type of medium large, circularly symmetric reflector is the *stressed parabolic reflector*.[8] The method of construction uses single radial members instead of trussed ribs. Construction is illustrated by Fig 23 and shown in Fig 1, where a central hub plate joins all the radial members to a central support column. The basic premise is that by pulling the ends of each radial member toward the central column with thin wires, they will be stressed into a shape that approaches parabolic. While this is acceptable for shallow reflectors, deeper dishes will require

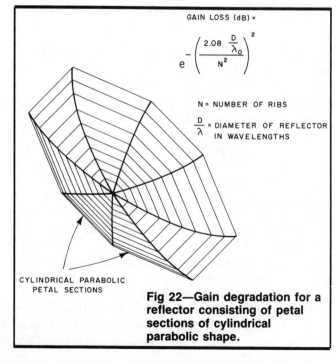

GAIN LOSS (dB) =

$$e^{-\left(\dfrac{2.08 \frac{D}{\lambda_0}}{N^2}\right)^2}$$

N = NUMBER OF RIBS

$\dfrac{D}{\lambda}$ = DIAMETER OF REFLECTOR
IN WAVELENGTHS

CYLINDRICAL PARABOLIC
PETAL SECTIONS

Fig 22—Gain degradation for a
reflector consisting of petal
sections of cylindrical
parabolic shape.

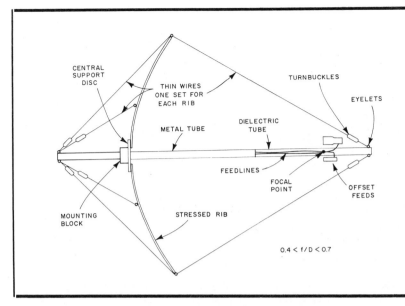

Fig 23—Stressed parabola design using multiple ribs. The length of the support tube is approximately equal to reflector diameter. Counterweights may be needed on the main support column.

additional trimming and stiffening; additional wires behind the radial members can be used to force them more closely to parabolic shape. Rigid sections are used to join the ends of the members, forming a fixed polygonal rim. Reflectors up to 40-ft diameter have been constructed in this manner.

The umbrella of thin wires in front of the reflector causes negligible loss in effective gain because the total blockage area is very small. Since the central support column passes directly through the focal point, it preferably should be made of a dielectric material, such as fiberglass. If the entire column cannot be made of an insulating material, the half nearest the focal point should be, to minimize shadowing of the feed.

For simplicity, the feed can be mounted directly to the side of the column, which will result in beam steering as discussed previously. Alternatively, any of the reverse feeds may be employed with good results.

SMALL REFLECTOR CONSTRUCTION

Molding

A reverse mold can be made from plaster, cement or any material that can be formed by rotating a template around a pivotal axis. After the mold has hardened, a "releasing" compound should be spread over it. Fiberglass or honeycomb material can be applied with an epoxy adhesive binder to build up the surface.[9] Materials for this type of construction can be found in boat and auto-body repair shops, but they are expensive.

After the dish is removed from the mold, a suitable mounting structure and rim can be cemented in place for structural integrity. Conductive material (screening, etc) can be cemented to the front surface. Reflectors up to 16-ft diameter have been fabricated in this manner.

Spin Casting

Small reflectors can be made with near optical surface accuracy by a method called *spin casting*. When a circular container of liquid is rotated about a vertical axis, gravity and centrifugal forces will form a perfect paraboloid at the surface of the liquid.[10] The focal length of the surface is equal to 1468.14 divided by the square of the rotational speed in revolutions per minute, regardless of the material used. The only requirement is that the fluid remain homogenous during the spin-forming operation.

Spin casting utilizes a casting resin for the liquid, and requires that the spinning speed be held constant for the time it takes the resin to harden. The container may be any convenient, circularly symmetric shape; however, in the interest of saving expensive resin and for the reduction of weight, the container should be an approximate paraboloid.

An acrylic casting resin with catalytic hardener material is available from art supply houses. Care should be used when handling large quantities of such material, as it is exothermic and will heat during the curing process. A slurry of non-shrinking casting plaster (also obtained from art supply houses) can also be used to spin cast paraboloids, which will be heavier than the resin type and must be carefully weatherproofed for outdoor use.

The spinning mechanism must be vibration free and have an inertia flywheel. For good accuracy and control of the focal length, an optional speed controller and shaft speed readout can be used. Typically, rotational speeds of less than 100 r/min will be required. For example, a 45 r/min record turntable will produce a focal length of 0.73 foot. To obtain a paraboloid with an f/D ratio of 0.5 will require a container about 18 inches diameter. If the first attempt produces an unsatisfactory surface, just apply a second thin layer of resin and repeat the operation.

The finished surface may be metalized with a coat of conductive paint or by cementing on a layer of aluminum foil with contact cement. A ball roller will minimize wrinkles.

Other Sources of Reflectors

Occasionally, an item not intended to be used as a focusing radio reflector may be found, which is quite suitable for that purpose. Large, shallow, circular trays, pot lids, bowls and even a popular form of child's aluminum snow sled are examples. Check the surface by making a close fitting template, then graphically check if the template curve is close to parabolic. Even if the item is not made from a conductive material, it can be easily covered with aluminum foil or a conductive paint.

Very good parabolic reflectors have been manufactured for the TVRO industry for many years and should not be overlooked as a source. These antennas are made with a surface accuracy sufficient to work well at 4 GHz and should give good results up to about 10 GHz. They are available in sizes from 4 to 14 feet in diameter.

Cylindrical Parabolic Reflectors

The cylindrical parabolic reflector antenna consists of a surface that is parabolically curved in only one plane, and a line-source feed, as shown in Fig 24. The primary advantage of this design is that the reflector is easier to construct than one for a circularly symmetric dish antenna. Greater surface accuracy can also be achieved through the use of screen or sheet material. The major disadvantage is the difficulty of designing and constructing a suitable line-source feed (a primary reason for its lack of popularity).

A line source is required since the cylindrical parabola focuses in only one plane. In the other plane (parallel to the line source), the reflector acts as a flat mirror, reflecting the broadside radiation of the line source. The line source must therefore be a relatively long, thin aperture or linear radiator

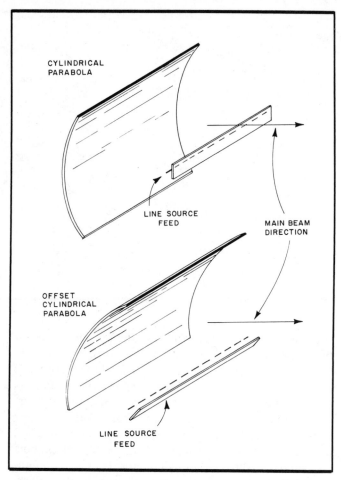

Fig 24—Standard cylindrical parabolic reflector (above) and offset arrangement (below), which eliminates feed blockage.

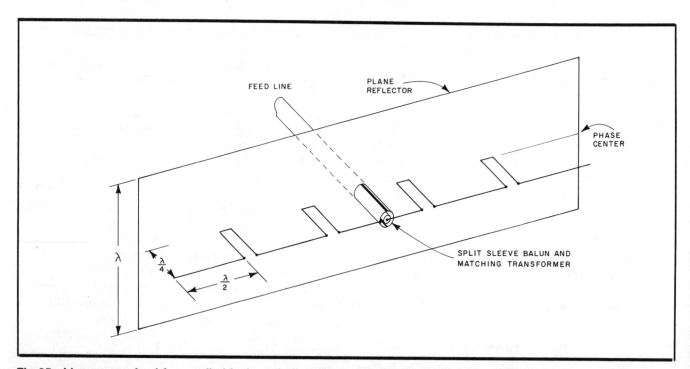

Fig 25—Line source feed for a cylindrical parabolic reflector, consisting of five λ/2 elements in phase, with a plane reflector. More elements may be added.

that radiates with uniform phase and amplitude along the total length. In the plane transverse to the line source, the feed must have a pattern similar to that of a dish feed—low side- and rear-lobe radiation, with the −10 dB level at the reflector edge.

Since the reflector can be in the near-field region of the feed, spillover from the broadside radiation will be negligible, provided the line source is no longer than the reflector is wide. However, there will be interaction between the feed and reflector, which can be eliminated by configuring the antenna as an offset cylindrical parabola (Fig 24, bottom). This arrangement has advantages similar to those of the offset, point-source fed reflector. (For additional information concerning offset-fed parabolic reflectors, see Chapter 10.)

The cylindrical parabolic reflector has a potentially higher aperture efficiency than does a circularly symmetric antenna, because spillover occurs in only one plane. A maximum aperture efficiency of 75% is attainable.

In practice, the line source can be a collinear radiator backed up with a 1-λ wide flat reflector, as shown in Fig 25.[11] Improved H-plane radiation characteristics can be obtained by employing two collinear radiators spaced λ/2 and fed in phase, similar to an extended double-dipole EIA feed antenna.

Notes

[1]Jasik, H., ed, *Antenna Engineering Handbook* (New York: McGraw-Hill, 1961) Ch 12.

[2]Love, A. W., ed, *Electromagnetic Horn Antennas* (New York: IEEE Press, 1976).

[3]Love, p 189.

[4]Love, p 181.

[5]Love, p 214.

[6]Naughton, T., "Parabolic Reflector Antennas," *Ham Radio,* May 1974, p 12.

[7]Jet Propulsion Laboratory Technical Report No. 32-1352.

[8]Knadle, R., "A 12 Foot Stressed Parabolic Dish," *QST,* Aug 1972, pp 16-22.

[9]Laakmann, P., "A Large Homebrew Parabolic Reflector," *Ham Radio,* Aug 1969.

[10]Roberson, J. and Crowe, C., *Engineering Fluid Mechanics* (Boston: Houghton Mifflin Company, 1975), p 119.

[11]Kennedy, J., "The Big Sail," *73,* Aug 1965, p 50.

Helical Antenna Design

By Bob Atkins, KA1GT
103 Division Ave
Millington, NJ 07946

The helical antenna provides a simple means of obtaining circular polarization, wide bandwidth and reasonable antenna gain in an easily constructed antenna. John Kraus, W8JK, the inventor of the helical antenna, goes so far as to say, "the dimensions of the helix are so non-critical that a helical beam antenna is one of the simplest types of antenna it is possible to make."[1] While this is true, it does not mean that careful design and construction of a helical antenna will not pay off in terms of increased gain, wider bandwidth and better circularity of polarization.

The radiation pattern and polarization characteristics of a helical antenna are dependent on the gross dimensions of the helix. Polarization may be circular, elliptical or linear, while the radiation may take place along the helix axis, at right angles to it, or in both directions simultaneously, as shown in Fig 1. When the helix diameter is small ($<1\ \lambda$), and the spacing between the turns is also small ($<0.05\ \lambda$), then the radiation from the antenna is predominantly at right angles to the antenna axis and the helix is said to be operating in the "normal" (meaning "at right angles" rather than "usual") mode.

The normal mode helix is not a very efficient antenna, but is of use in situations where an antenna is required which is very small compared to the wavelength of operation. The ubiquitous "rubber duck" antenna sometimes used on hand-held transceivers is an example of the normal mode helix. When the helix circumference is large ($>1.6\ \lambda$), and the spacing between turns is of the order of 1 wavelength then the helix may radiate with a four-lobed pattern when fed with a two-wire balanced transmission line. This is not a commonly utilized mode. The most common form of the helix antenna, and the one which will be described in detail here, is the *axial mode helix*. When the helix circumference is of the order of one wavelength and the spacing between turns in about a quarter wavelength, then radiation occurs mainly along the axis of the helix and the radiation is circularly polarized.

HELIX DIMENSIONS

The dimensions of the helix may be defined as shown in Fig 2. A number of investigators (see Note 2) have studied the relationship between the physical dimensions of the helix and the antenna gain, bandwidth and axial ratio (circularity of polarization). Most of the relationships are empirical, that is, they are derived from a comparison of the properties of many different antennas rather than being theoretically derived from basic principles. In the following analysis a helix pitch angle of 12.8 degrees will be assumed (see Fig 2), since most of the available data is for antennas with that pitch angle.

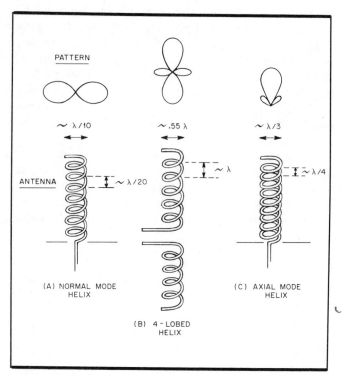

Fig 1—Dimensions and radiation patterns of different helix antennas.

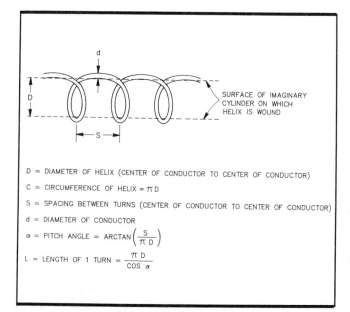

Fig 2—Dimensions of the helix.

Circumference

The first dimension of importance is the helix circumference. As has been mentioned, for an axial mode helix the circumference is of the order of one wavelength at the frequency of use. Research has shown that the helix circumference required to produce maximum gain at a particular frequency is related to the number of helix turns. The following empirical relationship has been found:

$$C = 1.066 + (N - 5) * 0.003 \qquad \text{(Eq 1)}$$

where

C is the circumference in wavelengths at peak gain (λ_p)
N is the number of helix turns
λ_p is the wavelength at helix peak gain

This relationship between C and N is shown graphically in Fig 3. Thus, for example, to yield maximum gain at 1296 MHz, a 20-turn 12.8-degree pitch helix should have a circumference of 1.126 wavelengths (26.05 cm).

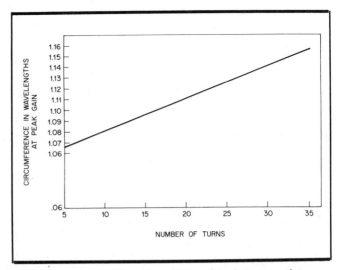

Fig 3—Graph showing the relationship between the circumference at peak gain and the number of helix turns.

Gain

The actual value of maximum gain has been shown to be given by the following somewhat complicated relationship:

$$G_p = 8.3 \left(\frac{\pi D}{\lambda_p}\right)^{\sqrt{N+2}\,-1} \left(\frac{NS}{\lambda_p}\right)^{0.8} \left(\frac{\tan 12.5}{\tan \alpha}\right)^{\frac{\sqrt{N}}{2}} \qquad \text{(Eq 2)}$$

where

α is the helix pitch angle (from 11.5 to 14.5 degrees)
D is the helix diameter
N is the number of helix turns
S is the spacing between helix turns,
λ_p is the wavelength at peak gain

Thus, a 20-turn, 12.8-degree pitch helix design for 1296 MHz using Eq 1 should show about 16.25 dBi gain at 1296 MHz according to Eq 2. The relationship between the number of helix turns and the helix peak gain is shown graphically in Fig 4.

Beamwidth

As with most antennas, as gain of a helix increases the beamwidth decreases. The usual measure of beamwidth is designated HPBW (half-power beamwidth), which is the angle between the half-power points on the major lobe. Fig 5 shows the relationship between the number of helix turns and HPBW at the frequency of peak gain. Another useful measure relating beamwidth and gain is the gain-beamwidth product, often designated $G\theta^2$, the product of the antenna gain and the square of the HPBW (in degrees). For 12.8-degree pitch helix antenna, the gain-beamwidth product varies from about 19,500 for a 35-turn helix to about 29,000 for a 5-turn helix, measured at the frequency of peak gain.

Bandwidth

A desirable property of the helical antenna is its relatively wide bandwidth. In general, the larger the

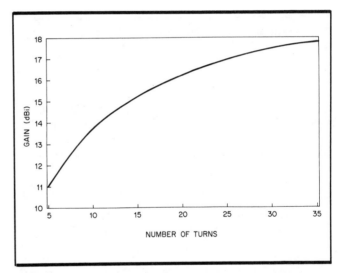

Fig 4—Gain v number of turns for a 12.8-pitch helix antenna.

number of helix turns, the higher the helix gain but the smaller the helix bandwidth. Actual bandwidth may be estimated by the following relationship:

$$FB = \frac{f_h}{F_l} \approx 1.07 \left(\frac{0.91 G_p}{G}\right)^{4/(3\sqrt{N})} \qquad \text{(Eq 3)}$$

where

N is the number of helix turns (from 5 to 35)
F_h is the upper frequency where the gain drops to G
F_l is the lower frequency where the gain drops to G
G_p is the gain at the maximum gain frequency
FB is the fractional bandwidth (or bandwidth frequency ratio)

Thus, for the 20-turn, 12.8-degree pitch helix, the -1-dB

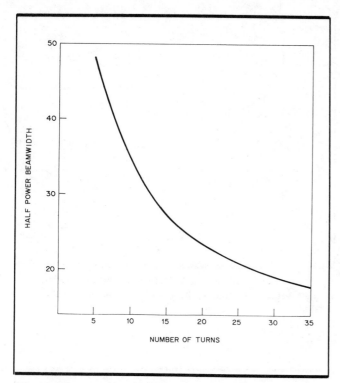

Fig 5—The number of helix turns and the half-power beamwidth (HPBW) are related this way.

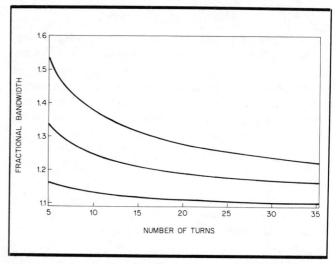

Fig 6—Bandwidth v number of turns for a 12.8-pitch helix antenna.

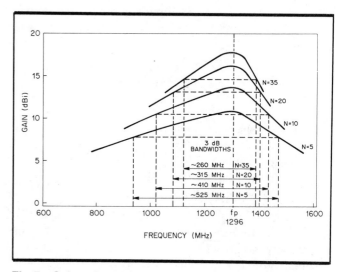

Fig 7—Gain v frequency for a 12.8-degree pitch helix with peak gain at 1296 MHz.

fractional bandwidth is 1.11, the −2-dB fractional bandwidth is 1.19 and the −3-dB fractional bandwidth is 1.28. A graphical depiction of the relationship between fractional bandwidth and number of helical turns is shown in Fig 6.

The actual shape of the gain v frequency curve for a given helix may be estimated from the following relationships:

$$G = 0.91G_p \left(\frac{1.04 \, f}{f_p} \right)^{\sqrt{N}} \text{ for } f \leq \frac{f_p}{1.04} \qquad \text{(Eq 4)}$$

$$G = 0.91G_p \left(\frac{f}{1.03 \, f_p} \right)^{-3\sqrt{N}} \text{ for } f \geq 1.03f_p \qquad \text{(Eq 5)}$$

where

    N is the number of helix turns
    G is the gain at frequency f
    G_p is the gain at the peak gain frequency f_p

These relationships hold to about ±0.5 dB for values of G to about 5 dB down from G_p. Computed gain v frequency curves for a number of helical antennas with f_p = 1296 MHz are shown in Fig 7. It will be noted that gain falls off much faster (three times as fast) at frequencies higher than f_p than at frequencies lower than f_p. This curve can be used to estimate gain at frequencies other than f_p or to determine the value needed to f_p when a given frequency range is desired to be covered.

POLARIZATION

As was mentioned earlier, an axial mode helix antenna generates circularly polarized radiation. There are of course two possible senses of circularly polarized radiation, "left-handed" and "right-handed." There has frequently been confusion as to which sense a given antenna radiates. Some of this confusion originates in the fact that the definitions of left and right handed used in classical physics and radio science (as defined by the Institute of Radio Engineers) are opposite, that is, left handed by one definition is right handed by the other! The definition used for all radio work is the IRE definition (see Note 3), which is that right circular polarization is the same as clockwise circular polarization—wave receding. That is, for a right-handed circular polarized antenna, looking from the rear of the antenna in the direction of radiation, the electric vector of the receding wave rotates in a clockwise direction. For a right-hand polarized helix antenna, the helix is also wound in a clockwise direction looking from the rear along the antenna.

The parameter used to define the uniformity of circular polarization is called the "axial ratio" (usually expressed in decibels). Perfectly circular polarization has an axial ratio of 0 dB, perfectly linear polarization has an axial ratio of infinity, and elliptical polarization has an axial ratio somewhere in between. The ratio is actually the ratio between the magnitude of the electric vector of the wave at its maximum to the electric vector of the wave at 90 degrees one-quarter wave later. For a uniform normal mode helix the axial ratio is about 1 dB over most of its operating range.

It has been experimentally observed that if the last few turns of the helix are tapered, then the axial ratio is improved slightly, at the expense of a slightly lower peak gain. For example, in one study (see Note 4) on an 18-turn helix the axial ratio at peak gain was reduced from about 1 dB to about 0.1 dB, while the gain fell by about 0.35 dB by tapering the last two turns from a diameter of D to 0.65D (see Fig 8). Different degrees of taper can produce antennas with extended bandwidth and/or improved axial ratio, but in all cases at the expense of peak again, which is the property that is usually of most concern in an amateur antenna system.

IMPEDANCE

The terminal impedance of an axial mode helix is close to 140 ohms resistive across its operating range when operating above a ground plane and fed as shown in Fig 9. Between the end of the helix and the feed point P the helix conductor lies in the plane of the helix axis and the angle [α] is the same as the helix pitch angle. For most amateur systems an impedance of 50 ohms is required. This may be achieved in a number of ways. One is to use a quarter-wave matching transformer (often a microstrip device at microwave frequencies) between the feed line and feed point of the helix. Another method is to increase the conductor size between the end of the helix and the feed point (see Fig 10 and Note 5). This may be achieved by soldering a flat metal strip to the helix conductor near the feed point. The resultant impedance is a function of the width and length of the strip, and the spacing between the strip and the ground plane. Adjustments should be made for a minimum SWR. A good starting point for a 1296-MHz helix (about 3 inches diameter) might be a flat metal point strip 1.5 inches long and 0.5 inch wide. The diameter of the conductor used for the helix has very little effect on helix characteristics when the helix is operating

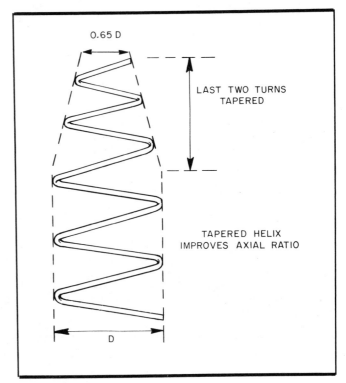

Fig 8—Tapered helix improves axial ratio.

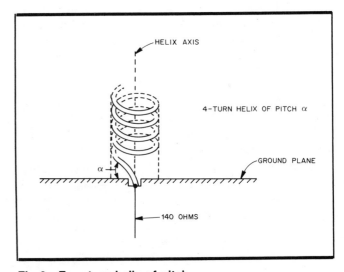

Fig 9—Four-turn helix of pitch α.

in the axial mode. Suggested diameters might be 1/4 inch below 1000 MHz, 3/16 inch at 1296 MHz and 1/8 inch at 2304 MHz. Copper tubing is available in these diameters from plumbing supply stores.

MULTIFILAR HELIX ANTENNAS

Although the axial mode helix antenna described above has a wide bandwidth compared to antenna designs

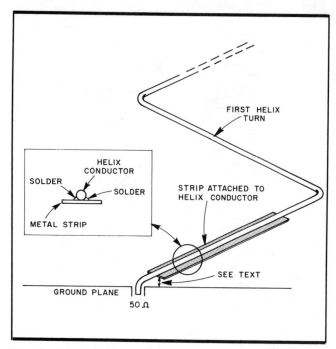

Fig 10—Matching helix antenna to 50-Ω feed line.

feed system is difficult to construct and has not found much application in amateur operation, though they are used in military avionics and space telemetry. Note 6 contains details of the theory and operation of the multifilar helix antenna.

Notes

[1]J. D. Kraus, *Antennas* (New York: McGraw-Hill, 1950), Ch 7.
[2]H. E. King and J. L. Wong, *IEEE Trans on Antennas Propagat*, vol AP-28, March 1980, pp 291-296.
[3]*IRE Standards on Radio Wave Propagation* (definition of terms) 1942, p 2, Supplement to *Proc IRE*, 30, No. 7, Part III.
[4]J. L. Wong and H. E. King, *IEEE Trans on Antennas Propagat*, vol AP-27, pp 72-78, January 1979.
[5]J. D. Kraus, *IEEE Trans on Antennas Propagat*, vol AP-25, November 1977, p 913.
[6]C. W. Gerst and R. A. Worden, *Electronics*, Aug 22, 1966, pp 100-110.

Design Example

Using the equations and graphs given earlier it is possible to design a helical antenna of given performance. Let's take as an example the design of an antenna for 1296 MHz. First, Eq 2 or Fig 4 is used to determine the number of turns required to give the desired gain. Let's say a gain of 17 dB is needed. Fig 4 shows that a 26-turn helix will be required. Eq 1 or Fig 3 may then be used to calculate the circumference of a 26-turn helix for peak gain at 1296 MHz. This turns out to be 1.129 wavelengths, or 26.11 cm. The other helix dimensions may then be determined from the relationships given in Fig 2. The results are:

Number of turns	= 26
Operational frequency	= 1296 MHz
Gain at 1296 MHz	= 17.08 dBi
Circumference	= 26.11 cm
Diameter	= 8.31 cm
Spacing between turns	= 5.78 cm
Length of each turn	= 26.75 cm
Length of wire needed	= 695.5 cm
Length of antenna	= 150.27 cm

such as the Yagi, the bandwidth can be further increased at the expense of design complexity. If the helix is regarded as a single wire wound around a cylinder, then a multifilar helix is an antenna in which multiple wires are wound around that same cylinder. The multiple wires may all be wound in the same direction (all clockwise) or they may be contrawound, that is, some wound clockwise and some wound anti-clockwise. Depending on the feed arrangement a multifilar contrawound helix may radiate linear or circular polarization of either sense. A quadrifilar counterwound helix may have a bandwidth of 5:1, say 800 to 4000 MHz. Such an antenna would have four feed points, and the beam pattern and polarization could be changed by changing the amplitude and phase of the signals supplied to the feed points. It is evident that such an antenna and

BASIC Program for Helix Design

The following BASIC program written in Apple BASIC may be used to obtain the physical parameters of a helical antenna for any given frequency based either on antenna gain, bandwidth or number of turns. A pitch of 12.8° is assumed.

```
1    DIM G(40)
2    DIM B1(40),B2(40),B3(40)
5    HOME
6 PI = 3.1415927
7 CA = 0.975149: REM COS 12.8
8 TA = 0.227194: REM TAN 12.8
10   REM   HELIX DESIGN PROGRAM
15   PRINT "HELIX DESIGN PROGRAM - KA1GT"
17   POKE 34,2
20   REM   BOB ATKINS KA1GT
30   HOME
32   FOR X = 5 TO 35
34   READ G(X),B1(X),B2(X),B3(X)
36   NEXT
40   PRINT "WHICH OF THE FOLLOWING PARAMETERS"
50   PRINT "DO YOU WISH TO BASE THE DESIGN ON ?"
55   PRINT
60   PRINT "1 - GAIN "
70   PRINT "2 - BANDWIDTH"
90   PRINT "3 - NUMBER OF TURNS"
95   PRINT
100  INPUT "ENTER #1-3 :";I
105  PRINT
200  ON I GOSUB 1000,2000,3000
250  C = 1.066 + (NT - 5) * .003
260  D = C / PI
270  S = C * TA
280  L = C / CA
290  TL = NT * L
295  INPUT "DIMENSIONS IN INCHES OR CM ? (I/C) ";I$
300  IF I$ = "C" THEN CV = 29979 / FP
305  IF I$ = "I" THEN CV = 29979 / (FP * 2.54)
306  IF I$ = "I" THEN I$ = "IN"
307  IF I$ = "C" THEN I$ = "CM"
310  HOME
400  PRINT "NUMBER OF TURNS"; TAB( 25);"= ";NT
410  PRINT "MAX GAIN"; TAB( 25);"= ";G(NT);"DB"
415  PRINT "FREQUENCY AT PEAK GAIN  = ";FP;"MHZ"
417 C =  INT (C * CV * 100) / 100
420  PRINT "CIRCUMFERENCE"; TAB( 25);"= ";C;" ";I$
425 D =  INT (D * CV * 100) / 100
430  PRINT "DIAMETER"; TAB( 25);"= ";D;" ";I$
435 S =  INT (S * CV * 100) / 100
440  PRINT "SPACING"; TAB( 25);"= ";S;" ";I$
445 L =  INT (L * CV * 100) / 100
450  PRINT "LENGTH OF TURN"; TAB( 25);"= ";L;" ";I$
455 TL =  INT (TL * CV * 100) / 100
460  PRINT "LENGTH OF WIRE NEEDED"; TAB( 25);"= ";TL;" ";I$
465 AL =  INT (NT * S * 100) / 100
470  PRINT "ANTENNA LENGTH"; TAB( 25);"= ";AL;" ";I$
500  PRINT : PRINT : PRINT
510  INPUT "RUN AGAIN ? (Y/N) ";I$
520  IF I$ = "Y" THEN  GOTO 55
999  END
1000  REM   DESIGN BASED ON GAIN
1010  PRINT "WHAT IS THE REQUIRED GAIN ?"
1020  INPUT "(IN THE RANGE 11-17.8DB) :";RG
1025  IF RG > 17.8 THEN  PRINT  CHR$ (7): GOTO 1000
1030  FOR X = 5 TO 35
```

```
1040    IF G(X) > RG THEN NT = X:X = 35
1050    NEXT
1060    PRINT "NUMBER OF TURNS REQUIRED = ";NT
1070    INPUT "OPERATIONAL FREQUENCY ? ";FP
1080    RETURN
1090    PRINT "CIRC = ";RC;" WAVELENGTHS"
2000    REM  BANDWIDTH
2010    PRINT : PRINT
2020    PRINT "WHICH BANDWIDTH ?"
2022    PRINT
2025    PRINT "1 - 1DB"
2030    PRINT "2 - 2DB"
2035    PRINT "3 - 3DB"
2037    PRINT
2040    INPUT "ENTER #1-3 :";WB
2045    PRINT
2050    PRINT "ENTER FREQUENCY RANGE (MHZ)"
2060    INPUT "(LOW FREQUENCY,HIGH FREQUENCY) :";F1,F2
2070 FB = F2 / F1
2080    ON WB GOSUB 2500,2600,2700
2085    IF NT < 5 THEN  PRINT "SORRY, NOT POSSIBLE - TRY AGAIN":
        PRINT : GOTO 2000
2090    PRINT "MAXIMUM NUMBER OF TURNS = ";NT
2095    PRINT
2100    PRINT "ASSOCIATED GAIN = ";G(NT);" DB"
2150    IF NT = 35 THEN FP = F1 + (.5618 * (F2 - F1)): GOTO 2277
2200    REM   ESTIMATE APPROX FREQUENCY OF PEAK GAIN BASED ON
        EXTRAPOLATION FROM LOWER FREQUENCY LIMIT
2205 G = G(NT)
2210 G1 = G - WB
2220 GA = 10 ^ ((G - WB) / 10)

2230 GB = 10 ^ (G / 10)
2240 X1 = GA / (.91 * GB)
2250 X2 =  LOG (X1) /  SQR (NT)
2260 X3 = 2.71828 ^ X2
2270 FP = (1.04 * F1) / X3
2272 REM CORRECT FOR GAIN SLOPE NEAR PEAK GAIN
2275 FP = FP - FP * .012885
2277 FP =  INT (FP + .5)
2280    PRINT "APPROX CENTER FREQUENCY = ";FP;" MHZ"
2300    RETURN
2500    FOR X = 5 TO 35
2505 NT = X
2510    IF B1(X) < FB THEN NT = X - 1:X = 35
2520    NEXT
2530    RETURN
2600    FOR X = 5 TO 35
2605 NT = X
2610    IF B2(X) < FB THEN NT = X - 1:X = 35
2620    NEXT
2630    RETURN
2700    FOR X = 5 TO 35
2705 NT = X
2710    IF B3(X) < FB THEN NT = X - 1:X = 35
2720    NEXT
2730    RETURN
3000    REM   DESIGN BASED ON NUMBER OF TURNS
3010    INPUT "NUMBER OF TURNS (5-35) ? ";NT
3020    INPUT "OPERATIONAL FREQUENCY (MHZ) ? ";FP
3030    RETURN
```

```
9999    REM THE FOLLOWING DATA STATEMENTS CONTAIN GAIN AND
        1,2 AND 3dB FRACTIONAL BANDWIDTH DATA ON 5-35 TURN
        HELIX ANTENNAS OF 12.8 DEGREES PITCH
10000   DATA  11,1.16,1.33,1.53,11.71,1.15,1.31,1.48,12.3,1.15,
        1.29,1.45
10010   DATA 12.82,1.14,1.27,1.42,13.28,1.14,1.26,1.39,13.69,1.13,
        1.25,1.38
10020   DATA  14.06,1.13,1.24,1.36,14.39,1.13,1.23,1.35,14.69,1.13,
        1.23,1.33
10030   DATA  14.97,1.12,1.22,1.32,15.23,1.12,1.21,1.31,15.46,1.12,
        1.21,1.31,15.68,1.12,1.2,1.3
10040   DATA  15.88,1.12,1.2,1.29,16.07,1.12,1.2,1.28,16.25,1.11,
        1.19,1.28
10050   DATA  16.41,1.11,1.19,1.28,16.56,1.11,1.19,1.27,16.70,
        1.11,1.18,1.26
10060   DATA  16.84,1.11,1.18,1.26,16.96,1.11,1.18,1.25,17.08,
        1.11,1.18,1.25
10070   DATA  17.18,1.11,1.18,1.25,17.28,1.11,1.17,1.24,17.38,
        1.11,1.17,1.24
10080   DATA  17.46,1.11,1.17,1.24,17.54,1.11,1.17,1.23,17.62,
        1.1,1.17,1.23
10090   DATA  17.69,1.1,1.16,1.23,17.75,1.1,1.16,1.23,17.81,1.1,
        1.16,1.22
```

Easy 50-Ω Feed for a Helix

By Joe M. Cadwallader, K6ZMW
13906 Fiji Way, #345
Marina del Rey, CA 90292

Recent interest in circular polarization (CP) on the VHF and UHF bands is growing, perhaps partially because of AMSAT-OSCAR Phase III and other satellite work. One of the most popular CP antennas is the helix, first described in depth by J. D. Kraus.[1] The helix is easy to build and very forgiving of minor dimensional errors owing in part to its rather broad (70%) bandwidth. For this reason the actual performance of a helix closely matches the theoretical performance.

PROBLEMS AND CURES

While working at 1296 MHz, where I've used both a quadhelix[2] and a helical feed for a dish, I found two deficiencies of the helix. First, terminating the helix at a connector in the center of the helix (Fig 1) is mechanically awkward and electrically rather undefined. I chose to terminate the helix in an N connector mounted on the ground screen at the periphery of the helix (Fig 2). Simply connect the helix conductor to the N connector as close to the ground screen as possible (Fig 3). Then adjust the first turn of the helix to maintain uniform spacing of the turns.

This modification goes a long way toward curing the second deficiency of the helix—the 140-Ω nominal feed-point impedance. Troetschel's approach[3] solves the feed impedance problem nicely in multiple helix arrays, but matching 50-Ω coax to a single helix is still a problem. The traditional quarter-wavelength matching section has proved difficult to fabricate and maintain. But if the helix is fed at the periphery, the first half turn of the helix conductor (leaving the N connector) acts much like a transmission line—a single conductor over a perfectly conducting ground plane. The impedance of such a transmission line is:

$$Z_0 = 138 \log \frac{4h}{d}$$

where
  Z_0 is the impedance of the line,
  h is the height of the center of the conductor above the ground plane, and
  d is the conductor diameter (both h and d must be in the same units of measure)

The cross-sectional detail of Fig 1 diagrams this. Clearly, the impedance of the helix is 140 Ω a turn or two away from the feed point. But as the helix conductor swoops down toward the feed connector (and the ground plane), h is getting smaller; therefore, the impedance is dropping. The 140-Ω nominal impedance of the helix is being transformed down to a lower value. For any

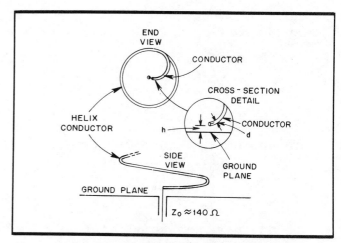

Fig 1—End view and side view of traditional helix configuration. Cross-sectional detail shows "standard" method for attaching feed line to the helix.

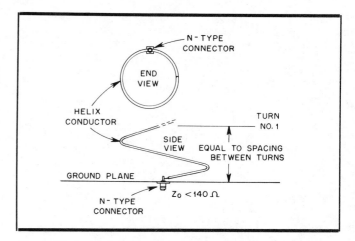

Fig 2—End view and side view of peripherally fed helix.

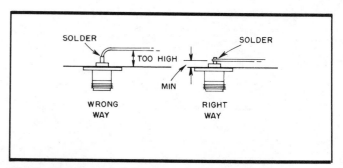

Fig 3—Wrong and right ways to attach helix to N connector.

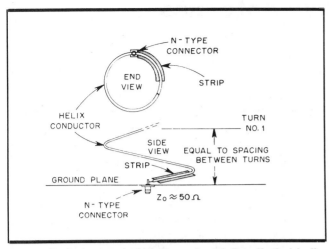

Fig 4—End view and side view of peripherally fed helix with metal strip added to improve transformer action.

particular conductor diameter, an optimum height can be found that will produce a feed-point impedance equal to 50 Ω. Preferably the height should be kept very small, and the diameter should be large. Apply power to the helix and measure the SWR at the operating frequency; adjust the height for an optimum match.

Typically, the conductor diameter may not be large

enough to result in a 50-Ω match at practical (small) values of h. In this case a strip of thin brass shim stock can be soldered to the first quarter turn of the helix conductor (Fig 4), as described by Kraus.[4] This effectively produces a larger diameter conductor which causes the impedance to drop further. The edges of this strip can be slit every ½ inch (12 mm) or so, and bent up or down (toward or away from the ground plane) to tune the line for an optimum match.

This approach will yield a perfect match to nearly any coax. The usually wide bandwidth of the helix (70% for SWR less than 2 to 1) will be reduced slightly to about 40% for the same conditions. This is not enough to be of any consequence for most amateur work. The improvements in assembly, adjustment and performance are well worth the effort to make the CP helix more practical to build and tune.

Notes

[1] J. Kraus, *Antennas* (New York: McGraw-Hill Book Co), 1950, Chap 7.
[2] Helix antennas are discussed in *The ARRL Antenna Book* (Newington, CT: ARRL, 1988), 15th ed., pp 19-22 to 19-33 and Chap 20.
[3] W. Troetschel "A Quadhelix Antenna for the 1215-Mc. Band," *QST*, August 1963, p 36.
[4] J. Kraus, "A 50-Ohm Input Impedance for Helical Beam Antennas," *IEEE Transactions on Antennas and Propagation*, Vol AP-25, No. 6, November 1977, p 913).

Aiming Microwave Antennas

By Bob Atkins, KA1GT
103 Division Ave
Millington, NJ 07946

One of the characteristics of antennas used at microwave frequencies is that high gain may be realized with small physical size. For most purposes the achievement of high antenna gain is highly desirable, since this will maximize communication range. Associated with increasing antenna gain is decreasing antenna beamwidth. This means that the higher the antenna gain, the more accurately it has to be pointed. The problem that arises is one of knowing in what direction to point the antenna with sufficient accuracy to take full advantage of its gain.

Antenna beamwidth can be roughly estimated from the gain figure. The relationship between gain and beamwidth holds quite well for parabolic dishes and reasonably well for optimized Yagi arrays. Non-optimized arrays (those with too large or small a stacking distance) have an appreciable number of side and back lobes, and the relationship given below may not hold:

Gain (as a power ratio) = 30000 / H° × V°

where

H° = horizontal 3-dB beamwidth
V° = vertical 3-dB beamwidth

For example, a 3-ft-diameter dish used at 10 GHz has a gain of about 37 dBi, or a power gain of 5000. Substitution in the above formula yields a horizontal × vertical 3-dB beamwidth of 6. Assuming equal horizontal and vertical beamwidths (which is a reasonable assumption with most dish feeds), the beamwidth in both planes is 2.45°. Thus, to take full advantage of the antenna gain, one must know in what direction to point it with an accuracy of better than 0.5° (Fig 1), and be physically able to point it with that accuracy. An aiming error of only 1.2° will result in a 3-dB loss of signal. Note that this applies to vertical as well as horizontal aiming!

So how do we know in what direction to point the antenna? Measuring bearings from a map is not an accurate method. The projection system used in drawing most maps does not reproduce great-circle bearings, which are the ones we need. There are maps that reproduce great-circle bearings, but they are only good for one particular point on the Earth's surface and have to be custom drawn for any given location.

In order to determine the bearing and distance between any two points on Earth, it is only necessary to know the pair of latitudes and longitudes. Relationships are as follows: If point 1 has a latitude R°N and longitude S°W, point 2 has a latitude X°N, longitude Y°W.

Distance between point 1 and point 2 in nautical miles is

$$D = 60 \cos^{-1} [\sin R \times \sin X + (\cos R \times \cos X \times \cos [Y - S])]$$

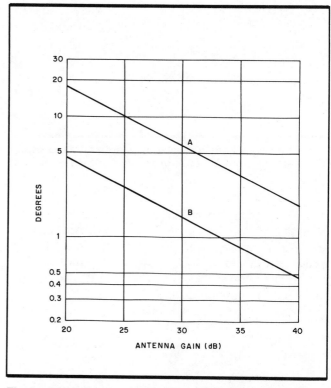

Fig 1—Approximate relationship between antenna gain and beamwidth. Line A is the antenna 3-dB beamwidth, while B is the aiming accuracy required for less than 1 dB of gain loss.

where 1 statute mile = 0.869 nautical mile.

Bearing from point 1 to point 2 is

$$\cos^{-1} \frac{[\sin X - (\sin R \times \cos Z)]}{(\sin Z \times \cos R)}$$

where $Z = \dfrac{\text{distance (nautical miles)}}{60}$

This assumes that point 1 is west of point 2. If point 1 is east of point 2, then the true bearing = (360 − calculated bearings).

The difference between a map-measured bearing and the true great-circle bearing between two points depends on where the points are and what type of map is used. Try measuring and calculating a few different points and see how much difference there can be. The points don't have to be close together, either. Remember that contacts over 1000 miles have been made on 10 GHz! For those of you with access to a microcomputer, the PATHLOSS program described in the Appendix will quickly and accurately calculate bearings for you.

Chapter 10

Earth-Moon-Earth (EME) Communications

By Dick Turrin, W2IMU,   and Al Katz, K2UYH
PO Box 65   Electrical Engineering Department
Colts Neck, NJ 07722   Trenton State College
                          Trenton, NJ 08650-4700

O f all the propagation mechanisms in the UHF and microwave spectrum, the Earth-Moon-Earth (EME) path has unique characteristics that make it an extremely rewarding challenge. "Moonbounce," as it's commonly known, allows communication between any two points on Earth. As the name implies, it involves the reflection of radio waves off the moon and receiving them back on Earth. The challenge of EME communication is in overcoming the natural laws of physics by making the most of our radio technology. This chapter provides information that will aid in realizing a successful amateur EME station.

HISTORY

There is little doubt that prehistoric man wondered about the moon, but it wasn't until early astronomers conceived of the solar system that our moon's nature became evident. Indeed, when it was realized that moonlight was simply reflected sunlight, the first glimmer of the moon as a passive, reflecting satellite was conceived. Several centuries were to pass before electromagnetic theory and the realization of practical radio transmission equipment would make the EME communication dream possible.

The development of high-power radar during WW II made available the equipment capable of receiving "real-time" EME signals. On January 10, 1946 the first lunar radio echoes were heard by engineers working at the Evans Signal Laboratory of the US Signal Corps, located in Belmar, New Jersey. Project Diana had succeeded on 111.5 MHz, using 15-kW output to a 64-element "bed-spring" array aimed at the eastern horizon.[1] Using much different equipment, a similar experiment by Z. Bay was also successful in Hungary on February 6, 1946.[2] For this experiment, a chemical integrator combined repeated echoes to detect the presence of the reflected signal. These experiments once and for all answered the question of whether or not radio signals could penetrate the

atmosphere and return back to Earth. The "space age" had arrived—even though 15 years would pass before the moon would be used for practical communication purposes.

Radio amateurs were among the first to recognize the moon's value for communication. The challenge of obtaining lunar echoes was compelling. Although the exact number of unsuccessful experiments is unknown, the three-year efforts of W4AO and W3GKP with W3LZD produced successful 144-MHz echoes in 1953.[3]

In the late 1950s, F. S. "Sam" Harris, W1FZJ (then VHF Editor of *CQ* magazine) started the infamous Rhododendron Swamp VHF Society, W1BU. Their goal: to make EME communications a reality. Sam heard his first weak echo on 50 MHz, then moved up to 144 MHz. He used a huge 128-element expanded collinear array mounted on a circular section of track. Echoes were heard with this antenna, but signals were again weaker than expected. This prompted his switch to 1296 MHz, using an 18-foot parabolic reflector antenna (Fig 1). In 1960 the first 1296-MHz EME contact was made between W1BU and W6HB, the Eimac Amateur Radio Club.[4] Shortly thereafter, KH6UK (operated by W2UK, on assignment in Hawaii) also worked W1BU. This was followed by the first 432-MHz EME contact between W1BU and KH6UK. Soon, others joined W1FZJ on 1296 MHz in this pioneering effort—HB9RG, DL3FM, G3LTF, W2CXY, W6NLZ and K6HCP, to name just a few. More contacts followed, with a greater number of stations becoming involved. Amateur EME communications had begun in earnest.

OSCAR III, which carried the first amateur satellite transponder, was launched in 1964. Although this caused a furor in satellite communications, serious EME work continued. The first 144-MHz EME contact was made on April 12, 1964 by W6DNG and OH1NL, in collaboration with K1HMU.[5] For technical reasons, interest began focusing on the 420-MHz band, where receiver noise

Fig 1—EME pioneer "Sam" Harris, W1FZJ, is shown in this 1960 photo adjusting the feed of his 18-foot dish.

Fig 2—Al Katz, K2UYH, sights the 28-foot dish that helped him earn the first 432-MHz WAC award.

figures were lower and power generation was easier than on 1296 MHz.

During July 1965, a monstrous EME signal appeared on 144 and 432 MHz from KP4BPU, using the 1000-foot (!) radio telescope antenna at Arecibo, Puerto Rico. In December of that same year, WA6LET provided a giant signal on 432 MHz using the 150-foot reflector antenna at Stanford University. Although these were only limited-time operations, they provided the first EME signals that *anyone* with a small antenna and good receiver could hear.

In early 1966, VK3ATN demonstrated that consistent echoes could be obtained on 144 MHz using only 150-W output to a stack of four rhombic antennas, each 50-λ long per leg. His experiments with W6YK, K6MYC and later K2MWA/2 resulted in the first W/VK EME contact in November 1966. The Crawford Hill VHF Club, K2MWA/2 (later W2NFA), used a commercial 60-foot reflector antenna for this achievement.

By 1968, W2NFA began promoting EME first on 432 MHz and later on 1296 MHz. At this time at least 10 stations in six different countries were active on 1296 MHz, with approximately 50 more operators busily assembling EME systems.

Regular 432-MHz activity began in 1971 with a contact between VE7BBG and WA6HXW. VE7BBG used a 20-foot, stressed parabolic reflector, while WA6HXW drove an array of 32 wooden-boom, Tilton (W1HDQ) Yagis. Within a month they were joined by K2UYH, W6FZJ (now W1JR), W9WCD, VK2AMW, and G3LTF; activity has steadily grown since then. Regular 2-meter

activity began in the mid-1970s, thanks to the efforts of W6PO and others. In 1976, K2UYH used 432-MHz EME operation to achieve the first VHF/UHF Worked All Continents Award (WAC). See Fig 2.

144-MHz EME activity increased greatly in the late 1970s when K1WHS, using a very large Yagi array, showed that contacts could be made with stations using only a *single Yagi*! This gain-trading approach made it possible for many stations unable to hear their own echoes to communicate with a "super station."

In addition to the perseverance of many experimenters, much of the recent progress in EME communication is due to the development of inexpensive, low-noise transistors. Today, ultra-sensitive receivers with noise temperatures lower than those of antennas are readily available. Large Yagi arrays and reflector antennas with improved feeds are being built, and the worldwide ranks of EME enthusiasts continue to grow. As a result, solid 432-MHz contacts are possible with only a four-Yagi array. On 1296 MHz, reflector antennas as small as 6-foot diameter can be successfully used. EME communication is finally within the grasp of most every amateur! Today, EME activity is on all bands 50 through 10,000 MHz, including 220 and 902 MHz.

EME PROPAGATION

By its very nature, the unique EME propagation path deserves special attention. The following information should be helpful in understanding and using this path. It is based on observations of nature and should remain valid for a long time.

Free-Space Path Loss

The single factor that makes EME difficult is the inordinately high path loss due to the approximate half-million mile round trip to and from the moon. Path loss in free space is simply the dilution of a radio wave as it expands spherically when propagating away from an antenna.

First EME on 2300 MHz

In April 1967, Bill "Smitty" Smith, W3GKP of Spencerville, Maryland and Paul Wilson, W4HHK of Collierville, Tennessee teamed-up to attempt the first EME QSO on the 13-cm (2300-2450 MHz) band. At the time, W4HHK had a fully steerable, az-el mounted 18-ft dish (theoretical beamwidth 1.7°, gain 39 dB) he had used on 432 MHz since 1964. (The same 18-ft dish is still in use in 1990 on 2304 MHz at W4HHK.) W3GKP had a 28-footer lying on the ground with brush growing through it. Smitty's antenna beamwidth and gain were a theoretical 1.1° and 43 dB respectively.

Project 2300 began with Smitty starting construction on a kilowatt (input) VA-802B Klystron amplifier transmitter and Paul building a crystal-controlled receiving converter. An operating frequency of 2304.000 MHz was agreed on because it is the 16th harmonic of 144.0 MHz and would make frequency measurements easy. A receiver first IF of two meters was chosen to make use of existing stable, narrowband receiving equipment. Smitty used a mixer system at 2.3 GHz for both transmit and receive. To find the frequency at 2304 MHz, 1-MHz secondary frequency standards with harmonic multipliers were employed. Lunar echoes were usually found within a kilohertz or two of the marker frequency.

Paul first tested his converter in May 1968 with a signal source located 250 feet from the dish and later at ½ mile. There were no locals on the band. Then he built a parametric amplifier ("paramp"—low-noise 2-GHz transistors were unavailable) from details found in Jim Fisk's (W1DTY) *Parametric Handbook*. It was pumped with a 9.6-GHz Klystron and exhibited an estimated 3-dB noise figure and 20 dB gain.

In early November 1968 both stations were ready for one-way tests. Smitty's transit-mounted dish could be manually steered vertically only, so window time for schedules was limited to about 20 minutes. In addition to Smitty's limited schedule window, a maximum of about two weeks of each month was usable when the moon was at high declination. Az-el data for antenna aiming was derived from the *Nautical Almanac* and conversion tables. Personal computers were still in the future at this time. It was a pencil and paper routine before each schedule. Although they tried AO, CW,

FSK and SSB emissions, slow CW proved best. About this time WA4HGN, 100 miles from W4HHK, gave Paul his first distant terrestrial signals to verify the EME equipment was on frequency and working. Solar noise was also regularly employed to test antenna and receiver.

Positive identification of Smitty's EME signal eluded Paul until March 29, 1969, when strip-chart recordings revealed 3-second dashes—dashes too weak to copy with headphones. Smitty confirmed that a 3-second format was used (he always kept it secret and changed often to prevent guessing at the receive end). Most of W3GKP's call sign was copied on April 24 that year.

Both participants curtailed all transmissions during NASA's Apollo Lunar missions (to avoid possible interference) at the suggestion of Army MARS. Apollo spacecraft operated just below the 2300-MHz band. Paul retuned his receiver for the Apollo frequencies and began listening with the Apollo 8 mission, but was unsuccessful until Apollo 10 was clearly received while in lunar orbit on May 23, 1968.

By early December 1969, Paul was ready to start transmitting to W3GKP with his VA-802B Klystron. Smitty heard an unidentified signal on December 20, but he did not positively identify Paul's signals until February 16, 1970. By the end of 1969, tests had been lengthened to about one hour. Smitty had mounted an ingenious mechanism at the feed of his dish that permitted steering the feed, thereby providing limited beam steering in azimuth.

Tests continued, becoming two-way in March 1970. There were signals heard and identified both ways on many schedules...some near misses at a two-way contact...and finally, a satisfying, real-time, slow CW QSO was realized on October 19, 1970 with headphone copy (chart recorder not required). The contact went so well that W4HHK added unscheduled 73s at the end that nearly caught W3GKP off guard. This first EME QSO on 2300 MHz covered a terrestrial distance of 750 miles.

Project 2300 spanned 3½ years, but for Smitty, W3GKP, it really began some 17 years earlier when he and Ross Bateman, W4AO achieved the first amateur EME echoes on any band.—*Paul Wilson, W4HHK*

Average EME path loss may be calculated by doubling the one-way path loss and including the additional lunar reflection losses. Table 1 gives this information for the principal amateur UHF/microwave bands. The lunar reflection coefficient is a scientifically measured quantity of close to 6.5% (−11.8 dB) for the UHF region, decreasing to about 5% at microwave frequencies.[6] It is related to the physical nature of the moon and does not change with time.

In addition, the distance between Earth and the moon is not constant, being greatest at *apogee* and least at *perigee*, changing on a 28-day cycle. Over an annual period, the distance can vary between 222,650 and 253,000 statute miles. This change, although small in percentage, results in a maximum path-loss variation of ±1.1 dB from the average value, regardless of frequency.

The reflection of radio waves is not affected by the optical phases of the moon. A new moon, which may be troublesome to locate, will reflect just as well as a full moon. Lunar phases are the result of sunlight being reflected and shadowed by the Earth.

Echo Delays

Radio waves propagate at a constant velocity of 186,000 miles per second. Because of the great distance between Earth and the moon, there will be a time delay of about 2.7 seconds from the instant a radio transmission originates to the time it returns. This time delay permits unique self evaluation of individual system echoes and assurance that communication with other stations is

3.4- and 5.7-GHz EME Experiments, Spring 1987

Until the late fall of 1986, there had never been much effort directed toward attempting EME QSOs on the 3.4- and 5.7-GHz bands. At that time, a group of amateurs from the North Texas Microwave Society (NTMS) decided it was time to take a serious look at EME experimentation on these bands. Their goal: the first two-way EME QSOs on 3.4 and 5.7 GHz. The NTMS group consisted of Les (Lucky) Whitaker, W7CNK, of Oklahoma City and Rick Fogle, WA5TNY, Carl Napper, KA5JPD, and Dave Hallidy, KD5RO, all of the Dallas/Fort Worth area.

Our calculations showed that low-noise GaAsFET preamp technology—coupled with the high antenna gains available from moderately sized dishes—would overcome most of the path losses encountered at these frequencies (280 dB at 3.4 GHz and 284 dB at 5.7 GHz). This meant that our search for transmit power would be a little easier, as 100 watts appeared to be enough power.

After spending the late fall of 1986 and the early winter of 1987 mounting the three- and five-meter diameter dish antennas used for these tests, we started building the necessary preamps and transverters. We also did some experimentation with feed designs for the dishes, finally settling on a design presented in February 1986 *Ham Radio* magazine by Norm Foote, WA9HUV. We were also fortunate to find surplus 100-watt TWT amplifiers that operated in the desired frequency ranges.

W7CNK's station was about ready to go, and he had a 5-m dish, so we decided to try to hear echoes on 5760 MHz first. On February 14, 1987, we ventured to Oklahoma City to make this historic attempt, but no echoes were to be heard that night. When WA5TNY hit the key, the TR relay locked up and the receive preamp instantly vaporized. What a disappointment! Undaunted, W7CNK reconfigured the station to operate on 3456 MHz the following weekend (February 20). With a little tweaking of the TWT, he became the first amateur to hear his own (weak) lunar echoes on 3456 MHz! This gave us the incentive we needed to press on. After repairs were made to the 5760-MHz preamp, another attempt was made to hear echoes on that band. On March 6, 1987, we were successful. The echoes were so good that at times SSB could be clearly heard.

In March, WA5TNY, KA5JPD and KD5RO started readying the Texas end of the link. We used a 3-m TVRO dish of mesh construction and feeds similar to those built for W7CNK. In addition, we also had over 100 watts of TWT power available. Finally, we were ready and set up a sked for the first 3456-MHz attempt. We were "quietly confident" that we would be successful.

On April 7 at 0120 UTC, KD5RO began calling W7CNK. KD5RO successfully worked W7CNK on 3456 MHz and each station heard every transmission made by the other. The only problem encountered was one of over-excitement by KD5RO. We heard W7CNK well enough that we forgot that the moon was at zenith (and libration fading was at its worst) and sent too fast. After slowing down a bit, everything went smoothly and the first-ever QSO off the moon on the amateur 9-cm band was history! Signals were not terribly strong, peaking 5 to 6 dB above the noise, but they were clearly audible without any additional filtering aids.

The tremendous success of our first attempt led us to believe that we would achieve even better results on 5760 MHz where antenna gains were higher. We made a sked for the next night (April 8) and, at the appointed time, clearly heard W7CNK calling WA5TNY. We answered, but to no avail. Throughout the entire schedule, Lucky never heard us. We later found out that our TWT was oscillating and was actually generating almost no power at the desired frequency. We needed to find another source of power for the 5.7-GHz attempt.

While we searched for another amplifier, W7CNK wasn't sitting on his laurels. He managed to work KØKE and several others on the evening of April 12 on 3456 MHz. This group was operating from a commercial site in Colorado. KØKE was running only 12 watts to a 10-meter dish! This QSO extended the EME distance record on this band to 489 miles.

WA5TNY finally located a TWT for 5760 MHz which ran about 20 watts output. The calculations showed this to be barely enough power for the link, so we decided to give it a try. At 1600 UTC on April 24, W7CNK began sending long strings of dashes so that we could peak our dish exactly on the moon. He was good copy, peaking 8 to 10 dB above the noise. Finally, he stood by and WA5TNY called him. In our haste and excitement, we forgot to account for the Doppler shift (about 8 to 10 kHz at that time) and Lucky had to find us. After he located us, the first-ever EME QSO on 5.7 GHz went very smoothly. Lucky later admitted that we were quite weak and there was no room for error—if the dish had not been kept exactly on the moon, he would have lost us. Efforts later by KØKE and his group to work W7CNK on 5760 MHz were unsuccessful, as they found that the 6-GHz feed system on their dish was configured for transmitting only.

In the short space of about six months, a lot was accomplished. Two groups, *working together as one team*, acquired the materials and constructed two complete EME stations. This team was able to break down some formidable barriers long thought to be insurmountable by amateurs—specifically, hearing the first lunar echoes on 3456 and 5760 MHz and then actually completing several EME QSOs on these bands. Teamwork was most certainly the prime factor in our success. Without it, and the guidance and expertise of other members of the NTMS and the amateur VHF/UHF community in general, our goals would have been much harder to achieve.—*David Hallidy, KD5RO*

Table 1

Two-Way EME Path Loss

Frequency (MHz)	Average Path Loss† (dB)
432	261.2
1296	271.1
2300	276.1
3400	279.5
5700	283.9
10,000	288.9

† ± 1.1 dB for elliptic lunar orbit

For any frequency:

$$\text{Path Loss (dB)} = 10 \log \frac{d_m \lambda_o \sigma_m}{(16\pi)^2 R^4}$$

where
  d_m = the moon's diameter, 2160 statute mi
  λ_o = free space wavelength in statute mi
  R = mean distance to the moon in statute mi (238,000)
  σ_m = average lunar reflection coefficient (0.065)

possible. The delay does not cause confusion in regular communication because amateurs typically use the simplex mode with pauses between transmissions.

A milestone in an EME operator's experience is first hearing his or her own echoes. Echo transmission is in the simplex mode, and TR switching must be done without much delay to receive as much of the transmission as possible. At a keying speed of 20 WPM it is possible to transmit and receive a complete call sign as an echo.

Atmospheric Effects

Propagation losses through the atmosphere are practically nil for all weather conditions at UHF and the lower microwave frequencies. Rain attenuation becomes an important factor only above 4 GHz.

For paths with low elevation angles (toward a rising or setting moon for example), other factors may influence the total propagation loss. Ground reflections from the antenna foreground can alter the effective path loss, depending on how the phase and amplitude of the reflected wave combines with the direct wave. A good specular reflection (often found over water) can result in a 6-dB increase in signal level, but can also cause significant losses. At low elevation angles, the signal must pass through a greater cross section of ionosphere, which can increase path loss by a maximum of 2 dB. Furthermore, antenna noise will increase, since part of the antenna beam "sees" the warm Earth at an approximate temperature of 300 K. The

rest of the antenna sees an atmospheric temperature ranging from 3 to 100 K.

Tropospheric propagation conditions can greatly influence effective EME path loss. The most pronounced effect is *refraction*, such as that experienced during tropospheric ducting. This can cause the optimum beam heading to point away from the moon! Even under normal conditions, sufficient refraction occurs to allow radio echoes when the moon is below the visible horizon. While rising and setting moon paths result in maximum point-to-point DX, they are also the most difficult to use successfully. The preferred EME path is one where the antenna beam is pointed well above the Earth's surface. In retrospect, project Diana, which resulted in the first EME echoes ever received, succeeded despite the most adverse choice of operating conditions.

Faraday Rotation

One type of fading is directly related to the rotation of linearly polarized radio waves as they propagate through the ionosphere. This effect is commonly known as *Faraday rotation*.[7] When a linearly polarized echo arrives back at Earth, the polarization orientation is not readily predictable and may actually be orthogonal (at right angles) to the transmitted wave. In this case, the return signal will be in the cross-polarized null of the transmitting antenna. Since the same antenna is usually employed for receiving, the echo will be very weak or not discernible.

Faraday rotation is a function of ionization density and signal path orientation with respect to the Earth's magnetic field. When the path is at right angles to the field, no Faraday rotation will occur—a rather unique situation for stations near the equator. Since ionization density is proportional to solar radiation, rotation effects are minimized on an all nighttime path. The most pronounced effects occur when the path is in the twilight region. Faraday rotation is also non-reciprocal, meaning that rotation on the path to the moon does not reverse sense on the return path; instead, it is cumulative. This makes it extremely difficult to predict initial linear polarization alignment, even to hear one's own echoes.

Some EME stations utilize a motorized polarization rotator to search for the best linear polarization orientation. Observations on 432 MHz indicate that moonbounce signals frequently have no apparent polarization orientation, while at other times they do. At 1296 MHz, there is almost always a preferred orientation.

Because the moon's surface is quite rough, reflected radio waves will be partially scattered into other polarizations (Fig 3). Measurements indicate that at UHF, average cross-polarized scattering can be as high as 15 dB below the principal polarization level. In practice, Faraday rotation fades are not always complete nulls.

The Cutting Edge: EME on 10 Gigs

On May 30, 1989, at 1215 UTC, Jim Vogler, WA7CJO (Arizona—grid locator DM33XL) and Al Ward, WB5LUA (Texas—EM13QC) made contact via 10-GHz EME for a new band/mode record of 888.5 miles. WA7CJO was running 80 W from a TWT amplifier to a 16-foot dish, and WB5LUA used a 9.5-foot dish and a 28-W TWT.

This report, published in September 1989 *QST*, describes a successful assault on the 10-GHz DX record. The narrative that follows confirms that EME DX records don't come easily!

Greetings from the Bedlam Microwave Society

By Jim Vogler, WA7CJO
2540 E Heatherbrae Dr
Phoenix, AZ 85016

March 12, 1988: The 4.8-m Ku-band dish and SCR-584 antenna positioner were picked up at Dick Kolbly's (K6HIJ) in Barstow, California (24 hours of no sleep and 864 miles in a 24-foot stake bed rental truck). Dave Chase (KY7B), Terry Wilkinson (WA7LYI), and yours truly participated.

May 14, 1988: Crane arrives at WA7CJO's. Dish and SCR-584 positioner are installed in about an hour and a half.

May 23, 1988: First sun noise measurement. Noise was 2.4 dB and antenna pattern was diffuse with at least 4 peaks. (This was before the feed was adjusted at the prime focus of the dish.) ("SSB" Transverter).

May 25, 1988: First moon noise measurement. Noise was 0.3 dB (sun noise was now 9 dB; system noise figure was approximately 5 dB). ("SSB" Transverter). Improvements continued on the feed, and after we discovered that the "SSB" transverter was prone to oscillation, we changed the transverter to the present image reject design.

June 24-26, 1988: First schedule with Kent (WA5VJB). WA7CJO transmitting (35 W). Due to a plethora of problems at both stations, nothing was heard. Dave Chase (KY7B), Terry Wilkinson (WA7LYI), Dick Raymond (WA7CTY), Charles Justinak (W7GBI), and yours truly participated.

June 26, 1988: Sun noise 10.2 dB, moon noise 1.2 dB. System noise figure is approximately 3 dB (thanks to the WB5LUA/WA5VJB X-band preamp board I had recently completed).

July 2-4: Second schedule with WA5VJB. Weather problems prevailed on both ends at times. WA7CJO heard his EME echo at approximately 3 AM MST July 3, 1988. This was the first coherent signal received on the system (other than signals from test equipment). The signal was 3-4 dB out of the noise and sounded like 2-meter aurora. Transmitter power is 35 W. Finally, at approximately 4 AM MST, WA5VJB hears my signal and is able to optimize his polarization and antenna position. By this time Kent is out of moon time and invincible fatigue overtakes us both. The next schedule (at perigee) should be a piece of cake! During August Dave and I (primarily Dave) worked on the 100-W TWT amplifier power supply, finally getting it going on the 18th.

August 20, 1988: Dave (KY7B), Wayne (K7JTG), Terry (WA7LYI), and myself work on the TWT. We find that

the beam has apparently become defocused and Wayne is busy taping magnets on the tube body (caution should be exercised in this because too strong a field could deflect the full beam current to the helix and instantly destroy the tube). We use all the magnets in the house and Terry and Dave raid the local stores in search of more magnets.

August 21, 1988: The 230-lb, 100-W TWT amplifier is installed on the antenna pedestal (15 feet above ground) by Dave (KY7B) and yours truly.

August 22, 1988: Third schedule with WA5VJB finds Kent armed with KY7B's Hughes 1277H TWT amplifier that happens to put out about 55 W. This should be easy! Poor weather prevails in Arizona. Kent is able to copy my signal with little difficulty although not much better than when I was running 35 W. I can barely detect his signal.

August 23, 1988: The fourth schedule with WA5VJB is a bloody nightmare. Weather problems had plagued us all weekend, first in Texas then in Arizona. It was overcast in Phoenix and I could only track the moon by using "moon noise" during much of the schedule. Normally, the moon is optically tracked by utilizing a television camera attached to the dish. I start out listening for WA5VJB, but his signals are very weak. It's 10 PM and the temperature in Phoenix is 100 degrees with the humidity at 100% as well! Additionally, during the schedule, the Collins KWM-2 driver became erratic and I switched to the 32S-3 that was standing by "just in case." This was to be the kiss of death for all the LNAs because of the faster CW timing of 32S-3. I had just enough spare Avantek 13135 GaAsFETs to repair my preamp and WB5LUA's 1.5-dB NF preamp (Al had graciously loaned me his winning preamp at the Central States Conference the month before). I repaired both preamps, remeasured the system noise figure (Al's was still 1.5 dB), and was back on the air. It only took about 10 minutes to blow Al's preamp again! From now on the transmit-to-receive cycle was preceded by removing and reconnecting my remaining preamp at the waveguide switch, which is located at the back of the dish, 18 feet in the air (remember the temperature and humidity?) The schedule runs until the moon sets on Kent's horizon. By this time Kent has complete call sets, and I only need his call to complete the contact (I had received my complete call and an "O" signal report). At this point, to say that invincible fatigue overcame us would be a profane understatement! Wayne Schlegel (K7JTG), and yours truly participated.

August 27, 1988: The fifth schedule with WA5VJB. I get

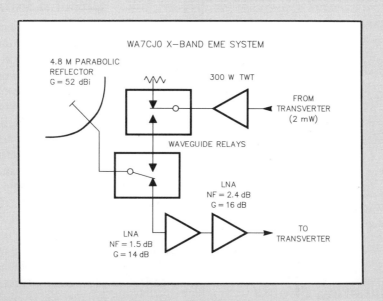

home from a California business trip at about 10 PM MST—3 hours late because of storms in the area (Phoenix had near total cloud cover). I called Kent to relay the bad news. Fortunately, he and his cohort, KF5N, decide to stick it out for a bit. At about midnight local time the clouds start to clear and I can see the moon. I call Kent and start to transmit (still using the previously mentioned transmit/receive system). It only took Kent about 10 minutes to get complete call sequences and optimize his polarization on my signal, even though he was not receiving my signal much better than he had during our second schedule when I was running 4 dB less power. Because I had been out of town since the previous ill-fated schedule, I hadn't rebuilt WB5LUA's preamp and my system noise figure was about 2.8 dB instead of 1.7 dB. For the next two

hours I struggled to pull Kent's signals out of the noise. This process was exacerbated by the phase modulation present on the signal (aurora-like). Finally, at 0930 GMT, the contact was complete! This was a solo operation by yours truly.

We have received advice and encouragement from numerous individuals throughout this project. In addition to the individuals mentioned above we would like to thank Tom Clark (W3IWI), Bill Ashby (K2TKN), Rod Blocksome (KØDAS), Barry Buelow (WAØRJT), Steve Krull (WB5DBS), Bill Plumer (local Avantek rep) and Greg Ruddell (Varian). Finally, it is our intention to keep this station active, and encourage others to attempt X-band EME. A good 10-foot dish and 20 W is what you need. You'll hear us!

WA7CJO X-Band EME System Specifications (8/27/88)

Antenna	4.8-m Ku-Band Parabolic Reflector
Feed	HB Scalar
Positioner	Modified SCR-584 (az-el), controllable to 30 s of arc.
Polarization	Horizontal
Power amplifier	Keltek power supply with Varian TWT (95 W)
IPA	Hewlett-Packard 495A
Transverter	HB Image Rejection[1]
Receive LNAs	WB5LUA/WA5VJB Avantek 13135 (2 stage)
Receive NF	1.5 dB
IF (Rx)	Collins 51S-1
IF (Tx)	Collins KWM-2 or 32S-3

[1]The transverter image rejection mixer is comprised of the following:

LO: Modified Frequency-West Model MS-740X phase-locked source (10.340 GHz, P_o = 20 mW)
Power divider: Narda 4315-2
Mixer: 2-Magnum Microwave MO64P (selected because of its excellent LO-to-RF isolation)
Hybrid coupler (Microwave): Narda 4035C
Hybrid coupler (IF): HB—Phase and amplitude are adjusted for best image rejection. The ferrite core used in this component provides an integral low pass filter response to the microwave components of the signal at the inputs of the hybrid.
Image rejection: 30-45 dB (LSB)
LO rejection at RF port: 40-45 dB
LNA (transverter): Modified Avantek AM-9923 (includes input and output isolators) NF = 3.2 dB, G = 23 dB
IF amplifiers (Rx & Tx): 2 Merrimac GAM-20-150

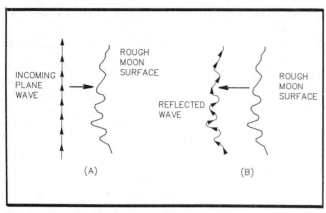

Fig 3—The rough lunar surface reflects a plane wave as one having many field vectors.

Antenna Mounting Effects

Complications are introduced by the antenna mounting geometry. If Faraday rotation were neglected, two antennas on polar mounts would remain in polarization alignment throughout an entire lunar orbit. This is not true with an az-el mounted antenna. (See the section on antenna mounts later in this chapter.) To maintain polarization alignment with this type of mount, the antenna will have to be rotated in polarization during the course of tracking.[8] At 432 MHz, where rapid Faraday rotation often occurs, the mounting complication is somewhat negated. However, it would be advantageous for all stations to use polar mounts.

Fig 4—KL7WE's 6 × 22-el array for 70 cm exemplifies the relative simplicity and elegance of stacked Yagis.

Circular Polarization

Faraday rotation fading may be eliminated by the exclusive use of circular polarization. By standardizing one sense of rotation for transmitting and the opposite for receiving, all stations would be optimized for reception and maintain compatibility with each other. The former point is so because the sense of a circularly polarized wave is reversed with respect to the original when reflected off the moon (or any other surface). A further benefit of circular polarization is that opposite senses are orthogonal in nature. This allows the same antenna to be independently equipped for both polarization senses. The arrangement is similar to crossed Yagis (linearly polarized), which can be mounted on the same boom with virtually no interaction or coupling between both feed points. By using appropriate hardware, it is possible to have two feed points on the same EME antenna, providing both left- and right-hand circular polarization with very low cross coupling. The implication is that the transmitter can be permanently connected to one port and the receiver to the other with only a modest protection device at the preamplifier to prevent overload damage. (A high power TR switch would not be required.) It is relatively easy to obtain 20 dB of isolation between feed points, and with care up to 40 dB at a single frequency.

For reasons of simplicity and historical convention, all stations still use linear polarization on 432 MHz. It is unlikely that this trend will change, because linearly polarized Yagi arrays are relatively easy and inexpensive to set up (Fig 4).

Libration Fading

One of the most troublesome aspects of receiving an EME signal is called *libration fading*.[9] It is characterized as a fluttery, rapid and irregular fading similar to that observed on tropospheric scatter paths.

This phenomenon is caused by multipath scattering from the lunar surface, exaggerated by the libration (rocking motion) between it and the Earth (Fig 5). There are three major components to this motion. The largest is due to the Earth's rotation and the remaining two are caused by the slightly elliptical lunar orbit and minor tilt in the moon's rotational axis.[10]

Consider that most of the returned energy emanates from a small region at the center of the moon's surface facing the Earth. Because the lunar terrain is quite rough, it does not provide a singular, specular, mirror-like reflection. Instead, the surface acts like a multitude of small mirrors, each at a slightly different distance from the Earth and randomly tilted. The net result is that each small reflection has a different phase and amplitude reflected back to the receiving antenna. Summation of these many vector echoes would provide a fixed signal level, were it not for the libration motion. This causes the phase and amplitude of the scattered components to vary with time, resulting in fades.

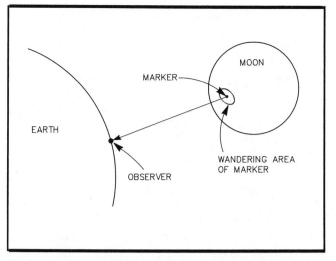

Fig 5—Various factors contribute to the apparent "wandering" of the moon's orbit about the Earth.

Nulls may be 20-dB deep or more, with the maximum fading rate directly related to the operating frequency. At 1296 MHz it is a maximum of 10 Hz, dropping to 3 Hz at 432 MHz. Samples of 1296-MHz echoes are shown in Fig 6A, illustrating that libration fading not only produces wide variations in signal level, but can also produce peaks well exceeding the average signal strength.

On a marginally readable EME signal, libration fading sounds like randomly keyed CW. Even when the average path-loss prediction indicates that signals should be below the receiving threshold, occasional signal bursts or "pings" are sometimes heard due to libration enhancement.

Minimizing Libration Fading

Severe libration fading may be somewhat alleviated by employing diversity reception techniques.[11] Interestingly enough, there are brief periods when libration ceases and EME echoes are rid of fading (Fig 6B), allowing even weak

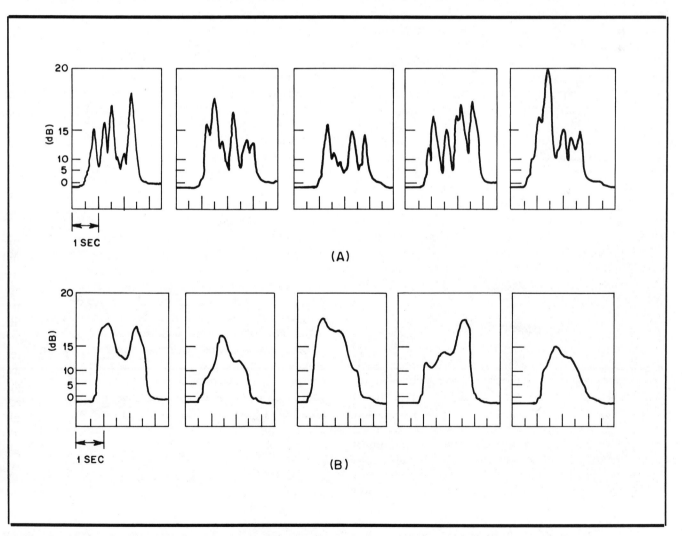

Fig 6—Recording of 1296-MHz lunar echoes representing periods of severe (A) and relatively low (B) libration fading. The recordings were made with 250 W to a 45-dB gain, 60-foot reflector utilizing circular polarization. System operating temperature was 400 K. The average theoretical echo return level is +15 dB.

signals to be copied easily. These periods only last for a few minutes and may not occur in a regular fashion during every lunar cycle. As a general rule, minimum libration fading on echoes will occur near moonrise or moonset. At lunar zenith, libration fading will always be near maximum. Because the Earth's rotational velocity is relative, stations at high latitudes will experience less libration fading than those near the equator. Stations on or near the same meridian should experience the same libration fading between them as on their own echoes. Other situations become more complex. Prediction of periods when minimum libration fading will occur can be achieved by using lunar ephemeris data and complex computer analysis.

Coherence Bandwidth

Closely allied with libration fading is the *coherence bandwidth* of an EME signal. This parameter is a measure of how well the sidebands of an EME echo resemble those of the original signal. Unfortunately, the same mechanism that produces libration fading also limits the usable EME signal bandwidth. Coherence-bandwidth effect is very similar to the selective fading experienced on the HF bands, only at a faster rate.

At 1296 MHz, a coherence bandwidth of a few kilohertz is typical, with no sharp demarcation. At low libration fading rates, usable bandwidth greatly increases. Additionally, coherence bandwidth is inversely proportional to frequency, which means that at higher frequencies it is more difficult to communicate using standard FM, AM and sometimes even SSB. At 1296 MHz, SSB is commonly used with success, whereas NBFM is unacceptable.

Additionally, libration fading will noise-modulate the EME signal, producing noise sidebands around the carrier frequency. This modulation increases with carrier frequency. At higher microwave frequencies, echoes do not sound like pure CW, but have a soft, "mushy" sound. At 10 GHz, it is difficult to use any standard form of voice modulation, with communication limited to CW or possibly some exotic form of modulation.

Doppler Shift

Another phenomenon of the EME path is *Doppler frequency shift*. When listening to a moonbounce signal, the frequency will rarely be the same as transmitted—it will be offset high or low. The amount of offset is proportional to the operating frequency and the relative velocities between the transmitting antenna, moon and receiving antenna. More directly stated, Doppler shift is proportional to the operating frequency and the rate of change of the total EME path length.

For the self-echo or "radar" path, frequency shift will be maximum near moonrise/moonset and will be zero around the time of lunar zenith. The Doppler shift will be high in frequency for a rising moon, since the moon and station antenna are approaching each other (Earth's rotation is faster than the moon's orbital revolution), and will be lower in frequency for a setting moon. Maximum Doppler shift occurs midway between lunar apogee and perigee. Fig 7 shows the typical S-shaped Doppler shift curve obtained for an echo path at 432 and 1296 MHz. A general formula is also included to show the dependence on station latitude, as well as on the declination of the moon. A correction curve for lunar orbit eccentricity can be found in Fig 8. At 432 MHz, a maximum deviation of ± 1200 Hz can be expected.

Between two stations at different geographic locations, the expected Doppler shift is the arithmetic mean of the individual echo paths plus the orbital correction factor. (The arithmetic mean is the sum of half the shift for each echo path.) An extreme situation would involve two stations diametrically opposed on the Earth. One station will experience a rising moon; the other a setting moon. The self-echo Doppler shifts will be near maximum for each station, but opposite in offset. In this case, the net frequency shift between the two stations will be almost nothing. Keep in mind that Doppler shift on the EME path changes very slowly with time; there is little need to retune during a normal contact.

Background Noise

In most cases, the EME antenna beamwidth is much wider than the moon's angular size, and noise from other sources will also be received. There are a number of sources intense enough to cause system S/N degradation. The ones of interest (in order of decreasing intensity) are: *solar radiation*, our own *galactic noise*, *radio stars*, *moon noise* and *cosmic background radiation*.

SOLAR NOISE

During the day, solar noise can pose a problem if the sun is in the same vicinity as the moon, or if the antenna has pronounced sidelobes. Because solar radiation is so high, excess receiver noise can be expected when the sun is quite a few beamwidths in angular position away from the moon. Solar noise is especially severe on the lower-frequency EME bands, where the relative noise output is higher and antenna beamwidths are wider. A simple test to determine the extent of system S/N degradation is to sweep the antenna through a wide angular range that includes the sun. The point at which solar noise drops below your receiving threshold will determine for any given band, how close (in angular degrees) the sun and moon must be before your receiving system becomes impaired.

OTHER SOURCES

At 432 MHz some galactic noise can be detected, but it is confined to a region in the center of the galactic plane called the Milky Way. At 1296 MHz and above, it is still observable.

Radio stars usually present little problem unless they fall within the main lobe of the antenna. At 432 MHz,

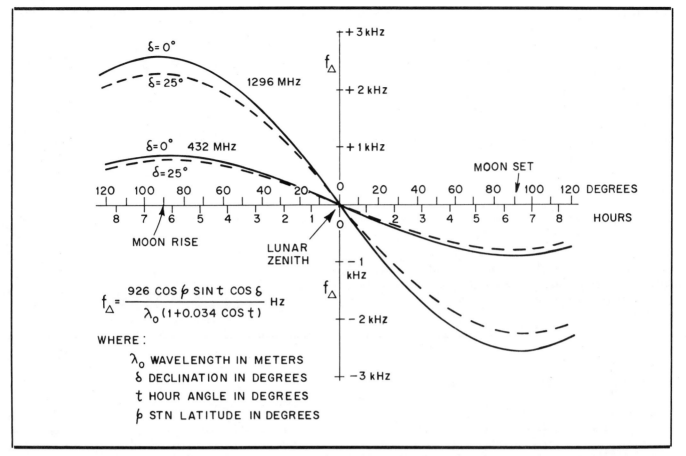

Fig 7—Graph for determining EME Doppler frequency shift at 50° latitude. *(from "432 MHz and Above EME Newsletter")*

The formula shown in the figure:

$$f_{\Delta} = \frac{926 \cos \phi \sin t \cos \delta}{\lambda_0 (1 + 0.034 \cos t)} \text{ Hz}$$

WHERE:

λ_0 WAVELENGTH IN METERS
δ DECLINATION IN DEGREES
t HOUR ANGLE IN DEGREES
ϕ STN LATITUDE IN DEGREES

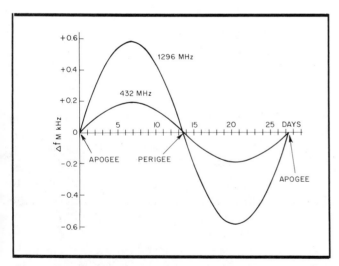

Fig 8—Doppler-shift correction factor curve for lunar orbit eccentricity.

some sources, such as Sagittarius, can cause significant system noise increase when the moon passes in front of this source. The strongest radio star has a noise output comparable to that of moon noise, which itself shouldn't be overlooked as it is intrinsic to EME communication. With present-day LNAs (preamplifiers) it should be detectable, since the moon has an apparent temperature of about 210 K.[13] When the antenna beamwidth becomes comparable with the subtended angle of the moon (about 0.5°), lunar noise will limit the operating system temperature to 210 K plus the receiver noise temperature. Today, practical limitations on antenna size precludes this noise-limiting effect. In the future, operation at higher frequencies will demonstrate the possibility of attaining this limiting condition.

Cosmic noise, like galactic noise, increases enormously at frequencies below 1 GHz.[14] At 432 MHz it can be as high as 15 to 3000 K, and a mere 3 to 15 K at 1296 MHz. This low-level cosmic background radiation extends through the microwave spectrum up to approximately 10 GHz, where other sources of noise and loss associated with the atmosphere become increasingly severe. Water-vapor and oxygen absorption are the principal factors that introduce noise above 10 GHz. Thus, in terms of low background noise the region between 1 and 10 GHz (known as the "space window") is preferred for any type of EME or space communication.

ANOMALOUS EFFECTS

Unusual effects, some transient and still not completely understood have been observed on EME paths. For example, fades lasting up to several hours sometimes occur on 432 MHz. These are believed to be caused by unusually high absorption and possible beam focusing effects in the ionosphere. EME station operators must have patience during these times, as the anomalous fades will dissipate and return the path to normal.

Double echoes and long delayed echoes (LDEs) have been reported on rare occasions. These transient effects are not reproducible, and their origin is still subject to speculation. One proposed mechanism is that solar winds produce highly ionized clouds of enormous proportions. These may refract radio waves back to Earth via circuitous paths of great distance.

Similarly, non-homogenous regions of ionization may act like a lens, increasing or decreasing path loss by focusing or dispersing the passing radio wave. Scintillation (rapid flutter) has also been reported on rare occasions. This phenomenon increases with decreasing frequency and can produce a variation of ± 3 to 4 dB at 1296 MHz. This is believed to be caused by turbulence in the ionosphere and is especially noticeable when the path traverses the ionosphere during twilight periods.[15]

Summary

All of the above EME path effects combine to create a variety of propagation conditions and challenges for the moonbouncer. Although the enormous signal-strength variations encountered in HF and terrestrial VHF propagation do not usually occur in EME work, there are times when conditions are exceptional and the path may be described as ''open.'' It is a challenge to the more technically minded radio amateur to use this method of communication, both for his own satisfaction and to make use of our vast FCC allocation of spectrum space.

The future of amateur EME communications can only improve as activity increases and technology meets the needs of high-power transmitters, better antennas and low-noise receivers. It is conceivable that EME communication will be the DX of the future—perhaps even supporting regular traffic nets and official broadcasting.

SYSTEM CONSIDERATIONS

To be successful at EME communication, it is first necessary to determine what is required in the way of equipment. There are three basic elements to an EME system: *transmitter*, *receiver* and *antenna*. Each has specifications that are interrelated to the total system performance.

For the transmitter, the primary specification is CW output power, which is currently limited by FCC regulation to 1500 W. The most important receiver parameter is sensitivity, which is related to noise figure and bandwidth. Antenna specifications include effective gain and equivalent temperature. Fig 9 shows how these elements combine to provide an EME system for one direction of transmission.

Transmitter power should be delivered to the antenna through a transmission line with as little loss as possible. This power is radiated in a concentrated beam, which increases effective power density in the direction of the moon through the effect of antenna gain. The transmitted

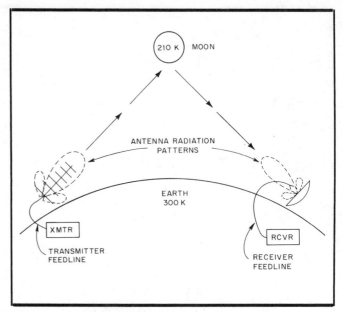

Fig 9—Major EME system components shown in a one-way path situation.

signal undergoes considerable attenuation by the very long EME path and is reflected back over an enormous area, of which the Earth is only a very small part. A very small proportion of the reflected power is collected by the receiving antenna, which concentrates it at the feed point. This concentration factor is the effective receiving antenna gain.

Received Power

Moon-reflected power received at the antenna feed point can be formulated by

$$\text{Power Received} = P_t \times L \times G_t \times \text{Path Loss} \times G_r$$

where

P_t = transmitter output power
L = transmitter feed-line loss
G_t and G_r = effective transmitter and receiver antenna gains.

For the self-echo case, G_t will usually equal G_r, since the same antenna is typically employed for both transmitting and receiving. Path loss for the popular EME bands can be found in Table 1.

The above equation is more readily expressed in dBm, or decibel power referenced to 1 mW, as the sum of the various factors expressed in decibel form. For example, at 1296 MHz the average path loss is 271.4 dB. Assume the transmitter output power is 500 watts (+ 57 dBm), feed-line loss is 1 dB and antenna gain is 30 dB (typical for a 12-foot diameter parabolic reflector). The received power at the antenna feed point is found by

$$\text{Power Received} = +57 \text{ dBm} - 1 \text{ dB} + 30 \text{ dB}$$
$$- 271.4 \text{ dB} + 30 \text{ dB} = -155.4 \text{ dBm}$$

To determine whether this level of received power is sufficient to be detected by the receiver, it is necessary to calculate the received noise power at the same antenna feed point. By comparing the two values, a signal-to-noise (S/N) ratio will be obtained, indicating our ability to hear the signal.

System Noise Power

Noise power in the radio spectrum is often expressed in terms of an equivalent black-body temperature.

$$p = kTB$$

where
- p = thermal noise power, in watts
- k = Boltzmann's constant (1.38×10^{-23} W/K/Hz)
- T = system operating temperature in kelvins
- B = effective system noise bandwidth in Hz.

For an operator listening to a CW signal, the minimum effective noise bandwidth is approximately 50 Hz, even if the receiver bandwidth is much larger.[16]

The sensitivity of a receiver, including the preamplifier, is usually rated by noise figure (NF), which is specified in dB. The effective noise temperature (T_{rcvr}) of a receiver is related to noise figure by

$$T_{rcvr} = 290 \, [10^{(NF/10)} - 1] \text{ kelvins}$$

If the receiver preamplifier is mounted at the antenna feed point (where it should be to minimize the effects of feed-line loss and maximize sensitivity), the total system temperature will be the effective receiver noise temperature plus the antenna noise temperature. At 1296 MHz, antenna temperatures are typically between 30 and 100 K, depending on design and where the main beam is pointed.

For example, a system at 1296 MHz might have a 0.7-dB NF, equivalent to a noise temperature of 50 K, and an antenna temperature of 50 K. The total system operating temperature in this case is 50 K + 50 K = 100 K. Using the noise-power equation (referenced to the antenna feed point) for a CW bandwidth of 50 Hz, we find

$$
\begin{aligned}
p &= 1.38 \times 10^{-23} \text{ W/K/Hz} \times 100 \text{ K} \times 50 \text{ Hz} \\
&= 6.90 \times 10^{-20} \text{W} \\
&= 6.90 \times 10^{-17} \text{ mW} \\
&= -161.6 \text{ dBm}
\end{aligned}
$$

Comparing this value to the received signal power (referenced to dBm) will provide the S/N ratio of this system as

$$
\begin{aligned}
S/N &= (-155.4 \text{ dBm}) - (-161.6 \text{ dBm}) \\
&= +6.2 \text{ dB}
\end{aligned}
$$

This signal level will be readily discernible, even though libration effects will produce fades below the audible threshold. A S/N ratio of +3 dB in an effective noise bandwidth of 50 Hz approaches the limit of detection by the human ear.

Introducing a lossy feed line, TR switch and connectors between the receiver preamplifier and the antenna feed terminals may be accounted for by altering the receiver

component of the system noise temperature to

$$T_{rcvr} = [(10^{(L/10)} - 1) + 10^{(L/10)} \, (10^{(NF/10)} - 1)] \, 290 \text{ K}$$

where
- T_{rcvr} = modified receiver noise temperature in kelvins due to lossy feed line
- NF = receiver noise figure in dB
- L = total loss in dB between the preamplifier and antenna feed point, including impedance mismatch loss.

With a receiver NF of 0.7 dB, a loss of 1 dB between the preamplifier and antenna will increase the effective receiver noise temperature from 50 K to 138 K! Each 0.1-dB loss ahead of the preamplifier adds at least 7.5 K to receiver noise temperature. For this reason, great care should be taken when connecting the preamplifier to the antenna. Since low-noise GaAsFET or HEMT devices used in preamplifiers are operated under input-mismatch conditions for best noise performance, it is even more imperative that the antenna-to-preamp line be of minimum length to satisfy best overall receiver noise performance. Losses in switching relays, cables and connectors can add up, noticeably degrading the performance of an otherwise good receiving system. This point cannot be overstressed, since present technology makes very low-noise preamplifiers commonplace.

The purpose of this exercise was to indicate how the system signal-to-noise ratio may be calculated and how the various system parameters are introduced. In this way, trade offs can be made and system deficiencies made evident.

TRANSMITTER CONSIDERATIONS

Although the single most important specification for an EME transmitter is power output, there are other considerations. Good frequency stability and low harmonic and spurious emissions are not only good engineering practice, but are also required by FCC regulation.[17] Short-term stability is perhaps the most important criteria since a drifting, weak, libration-fading signal is very difficult to copy.

Frequency stability is largely determined by the crystal oscillator(s) employed and the degree of multiplication required. The crystal should be in the 5- to 100-MHz region, with higher frequencies preferred due to lower phase noise and easier harmonic filtering (see Chapter 6). Temperature compensation may be designed into an oscillator circuit to obtain the high degree of long-term frequency stability required. Long-term stability should be adequate for repeatability during a QSO and maintaining schedules within a few hundred hertz accuracy. At 2300 MHz, this requires an oscillator to be stable to 0.1 parts per million (ppm). This is not too difficult to meet with a well-designed, temperature-compensated 50-MHz crystal oscillator circuit.

Current trends favor the transverter approach to transmitter design. This is a heterodyne system in which a low-power HF signal of any mode is mixed with the UHF output of a crystal oscillator/multiplier (see Chapter 7). The mixer output is then filtered and amplified to obtain the desired output product. A more basic approach uses a crystal oscillator/multiplier followed by a filter and one or more power amplifiers. This only allows the basic CW mode, which is most commonly used in the weak-signal EME environment. Frequency-shift keying, which offers the advantage of redundancy, is seldom used. SSB is the most effective voice mode because it is less subject to distortion from libration fading effects.

A means of incrementally adjusting the transmitter frequency is desired in order to set the operating frequency to an accurate marker generator. By convention, most EME operating is done within a 100-kHz subband, so the tuning requirement can be easily met with an adjustable crystal oscillator, or VFO in the transverter case.

Power Generation

In general, frequency of operation determines the maximum power output practically achievable by amateurs. At frequencies below 1000 MHz, triode or tetrode vacuum tubes with conventional construction provide ample gain and power output exceeding 1 kW. Some popular tubes of this type are the 4CX250B, 4CX250R, 8930, 7650, 8874, 8877, 8938, 3CX800A7 and 7213. Amplifiers using these tubes can provide full legal output power on the 70-cm band. A few commercial designs are now available in fully built or kit form.

At frequencies above 1000 MHz, transit-time limitations and physical structures prevent the aforementioned tubes from performing well. At the present time, planar triodes are the mainstay of amateur microwave power amplifiers. Solid-state amplifiers are available, but are expensive and relatively limited in power capability. As prices go down and power levels go up, these devices will become increasingly popular with EME operators.

While high-power planar triodes are available, they too are expensive. The "work horses" of planar triodes are the 3CX100A5 and 7289 (ceramic sealed). Higher-power types are the Y730 and TH308. Although most of the medium-power (2C39 family) planar triodes are conservatively rated at 50-W output, intermittent service in amateur use permits much higher levels. Single-tube[18] and multitube[19,20] designs are available, which can produce outputs in the range of 200-800 W at 1296 MHz. Multitube designs generally combine several tubes in a single tuned cavity to obtain highest efficiency with water cooling.

Personal Safety

EME operation, by its very nature, involves extremely high levels of effective radiated power (ERP). Good RF safety practices are your best protection. Before attempting EME or any high-power operation, it is strongly advised that you read Chapter 2 *first*. It is important to note that *dangerous levels of incidental radiation can exist at short distances from power amplifiers and antennas*.

Sources of unwanted radiation can come from poorly designed and constructed power amplifiers, "leaky" tuning screws, braided-shield coaxial cable, connectors, open-shield enclosures and exposed microstrip circuits. If your power amplifier is behaving erratically or showing poor efficiency, look for possible sources of leakage.

Radiation from antennas is obviously necessary for RF communications to occur. However, RF density is highest in the immediate vicinity of small, low-gain antennas, such as reflector feeds. Radiation levels in the aperture of a high-gain reflector antenna is greatly reduced because the energy is distributed over a large area. To be safe, measure RF density levels in the vicinity of antennas by using the methods described in Chapter 2.

RECEIVER CONSIDERATIONS

EME receiver design must strive for maximum sensitivity to detect the very weak signals normally encountered. This translates to low inherent noise and narrow effective noise bandwidth. (*Noise figure* or its equivalent noise temperature are the terms commonly used to describe intrinsic noise in the overall receiver.) In addition, linearity, low intermodulation (IM) distortion and frequency stability are all desirable in a good receiver.

Most EME station receivers are single-conversion, employing a good HF communications receiver as a tunable IF. This system greatly simplifies receiver design. At frequencies up to 432 MHz, single conversion with a 28-MHz IF will provide satisfactory image rejection. Above 432 MHz, it is advisable to use a higher-frequency IF (144 and 432 MHz are common) or even better, to use double conversion along with a high-frequency first IF. This minimizes image noise originating at the relatively broadband preamplifier from appearing at the tunable IF. This noise can degrade the sensitivity of a receiving system by as much as 3 dB. Recently, *image-reject mixers* have become popular in the commercial microwave industry and should also work well in a single-conversion amateur design. Various receiving converters can be found in the project chapters of this book.

Fig 10 shows a typical EME installation utilizing single conversion and a tunable, high-frequency IF. Since any feed line between the antenna and receiver introduces attenuation and noise, it is imperative that the low-noise preamplifier (LNA) be mounted directly at the antenna terminals. LNA gain should be sufficient to overcome feed-line losses and mask noise in the next stage. (At 2300 MHz and above, it may be advantageous to mount both the LNA and the final power amplifier at the antenna because of line loss and the relative difficulty of generating power.) A further improvement in design might include mounting the receive converter at the antenna, thus mitigating some receiver feed-line loss by running the lower IF through it.

Current practices employ one or two low noise, Gallium Arsenide field-effect transistors (GaAsFET) or High Electron Mobility Transistors (HEMT) in the preamplifier, with only a simple noise impedance matching circuit between it and the antenna. Only if severe IM is present should a filter be placed ahead of the LNA. If necessary, it preferably should be designed into the

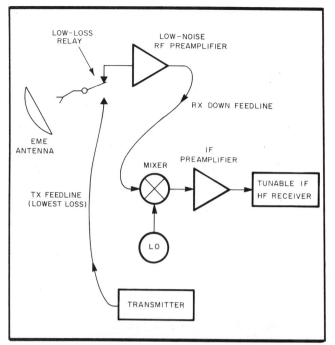

Fig 10—A typical EME system utilizing a single-conversion receiving converter with a tunable IF. The LNA is mounted at the antenna for highest efficiency.

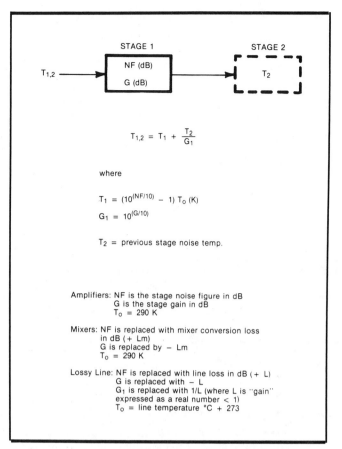

$$T_{1,2} = T_1 + \frac{T_2}{G_1}$$

where

$$T_1 = (10^{(NF/10)} - 1)\, T_0 \;(K)$$

$$G_1 = 10^{(G/10)}$$

T_2 = previous stage noise temp.

Amplifiers: NF is the stage noise figure in dB
        G is the stage gain in dB
        T_0 = 290 K

Mixers: NF is replaced with mixer conversion loss
        in dB (+ Lm)
        G is replaced by − Lm
        T_0 = 290 K

Lossy Line: NF is replaced with line loss in dB (+ L)
        G is replaced with − L
        G_1 is replaced with 1/L (where L is "gain"
        expressed as a real number < 1)
        T_0 = line temperature °C + 273

Fig 11—A universal formula to evaluate noise in cascaded stages of receiving system amplifiers, mixers and transmission lines (see text).

preamplifier to minimize losses. Some antenna designs will inherently provide filtering. For example, a waveguide feed acts as a high-pass filter, and a Yagi displays passband characteristics.

A popular trend among EME stations is to use two separate feed lines. The lowest-loss line is used to carry transmitter power, while another line with somewhat greater loss but reduced cost, runs from the LNA to the receiving converter. A relay is used at the antenna terminals for TR switching.

Inherent in all antenna-mounted active hardware is the need for weather and insect protection, and in some cases, temperature control. These factors should not be overlooked in a complete installation.

Receiver Noise Analysis

Once you have a conception of the various receiving system options, how can relative performance be evaluated and the proper system elements be chosen? A receiving system *noise analysis* referred to the antenna terminals will indicate how to apportion preamplifier gain and feed-line losses to receive mixers and IF amplifiers. This analysis requires that all system component impedances be matched to each other, so that amplifier gains and line losses are not compromised.

Fig 11 contains a simple block diagram and noise formula that permits the evaluation of a receiving system on a stage-by-stage basis. It is the basic key to designing for maximum sensitivity (minimum noise). The procedure is to start somewhere in the system where noise temperature

can be predicted with reasonable accuracy, then proceed backwards stage-by-stage until the antenna is reached.

A typical example, shown in Fig 12 starts at the mixer input, where a NF of about 6 dB is typical. A noise temperature of 870 K was calculated by solving for T1. The next "stage" back is the feed line, which in this case is assumed to have a 3-dB loss. To calculate the cascaded noise temperature at the input to this stage, consider it stage 1 and the mixer stage 2. Assuming the feed line is at a temperature of 17 °C, and that L = 0.5, solving for T1,2 yields a temperature of 2030 K.

Consider that a 1-dB NF, 23-dB gain preamplifier is mast-mounted ahead of the feed line. Using the basic formula again, consider the preamplifier stage 1 and all stages downstream as stage 2. Solving for T1,2 gives an 85.2 K noise temperature at the input to the preamplifier. Finally, any jumper cables and switching relays between the antenna and the preamplifier must be accounted for with the same procedure used on the feed line. Loss here may be surprisingly high, amounting to 0.5 dB or more. In the Fig 12 example, only 0.5-dB loss in this stage increases the noise temperature at the antenna to 130.9 K. The antenna noise temperature must be added to this figure to obtain the system operating temperature, which is crucial

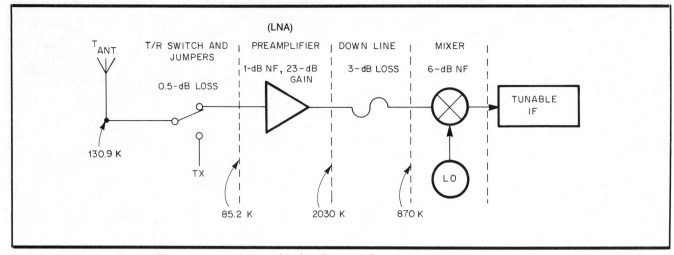

Fig 12—Example of receiving system noise evaluation (see text).

to evaluating the complete EME system performance.

It will come as no great surprise that the most significant improvement in overall system noise performance usually results from eliminating losses *ahead* of the LNA, which should be the very best available. Every 0.1-dB loss ahead of the LNA contributes at least 7.5 K to the system operating temperature, which is a significant amount.

A final note must be made about the relationship between antenna temperature and receiver input temperature. When the receiver temperature begins to approach the antenna temperature, there will be diminishing returns in lowering the system temperature. A general rule of thumb for weak-signal EME systems is to not invest in a better preamplifier when the existing one is already rated at half the antenna temperature. This is especially true at VHF, where antenna temperature is limited by the background noise of the universe. The following section on antenna considerations provides a method of estimating antenna temperature.

Preamplifier/Antenna Interface

Caution must be exercised regarding the interfacing of your preamplifier and antenna. In most instances, NF is measured and optimized using apparatus with a nominal 50-Ω source impedance. Since LNA gain and NF are somewhat interrelated to the source impedance, it is advisable to first measure the impedance of the antenna. Seldom are antennas purely 50-Ω resistive, so the noise match between antenna and preamplifier should be optimized. One procedure is to "leak" noise into the EME antenna by means of a small probe or horn. Adjust the preamplifier input match for a maximum *change* in receiver output noise as the source is switched on and off. This procedure is recommended, even when no other measurements can be made.

ANTENNA CONSIDERATIONS

The antenna is the single most important element in an EME communication system. Antenna gain must make up for transmit power limitations, tremendous path loss and limits in receiver sensitivity. At the same time, antenna noise must be minimized to further enhance receiver sensitivity. In other words, the requirements for a good EME antenna are: (1) highest gain efficiency for transmitting and, (2) highest gain/temperature ratio for receiving. Unfortunately, these two requirements are somewhat mutually exclusive; obtaining lowest antenna noise necessitates some compromise in gain. This paradox is not significant until very low-noise receiving systems are used.

Gain

Antenna gain is simply a measure of how well the antenna can concentrate available power in a single direction, which is referred to as the *main beam* or *lobe*. Gain is more precisely defined as the product of directivity and efficiency. In high-gain antennas, the efficiency factor is usually very high (approaching unity) and the term gain can then be used synonymously with directivity. It is also customary to specify gain in dBi, which is decibels referenced to an isotropic radiator (a hypothetical model that radiates power equally in all directions and in one polarization). Throughout this chapter, antenna gain is given in dBi. For reference, a ½-λ dipole has a gain of 2.14 dBi.

The System Considerations section revealed that the minimum gain requirement for receiving echoes is around 25 dBi. Although somewhat lower gain can be used for communicating, success will be limited. Where one station has a low-gain antenna, communication is possible provided the other station antenna gain makes up for the

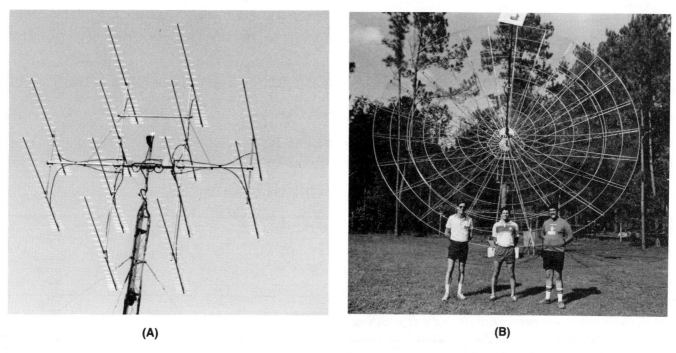

(A)   (B)

Fig 13—Two primary EME antenna types. At (A) is a 12 × 22-el Yagi array for 70 cm (K1FO), while KU4F's 28-foot dish is shown in (B).

deficiency. In general, hearing your own echoes is the best assurance that communication with other stations of the same stature *is* possible.

Antenna Types

There are various antenna designs that can achieve the required gain in the UHF and above region. Considerations of efficiency and practicality narrow the choice down to two general types—*parabolic reflectors* and *Yagi arrays* (Fig 13). Other designs that have been used are: (1) the rhombic, which takes up more space than the gain warrants; (2) very long Yagis, which like the rhombic, suffer from decreased gain efficiency as the length increases; (3) the dipole array, which requires a complex, multiport power divider and phased feed lines for the individual dipoles and (4) the cylindrical parabolic reflector, which requires a difficult-to-construct line-source feed.

Yagi Arrays

Advantages of Yagi arrays include relatively low wind loading (therefore less risk of losing the antenna) and easier fabrication than required for a large reflector. The disadvantages are that Yagis are inherently narrow, single band antennas requiring careful tuning to work well. They also can exhibit poor noise performance due to excessive side and rear radiation, although proper stacking will improve this.[21] Yagis are also linearly polarized, which is a disadvantage when circular polarization is desired. While crossed Yagis on a single boom can produce circular polarization, the additional complexity makes it a seldom-used technique on EME arrays. Short rear-mounted Yagis with rotatable polarization are becoming popular.

Stacking Yagis in an array is necessary to achieve the required gain. Individual Yagis in the array shouldn't be longer than seven wavelengths to maximize gain efficiency versus size. The interaction between Yagis stacked side-by-side places additional requirements on stacking distances. In general, close spacing is preferred because it reduces the physical size of the array and also improves the noise performance by reducing "grating lobes" associated with stacked antennas. For optimum noise performance without sacrificing too much gain, stacking distances must be carefully set and will depend on the individual Yagis used and their radiation characteristics.

Each Yagi must be connected to a common RF distribution point through a power divider and phasing line harness. This network can be a source of additional loss, and must be carefully constructed with an efficient power divider and low-loss transmission line. If all phasing lines are the same length, the total loss (excluding that of the power divider) is that of just one phasing line section. Although weatherproof coaxial cable is the usual choice for phasing lines, impedance-matched, open-wire line harnesses have been used with good results at 432 MHz. Yagis are not recommended for the microwave bands.

Parabolic Reflectors

A parabolic antenna collects RF energy over the entire reflector surface and directs it to the *focal point*, where a small "feed" antenna can receive it. In this manner, the parabola essentially concentrates energy collected from a large area, resulting in high gain. Because of practical limitations in the small feed antenna, all of the focused energy cannot be captured and some loss of efficiency results.

Basic Reflector Geometry

Although there are many types of reflector antennas, two specific designs are considered optimum for EME application—the circularly symmetric, paraboloidal reflector with prime-focus feed, and the offset-fed, parabolic reflector design. The symmetric reflector (Fig 14) is the most widely used and commonly referred to as a "dish" antenna.

Dish antennas are popular because of their high gain and relatively simple construction, but also for historical reasons. Other advantages are ease of polarization rotation (just rotate the feed) ease of implementation of circular polarization at the feed. Also, dish antennas have broad bandwidth, which permits one reflector to be used for several bands by simply changing the feed. This type of antenna is capable of an effective gain between 50 and 70% of the aperture area gain, depending on the type of feed used. When properly used, the dual-mode feed described in Chapter 9 offers the highest efficiency for a simply fed reflector.

The primary specification for dish antennas relates aperture diameter to focal length as a ratio called the *f/d ratio*. This ratio largely prescribes the radiation characteristics of the feed required for maximum gain. For practical feeds, such as small horns, maximum gain is achieved when the dish illumination is tapered from maximum in the center to − 10 dB at the rim of the reflector. Best noise performance (gain/temperature) is achieved with a somewhat greater taper of approximately − 15 dB at the rim. Since both tapers cannot be achieved with the same feed, a compromise of − 12 to − 13 dB can be made. In this case, maximum gain is compromised by less than 1 dB.

Another type of reflector antenna is a variation of the symmetric paraboloid known as an offset-fed parabolic reflector (Fig 15). In this design, the feed is actually not offset from the focal point, but is tilted to illuminate an offset section of the paraboloid. This approach is relatively new in antenna technology. The primary advantage of this design is elimination of blockage to the aperture by the feed, thereby improving both the gain and noise performance. Additionally, the feed is located at a more accessible position and adjustments can be made without interaction between the antenna and your body. The principal disadvantage is the rather awkward geometry, which makes construction more difficult.[12]

Reflector Surface

All reflector antennas require special attention to their reflecting surface. It should be conductive, although high conductivity is not a primary consideration; reflectors are low Q, with surface currents distributed over a wide area. The curve must not deviate from a perfect parabola by more than about $1/10 \lambda$ to maintain phase integrity over the entire aperture, thus preserving highest gain. Reflec-

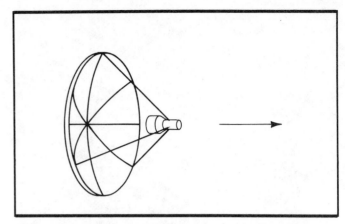

Fig 14—Geometry of a circularly symmetric, prime-focus fed parabolic reflector.

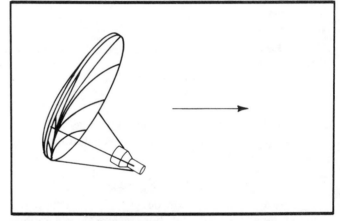

Fig 15—An offset-fed parabolic reflector provides no blockage to the aperture.

tor surface material may be a grid-like mesh that does not contain open spaces greater than $1/10 \lambda$. Electrical bonding at the mesh crossovers is optional and area joints may be either butt or overlapping, provided that they are tight. Paint or surface corrosion does not significantly degrade performance.

Antenna Noise

Antenna noise is the aggregate of whatever noise sources are in the field of view of the antenna, weighted by the normalized radiation characteristics. EME antennas normally have their main beam pointed toward the moon, where background noise is usually low. Therefore, most of the noise comes from outside of the main beam, through the side and rear lobes of the antenna. Even though the weighting factor in these lobes is small, the sum of these sources may be significant. For dish antennas, a main source of noise is feed spillover beyond the rim, which usually points toward the warm Earth.

Although somewhat difficult, an estimate of noise for dish antennas can be obtained by direct measurement. The only requirement is that side and rear radiation from the feed is down at least 30 dB from the main lobe, as in the dual-mode horn. First obtain a reference noise-level output from the receiver with only the feed horn pointed directly at the zenith. This is a measure of receiver noise plus the background noise of the universe. Next, the feed is remounted in the dish and the reflector beam is pointed near the zenith, where background noise is found to be minimum, or preferably a "cold spot" in the sky. The receiver noise output level now corresponds to the sum of receiver and universe noise, plus antenna noise temperature. Since noise temperature is proportional to noise power, a simple ratio may be formulated by

$$R = \frac{T_r + T_b + T_a}{T_r + T_b}$$

where

R = the measured receiver output-noise ratio expressed as a real number greater than 1.

T_r = receiver noise temperature (refer to Receiver Considerations section)

T_b = background noise of the universe (taken from Fig 16)

Solving for T_a

$T_a = (T_r + T_b) \times (R - 1)$

Receiving system gain stability must be very good during the period it takes to physically switch the feed, as the measured noise ratio can be only 1.25 dB for a low-noise antenna! The above method is preferred over another, in which the preamplifier is switched between a room-temperature termination and the feed antenna. The latter method is not always accurate because preamplifier gain and noise is dependent on input impedance match.

Direct measurement of antenna gain is much more difficult. Although methods are given in Chapter 7 and a latter part of this chapter, it is prudent to not attempt gain measurement with large, high-gain antennas. Care in construction and attention to details will be more important in attaining expected performance. Use direct gain measurements only as a last-resort diagnostic tool when no other factor in the EME system is accountable for poor observed performance.

Antenna Mounts

Large, high-gain antennas have a characteristically narrow, pencil-like main beam that must be properly aimed. To accomplish this, the mount should position the antenna with high accuracy while being able to withstand extreme weather conditions. Integrity in the structural design is the key factor to successful mount construction. Two basic mount types are considered here: (1) the *polar mount*, and (2) the elevation-over-azimuth type, which is commonly referred to as an *az-el mount*.

Polar Mount

This type of mount is recommended strictly for EME operation, being of little use to satellite experimenters. A polar mount requires the principal axis, or *polar axis*, to be aligned exactly parallel with the rotational axis of the Earth (Fig 17A). The antenna is mounted upon this axis with the main beam at right angles to it, with provisions for adjusting the antenna beam ± 30° from the right-angle position. This latter provision is known as the *declination axis* and is required to accommodate monthly declination variations of the moon. Since lunar declination changes only a few degrees during a single orbit, this adjustment may usually be set once for any given operating period.

The great advantage of a polar mount is that the polar axis may be rotated by a low-speed, constant drive. It must simply keep pace with the rotation of the Earth, approximately 15° per hour. A properly set up and operated polar mount greatly simplifies moon and sun tracking (for noise evaluation procedures). The disadvantages of a polar mount are the relatively difficult construction and initial alignment of the polar axis. Also, the beam pointing range is usually limited to lunar and solar orbits, that is, far-distant objects.

Az-el Mount

This is the most popular EME antenna mount, permitting the greatest flexibility in beam pointing but requiring two-axis rotation to track the moon (Fig 17B). The popularity of this mount stems from the straightforward construction. Today, the use of microcomputers to provide azimuth and elevation pointing information, along with automated drive, has most likely preserved this

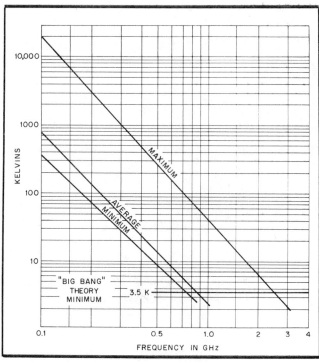

Fig 16—Cosmic noise levels (including galactic noise) for the UHF/lower microwave region.

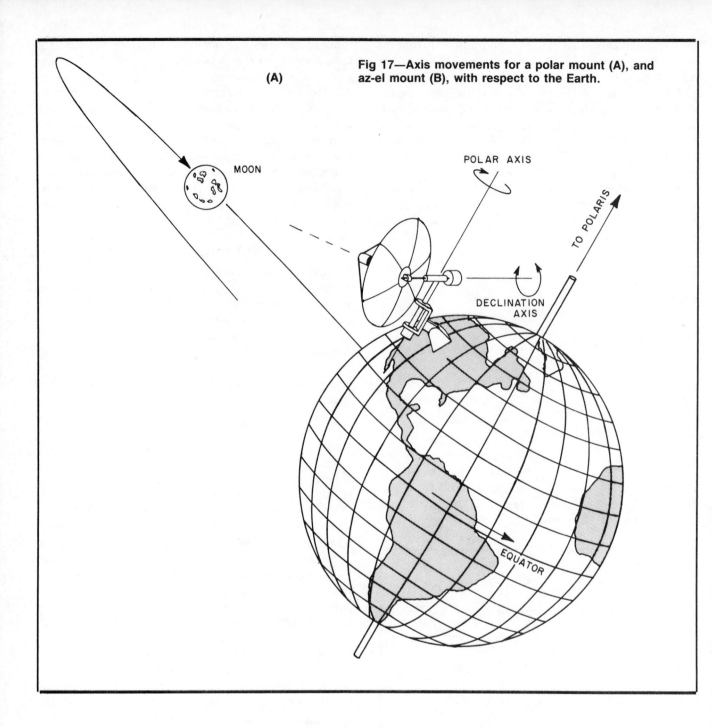

(A)

Fig 17—Axis movements for a polar mount (A), and az-el mount (B), with respect to the Earth.

type of mount over the less complicated drive mechanism of the polar mount.

Az-el mounts have a vertical axis, the *azimuth axis*, which is secured to the Earth and provides a rotating platform upon which a horizontal axis, the *elevation axis* is mounted. Even though it is convenient to mount the center of gravity at the intersection of the axes, it is not good engineering practice to place the mounting structure within the active region of the antenna. Various mount designs have been devised to alleviate this problem, including an elevation yoke arrangement and offset mounting with counterbalancing to relieve torque stress on the elevation axis. An exception to the rule is found in horizontally polarized Yagi arrays. This configuration can have the azimuth axis support extend through the center of the array, with the intersection of the axes located at the center of gravity. Serious consequences to the antenna radiation pattern usually will not result.

General Antenna Mounting Considerations

Tracking the moon requires very slow antenna movement, allowing the use of rather crude axle bearings. Precision units are not necessary. Since axle rotation is limited to less than a single turn, nested or even large-threaded iron pipe may be used as a bearing. If the structure is properly counterbalanced, torque on either axis of rotation can be reduced to the bearing friction and wind

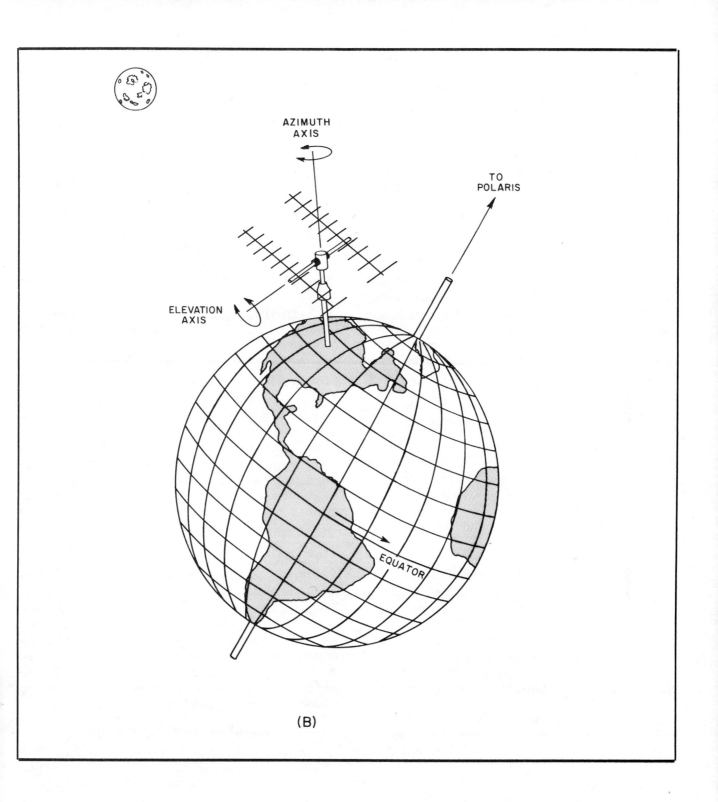

(B)

loading. In most cases a low-power, self-locking, worm-drive system will suffice. Cable and winch elevation drive is popular but requires a counterbalance to apply torque in the opposite direction. This drive works best where a large radius arm is available or can be provided on the antenna structure. Suitable stops for both rotational axes should always be incorporated to prevent excess rotation accidents from damaging mount and antenna structures.

Large reflector antennas exhibit high wind loading even with mesh surface construction, requiring the mount to withstand a considerable overturning moment. The structure should be well anchored to the ground, either with heavy guying, a concrete foundation, or both. A rough estimate of horizontal wind force in pounds at the top of the mount structure may be obtained by multiplying the total aperture area of the reflector in square feet by 0.004 times the square of the wind velocity in miles per hour. The recommended stow position for a reflector antenna is with the beam pointed toward the zenith to minimize wind loading.

How high above Earth to mount an EME antenna is a matter of your local foreground clearance and how much orbital coverage is desired (full moonrise to moonset will maximize DX potential). In residential backyards, the trend is to mount the antenna just high enough to afford radiation clearance of buildings and low foliage, both of which can cause excessive signal attenuation. If limited access to the lunar orbit is acceptable, a lower mount will greatly simplify the system. For personal safety, it is advisable to allow a minimum clearance of about 8 feet from the lowest point on the antenna to the ground. A careful survey of your particular environment should always be made before placing the antenna mount. Look for best clearance in the direction of moonrise and moonset, allowing for maximum declination variation. Avoid placing the mount where the antenna beam will pass through buildings or dense foliage.

Even with large EME antennas, RF density falls off quite rapidly and should present no serious threat to individuals, *provided that safety precautions are heeded*. Consult Chapter 2 for a thorough discussion on this subject. Consider your neighbors' concerns about RF radiation and do your best to prevent future problems.

MOON ORBIT AND TRACKING

The lunar orbit is slightly elliptical and has a mean distance of 238,000 statute miles from Earth. Although the orbit is essentially in our equatorial plane, the path as seen from Earth seems to spiral north and south of the equator at regular intervals of a lunar month—about 28 days long. This variation above and below the equator is referred to as the *lunar declination*.

Polar-Mount Tracking

With this mount, usually only one axis is rotated to track the moon. As the Earth rotates, the antenna can be kept in nearly constant alignment with the moon by counter-rotation of the polar axis. The rotational speed of the Earth is about 15° per hour, therefore the drive need only rotate at this very slow speed. In practice, antenna beamwidths used for EME are several degrees wide; common procedure is to rotate the polar axis at intervals frequent enough to keep the moon within the beam. This method of updating the antenna position every few minutes is more popular than using a constant-speed clock drive.

In the northern hemisphere, alignment of the polar axis can be achieved by first pointing it at the North Star (Polaris), and then moving it 1° west. The southern hemisphere has no equivalent to the North Star and other means must be used to determine true south. The acute angle of the polar axis relative to the horizon is always equal to your latitude.

If the moon remained directly over the equator (0° declination), the antenna would always be pointed at right angles to the polar axis. However, because the moon periodically moves above and below the equator by as much as 27°, it is necessary to point the antenna away from this right-angle position. The declination axis is used for this purpose. With most EME antennas, the declination need be changed only once for each daily orbit. This is because the maximum change in declination angle for any one orbit is about 2°. The maximum rate of declination change occurs as the moon crosses the equator.

The information needed to properly point your antenna with a polar mount can be obtained from the *Nautical Almanac*.[22] This document can be obtained from the US Government Printing Office, or found in many large libraries. It is issued in advance on a yearly basis, and contains tabulations of the Greenwich Hour Angle (GHA) and declination of the moon for each hour in Universal Coordinated Time (UTC), as well as similar information for the sun and planets.

GHA is the rotational angle of a polar-mount axis located on the Greenwich, or prime meridian. Zero degrees GHA corresponds to the zenith position of the moon at Greenwich, England. To find the Local Hour Angle (LHA) of the moon at your location, subtract your longitude west of Greenwich from the tabulated value of GHA.

LHA = GHA − Degrees West Longitude

Zero degrees LHA corresponds to the zenith position of the moon at your location. (Polar axes are calibrated with an angular scale of ±90°; moonrise and moonset correspond to LHAs of +90° and −90°, respectively.

The declination angle is obtained directly from the *Nautical Almanac* tables. Since it changes so slowly for a daily orbit period, a value midway between moonrise and moonset may be used. At times other than those found in the tables, GHA may be obtained with sufficient accuracy by linear interpolation.

In practice, the antenna may not be exactly aligned with the geometry of the mounting structure and calibration adjustments may be necessary to ensure high accuracy. Final adjustments are most easily made once an operational system can receive solar noise or lunar echoes. The process is to first experimentally peak the antenna on the moon or sun, note the exact time, and lock the rotational axes. You can then obtain the GHA and declination by interpolation from the *Nautical Almanac* and calibrate the readouts to the corresponding LHA and declination.

Az-el Mount Tracking

The az-el mount is generally easier to construct and initially align than a polar mount. It is essentially nothing more than a conventional rotating mechanism used to point an antenna on the horizon, with the addition of a tilting (elevation) mechanism mounted above the azimuth rotator. The elevation rotator need only tilt the antenna up by 90° from the horizon, which is at 0° elevation. An advantage of this mount is that the antenna system can be used for other modes of communication, such as satellite and terrestrial.

It is very important that the azimuth axis be exactly vertical with respect to the Earth and that the elevation axis be at right angles to the azimuth axis. Rough calibration of the elevation scale may be easily achieved at 0° with a spirit level, or at 90° with a plumb bob. Final calibration of the azimuth and elevation readouts is most easily done in the same manner as with the polar mount.

Information necessary to point an az-el mount at the moon may be computed using the tabulated GHA and declination angles from the *Nautical Almanac*. The LHA must be calculated first, then formulas to convert LHA and declination to azimuth and elevation must be used. Following are equations with an accuracy of approximately 1°

Elevation in degrees = arcsin [sin (DEC) × sin (LAT) + cos (DEC) × cos (LAT) × cos (LHA)]

Azimuth in degrees = arcsin $\dfrac{\cos \text{(DEC)} \times \sin \text{(LHA)}}{\cos \text{(ELEVATION)}}$

In the early days of EME communication, the cumbersome mathematics required to use an az-el mount were considered a major disadvantage. Today, with the availability of inexpensive microcomputers and programmable calculators, these calculations are no longer a problem.

Many programs are available from various computer bulletin-board services as freeware to compute the lunar azimuth and elevation directly, from date and time only, without any information from the *Nautical Almanac*. Notable among these is one available from VK3UM. Another such program, written by W8MIF, appears in the companion disk to this *Manual* under the name of SUNMOON.

Angular Readouts

In addition to calibrating the readouts of the mount axes, it is also necessary to have a convenient means of reading the angular scales. Various methods have been devised, which can provide a precision of about ±1°, sufficient for most EME applications. Large, calibrated protractors can be used for direct observation. Pairs of selsyns geared to 1:1 and 36:1 ratios may be used for remote indication. Perhaps the best form of readout is the remote digital type. The simplest form uses multi-turn linear potentiometers and a digital voltmeter. Fig 18 shows a remote readout circuit designed by W4UDH, which can be adapted to most mounts and is easily calibrated.

SYSTEM EVALUATION BY MEASUREMENT

Direct or indirect measurement of EME system parameters is the only way to ensure that the system is working as expected, or to check for performance deterioration over extended periods. The measurement procedures used in this section will require little in the way of specialized equipment, but rely more on attention to detail.

Operating System Noise Temperature

One of the basic evaluations is a measure of the operating system noise temperature, which encompasses both receiver noise temperature and the antenna temperature. A method of making this measurement is to use sun noise as a reference. To do this, the receiving system should

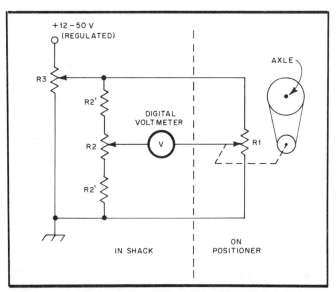

Fig 18—A simple analog-to-digital angle readout for antenna position. R1 is a multiturn linear potentiometer that is coupled to the axle by a 3:1-10:1 pulley system. R2 is the calibrate set adjustment, while R3 expands or compresses the scale. Resistors R2' may be needed to provide bandspread for R2. The digital voltmeter must "float" above ground and may require RF filtering. The circuit can provide accuracy limited only by the linearity of R1, typically 0.5% or less.

be operated at the maximum bandwidth possible and in a linear mode, which means that the AGC should be off. The receiver should also be checked for linearity at least 15 dB above the highest solar noise level expected. This ensures that receiver compression will not cause erroneous noise output readings.

A low-level signal source and calibrated RF attenuator are all the pieces of equipment necessary to check for receiver compression. Without gain compression, a 15-dB increase in signal level above the expected noise maximum should result in a 15-dB increase in receiver noise output. This may be taken directly at the audio output of the receiver and read with an averaging type ac voltmeter with a time constant of about 2 seconds.

The system noise temperature measurement consists of recording the receiver output noise level when the antenna is pointed directly at the sun, and again with the beam pointed toward a "cold" sky. The ratio of these two readings can be used to determine the system operating temperature by

$$T_{\text{operating system}} = \frac{T_{\text{sun-ant}}}{k - 1}$$

where
  k = the ratio of output voltages squared
  $T_{\text{sun-ant}}$ = antenna temperature due to solar radiation only.

It is given by

$$T_{\text{sun-ant}} = T_{\text{apparent}} \frac{(\text{subtended sun angle})^2}{(\text{half power beamwidth})^2}$$

where the subtended sun angle is close to 0.5° and the antenna half-power beamwidth is in degrees. If the half-power beamwidth is unknown, it may be measured by the method given below or estimated using data found in Chapter 9. The apparent sun temperature ($T_{apparent}$) can be taken from Fig 19 if the noise measurement was taken during a quiet solar period.

System temperature determination is only as accurate as the value used for $T_{apparent}$. In general, solar noise increases with sunspot activity—varying over a considerable range, with short-term effects caused by solar flares. These effects are quite pronounced at VHF and tend to become smaller above 2 GHz.

Accurate solar radiation data may be obtained from agencies in a number of countries. The National Bureau of Standards (NBS) at Boulder, Colorado maintains a real-time forecasting service that can be reached by telephone at 303-497-3171. The World Data Center, also at Boulder (303-497-6223) maintains long-term records on solar radiation. Data of interest to EME operators is available for 605, 1415 and 2659 MHz and is given in solar flux units (SFUs). An SFU can be converted to apparent sun temperature by

$$T_{apparent\ (K)} = 2.726 \times 10^9\ \frac{solar\ flux\ units}{(f\ MHz)^2}$$

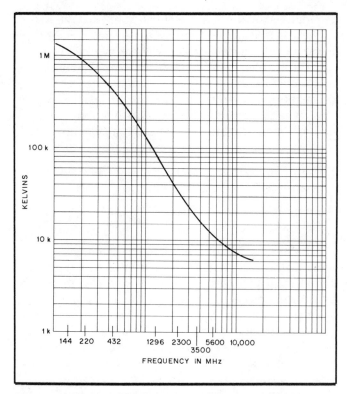

Fig 19—Apparent sun temperature during "quiet" conditions.

Obtain solar data for the frequencies listed above and interpolate for the band of interest. Make every effort to conduct your measurements during quiet solar periods for highest accuracy. Take several readings over a period of an hour or more to determine if a minimum level has been observed. Otherwise, use the measured value at a time for which NBS data is available.

An alternative method of estimating the system operating temperature requires aiming the antenna beam from "cold sky" to a negative elevation angle, such that the −3 dB beamwidth is all aimed toward the earth. Then, $T_{sun-ant}$ can be replaced by 290 K in the $T_{operating\ system}$ equation (see previous page).

If the measured system temperature is 50 kelvins higher than expected, it may be advisable to separate parts of the system and measure them individually. A good place to start is to measure your LNA with calibrated instruments. At the same time, determine LNA gain to within 1 dB. With this information and the method given in the Receiver Considerations section, recalculate the system operating temperature. Next, optimize the LNA/antenna interface for best noise match and repeat the measurement evaluation. Finally, determine the antenna temperature and check for inconsistencies. This procedure should indicate which part of the system needs improvement.

Using Antenna Beamwidth

A sun-noise measurement that can aid in antenna evaluation is to observe the antenna half-power beamwidth. This is an indicator of effective directivity, which in turn can be an indicator of gain. If the ratio of received noise power with the antenna pointed at and away from the sun is greater than 2, this technique can be used. Measuring antenna characteristics with this method is highly desirable, since the range conditions are ideal. The signal source is very far away and the antenna can be pointed away from the Earth, virtually eliminating ground reflection effects.

The sun is not a point source, but one whose angular size depends on frequency. This may be a consideration when evaluating antennas with 3-dB beamwidths of less than 2°. The correction factor details are beyond the scope of this book; most amateur EME antennas will not require this refinement.[23]

A more practical consideration is the effective signal-to-noise ratio during measurement. To find the effective 3-dB points, a correction factor must be included with the measured data.

$$Correction\ factor = 10 \log\left(\frac{N_o}{N_o + 1}\right)$$

where N_o is the measured noise ratio between aiming the main beam toward and away from the sun. The correction factor will always be a dB value to be subtracted from 3 dB, the half-power level.

For example, if the difference in noise when pointed at or away from the sun is 8 dB, N_o is 6.31 and the correction factor is 0.64 dB. Subtracting this from 3 dB yields an effective half-power point of 2.36 dB. As the antenna is scanned across the sun, the half-power beamwidth should be measured between the two points 2.36 dB down on either side of the peak, rather that at 3 dB. This correction factor is especially significant when the noise ratio is low.

The preferred way to make a beamwidth measurement does not depend on the accuracy of your antenna position readout. Keep the antenna stationary and let the sun drift through the peak of the main beam. This may require some trial-and-error positioning to anticipate the path. Since the sun drifts at 15° per hour, it takes 24 minutes to drift from one half-power point to the opposite one on a 3° beamwidth antenna. Avoid measurements at elevation angles below 20° and when the sun is disturbed.

Half-power beamwidth measurements should be made in both the polarization and orthogonal planes. This can be achieved by rotating the entire antenna 90°. On a dish antenna, only the feed need be rotated. The two planes being measured should align with and be orthogonal to the path of the sun, if possible. Using sun noise as a reference for both planes works because solar noise is randomly polarized.

Successful measurements of 3-dB beamwidths in the two principle planes allows a good estimate of antenna directivity by using the formula

$$\text{Antenna Directivity (in dB)} = 10 \log \frac{27,000}{\phi E \times \phi H}$$

where ϕE and ϕH are the half-power beamwidth angles in degrees for the E and H planes, respectively.

The above procedure can be a diagnostic aid in finding poorly constructed reflector surfaces or improper phasing in arrays, as well as for reflector illumination evaluation. However, the methods outlined in this section are subject to errors both in measurement accuracy and in absolute solar radiation levels. Your results should only be used as guidelines to aid in system evaluation.

By pointing the antenna toward and away from the sun, the ratio of output noise can be used to periodically check for system performance deterioration. It can also be used for evaluation of modifications. For the latter purpose it is most valuable, permitting a fairly accurate assessment of relative performance after changing LNAs or a reflector feed. Just think—you can do all this without elaborate test equipment!

OPERATING PROCEDURES

In addition to VHF EME, regular activity exists on the 432, 1296 and 2300-MHz bands. There have also been contacts on 902, 3456 and 5760 MHz. A conservative estimate is that 1000 amateur stations worldwide are currently setup for some type of EME communication.

With the exception of 144 MHz, the most popular EME band is 432 MHz, with several stations having contacted more than 400 others at this time. A minimum antenna for this band is a single long Yagi. Some stations using only four Yagis have worked more than 100 different stations and received the Worked All Continents (WAC) award! Linear polarization is used almost exclusively on 432 MHz, and many stations have the ability to rotate antenna polarization.

Next in popularity is 1296 MHz, where OE9XXI and

others have worked more than 80 different stations. On this band, contacts have been made by stations using dish antennas as small as 6-feet diameter; a number of "regulars" use 8-foot dishes. Almost all stations use circular polarization, although some operators have had success using large Yagi (both loop and linear element) arrays. Unfortunately, these are at a great disadvantage compared to the circularly polarized antennas.

SIGNAL REPORTING

Because short-term fading can turn a "dah" into a "dit" or even a pair of dits, the "T M O R" system is used for reporting during initial schedules on 432 MHz and higher. The meanings of these symbols is given in Table 2. If signal levels are strong enough, standard RST reports can be used.

On 432 MHz and above, 2½-min sequencing is used for schedules, with the station easternmost of the International Date Line usually transmitting first. (A slightly different timing sequence is used on 144 MHz.)[24] Table 3 lists a typical sequence. During the initial transmission period for each station, call signs are repeated for 2 minutes. The procedure for subsequent transmission periods depends on what has been previously copied.

On CW, keying speeds of 12-15 WPM are generally used. Very slow speeds should be avoided because of fading. When transmitting call sequences, it is advised that you send the other station call sign once, followed by "DE" then your call sign one time. Pause and repeat the sequence. This cadence sets a rhythm to anticipate copy. Send with proper spacing; the use of a programmable keyer is especially useful and encouraged. Remember that a signal in the noise accompanied by fading is difficult enough to copy without the complication of bad sending!

Table 2

Signal Reports Used on 432-MHz EME

T—Portions of call sign copied
M—Complete call signs copied
    Minimum required for QSO
O—Good signal, solid copy (possible enough for SSB work)
R—Call signs and reports copied
SK—End of contact

Table 3

432-MHz Procedure—2½ Minute Sequence

Period	2 Minutes	30 Seconds
1	NC1I DE DL9KR	
2	DL9KR DE NC1I	
3	NC1I DE DL9KR	O O O O O
4	RO RO RO RO	DE NC1I K __
5	R R R R R R	DE DL9KR SK

Faraday rotation makes the EME path one of the few non-reciprocal communication media that amateurs use. For this reason, do not expect stations to copy each other equally well. To compensate for the difference in optimum polarization angle between transmit and receive, a station with rotatable linear polarization should seek the angle corresponding to the best received signal. If both stations have this capability, each should peak up the received signal. Once this angle has been found, it will not change appreciably during the period of a QSO.

Optimum transmit polarization may be at quite a different angle. It should be anticipated that polarization rotation will have to take place between each transmission. If only one out of two stations in communication is equipped to rotate polarization, the optimum transmit angle can only be found by trial-and-error. Keep in mind that the orientation tolerance is quite broad; an error of $\pm 20°$ will result in only 0.5-dB loss of signal strength.

Activity and Scheduling

Activity on 432, 1296 and 2300 MHz is centered around ''activity weekends,'' which are scheduled once each month. Their choice is based on the location of the moon. The weekend closest to the lunar perigee (when the moon is closest to the Earth) is usually preferred because of lower path loss. High northern declination is also desirable to afford the greatest lunar orbit time for stations in northern latitudes, where most EME operators are located. Consideration is also given to the position of the sun and cosmic noise level when setting the activity period.

Schedules on 70 cm are normally arranged for both Saturday and Sunday, running simultaneously on 432.000 and 432.025 through 432.060 MHz. Random activity occurs between 432.005 and 432.020 MHz, with 432.010 MHz considered the calling frequency. Seventy centimeter activity can be found at other times but is sparse compared to activity weekends, when signals can almost always be heard off the moon. Operators wishing schedules should correspond with a schedule coordinator. At the time of this writing, schedules are listed in K2UYH's monthly *432 MHz and Above EME Newsletter*.[25]

Sunday is when schedules on 23 cm are set, usually on either 1296.000 or 1296.025 MHz. The calling frequency is 1296.010 MHz, and random activity can be found anywhere from 1296.005 to 1296.020 MHz. Because of lower activity, schedules on 2300 MHz are not arranged every month, but are set on Saturdays to not conflict with 1296-MHz operation. Activity occurs mainly on 2304.000 and sometimes on 2320.150 MHz or on a cross-frequency combination. This frequency offset is often required since US regulations permit operation in the band 2300-2320 MHz, while some European countries only permit operation above 2320 MHz. For US amateurs, the 2400-2450-MHz segment is reserved for satellite communication.

Additional information on schedules and operation can be obtained by participating in the ''70 cm and Above Net,'' which meets every Saturday and Sunday at 1600 UTC on 14.345 MHz. Although regular schedules occur during activity weekends, it should be emphasized that a greater share of contacts are made on a random basis, both on 432 and 1296 MHz.

Notes

[1]T. Clark, ''How Diana Touched the Moon,'' *IEEE Spectrum*, May 1980, pp 44-48.
[2]Z. Bay, ''Reflections of Microwaves from the Moon,'' *Hungarica Acta Physica*, Vol 1, 1946, p 1.
[3]E. Tilton, ''Lunar DX on 144 Mc.!,'' *QST*, Mar 1953, pp 11-12, 116.
[4]S. Harris and W. Orr, ''Project Moon Bounce,'' *QST*, Sep 1960, pp 62-66, 158.
[5]S. Harris, ''The World Above 50 Mc.,'' *QST*, Jun 1964, pp 95-98.
[6]MIT Lincoln Laboratory, ''Radar Studies of the Moon, Final Report,'' Vol 1, Aug 1967, p 19.
[7]Kressner and Michaels, *Introduction to Space Communication Systems* (New York: McGraw-Hill Publishing Co).
[8]J. A. Klobucher, ''Correspondence,'' *IEEE Transactions on Antennas and Propagation*, Sep 1966, p 650.
[9]S. J. Fricker, et al, ''Characteristics of Moon-Reflected UHF Signals,'' *MIT Technical Report No. 187*, Dec 1958.
[10]MIT Lincoln Laboratory, *Radar Studies of the Moon, Quarterly Progress Report*, Feb 1966, p 15.
[11]Jakes, *Microwave Mobile Communications* (New York: Wiley Publishing Co, 1974), Ch 5.
[12]Crawford Hill VHF Club EME Technical Reports, Number 18.
[13]Zheleznyakov, *Radio Emission of the Sun and Planets* (London: Pergamon Press Ltd, 1970), p 287.
[14]Kraus, *Radio Astronomy* (New York: McGraw-Hill Publishing Co, 1966).
[15]R. R. Taur, ''Ionosopheric Scintillation at Frequencies Above 1 GHz,'' *COMSAT Technical Review*, Vol 4, No. 2, 1974.
[16]R. H. Turrin, ''Simple Super Selectivity,'' Technical Correspondence, *QST*, Jan 1967, p 48.
[17]FCC regulations, Part 97.
[18]E. R. Angle, ''A Quarter-Kilowatt 23-cm Amplifier,'' *QST*, Mar 1985, pp 14-20 and Apr 1985, pp 32-37.
[19]R. E. Fisher, et al, ''A Power Amplifier for 1296 MHz,'' *Ham Radio*, Mar 1970, pp 43-50.
[20]H. E. Holshouser, K4QIF, ''800 watts with a UPX-4'' (unpublished).
[21]S. Powlishen, ''Stacking Yagis is a Science,'' *Ham Radio*, May 1985, pp 18-33.
[22]Available from the Superintendent of Documents, US Govt Printing Office.
[23]A. R. Giddis, ''Effects of the Sun upon Antenna Temperature,'' *Philco WDL Technical Report E320*, Mar 1963.
[24]*The ARRL Handbook*, Chapter 23.
[25]Allen Katz, K2UYH, 1621 Old Trenton Rd, RD 4, Trenton, NJ 08691.

Chapter 11

Getting Started in Microwave Measurements

By Keith R. Ericson, KØKE
11090 N Forest Hills Dr
Parker, CO 80134-8128

Getting started in microwave work needn't be difficult or intimidating. There's no magic involved, but if you adhere to a few general principles, you'll be more successful.

This is not a treatise on how to perform specific measurements—it's a general overview that will help you get started with microwave measurements, and hopefully solve a problem or two.

Getting Started

Having the right test equipment is one of the most important keys to successful measurements at microwave frequencies. It's not necessary to have the latest 26-GHz, digital-readout spectrum analyzer—nice, maybe, but not necessary. There are many sources of used test equipment. Take the time to look through a few catalogs and become familiar with the available equipment and its cost. Tucker Electronics, Davilyn Corporation and Lectronic Research Labs all have comprehensive illustrated catalogs. [Look in your local commercial telephone directory for their nearest offices.—Ed.]

When visiting another city on business or vacation, investigate the local surplus electronics dealers. Almost every large city has one. Chances are you'll find something of interest at a reasonable price. Don't be afraid to haggle—many dealers enjoy it, whether they'll admit to it or not. Be sure you have a good idea of the unit's current price. Sometimes it helps to amass a pile of things and then negotiate a bargain "volume" rate. Don't be afraid to get your hands dirty. Look in all of the store's nooks and crannies for smaller items. Plug in the items before paying for them. Do they light up? Are the fuses good? Do the meters work?

Power Meters

Without a doubt, the first piece of test gear you should acquire is a power meter calibrated in decibels. This meter will indicate power output, power loss, filter response, impedance matching, drive levels and much more. A good power meter is definitely a necessity (see Fig 1). Such meters are frequently found on the surplus market, minus their most important part, the power sensor. The power sensor is often called a bolometer, which is really nothing more than a thin piece of wire that heats up, changes resistance and unbalances a bridge circuit, causing the unit's meter to deflect. The meter is useless without the power sensing head, and is frequently available in this condition for a reasonable price. Similar units have been manufactured by General Microwave, PRD and others.

Most of the "headless" power meters you'll find have been scrapped for a good reason—the sensor head has been blown by carelessness. The sensor heads can usually handle a maximum power level of +10 dBm (10 mW) and are easily destroyed by excessive power. You should have a good idea of the output level of any device being tested, before connecting the power meter! If in doubt, place a resistive pad in-line to attenuate the power to a level that will not overload the meter. Most meters are most stable at higher power levels, and suffer from drift at the low-power ranges (the meter is trying to sense minute changes in the bolometer head). The average dynamic range for most surplus power meters is about 30 dB (from −20 dBm to +10 dBm). Newer models will have greater dynamic range and a correspondingly higher price tag. Being inherently broadbanded devices, they respond equally well to the fundamental signal, harmonics and other spurious energy. This can sometimes lead to inaccurate results.

(A)

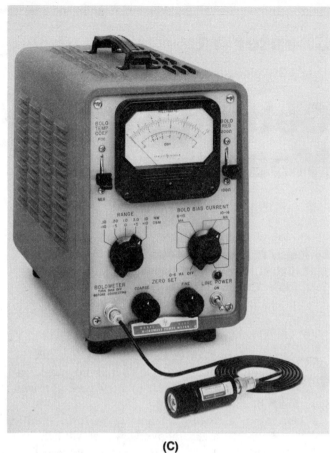

(C)

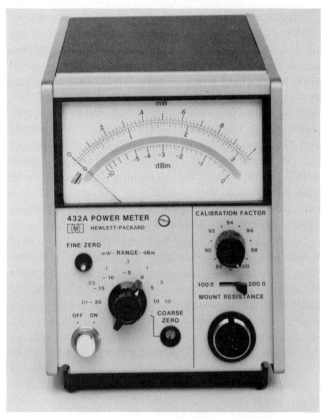

(B)

(D)   (E)

Fig 1—Here are several popular power meters manufactured by Hewlett-Packard. Photos A, B and C are the 431A, 432A and 430C (with the HP478 bolometer head) models, respectively. Close ups of bolometers appear in D and E.

A Bird #43 wattmeter is also useful for measuring microwave power. Slugs are available through 2304 MHz (they're expensive). The more common "E" slugs can be used at low power levels (5 to 10 watts) through 3456 MHz, with reduced accuracy.

Attenuators

The easiest way to extend a power meter's useful range is to have on hand a large supply of attenuators (see Fig 2). A good selection contains 3, 6, 10 and 20-dB pads, with an assortment of connectors and adapters. Sometimes you can find oddball values such as 5- or 7-dB attenuators. These are just as handy, and can be combined to form new values (a 3- and 7-dB pad combine to form a 10-dB pad). It's nice to have two of each value to compare accuracy. You can never have too many attenuator pads!

Adapters, Coax and Connectors

Many different types of connectors are found on today's microwave devices. As with attenuator pads, you can never have too many connectors and adapters. Some of the more common types include N-SMA, N-BNC, BNC-SMA, waveguide to N, SMA, and many other combinations both male and female. It's not always necessary to purchase specific adapters. A short length of coax with different connectors on each end can also be used.

0.141-inch semi-rigid coax is used extensively above 1 GHz (it's not very flexible), and is often available on the surplus market in a pre-bent condition. Murphy's Law for semi-rigid coax states that the bend will always be in the wrong direction, or the piece will be too long (naturally). To get around this problem, use a piece of flexible 0.141-inch equivalent (Belden #1168A). When bending semi-rigid coax, use a mandrel such as a ½-inch drill bit or wooden dowel to avoid kinking or tearing the outer shield. The radius of the bend can be changed, but never completely straightened out. It will always retain some distortion and produce an impedance bump. This may be acceptable at 1296 MHz, but certainly not at 10 GHz. Attempting a second bend will probably destroy the coax.

When making connections to microwave circuits, be sure the connectors are snug (not crescent-wrench tight, however). At 10 GHz, the "tightness" of the connector can affect the impedance of the connection (due to a slight deformation of the connector geometry). If the connector is too loose, there is a small percentage of a wavelength within the connector that no longer has a 50-ohm impedance. It acts as a mismatching impedance bump. The measured gain of an amplifier can actually change by several decibels, depending upon the geometry of the connectors. SMA connectors should usually be tightened to 6-8 in-oz. In the real world that's a little tighter than finger snug. BNC connectors become erratic at about 2 GHz, because each time a new connection is made, the geometry inside the mating connectors is slightly different.

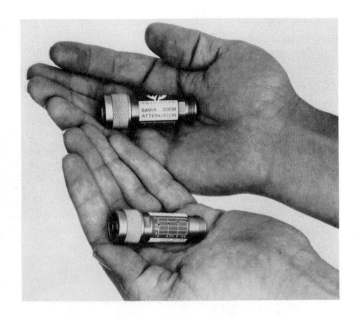

Fig 2—Attenuators are used to extend the useful range of a power meter.

Diode Detectors

Another useful and inexpensive piece of test equipment is the diode detector. It functions as a power meter, sampling the voltage at the output of an RF test circuit, and providing a voltage that can be read on a simple VOM. In general, expect the detector to provide a 100-mV output for a 0-dBm input. The detector is usually used to indicate relative power levels (for peaking circuit response), and not for absolute power measurements. Typical diode detectors are several inches long (see Fig 3) with a Type N input connector (RF) and a BNC output connector (dc). They are also available in a waveguide-to-BNC form for low-power microwave measurements.

Directional Couplers

Directional couplers are useful, passive devices used to obtain valid test data. They usually cover a one-octave frequency range (1 to 2 GHz, 2 to 4 GHz, etc) and have a sampling port that has an output 10 or 20 dB less than the signal passing through it. The pass-through signal is

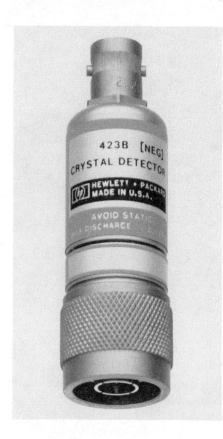

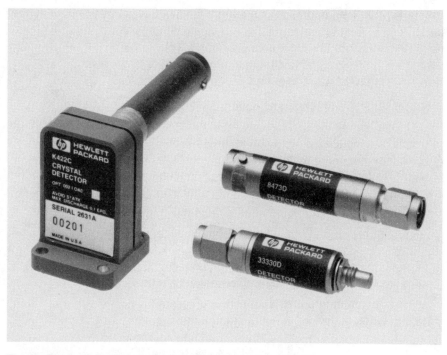

Fig 3—Diode detectors may function as power meters by providing a voltage that can be read on a VOM. They are available with various input/output connector combinations.

subject to negligible loss (insertion loss). The attenuated output from the sampling port can be used to drive an RF power meter. These couplers come in two varieties: waveguide and coaxial (see Fig 4). For example, you can place a 20-dB directional coupler in line with a 1-W, +30-dBm amplifier (terminate the through port in a dummy load and connect a power meter to the −20-dB sampling port). The output from the sampling port will now be +10 dBm—a power level that your power meter can handle. If a 20-dB directional coupler is used at the output of a 10-W amplifier, an additional 10-dB pad connected in series with the

sampling port will attenuate the output to +10 dBm (this allows you to effectively measure a 10-W signal on a bolometer-type power meter). Other uses for these devices include measuring return loss. When measuring return loss, reverse the direction in which you connect the coupler (the sample port is fed by the reflected power from the antenna or load in question).

Let's apply a 1-W (+30 dBm) signal to our test load. If the load in question has a 20-dB return loss (1.22 to 1 SWR), the power reflected from the load is 20 dB less than the 1-W drive signal (+10 dBm). This reflected power is

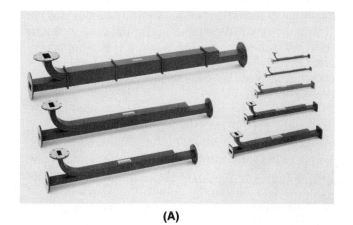

(A)

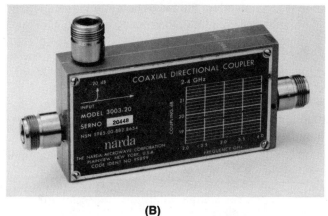

(B)

Fig 4—Directional couplers, used to drive an RF power meter and to measure return loss, come in two varieties: waveguide (A) and coaxial (B).

attenuated another 20 dB by the coupler's sampling port, putting the measured signal at -10 dBm. As you can see, the 1-W level is appropriate for making accurate return loss measurements with a directional coupler and a power meter. When working with substantial amounts of RF at microwave frequencies, do not stand in front of the antenna—the strong RF field can be harmful, and body tissue heating will occur.

Narda, HP, PRD and Sage Labs manufacture high-quality couplers, frequently found on the surplus market at a reasonable price. The frequency response of these directional couplers is often stamped on the cover of the device. They come in two varieties: single and dual directional. Dual directional couplers are easier to work with, but single direction couplers are just as accurate (turn them around).

Now that you have accumulated a selection of basic microwave test instruments, let's add to your shopping list as your needs, interests and, of course, your pocketbook allow.

Signal Generators

Signal generators are useful for testing low-level circuits and their respective frequency response. They come in all manner of frequency coverage, price, stability, etc (see Fig 5). Most have variable output attenuators and a maximum output level of about 1 to 10 mW. Common ranges are 1 to 2 GHz, 2 to 4 GHz, 4 to 8 GHz, and 7 to 11 GHz. Many of the older units are not solid state, and their tubes can be obtained at a reasonable price. These are sufficient for most amateur tasks. The older units sometimes suffer from frequency drift and phase noise, but these are not necessarily problems. The older signal generators usually produce CW, FM and PWM (pulse width modulation). HP, Polarad, General Microwave and Sierra Research manufacture units that are available surplus for about $150.

Sweep Generators

The logical extension of a simple signal generator (more expensive) is called a sweep generator. As the name implies, this device will sweep its signal across a broad range (usually one octave) of frequencies, with a relatively flat output level. The sweep generator is used to check the frequency response of a circuit or filter, or the SWR passband of an antenna, among others. It's often used in conjunction with a spectrum analyzer (looking at a wide passband), but meaningful results can be had using a power meter and restricting the sweep range to the passband response.

Power Supplies

No shop would be complete without several regulated power supplies (see Fig 6). Useful ranges include 3 to 5 V dc (for GaAsFETs), 12 V dc, 19 V dc (for Frequency West/California Microwave local oscillators), and 24 to 28 V dc. A separate 28-V supply should be used to power T/R relays so that voltage spikes from the relay coils will not damage sensitive devices. Lambda makes a broad range of high-quality power supplies. These are often available at swap meets and hamfests for a reasonable price ($10 to $25). Building power supplies is a major part of microwave experimentation—it's not very exciting, but it is necessary.

Frequency Counters

A good counter (sensitive to 1296 MHz) is a useful addition to any workbench. Microwave counters and transfer oscillators are available to extend the useful frequency of your counter. They are, however, expensive, cumbersome and insensitive.

Fig 5—Signal generators test the frequency response of low-level circuits. They are available on the surplus market.

Fig 6—Every microwave experimenter needs at least a few regulated power supplies. They're available on the used market or can be built inexpensively.

Spectrum Analyzers

The ultimate piece of microwave test gear has to be the spectrum analyzer (see Fig 7). In simplest terms, this unit is nothing more than a tunable receiver with its output connected to an oscilloscope, allowing you to accurately measure the output of the receiver. The spectrum analyzer can be used to display RF power, harmonics, oscillations, frequency, pulses and many other measurements depending on your interests. This is a sizable investment (one you will not regret) that should be considered carefully. With the money you invest in a spectrum analyzer you could probably buy another transceiver, a vacation or a used car. Determine your needs carefully! Older units rely on tubes, Klystrons and BWOs (backwave oscillators) for their LOs. Replacing these tubes is expensive (they're hard to find, too). It's probably why they're so "reasonably" priced. If the tubes burn out, your analyzer is basically worthless, so consider the unit's history and condition carefully.

Analyzers to look for include the HP 8551B, Tektronics 491 and other models manufactured by Singer and Polarad. The HP unit can display a 2-GHz range of frequencies centered around the frequency in question. (This is called dispersion.) It's a good buy ($700 to $1200), although it's heavy and bulky. The Tektronics unit, while smaller, does not have the dispersion range of the HP unit (± 35 MHz). Both units suffer from image problems, which can usually be eliminated if you know what to look for. The UPM-84 (military surplus) is frequently available on the surplus market for about $250. It's not a bargain. This unit has many images, birdies and other spurious responses, making it quite difficult to use. Newer units, while improved, have accordingly higher price tags. Most units will have coverage extending to 12 GHz, sufficient to cover most amateur microwave bands. Newer units with coverage limits of 1.8 GHz are becoming more common, and should not be rejected because of their frequency limitations (they have other desirable features such as digital readout, good image rejection, reliable calibration and portability). Their coverage range can be easily extended with a home-brew down-converting mixer that converts the desired frequency to one the analyzer can handle. The application notes on spectrum analyzers (provided by the manufacturers) describe many types of possible measurements.

A receiving down-converter feeding a receiver such as an ICOM R-7000 (a wide-range VHF/UHF receiver) with its output connected to an oscilloscope is, in effect, a home-brew spectrum analyzer. The down-converter can be as simple as a DBM (doubly balanced mixer) and a "Frequency West" type LO, or a commercial down-converter, available surplus from Collins Radio.

Now that your shop is well-supplied with test equipment, let's discuss some ways to make microwave measurements a little easier (and make your projects work better).

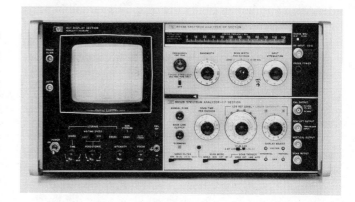

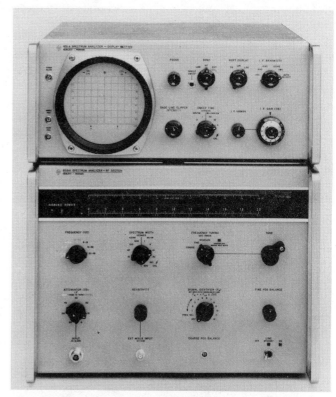

Fig 7—The spectrum analyzer allows you to measure RF power, harmonics, oscillations, deviation and pulses—among other things. New ones can be expensive, but if you decide to purchase a used model, make sure the tubes are good (or readily available).

Decibels

An intimate knowledge of decibels is valuable, and easily acquired. The reference for most microwave work is 1 mW (0 dBm). From here it's easy to go up and down in 3- and 10-dB steps, converting the dBm figures to more familiar values such as watts. See Table 1.

Note that the $\times 5$ column is the same as the $\times 10$ column (10-dB multiple) minus 3 dB. If you learn to keep

Table 1
Decibel Reference Table

Reference		×2		×4		×5		×10	
+ 0 dBm =	1 mW	+3 dBm =	2 mW	+6 dBm =	4 mW	+7 dBm =	5 mW	+10 dBm =	10 mW
+10 dBm =	10 mW	+13 dBm =	20 mW	+16 dBm =	40 mW	+17 dBm =	50 mW	+20 dBm =	100 mW
+20 dBm =	100 mW	+23 dBm =	200 mW	+26 dBm =	400 mW	+27 dBm =	500 mW	+30 dBm =	1 W
+30 dBm =	1 W	+33 dBm =	2 W	+36 dBm =	4 W	+37 dBm =	5 W	+40 dBm =	10 W
+40 dBm =	10 W	+43 dBm =	20 W	+46 dBm =	40 W	+47 dBm =	50 W	+50 dBm =	100 W
+50 dBm =	100 W	+53 dBm =	200 W	+56 dBm =	400 W	+57 dBm =	500 W	+60 dBm =	1 kW

track of these multiples it will make your microwave test work simpler. Also note that most power meters are calibrated in two scales: dBm and multiples of 1 watt. For example, if your power meter reads + 3 dBm, and you're feeding it through a 20-dB pad, the signal is actually at + 23 dBm. On the upper scale you will see a 2, indicating in this case, 200 mW. Decibels are also useful when it comes to measuring antenna gain or interstage matching (via the concept of return loss). The greater the return loss, the better the impedance match. Return loss reference points are listed in Table 2.

An attenuator pad placed between the source and the load will improve the impedance match. It makes for an additional return loss, making the load look more like 50 ohms. For example, a 3-dB pad placed ahead of a load with a 9-dB return loss will improve the SWR from 2 to 1, to 1.4 to 1. The signal is reduced by 3 dB in the forward direction, and 3-dB in the reverse direction! The net effect is a 6-dB loss, making the total return loss 15 dB (6 dB accounts for the difference between the 2 to 1 and 1.4 to 1 SWR).

Isolators/Circulators

Isolators are used in the microwave industry as a buffer between circuit stages, or between a stage and its load. They present a 50-ohm load with an excellent return loss (20 dB), and help to increase circuit stability (in case the circuit under test is not so stable). An isolator is a two-port device. A similar three-port device is called a circulator. Both devices pass signals with little loss in one direction, while exhibiting a high degree of isolation in the opposite direction.

Unfortunately, most isolators are frequency dependent, and function only over a small range of frequencies, such as 1 to 1.4 GHz, 3.7 to 4.2 GHz, etc. The higher-frequency circulators, constructed inside waveguides, have characteristics that depend upon the response of the waveguide itself. Being ferromagnetic devices, exposure to magnetic fields will change their characteristic response patterns. Some experimenters have had success with placing a magnet on top of the isolator, thereby improving the return loss at another frequency.

Table 2
Return Loss vs SWR

Return Loss	SWR
6 dB	3 to 1
9 dB	2 to 1
10 dB	1.9 to 1
15 dB	1.4 to 1
20 dB	1.2 to 1
25 dB	1.1 to 1
30 dB	1.06 to 1

Waveguide transitions frequently contain an isolator between the waveguide and the coaxial port. That makes the transition useful in only one direction. Sometimes the isolators can be removed, making the transition bi-directional.

Circuit/Interstage Terminations and Matching

Along the way I have alluded to various devices designed to be placed in between other microwave circuits/stages. Most microwave circuits and antennas are designed around a standard 50-ohm impedance. If the output of a stage is designed to operate into a 50-ohm load, feeding it into any other load may degrade its performance (for example, a preamp may oscillate). A 3-dB pad placed after the preamp will load the circuit enough to ensure its stability. An isolator placed after the preamp will achieve the same result without the 3-dB loss. The response of a filter designed for a 50-ohm load will change if operated at another impedance. When measuring the response of any filter, be sure to place at least a 6-dB pad or an isolator at the input and output to ensure reliable results.

Low-noise preamps achieve their low noise figure through input mismatching. If the preamp is connected to an antenna that is not close to a 50-ohm impedance, it may oscillate. A pad in front of the preamp will reduce this tendency (and, unfortunately, increase the preamp's noise figure by the dB rating of the pad!). A better approach is to improve the impedance of the antenna. If that is not possible, it's often necessary to place an isolator ahead of the preamp (stabilizing the preamp while adding a negligible 0.5-dB loss).

Slug tuners (see Fig 8) are useful matching devices, being the microwave equivalent of a matchbox. While they work best on the band they were designed for, they can also be utilized at higher frequencies (a 1296-MHz slug tuner works well on 2304 MHz).

Waveguide and Feed Lines

At the lower end of the microwave spectrum, coax is an acceptable alternative to waveguide transmission lines. 7/8-inch coax is a good choice for 1296, 2304 and 3456 MHz. Long runs at higher frequencies require the use of waveguides for low loss.

Losses for waveguides run about 1.5 dB per 100 feet (at 5.7 GHz). Losses approach 10 dB per 100 feet at 5.7 GHz for ½-inch coax, making it suitable only for short runs or rotator loops.

The low-frequency cutoff characteristic of waveguides is useful. Loss increases rapidly as the waveguide becomes less than a half-wavelength across its broadest dimension. Therefore, a short piece of waveguide can be used as a filter to reject image products that fall below this cutoff point. Two back-to-back waveguide-to-coax transitions can be used (waveguide ends bolted together) to make an effective filter. Various waveguides are used by commercial utility companies, which often have surplus pieces available. Your local tower rigger will probably have some on hand.

In general, a signal is coupled into a waveguide through a transition—nothing more than a ¼-λ vertical antenna (probe) placed at the correct position within the waveguide. The waveguide is then shorted ¼ λ behind the probe. If the waveguide does not come with the necessary flanges and transitions, it's still usable. Mount a coaxial connector (with a ¼-λ probe soldered to the center pin) ¼ λ on the waveguide. Solder a cover plate over the open end of the waveguide, ¼ λ behind the connector. A small tuning screw mounted opposite the probe can be used to tune the transition for the best return loss.

Conclusion

While far from a complete treatise on the subject, this paper should help take some of the mystery out of getting

Fig 8—Slug tuners are the microwave equivalent of matchboxes.

started in the exciting world of microwave experimentation. Many references, newsletters and books are available to you. Past proceedings of Microwave Update, Central States VHF Society and East Coast meetings should be collected. Other newsletters include those published by the Packrats and North Texas Microwave Society, and the *EME Letter* by K2UYH. *QST*, *QEX*, *Ham Radio* and *VHF Communications* frequently contain excellent material.

The section titles of this paper can be used as a shopping list for microwave equipment. It may take a few years to accumulate these items (at the right price). Each added item will enhance your capabilities, knowledge and enjoyment.

Chapter 12

Tackling Microwaves with Microcomputers

By Dr James C. Rautio, AJ3K
4397 Luna Course
Liverpool, NY 13090

A soldering iron, a few scraps of copper and a razor knife are among the important microwave circuit "optimization" tools used by most experimenters. With this chapter, we will add one more tool—the microcomputer. Faster than a speeding Smith Chart, the microcomputer can calculate—in minutes—answers that could take a skilled experimenter hours or days. But, since microcomputers cannot solve every problem, the soldering iron is still an important tool; the microcomputer will simply make your job easier.

COMPUTER-BASED DESIGN TECHNIQUES

Ideally we want software that is fast, accurate, and compatible with microcomputers. For example, what is the gain of a particular amplifier? What is its bandwidth? Will it oscillate? To get these answers, we will use circuit theory to approximate true microwave analysis.

A full electromagnetic microwave analysis (such as that provided by the method of moments) could define all the electric and magnetic fields in our microwave test circuit. Circuit theory is concerned with voltages instead of electric fields and currents instead of magnetic fields. Circuit theory assumes all components are small compared to wavelength. If a lumped element, such as a resistor or capacitor, becomes larger than, say, a tenth of a wavelength, we can still use circuit theory by modeling. We build the model out of lumped (that is, ideal) elements and analyze it using circuit theory. A resistor may have series inductance and shunt capacitance; a capacitor may have series resistance and inductance. Even transmission lines can be approximated with circuit theory models in most practical circuits.

Properly applied, circuit theory can give us fast answers to difficult problems. On top of that, the equations providing those answers are, for the most part, simple. In fact, most of the equations are related to Ohm's Law—with a slight twist. Simple equations also enable the software to fit on a microcomputer.

Circuit theory, microwaves and computers have been working together for the last 20 years. There is a considerable amount of circuit theory software available to the microwave industry. One of the popular programs is called Super-Compact (trademark of Compact Software, Inc). With all the "bells and whistles," it costs nearly as much as a moderately-priced house. If you can't yet afford a "second home," but want to put your microcomputer to work on your next microwave project, home-brew software is a good alternative.

Before we can write any software, we will have to become familiar with a couple of important equations. A good place to start is with the familiar equations for resistors, capacitors and inductors.

COMPLEX SCALAR ARITHMETIC AND LUMPED ELEMENTS

A philosopher once said, "At times life seems so real while, at other times, life seems to be totally imaginary." A mathematician then replied, "Summing it up, life is complex." And so it goes with microwave circuit theory. Complex numbers, which have a real and imaginary components, simplify some very complicated equations. (If you are a little rusty with complex numbers, you may want to review the appropriate section in *The ARRL Handbook*, or read "How to Perform AC Circuit Analysis," F. W. Napurano, May 1985 *QST*, pp 19-22.)

So how can we use complex numbers to analyze a network that has *real* electrons, *real* currents and *real* voltages? It's simple—we can't! That is, until we make a simplifying assumption. Take, for example, a sine wave with a given frequency, magnitude and phase. *Magnitude* and *phase*, now there's the key. Don't complex numbers have a magnitude and phase? They sure do. Let's agree that whenever we have a single complex number that has a certain magnitude and phase, what we are really talking about is a sine wave with the same magnitude and phase. We find that adding, subtracting, multiplying and dividing complex numbers is much easier than performing the same calculations with sine waves.

Software Details

Now, let's get into some software details. In order to represent one complex number in a computer we will need two floating-point (with a decimal point) numbers. For fastest "number crunching," we will let one of the numbers represent the real part, and the other represent the imaginary part. We could also choose magnitude and phase as our two numbers, but this would slow down computing speed.

After we do all the number crunching and want to display the answer, we may want to convert the complex number from its real and imaginary parts to magnitude and phase angle. The magnitude is the square root of the sum of the squares of the real and imaginary parts. The magnitude may then be converted to dB before being printed out (20 times log base 10 of the magnitude). If the complex number represents an impedance or admittance (rather than a voltage or current), it should not be converted to dB.

Things get a little trickier when we look at phase. Sure, the theory books say phase is the arctangent of the imaginary part, divided by the real part. So what happens when the real part is zero? If the computer language your machine uses crashes when it divides by zero, you will have some problems. There is an even more subtle and dangerous problem that can occur when calculating arctangents. Suppose we divide the imaginary part by the real part and get a positive result. That means that both the real and imaginary parts are positive and the result is in the first quadrant (0-90 degrees in the cartesian coordinate system), right? But suppose the real and imaginary parts are both negative; the angle would actually be in the third quadrant (180-270 degrees in the cartesian coordinate system), but we would still think it is in the first quadrant. (A negative number, divided by another negative number, leads to a positive answer.)

To get around this problem in BASIC, use the following:

```
100 REM RE = REAL PART, IM = IMAGINARY PART,
    AN = ANGLE
110 AN = ATN(IM/RE)
120 IF AN < = 0 GOTO 150
130 IF RE + IM < 0 THEN AN = AN-3.1415926
140 GOTO 160
150 IF RE < 0 THEN AN = AN + 3.1415926
160 PRINT AN*57.2957795
```

In statement 160, the angle is converted from radians to degrees, an important step to remember. If divide-by-zero errors are to be avoided, your software should check to see if the real part is close to, or equal to zero prior to dividing. (Line 110.)

FORTRAN has an ATAN function identical to the above, and an ATAN2 function that makes the conversion very simple:

```
C   RE = REAL PART, IM = IMAGINARY PART,
    AN = ANGLE
    AN = ATAN2(IM,RE)
    WRITE(6,900) AN*57.2957795
900 FORMAT(F9.3)
```

The ATAN2 function takes care of all the checking and doesn't mind if the real part is zero. Note that a comma, not a divide symbol, separates the arguments of the ATAN2 function. In the case of FORTRAN, you also want to be sure the variable IM is explicitly declared as REAL, otherwise it will default to INTEGER, causing an error. You could also use a variable name for the imaginary part that does not begin with the letters I through N.

Manipulating Complex Numbers

We will also need to add, subtract, multiply and divide complex numbers. It is common to write a complex number as "a + jb" where a is the real part and b is the imaginary part. The j indicates the imaginary part follows (j is also referred to as the square root of −1). When we add them together (recall the mathematician's comment), we have a single (scalar) complex number. Table 1 uses this notation in describing how to manipulate the real and imaginary parts of the four basic math functions. Note that if b and d are both zero, we have two real numbers and the results simplify to what we would expect for real numbers. You may also notice that if both a and c are zero we have two imaginary numbers and the results simplify as well. Examples of the equations in Table 1 translated into BASIC are found in the program at the end of this section.

Now we can use the four basic functions of complex arithmetic, and once our calculations are finished we can convert the real and imaginary parts to magnitude and phase angle. So how do we do the calculations? For lumped elements, the key is to calculate the impedance (or admittance, if you prefer). Table 2 shows several impedance equations in complex number format. The real part of the complex number represents resistance, and the imaginary part represents reactance.

Notice that we use fundamental units: ohms, henrys and farads. In this way, we don't have to worry about converting between inconsistent units. It is best to keep unit conversions in the input/output routines. Ask the user for say, picofarads, but convert the value to farads for processing.

Table 1

The Basic Four Functions Applied To Complex Numbers

ADDITION	$(a + jb) + (c + jd)$	$--->(e + jf)$
where $e = a + c$		
$f = b + d$		
SUBTRACTION	$(a + jb) - (c + jd)$	$--->(e + jf)$
where $e = a - c$		
$f = b - d$		
MULTIPLICATION	$(a + jb) \times (c + jd)$	$--->(e + jf)$
where $e = a \times c - b \times d$		
$f = b \times c + a \times d$		
DIVISION	$(a + jb) / (c + jd)$	$--->(e + jf)$
where $e = (a \times c + b \times d) / (c^2 + d^2)$		
$f = (b \times c - a \times d) / (c^2 + d^2)$		

Table 2
Complex Impedance of Lumped Elements

RESISTOR $Z = R + j0$
(R in ohms, zero reactance)

INDUCTOR $Z = 0 + j(\omega \times L)$
(L in henrys, ω in radians/second)

CAPACITOR $Z = 0 - j(1/(\omega \times C))$
(C in farads, ω in radians/second)

Note also that the frequency, ω, is specified in radians-per-second ($2\pi f$, with f in hertz). Again, this is to keep the equations simple and to speed the number crunching. Convert MHz or GHz to Hz, and multiply by 2π before doing any number crunching.

Now that we can calculate the impedance (or admittance), and since we already know how to combine impedance and admittance in series and parallel, what kind of circuit can we analyze? Let's start with a simple one. We can put a simple circuit into a box and connect it to a single coaxial connector. A circuit with only one coaxial connector is known as a one-port network. A one-port network has two terminals: the grounded outer conductor, and the center conductor. A two-port network, of course, would have two connectors and three terminals. Two of the terminals are the center conductors of the two connectors, and the third terminal is ground (which is the same for both ports). We discuss two-port networks in the next section.

A typical one-port device is shown in Fig 1. It has two terminals comprising a single port. To analyze the circuit, we first calculate the conductance of R2, and add it to the admittance of C1. Next, we invert the admittance of the RC network (R2-C1) and add it to the impedance of L1. Next add that value to R1. This particular one-port network is the start of a low-pass filter. The 50-ohm resistor (R2) is a simple model of, say, a resonant antenna. The impedance across the input terminals, which we will calculate, is the impedance that a transmitter would see when connected to the input port. We are not restricted to low-pass filters. For example, instead of a 50-ohm resistor, we could have used a series RC circuit as a model of the input of an FET amplifier. Then we could use inductance and capacitance to match the FET to a 50-ohm input.

ONEP: A SIMPLE ANALYSIS PROGRAM

Fig 2 shows a BASIC program, ONEP (short for one-port), that can be used to analyze nearly any one-port network. We will examine the program and use it to analyze the one-port network in Fig 1.

ONEP was written on an IBM PC. It does not contain any unusual statements that other versions of BASIC might not understand. This makes the program more "transportable" than it might otherwise be. Let's dig into the source listing.

Line 110 sets two constants that should be familiar to you. For non-IBM users, ignore the "#" designator that follows the numbers. Lines 120 and 130 input the desired frequency for analysis in GHz and convert it to radians-per-second.

Lines 140-160 input the type of the first component (resistive, capacitive or inductive). The component type (in C$) is then checked to make sure it is a valid input. Checking all input for validity is a basic rule of programming. In fact, a good program will take into account any possible input data, especially wrong data. Another example of good programming style is line 140, which specifies the desired user response. It does not leave the user wondering what the program wants. Too many frustrated users have walked away from computers thinking, "Boy, I just don't know how to use computers," when it is really the programmer who doesn't know how to write user-friendly software.

Lines 170-190 input the value of the first component and convert it to fundamental units (ohms, henrys or farads). By the way, negative values are allowed, and although such components cannot be realized (at least not with passive components), they can be interesting to examine. Line 195 clears the real and imaginary parts of the impedance prior to the initial number crunching.

Lines 200-220 (which are skipped over the first time through) check variable ZY$. If ZY$ equals "Y" then RE and IM contain the real and imaginary parts of the admittance, not the impedance. If that is the case, the admittance is inverted to give us the impedance. Lines 300-330 calculate the impedance of the next component and add it to RE and IM. Control then transfers to line 600, which outputs the results (if desired) and asks for the next component.

The first component always has its impedance (not its admittance) calculated. But suppose we want to connect the second component in parallel with the first? Lines 620-670 input the value for the second (and subsequent) components. Line 680 determines whether the second or subsequent components will be connected in series or parallel. If you want to connect the next component in series, the program jumps to line 200 and adds the appropriate impedance. If you want to connect it in parallel, however, the program jumps to line 400. Here, it converts RE and IM to admittance (if they aren't already), and calculates the admittance of the new component and adds that admittance to RE and IM. It also sets ZY$ to "Y" so the program now knows

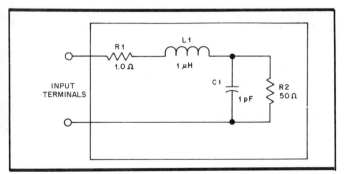

Fig 1—A one-port network has a single input port, with two terminals, one of which is ground. Any number of resistors, inductors and capacitors can be connected inside the one-port network.

```
100 REM CALCULATE THE Z OR Y PARAMETERS OF A ONE-PORT
110 PI=3.1415926# : RD=57.2957795#
120 INPUT "ENTER FREQUENCY (GHZ) = ", W
130 W=2E+09*PI*W
140 INPUT "ENTER FIRST COMPONENT (R/L/C) = ", C$
150 IF C$="R" GOTO 170
151 IF C$="L" GOTO 170
152 IF C$="C" GOTO 170
160 PRINT "PLEASE INPUT R OR L OR C." : GOTO 140
170 INPUT "ENTER COMPONENT VALUE (OHMS/NANOHENRIES/PICOFARADS) = ", VL
180 IF C$="L" THEN VL=VL*1E-09
190 IF C$="C" THEN VL=VL*1E-12
195 RE=0 : IM=0 : GOTO 300
200 IF ZY$="Z" THEN GOTO 300
210 REM INVERT ADMITTANCE TO GET IMPEDANCE
220 DE=RE*RE+IM*IM : RE=RE/DE : IM=-IM/DE
300 ZY$="Z"
310 IF C$="R" THEN RE=RE+VL
320 IF C$="L" THEN IM=IM+W*VL
330 IF C$="C" THEN IM=IM-1/(W*VL)
340 GOTO 600
400 IF ZY$="Y" THEN GOTO 500
410 REM INVERT IMPEDANCE TO GET ADMITTANCE
420 DE=RE*RE+IM*IM : RE=RE/DE : IM=-IM/DE
500 ZY$="Y"
510 IF C$="R" THEN RE=RE+1/VL
520 IF C$="L" THEN IM=IM-1/(W*VL)
530 IF C$="C" THEN IM=IM+W*VL
600 INPUT "PRINT RESULT (Y/N) ? ", YN$
610 IF YN$="Y" GOTO 900
620 INPUT "ENTER NEXT COMPONENT (R/L/C) = ", C$
630 IF C$="R" GOTO 650
631 IF C$="L" GOTO 650
632 IF C$="C" GOTO 650
640 PRINT "PLEASE INPUT R OR L OR C." : GOTO 620
650 INPUT "ENTER VALUE (OHMS/NANOHENRIES/PICOFARADS) = ", VL
660 IF C$="L" THEN VL=VL*1E-09
670 IF C$="C" THEN VL=VL*1E-12
680 INPUT "CONNECT IN SERIES OR PARALLEL (S/P) ? ", SP$
690 IF SP$="S" GOTO 200
700 IF SP$="P" GOTO 400
710 PRINT "PLEASE INPUT S OR P." : GOTO 680
900 IF ZY$="Z" GOTO 920
910 DE=RE*RE+IM*IM : RE=RE/DE : IM=-IM/DE : ZY$="Z"
920 PM$="+" : IF IM<0 THEN PM$="-"
930 PRINT : PRINT "IMPEDANCE = ";RE;" ";PM$;" J ";ABS(IM)" OHMS"
940 AN = ATN(IM/RE)
950 IF AN<=0 THEN GOTO 980
960 IF RE+IM<0 THEN AN=AN-PI
970 GOTO 990
980 IF RE<0 THEN AN=AN+PI
990 AN=AN*RD : MG=SQR(RE*RE+IM*IM)
1000 PRINT "IMPEDANCE = ";MG;" OHMS AT ";AN;" DEGREES."
1010 PRINT : INPUT "CONTINUE (Y/N) ? ", YN$
1020 IF YN$="N" THEN STOP
1030 GOTO 620
```

Fig 2—A BASIC program to calculate the one-port Z parameter (the impedance) of nearly any RLC circuit.

that RE and IM represent admittance rather than an impedance.

When describing a program, always include a numeric example. This makes it easy to check that all the equations are typed in correctly. We will use the circuit in Fig 1 at a frequency of 1 GHz as an example. For the first element, type in R. Then when asked for its value, specify 50. If you print out the current result, it should be $50 + j0$ ohms, and 50 ohms at 0 degrees. For the next component, specify C with a value of 1. This time, ONEP will ask if you want it connected in series or parallel. Type in P for parallel. Now, if you print out the result, it will be $45.5 - j14.3$ ohms (rounded to the nearest tenth) and 47.7 ohms at -17.4 degrees. Next specify L with a value of 1, connected in series. The result should be $45.5 - j8.0$ ohms and 46.2 ohms at -10.0 degrees. When we connect the 1-ohm resistor in series (our model of a lossy inductor), the result is $46.5 - j8.0$ ohms and 47.2 ohms at -9.8 degrees. The circuit in Fig 1 has now been analyzed.

ONEP is not meant to be the last word in one-port network analysis. For example, the program could be expanded to analyze a one-port network at a series of frequencies instead of just one. Also, the circuit information could be read in from a disk file. This would allow you to analyze the same circuit repeatedly, each time making a small change in one or two components. This allows you to "tweak" the circuit response. It is even possible to let the computer do the tweaking automatically.

Graphics would be another valuable addition to ONEP. Lists of numbers contain useful information, but a graph is often easier to understand.

These ideas could easily form the basis for a number of weekend software projects.

Z and Y Parameters

Let's review how we analyze one-port networks. We will do so in terms of Z parameters and Y parameters. It may seem complicated, but the transition to two-port networks will easily follow.

In Fig 3A we have two one-port networks. They could contain one component, such as a resistor or capacitor, or they could be complex circuits such as Fig 1. The important point is that both one-port networks have only two terminals. All of the components, whatever they may be, can be considered to be inside the "black box." When we want to combine two one-port networks in series, we calculate the Z parameter (impedance) of each one-port network and add them together. The result is the Z parameter of the network in Fig 3B. (The one-ports of Fig 3A are combined as shown by the heavy dark lines.)

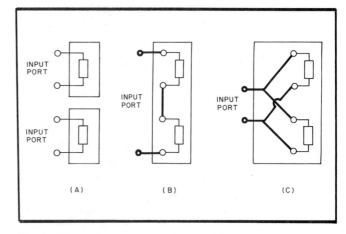

Fig 3—There are two ways to combine one-port networks. We can add the Z parameters of the two networks, as shown in 3A, to find the Z parameters of the one port network in 3B. Or we can add the one-port Y parameters to find the Y parameter of the one-port network in 3C.

When we want to combine one-port networks in parallel, as shown in Fig 3C, we calculate the Y parameter (admittance) of each network and add them together to obtain the Y parameter of the resulting circuit.

Keep Fig 3 and the previous discussion in mind because we will use these ideas again when we examine two-port networks.

We often like to calculate the reflection coefficient of a one-port network. The equations are summarized in Table 3. Note that the reflection coefficient is referred to as an "S parameter." The equations are very similar, except the inverse is indicated by a power of minus one. The reason for the unusual notation is to ensure the same equations will work when analyzing two-port networks.

Table 3
Conversion Between Z, Y and S Parameters

From \ To	Z	Y	S
Z	Z	Z^{-1}	$(Z - Z_0)(Z + Z_0)^{-1}$
Y	Y^{-1}	Y	$(Y_0 - Y)(Y_0 + Y)^{-1}$
S	$Z_0(1 + S)(1 - S)^{-1}$	$Y_0(1 - S)(1 + S)^{-1}$	S

(Z_0 = system impedance, almost always 50 ohms. $Y_0 = 1/Z_0$)

TWO-PORT ANALYSIS

If we know the current flowing through a one-port network and we want to calculate the voltage across its two terminals, we use the network's Z parameter in Ohm's Law: $V = ZI$. Correspondingly, if we know the voltage and want the current, we use the Y parameter in Ohm's Law: $I = YV$, where Y is the inverse of Z. Wouldn't it be nice if we could do the same thing for two-port networks?

Let's take a look at the two-port network in Fig 4. Rather than one voltage and one current, we have two voltages and two currents. What shall we use for Z parameters? When we multiply a Z parameter by the network's current, its voltage is the result. Let's apply power to port 1 (that is, I_1 equals some value in amps). At the same time, we will make sure that there is no current flowing into port 2, by leaving its terminals open. The current flowing into port 1, and its associated voltage (just like in a one-port), are proportional. The constant of proportionality is called Z_{11}. If we now measure the voltage across port 2 caused by the current flowing into port 1, we will find that it too is proportional. This constant of proportionality is called Z_{21}.

Summarizing what we have so far:

$$V_1 = Z_{11} \times I_1 \qquad V_2 = Z_{21} \times I_1$$

We have two equations, and in each one the current multiplied by the Z parameter equals the voltage. The only problem is that we haven't considered the possibility of current flowing into port 2. Let's say a current, I_2, is flowing into port 2, and no current is flowing into port 1 ($I_1 = 0$). As before, the voltage across port 2 and port 1 are proportional to the current flowing into port 2. This time the constants of proportionality are called Z_{22} and Z_{12} respectively.

What happens if we have both a current, I_1, on port 1 and another current, I_2, on port 2? We add the voltages caused by I_1 and I_2 together:

$$V_1 = Z_{11} \times I_1 + Z_{12} \times I_2$$
$$V_2 = Z_{21} \times I_1 + Z_{22} \times I_2$$

This is Ohm's Law for two-port networks. To make things simpler, let's see if we can get the equations to look like Ohm's Law, too.

First, put all the Z parameters into a matrix:

$$\mathbf{Z} = \begin{pmatrix} Z_{11} & Z_{12} \\ Z_{21} & Z_{22} \end{pmatrix}$$

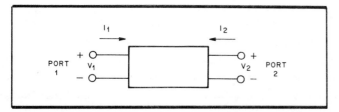

Fig 4—A two-port network has two voltages and two currents.

A matrix can be any size. This particular **Z** matrix is called a 2 by 2 matrix (the number of rows by the number of columns, commonly written 2×2). If you have ever used arrays of numbers in a computer, you will see that a matrix is an array with two dimensions. We use a boldface **Z** to indicate a matrix.

Next, we will convert the voltages and currents into vectors. A vector is an array with only one dimension:

$$\mathbf{V} = \begin{pmatrix} V_1 \\ V_2 \end{pmatrix} \qquad \mathbf{I} = \begin{pmatrix} I_1 \\ I_2 \end{pmatrix}$$

A vector can also be thought of as a 2×1 matrix. Again, we are using a boldface **V** and **I** to indicate that we are dealing with more than just a single number. Now we can write our Z parameter equations as:

$$\mathbf{V} = \mathbf{Z} \times \mathbf{I}$$

This looks like Ohm's Law, but what does $\mathbf{Z} \times \mathbf{I}$ mean? Let's expand the matrix equation and see.

$$\begin{pmatrix} V_1 \\ V_2 \end{pmatrix} = \begin{pmatrix} Z_{11} & Z_{12} \\ Z_{21} & Z_{22} \end{pmatrix} \times \begin{pmatrix} I_1 \\ I_2 \end{pmatrix}$$

Say we want to calculate V_1 and we have values for the Z parameters and the two currents. First, put a left hand finger on Z_{11} and a right hand finger on I_1 and say, "Z_{11} times I_1." Now move your left hand finger horizontally to Z_{12} and your right hand finger down to I_2 and say, "plus Z_{12} times I_2." That's the equation for V_1! To get the equation for V_2, start on Z_{21} (times I_1), then move to Z_{22} (times I_2).

What we have done illustrates the general rule for multiplying any two matrices, regardless of how large they are. In short, for the first matrix (in this case, **Z**) go across each row, and for the second matrix, go down each column (**I** has only one column here), multiplying and adding as you go. We will work through more examples later.

There is one important difference between Ohm's Law and $\mathbf{V} = \mathbf{Z} \times \mathbf{I}$. For Ohm's Law, we can also write $V = I \times Z$. We can't do this with the matrix equation. The reason will be easy to see if you write out $\mathbf{V} = \mathbf{I} \times \mathbf{Z}$. The rule for matrix multiplication simply won't work.

Suppose we know the voltages, V_1 and V_2, and we want to calculate the currents, I_1 and I_2. We would like a matrix equation that looks like **I** equals a matrix multiplied by **V**. To make the equation look like Ohm's Law, let's call the matrix **Y**. For Ohm's Law, $Y = 1/Z$ (Y is the inverse of Z). As it turns out, it is quite simple to calculate the inverse of a 2×2 matrix. If we take the inverse of the **Z** matrix we have the required **Y** matrix and our new form of Ohm's Law is:

$$\mathbf{I} = \mathbf{Y} \times \mathbf{V}$$

where $\mathbf{Y} = \mathbf{Z}^{-1}$

As you've probably guessed by now, the key to two-port network analysis is to calculate the Z parameter matrix (also known as the impedance matrix) or, equivalently, the Y parameter matrix (also known as the admittance matrix). Once we know one, we can calculate the other by matrix

Table 4
Two-Port Z and Y Parameters

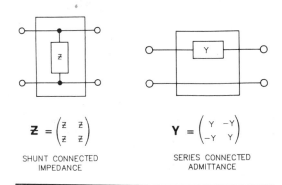

$$\mathbf{Z} = \begin{pmatrix} z & z \\ z & z \end{pmatrix} \qquad \mathbf{Y} = \begin{pmatrix} Y & -Y \\ -Y & Y \end{pmatrix}$$

SHUNT CONNECTED IMPEDANCE   SERIES CONNECTED ADMITTANCE

Table 5
The Four Basic Functions for Matrix Arithmetic

ADDITION

$$\begin{pmatrix} a_{11} & a_{12} \\ a_{21} & a_{22} \end{pmatrix} + \begin{pmatrix} b_{11} & b_{12} \\ b_{21} & b_{22} \end{pmatrix} = \begin{pmatrix} c_{11} & c_{12} \\ c_{21} & c_{22} \end{pmatrix}$$

$$c_{11} = a_{11} + b_{11}$$
$$c_{12} = a_{12} + b_{12}$$
$$c_{21} = a_{21} + b_{21}$$
$$c_{22} = a_{22} + b_{22}$$

SUBTRACTION

$$\begin{pmatrix} a_{11} & a_{12} \\ a_{21} & a_{22} \end{pmatrix} - \begin{pmatrix} b_{11} & b_{12} \\ b_{21} & b_{22} \end{pmatrix} = \begin{pmatrix} c_{11} & c_{12} \\ c_{21} & c_{22} \end{pmatrix}$$

$$c_{11} = a_{11} - b_{11}$$
$$c_{12} = a_{12} - b_{12}$$
$$c_{21} = a_{21} - b_{21}$$
$$c_{22} = a_{22} - b_{22}$$

MULTIPLICATION

$$\begin{pmatrix} a_{11} & a_{12} \\ a_{21} & a_{22} \end{pmatrix} \times \begin{pmatrix} b_{11} & b_{12} \\ b_{21} & b_{22} \end{pmatrix} = \begin{pmatrix} c_{11} & c_{12} \\ c_{21} & c_{22} \end{pmatrix}$$

$$c_{11} = a_{11} \times b_{11} + a_{12} \times b_{21}$$
$$c_{12} = a_{11} \times b_{12} + a_{12} \times b_{22}$$
$$c_{21} = a_{21} \times b_{11} + a_{22} \times b_{21}$$
$$c_{22} = a_{21} \times b_{12} + a_{22} \times b_{22}$$

INVERSION

$$\begin{pmatrix} a_{11} & a_{12} \\ a_{21} & a_{22} \end{pmatrix}^{-1} = \begin{pmatrix} c_{11} & c_{12} \\ c_{21} & c_{22} \end{pmatrix}$$

$$c_{11} = a_{22} / D$$
$$c_{12} = -a_{12} / D$$
$$c_{21} = -a_{21} / D$$
$$c_{22} = a_{11} / D$$
$$D = a_{11} \times a_{22} - a_{12} \times a_{21}$$

inversion. Notice that the equations in Table 3 still hold even though we are now working with 2×2 impedance matrices instead of one-port impedances.

Before we can do any number crunching with **Z** or **Y** matrices, we need to know how to calculate the numbers within them. For starters, let's examine a one-port network. It could contain a resistor or a capacitor or an RC circuit, and so forth. The important thing is that we have only two terminals to consider. Now take a two-port network. This can be visualized as an empty box with two coax connectors. There are two different ways we can connect our two-terminal device inside the two-port box. The obvious way is to connect one terminal to the center conductor of one connector and the other terminal to the center conductor of the other connector (connecting the device in series).

The second way to connect the two-terminal device within the "black box" is to short the center conductors of both coax connectors together, and connect one terminal of the device to the shorted center conductors, and the other to ground (connecting the device in shunt).

Table 4 shows the two-port Z parameters for a device connected in shunt and the Y parameters for a device connected in series. We don't show the Z parameters of a device connected in series because they don't exist. Recall that we can find the Z parameters by applying current to port 1, while leaving port 2 open. For a lumped element device connected in series with port 2 open, there is no way to get current to flow into port 1. A similar situation applies to Y parameters and devices connected in shunt.

Manipulating Matrices

Before we can start number crunching with the matrices, we must know how to add, subtract, multiply and invert them. Table 5 summarizes these four basic operations. Adding or subtracting matrices is done by adding or subtracting each element in each matrix. We have already seen how to multiply a 2×2 matrix by a 2×1 matrix (vector). Table 5 shows how to multiply 2×2 matrices. For each row/column pair we come up with one number in the resulting matrix. When multiplying two 2×2

matrices, we will have four row/column pairs, thus our answer will also be a 2×2 matrix. The fourth function, matrix inversion, is simple for a 2×2 matrix. The inversion operation can get quite complicated for larger matrices.

Let's check out an interesting property of an inverted matrix. Pick any four numbers (it is probably easiest to pick real numbers, but this will work just as well with complex numbers). Arrange them in a 2×2 matrix, and then invert the matrix using the rules in Table 5. Now multiply the inverted matrix by the original matrix, again, using the rules in Table 5. The answer will always be the same—the unit matrix. If there are no arithmetic errors, the answer matrix will have 1.0 in the top left corner and lower right corner. The other two numbers will be zero. Why is this called a unit matrix? When we multiply a real number by its inverse, we get 1.0. When we multiply a matrix by its inverse, we similarly get a unit matrix.

Keep in mind that the numbers in Table 5 can be complex, in which case we use the rules for addition and multiplication of complex numbers (like we did for one-port networks). We can now fill our matrices with Y and Z parameters and add them together. What happens if we add the Z parameters of two different two-port networks? When we added the Z parameters of two different one-port networks, we got the Z parameter of the one-port networks connected in series. The same thing happens with two-port networks. (See Fig 5B.) You may notice that Fig 5B looks a lot like Fig 3B. As an example of how to add Z parameters, the top two-port network in Fig 5B could be a capacitor connected in shunt, and the second two-port could be an inductor connected in shunt. Adding the Z parameter matrices would give you the Z parameters of a

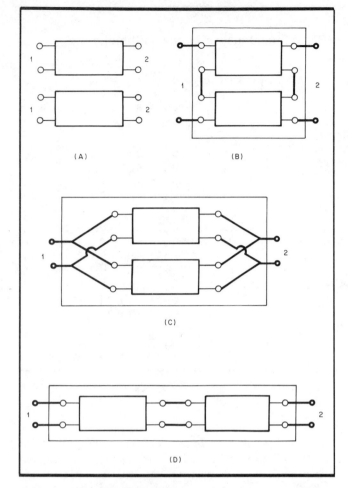

(A)

(B)

(C)

(D)

Fig 5—Adding the Z parameters of the two-port networks in 5A results in the Z parameters of the two-port networks connected in series, 5B. Adding their Y parameters results in the Y parameters of the parallel connection, 5C. Multiplying the ABCD parameters results in the ABCD parameters of the cascaded combination, 5D.

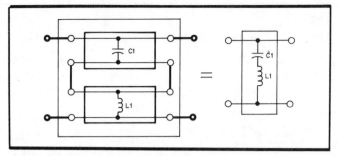

Fig 6—When the Z parameters of a shunt-connected capacitor and a shunt-connected inductor are added, we get the Z parameters of a series LC network connected in shunt.

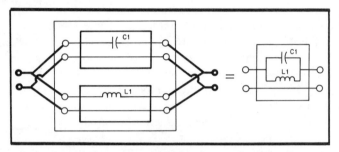

Fig 7—When the Y parameters of a series-connected inductor and a series-connected capacitor are added, we get the Y parameters of a parallel 2-port LC network connected in series.

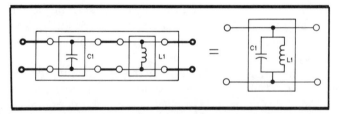

Fig 8—When the 2 × 2 ABCD matrices of two-port networks are multiplied, we get the ABCD parameters of the networks connected in cascade, in this case a shunt-connected parallel LC circuit.

series LC circuit connected in shunt. See Fig 6.

As we might suspect, adding the Y parameters of two two-port networks results in the Y parameters of the networks connected in parallel. This is illustrated in Fig 5C, which is similar to Fig 3C. An example is shown in Fig 7. Here we have the Y parameters of a series-connected capacitor and a series-connected inductor. By adding their Y parameters, we get the Y parameters of a two-port network connected in parallel (see Fig 5C). After we untangle the wiring of the left half of Fig 7, we see that it is the same as the right half, a parallel LC circuit connected in series (got that?).

If, instead, we want to analyze a parallel LC circuit connected in shunt (rather than connected in series), it would be nice if we could cascade the two-port networks as in Fig 5D. But, this cannot be done with one-port networks. With two-port networks we calculate the ABCD parameters. (It takes real imagination to come up with some of these parameter names!) Once the ABCD parameters are calculated for each network, we multiply the ABCD matrices, which results in the ABCD parameters of the two-port networks cascaded.

When adding Z or Y parameters, a quick check of the rules for matrix addition will show that the order in which the matrices are added does not matter. We will get the same result either way. With ABCD matrices, we will, in general, obtain different results depending on the order in which we multiply them. If a two-port network, A, is connected first, and a two-port network, B, is second, then be sure to multiply matrix A × matrix B and not the other way around!

Cascading two-port networks is illustrated in Fig 8. First we calculate the 2 × 2 ABCD matrix of the shunt-connected capacitor, C1. Then calculate the 2 × 2 ABCD matrix of the shunt-connected inductor, L1. Then we multiply the two matrices together (using the rules of Table 5) and we have the ABCD parameters of a shunt-connected parallel LC circuit.

Table 6

Conversion Between Z, Y, S and ABCD Parameters

From / To	Z	Y	S
$\begin{pmatrix} AB \\ CD \end{pmatrix}$	$A = \dfrac{Z_{11}}{Z_{21}}$	$A = -\dfrac{Y_{22}}{Y_{21}}$	$A = \dfrac{[(1 + S_{11})(1 - S_{22}) + S_{12}\,S_{21}]}{2S_{21}}$
	$B = \dfrac{Z_{11}\,Z_{22}}{Z_{21}} - Z_{12}$	$B = -\dfrac{1}{Y_{21}}$	$B = \dfrac{Z_0\,[(1 + S_{11})(1 + S_{22}) - S_{12}\,S_{21}]}{2S_{21}]}$
	$C = \dfrac{1}{Z_{21}}$	$C = -\dfrac{Y_{11}\,Y_{22}}{Y_{21}} + Y_{12}$	$C = \dfrac{[(1 - S_{11})(1 - S_{22}) - S_{12}\,S_{21}]}{2S_{21}\,Z_0}$
	$D = \dfrac{Z_{22}}{Z_{21}}$	$D = -\dfrac{Y_{11}}{Y_{21}}$	$D = \dfrac{[(1 - S_{11})(1 + S_{22}) + S_{12}\,S_{21}]}{2S_{21}}$

To / From	Z	Y	S
$\begin{pmatrix} AB \\ CD \end{pmatrix}$	$Z_{11} = \dfrac{A}{C}$	$Y_{11} = \dfrac{D}{B}$	$S_{11} = \dfrac{A + \dfrac{B}{Z_0} - C\,Z_0 - D}{A + \dfrac{B}{Z_0} + C\,Z_0 + D}$
	$Z_{12} = \dfrac{AD}{C} - B$	$Y_{12} = -\dfrac{AD}{B} + C$	$S_{12} = 2\,\dfrac{AD - BC}{A + \dfrac{B}{Z_0} + C\,Z_0 + D}$
	$Z_{21} = \dfrac{1}{C}$	$Y_{21} = -\dfrac{1}{B}$	$S_{21} = \dfrac{2}{A + \dfrac{B}{Z_0} + C\,Z_0 + D}$
	$Z_{22} = \dfrac{D}{C}$	$Y_{22} = \dfrac{A}{B}$	$S_{22} = -\dfrac{A - \dfrac{B}{Z_0} + C\,Z_0 - D}{A + \dfrac{B}{Z_0} + C\,Z_0 + D}$

How do we calculate the ABCD parameters? If we have the Y or Z parameters, it is a simple matter. Just refer to Table 6 for the equations to convert from one to the other.

There are about a dozen different kinds of circuit parameters, all with different characteristics. So far, we have examined Y, Z and ABCD parameters. The last parameters we'll look at are called S parameters, also known as scattering parameters. S parameters are important in microwave work. The computer itself really doesn't need them, but S parameters are useful because they are easily measured and understood.

Just like Y, Z and ABCD parameters, S parameters for a two-port network take the form of a 2 × 2 matrix. S_{11} is the reflection coefficient of port 1, when a dummy load (50 ohms) is connected to port 2. Likewise, S_{22} is the reflection coefficient of port 2 when a dummy load is connected to port 1. S_{21} is the forward gain (or loss) into a matched load, and S_{12} is the loss in the reverse direc-

tion. S parameters are always measured (and calculated) with both ports terminated in a reflectionless load. If we are working in a 50-ohm system, the reflectionless load will be a 50-ohm resistor.

For example, in a given microwave amplifier we would like to see S_{11} to be as small as possible (which means very little power is reflected from the amplifier input), and S_{21} to be as large as possible, as long as the amplifier gain (S_{21}) doesn't get so large that it starts oscillating. For a bandpass filter, we would like to see S_{21} equal to 1.0 (0.0 dB) in the pass band, and less than, say, 0.01 (−40.0 dB) in the stop band. It is usually most convenient to look at S parameter magnitudes in dB. Of course, S parameters can be complex, so we can calculate the angle of an S parameter too.

It turns out that S parameters are relatively easy to measure. Although the test equipment required is too expensive for most budgets, many microwave transistors come with S parameter data on their data sheets. We can program the computer to convert the S parameter data to the desired parameters.

Table 6 shows how to convert between S parameters and ABCD parameters. Table 3 shows how to convert between S parameters and Y or Z parameters. Even though it may not be readily apparent, Table 3 works for 2×2 matrices as well as the one-port networks we originally used it for. To use the equations for matrices, let each Y, Z and S be a matrix, and be sure the equations contain the constant 1.0 (use a unit matrix). Where the equations have a constant other than 1.0 (eg, Z_0 or Y_0), use a unit matrix with that constant substituted for the 1.0s on the diagonal. Then apply the four basic functions for matrices listed in Table 5 and make the conversion. There is an example in the program coming up.

We have been working with matrix equations like $V = Z \times I$ and $Y = Z^{-1}$. In terms of matrices, these equations are simple. If we start converting matrix equations to equations in terms of regular numbers, things will get complicated. If you want a vivid example, just try writing the matrix equation to convert from S parameters to Z parameters, in terms of real numbers. It will be a real mess.

In order to keep our programs simple, we will write subroutines or procedures to perform matrix multiplication and inversion. We can call these subroutines whenever we need them. The subroutines will take care of the actual numbers and we can write our program in terms of simpler matrix equations.

There is just one catch. We chose BASIC for the previous program because BASIC is available on just about any computer. Unfortunately, only the most advanced forms of BASIC have full subroutine capability. We will use another language for the next example. Don't worry, it will be easy to follow for those with even a moderate knowledge of BASIC.

TWOP: A PROGRAM FOR ANALYSIS OF TWO-PORT NETWORKS

Most microwave software is now written in FORTRAN, Pascal or C. Of the three languages, Pascal is most widely available for microcomputers. We will use Pascal for our next example. You will need a Pascal compiler for your computer if you want to type this listing and run the program. *The ARRL Microwave Software Diskette* for the IBM® PC includes a compiled version of the program, which will run from DOS. The example program will analyze the circuit in Fig 9. The required inputs are the FET S parameters, the source impedance, Z, and the gate admittance, Y. The program will output the S parameters of the amplifier.

The program we will use to analyze our circuit, TWOP (for two-port analysis), is shown in Fig 10. The program name is followed by "(INPUT,OUTPUT)," indicating that READ statements will take input from the keyboard and write statements will send output to the screen (there are other possibilities). The next line is a comment, which in BASIC programs, is set off by a REM statement. In Pascal, a portion of a line, or several lines may be set off for comments by means of braces {like these}.

The next portion of the program defines data types. Both Pascal and BASIC have a big disadvantage in that they have no COMPLEX data type (as there is in FORTRAN). Pascal can work around the problem by creating a COMPLEX data type. Then the programmer can write procedures (FORTRAN programmers call them subroutines) to do things such as complex multiplication. The TYPE section of TWOP creates the complex data type. The complex data type is defined here as a RECORD with two parts, Re and Im (for real and imaginary). A RECORD is similar to an array, except that subscripts are not used to access its elements. If we want to access the real part of a complex record say, Z, we use "Z.Re". If we want to access the imaginary part, we use "Z.Im". When we want to access the whole record (say, to pass it to another procedure), we use "Z" by itself.

The second data type defined in this section is Matrix. Matrix is a 2×2 array of Complex, used to store two-port parameters. If we want to access the Complex number stored in the $_{21}$ element of a Matrix, say Mat_a, use "Mat_a[2,1]". Pascal uses square brackets for array subscripts. You may be familiar with BASIC's and FORTRAN's parentheses for array subscripts. To access only the real part of the $_{21}$ element, use "Mat_a[2,1].Re".

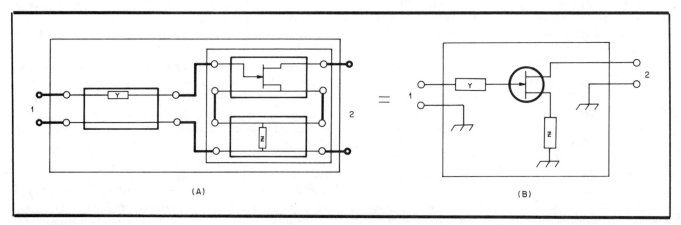

Fig 9—The amplifier to be analyzed by the example program. The Z and Y elements, and the S parameters of the FET may be adjusted.

Fig 10—A Pascal program is used to illustrate two-port network analysis. This program is set up to analyze an FET amplifier with source feedback and an input matching impedance. By changing only the main procedure (which is at the end of the program), other circuits can be analyzed.

```pascal
PROGRAM TWOP(INPUT,OUTPUT);   {Analyze a circuit using two-ports.}

  TYPE
    Complex = RECORD
                 Re : REAL;      {Real part}
                 Im : REAL;      {Imaginary part}
              END;
    Matrix = ARRAY[1..2,1..2] OF Complex;   {Used for two-port parameters.}

  VAR
    Mat_a, Mat_b : Matrix;  {Store results here.}
    Z,Y          : Complex; {Impedance, Admittance of circuit elements.}
    I,J          : INTEGER; {Loop indices.}
    M_temp       : Matrix;  {Temporary storage.}
    C_temp       : Complex; {Ditto.}

  PROCEDURE C_add(VAR C1,C2,C3:Complex);   { C1+C2 --> C3 }
    BEGIN
      C3.Re := C1.Re+C2.Re;   C3.Im := C1.Im+C2.Im
    END;

  PROCEDURE C_sub(VAR C1,C2,C3:Complex);   { C1-C2 --> C3 }
    BEGIN
      C3.Re := C1.Re-C2.Re;   C3.Im := C1.Im-C2.Im
    END;

  PROCEDURE C_mult(VAR C1,C2,C3:Complex);   { C1*C2 --> C3 }
    VAR Temp : REAL;
    BEGIN
      Temp := C1.Re*C2.Re - C1.Im*C2.Im; {Real part of answer.}
      C3.Im := C1.Re*C2.Im + C1.Im*C2.Re;
      C3.Re := Temp
    END;

  PROCEDURE C_div(VAR C1,C2,C3:Complex);   { C1/C2 --> C3 }
    VAR Denom,Temp : REAL;
    BEGIN
      Denom := sqr(C2.Re) + sqr(C2.Im); {sqr = square, sqrt = square root.}
      Temp := (C1.Re*C2.Re + C1.Im*C2.Im) / Denom; {Real part of C3.}
      C3.Im := (C1.Im*C2.Re - C1.Re*C2.Im) / Denom;
      C3.Re := Temp
    END;

  PROCEDURE Mat_add(VAR M1,M2,M3:Matrix);   { M1+M2 --> M3 }
    BEGIN
      FOR I:=1 TO 2 DO FOR J:=1 TO 2 DO C_add(M1[I,J],M2[I,J],M3[I,J])
    END;

  PROCEDURE Mat_mult(VAR M1,M2,M3:Matrix);   { M1*M2 --> M3 }
    VAR M_temp : Matrix;  C_temp : Complex;  I,J,K : INTEGER;
    BEGIN
      FOR I:=1 TO 2 DO FOR J:=1 TO 2 DO BEGIN   { Calculate M3[I,J] }
        M_temp[I,J].Re := 0.0; M_temp[I,J].Im := 0.0;
        FOR K:=1 TO 2 DO BEGIN
          C_mult(M1[I,K],M2[K,J],C_temp);
          C_add(C_temp,M_temp[I,J],M_temp[I,J])
        END   {K loop.}
      END; {I and J loops.}
      M3 := M_temp
    END;
```

Fig 10—Continued on next page

```
PROCEDURE Mat_inv(VAR M1,M2:Matrix);   { M1**-1 --> M2 }
  VAR Det,C_temp : Complex;
  BEGIN
    C_temp := M1[1,1];  M2[1,1] := M1[2,2];  M2[2,2] := C_temp;
    M2[1,2].Re := -M1[1,2].Re;  M2[1,2].Im := -M1[1,2].Im;
    M2[2,1].Re := -M1[2,1].Re;  M2[2,1].Im := -M1[2,1].Im;
    {Get the determinant.}
    C_mult(M2[1,1],M2[2,2],C_temp);  C_mult(M2[1,2],M2[2,1],Det);
    C_sub(C_temp,Det,Det);
    {Divide each element of the matrix by Det.}
    C_div(M2[1,1],Det,M2[1,1]);   C_div(M2[1,2],Det,M2[1,2]);
    C_div(M2[2,1],Det,M2[2,1]);   C_div(M2[2,2],Det,M2[2,2])
  END;

PROCEDURE Conn_shunt(VAR M1:Matrix);
  BEGIN   {Connect Z in shunt, return the two-port Z-parameters in M1.}
    FOR I:=1 TO 2 DO FOR J:=1 TO 2 DO M1[I,J] := Z
  END;

PROCEDURE Conn_series(VAR M1:Matrix);
  BEGIN   {Connect Y in series and return the Y-parameters in M1.}
    M1[1,1] := Y;   M1[2,2] := Y;
    M1[1,2].Re := -Y.Re;   M1[1,2].Im := -Y.Im;
    M1[2,1] := M1[1,2]
  END;

PROCEDURE S_to_Z(VAR M1:Matrix); {Convert S parameters in M1 to Z parameters.}
  BEGIN   {Put S-1 into M_temp and invert it.  Mult. the whole thing by
           -50.0 Ohms later to take care of the sign.}
    M_temp := M1;
    M_temp[1,1].Re := M1[1,1].Re-1.0;  M_temp[2,2].Re := M1[2,2].Re-1.0;
    Mat_inv(M_temp,M_temp);
    {Now change M1 to 1+S}
    M1[1,1].Re := M1[1,1].Re+1.0;   M1[2,2].Re := M1[2,2].Re+1.0;
    Mat_mult(M1,M_temp,M1);
    {Now multiply by Zo = 50 Ohms.}
    FOR I:=1 TO 2 DO FOR J:=1 TO 2 DO BEGIN
      M1[I,J].Re := -50.0*M1[I,J].Re;   M1[I,J].Im := -50.0*M1[I,J].Im
    END
  END;

PROCEDURE Z_to_ABCD(VAR M1:Matrix); {Convert Z param in M1 to ABCD param.}
  BEGIN   {Invert Z21 to get C.}
    C_temp.Re := 1.0;  C_temp.Im := 0.0;
    C_div(C_temp,M1[2,1],M1[2,1]);    {C is done.}
    C_mult(M1[2,1],M1[1,1],M1[1,1]);  {A is done.}
    C_mult(M1[1,1],M1[2,2],C_temp);
    C_sub(C_temp,M1[1,2],M1[1,2]);    {B is done.}
    C_mult(M1[2,1],M1[2,2],M1[2,2])   {D is done.}
  END;

PROCEDURE Y_to_ABCD(VAR M1:Matrix); {Convert Y param in M1 to ABCD param.}
  BEGIN   {Change some signs.}
    M1[1,2].Re := -M1[1,2].Re;  M1[1,2].Im := -M1[1,2].Im;
    M1[2,1].Re := -M1[2,1].Re;  M1[2,1].Im := -M1[2,1].Im;
    {Do a Z to ABCD and then swap some elements...}
    Z_to_ABCD(M1);
    C_temp := M1[1,1]; M1[1,1] := M1[2,2];  M1[2,2] := C_temp;
    C_temp := M1[2,1]; M1[2,1] := M1[1,2];  M1[1,2] := C_temp
  END;
```

Fig 10—Continued on next page

```
PROCEDURE ABCD_to_Z(VAR M1:Matrix); {Convert ABCD param in M1 to Z param.}
  BEGIN
    Z_to_ABCD(M1);  {This will get the job done!}
  END;

PROCEDURE Z_to_S(VAR M1:Matrix); {Convert Z parameters in M1 to S param.}
  BEGIN  {Move M1 to M_temp, add Zo and invert it.}
    M_temp := M1;
    M_temp[1,1].Re := M1[1,1].Re+50.0;  M_temp[2,2].Re := M1[2,2].Re+50.0;
    Mat_inv(M_temp,M_temp);
    {Subtract Zo from M1.}
    M1[1,1].Re := M1[1,1].Re-50.0;  M1[2,2].Re := M1[2,2].Re-50.0;
    Mat_mult(M1,M_temp,M1)
  END;

PROCEDURE Mat_print(VAR M1:Matrix);  {Print out the numbers in M1.}
  BEGIN
    FOR I:=1 TO 2 DO BEGIN
      WRITELN;
      FOR J:=1 TO 2 DO WRITE('(',M1[I,J].Re:7:3,',',M1[I,J].Im:7:3,')  ');
    END;
    WRITELN
  END;

PROCEDURE Mat_get(VAR M1:Matrix); {Ask user for matrix data.}
  BEGIN
    WRITELN; WRITELN('Input real followed by imaginary and press return.');
    FOR I:=1 TO 2 DO FOR J:=1 TO 2 DO BEGIN
      WRITE('Mat[',I:1,',',J:1,'] = ');  READLN(M1[I,J].Re,M1[I,J].Im)
    END;
    WRITELN; WRITELN('The following numbers were typed in...');
    Mat_print(M1)
  END;

BEGIN {Main}
  WRITELN; WRITELN('Input S-parameters of FET.');
  Mat_get(Mat_a);
  S_to_Z(Mat_a);

  WRITELN; WRITE('Input source feedback impedance (real,imag., Ohms) = ');
  READLN(Z.Re,Z.Im);
  Conn_shunt(Mat_b);

  Mat_add(Mat_a,Mat_b,Mat_b); {Mat_b now has Z param. of FET + source fdbk}
  Z_to_ABCD(Mat_b);

  WRITELN; WRITE('Input gate matching admittance (real,imag., mhos) = ');
  READLN(Y.Re,Y.Im);
  Conn_series(Mat_a);
  Y_to_ABCD(Mat_a);
  Mat_mult(Mat_a,Mat_b,Mat_a);

  WRITELN;  WRITELN('For source impedance = (',Z.Re:8:2,',',Z.Im:8:2,')');
            WRITELN('and gate admittance  = (',Y.Re:8:4,',',Y.Im:8:4,')');
  WRITELN;  WRITELN('The resulting circuit S parameters are:');
  ABCD_to_Z(Mat_a);
  Z_to_S(Mat_a);
  Mat_print(Mat_a)
END.
```

The next section, (VAR), declares several variables. The comments following each section describe the purpose of the variables. In addition, each variable name is descriptive of its use, a practice common in Pascal. The underline character, "_", aids readability of the variable names. Since this list of variable declarations is at the very beginning of the program, they are global. This means that every procedure, anywhere in the program, can use them. No FORTRAN "COMMON" statements are required.

A series of procedures follow, all of which are called by the main procedure. Since Pascal does not allow forward references (that is, calling a procedure prior to the procedure's location in the listing) except with special consideration, the main procedure is at the end of the listing. You might say Pascal programs start at the end.

Twenty-five lines before the end of the program, the main procedure starts with the line "BEGIN {Main}". The main procedure ends at the "END" statement. The period is used in Pascal to indicate the end of the entire program.

The first statement of the program, "WRITELN;" prints a blank line. Since the semicolon marks the end of a statement (much like a colon does in BASIC), a second statement can be added to the same line. The second statement here prompts the user for the S parameters of an FET. The next line calls procedure Mat_get. In Pascal, it is not necessary to use CALL or GOSUB. You reference the name of the procedure and it is executed. Mat_get, of course, prompts the user for numbers to fill up a matrix, in this case, the matrix Mat_a.

The next procedure reference is S_to_Z. It converts S parameters in Mat_a, to Z parameters.

The next section inputs the source feedback impedance. Two numbers are entered: the real part (Z.Re) and the imaginary part (Z.Im). This impedance is then connected in shunt inside a two-port network according to the rules in Table 4. This puts the Z parameters of the source impedance into Mat_a. Comparing the transistor and source impedance in Fig 9A with Fig 5B, we can see that we want to add the Z parameter matrices. The procedure Mat_add adds Mat_a (the source impedance) with Mat_b (the FET Z parameters) and puts the result back into Mat_b.

To complete the circuit, we want to cascade the FET/source impedance with the gate matching admittance. To cascade, Mat_b gets converted to ABCD parameters and the user is prompted for the gate matching admittance. The gate admittance is connected in series and Mat_a is loaded with the two-port Y parameters. The Y parameters are converted to ABCD parameters and Mat_a is multiplied by Mat_b (in that order!). The resulting ABCD parameters of the whole amplifier are placed back in Mat_a.

If we now wanted to cascade two identical amplifiers back to back, they could be analyzed simply by multiplying the ABCD parameters of the amplifier (in Mat_a) by themselves: "Mat_mult(Mat_a,Mat_a,Mat_a);". You can cascade any number of stages together.

As a last step, the user's data is printed out. This allows the user to make sure the correct data was entered. (This is an important rule of programming which, you may have noticed, was not used in ONEP.) Rather than converting directly from ABCD parameters to S parameters, it is easier (for the programmer) to convert to Z parameters and then to S parameters. This is permissible as long as the circuit has a path for current to flow to ground from both ports. Finally, the procedure Mat_print lets the user view the contents of Mat_a.

Procedure Details

The main procedure gives us a good overview of how TWOP operates without getting lost in too many details. It is however, interesting to dive into some of the procedures in detail. We will start with PROCEDURE Z_to_S.

It should be no surprise to find that Z_to_S converts Z parameters to S parameters. The section starts out with "PROCEDURE Z_to_S(VAR M1:Matrix);". The procedure is invoked in the main procedure with "Z_to_S(Mat_a);". This means that Mat_a is passed to Z_to_S. Anything that Z_to_S then does with M1 (which is defined to be matrix), it does with Mat_a. If we had used "Z_to_S(Mat_b);" in the main procedure, then anything Z_to_S did with M1 would be done with Mat_b. The VAR statement means that M1 can be changed by the procedure.

Z_to_S first moves a copy of M1 (that is, Mat_a), to M_temp, a global matrix to store temporary results, with the line "M_temp := M1;". The ":=" is the assignment operator in Pascal. It performs much the same function as "=" in BASIC and FORTRAN. Pascal reserves "=" for the Boolean operator (for example, IF A = B THEN...).

Next, Z_to_S adds 50.0 ohms to the 11 and 22 elements of M_temp (see the equation in Table 3). Since 50.0 ohms is a real value, we need only reference the real parts: M_temp[1,1].Re and M_temp[2,2].Re. Since Z + 50.0 ohms will need to be inverted, Mat_inv does the job.

The last two lines subtract 50.0 ohms from M1, and multiply M1 by M_temp, resulting in the S parameters. We made the point earlier that matrices are multiplied in a specific order. This is one of few situations where order does not matter.

Notice how simple matrix equations have led to simple software. If we had attempted this procedure by actually manipulating real numbers, we would now be hopelessly lost.

Three matrices are passed to procedure Mat_mult (as is done at the end of Z_to_S). The first two are multiplied and the result placed in the third. Inside Mat_mult, the matrices are known as M1, M2 and M3 respectively.

You will notice an extra VAR line in Mat_mult that is not present in Z_to_S. This VAR declares temporary storage variables. Since these variables are declared only within Mat_mult, Mat_mult is the only procedure that can use them. These are known as local variables. That they happen to have the same name as some global variables is of no importance to Mat_mult, since the local variables are completely independent of the global variables with the same name.

The result of the matrix multiplication is stored in the temporary matrix M_temp. We could put the result directly in M3 except that M3 might be the same as M1 or M2. In that case, placing the result in M3 would destroy part of M1 or M2 as we were using it. When we are finished with the matrix multiplication, M_temp is transferred to M3 and passed back to the calling procedure.

Mat_mult has three FOR loops. These are similar to BASIC FOR loops except the body of the loop (if it is more than one statement) is contained between a BEGIN and an END statement (rather than a FOR and NEXT statement). For nested loops, each BEGIN can be matched with its END in the same manner that open parentheses can be matched with close parentheses in equations. If the programmer is courteous, the body of each FOR loop will be easily identifiable.

Mat_mult was set up so that if you want to multiply, say, 3 × 3 matrices instead of 2 × 2 matrices, simply change the upper limit of each of the three loops from 2 to 3 (eg, change "FOR I: =1 TO 2 DO" to "FOR I: =1 TO 3 DO").

Mat_mult makes use of C_mult, a procedure that multiplies two complex numbers. C_mult stores the real part of the answer in a temporary variable while it calculates the imaginary part. This is necessary, again, in case C1 or C2 is the same as C3.

Improvements to TWOP

An important skill for writing software is the ability to look at a program critically and see what can be improved. We have taken some short cuts with TWOP to keep the listing as short as possible and still demonstrate the important points discussed in this chapter. One shortcut is the input and output of complex numbers, which is done in real and imaginary formats. It would be a good idea to change them to magnitude and phase angle. S parameters are probably best discussed in dB.

As the program stands, to analyze different circuits, the main procedure must be modified. TWOP could be set up so that circuit elements and the conversion between various parameters could be read from a disk file. That way, to change the circuit, only a file must be changed, not the program itself. If you really want to get fancy, set the program up so it can analyze a series of frequencies, instead of just one. As with ONEP, TWOP offers the makings of a number of good weekend software projects.

An Example: Using TWOP to Analyze a Simple Amplifier

We will end our discussion of TWOP with a numeric example. Consider an Avantek AT-8250 FET operating at 5.0 GHz. The S parameter data, taken from a data sheet and converted to real and imaginary components is:

$$S_{11} = -0.67 - j0.31$$
$$S_{12} = 0.11 - j0.03$$

$$S_{21} = 2.14 + j1.86$$
$$S_{22} = -0.17 - j0.31.$$

The source feedback is a parallel RC circuit with R = 5.0 ohms and C = 1.0 pF. Using ONEP, we find that the one-port Z parameter is $4.88 - j0.77$ ohms. The gate matching admittance is a 1.0 nH inductor connected in series, its impedance is $0.0 + j31.42$ ohms (again, using ONEP). The admittance is then $0.0 - j0.0318$ mhos.

Several Mat_print statements are scattered through the main procedure to help with program validation. At the start of the main procedure, the FET S parameters are typed in and then converted to Z parameters. A Mat_print statement was placed at this point giving:

$$Z_{11} = 18.702 - j12.664$$
$$Z_{12} = 5.001 - j4.277$$
$$Z_{21} = 157.534 + j44.315$$
$$Z_{22} = 44.796 - j24.990.$$

After the source feedback impedance is added, and the results converted to ABCD parameters:

$$A = 0.115 - j0.113$$
$$B = -7.103 - j3.547$$
$$C = 0.006 - j0.002$$
$$D = 0.246 - j0.224.$$

After multiplying the ABCD parameters by the ABCD parameters of the matching inductor, we find:

$$A = 0.163 + j\ 0.067$$
$$B = -0.044 + j4.179$$
$$C = 0.006 - j0.002$$
$$D = 0.246 - j0.224.$$

When the ABCD parameters are converted to S parameters for the final answer, we find:

$$S_{11} = -0.644 + j0.511$$
$$S_{12} = 0.161 - j0.092$$
$$S_{21} = 2.748 + j0.596$$
$$S_{22} = -0.243 - j0.241.$$

The amplifier gain with a 50.0-ohm input and output is the magnitude of S_{21}, which is 2.81, or about 9 dB.

Amplifier Stability

While we are on the subject of amplifiers, let's throw in a very useful equation used to determine amplifier stability:

$$K = \frac{1 + |S_{11}S_{22} - S_{12}S_{21}|^2 - |S_{11}|^2 - |S_{22}|^2}{2|S_{12}S_{22}|} \quad \text{(Eq 1)}$$

Note: $|a + jb|^2 = a^2 + b^2$

K is called Rollett's stability factor (1/K is known as C or Linvill's stability factor). If K is greater than 1.0, the amplifier is unconditionally stable for any passive input or output load, provided there is no external feedback path (such as bias leads). If K is less than 1.0, the amplifier will oscillate at some combinations of input and output loads. Whether K is greater than or less than one is the important criterion; to a large extent, how much greater or less than one is not an indication of how stable or unstable the amplifier is.

TRANSMISSION LINES

As we push to ever higher frequencies, lumped elements become more difficult to use. At some point, even our models of the lumped elements break down. We have to start using distributed elements. One such element is the transmission line. Again, the way we include transmission lines in circuit analysis is to build a circuit model.

Any transmission line can be characterized by a certain amount of shunt capacitance and series inductance, which looks like a low-pass filter. Trouble is, if we make a circuit model with a shunt capacitor and a series inductor, it will break down as we approach the cutoff frequency of the low-pass filter. A real transmission line will still transmit power, but a low-pass filter will not. To counter that, we can cut the value of each inductor and each capacitor in half, and make twice as many LC sections. This doubles the cutoff frequency and makes our model better. If it still isn't good enough, cut everything in half again and again. After a point, the model gets much too complicated. After all, we might have a circuit that is approaching infinite size! Fortunately, mathematics is up to the task.

Calculating the ABCD Parameters

When the model is taken to infinite size, the ABCD parameters simplify:

$$\begin{pmatrix} A & B \\ C & D \end{pmatrix} = \begin{pmatrix} \cos(\beta\ell) & j \times Z \times \sin(\beta\ell) \\ j \times Y \times \sin(\beta\ell) & \cos(\beta\ell) \end{pmatrix}$$

where

β = propagation constant = $2\pi/\lambda$
ℓ = transmission line length
Z = transmission line impedance.
$Y = 1/Z$

The above equations can be used to calculate the two-port ABCD parameters for a cascadable transmission line like the one illustrated in Fig 11A. The transmission line (inside the box) is drawn as though it were a microstrip (that is, on printed circuit board) line, but it could be any kind of unbalanced transmission line.

Be careful when using the above equations. Make sure you use the same units (preferably meters) for the transmission line length, and the wavelength used to calculate β. Also, when you calculate the wavelength, be sure to include any velocity factor. For homogeneous media (that is, media that have the same dielectric everywhere, like coaxial cable), the velocity factor is the square root of the dielectric constant. For microstrip lines (inhomogeneous media), use the square root of the effective dielectric constant (which is closer to the dielectric constant of the substrate than that of air).

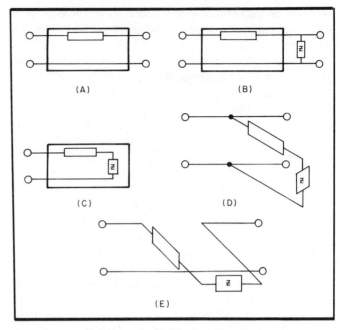

Fig 11—A cascadable two-port transmission line in (A) can be cascaded with an impedance (B), then converted to a one-port network (C). The one-port may then be connected in shunt, forming a shunt stub (D) or in series, forming a series stub (E).

Given β, the line length and its impedance, we can now calculate the ABCD parameters. If we want to cascade a length of transmission line in front of the amplifier we analyzed with TWOP, we calculate the ABCD parameters of the transmission line. Then, immediately after calculating the ABCD parameters of the amplifier, we would multiply the two ABCD matrices together to get the ABCD parameters of the transmission line and amplifier. If we were finished with the amplifier analysis at that time, the ABCD parameters could be converted to S parameters and printed out.

Transmission-Line Stubs

Another important microwave circuit element useful when lumped elements no longer work is the transmission line stub. A stub has one end connected to the main circuit path while the other end is usually either grounded (a shorted stub) or left open (an open stub). The impedance of a shorted or open circuit stub (the process is familiar to any Smith Chart user), properly chosen, can be used as a matching element.

If we could calculate the input impedance of the stub, then we could treat it like a one-port network. Let's look at an open stub. First we calculate the ABCD matrix of the two-port cascadable transmission line, and convert the results to Z parameters. When we write out Ohm's Law using the Z parameters we get:

$$\begin{pmatrix} V_1 \\ V_2 \end{pmatrix} = \begin{pmatrix} Z_{11} & Z_{12} \\ Z_{21} & Z_{22} \end{pmatrix} \times \begin{pmatrix} I_1 \\ I_2 \end{pmatrix}$$

This should look familiar. To make an open stub, we

will leave port 2 open. This means that I_2 will be zero at all times. When we use matrix multiplication to multiply $\mathbf{Z} \times \mathbf{I}$ we find that Z_{12} and Z_{22} are always multiplied by zero. This means Z_{12} and Z_{22} are no longer needed. What about Z_{21}? Since we are leaving port 2 open, we don't care what V_2 is, and the only purpose for Z_{21} is to calculate V_2. The one-port Z parameter of an open stub is simply Z_{11} of the two-port transmission line's $\mathbf{Z}$ matrix. By a similar argument, we find that the input admittance of a shorted stub is just Y_{11} of the $\mathbf{Y}$ matrix.

In the above discussion, we used Z parameters (and Y parameters) for converting a two-port network (the cascadable transmission line) into a one-port network. Actually, the two-port network could be any circuit. For example, if we want to analyze a stub terminated not in a shorted or open circuit, but an impedance, Z, we could construct the two-port network shown in Fig 11B (by multiplying ABCD matrices). Then, by converting the resulting ABCD matrix to Z parameters, Z_{11} would be the one-port Z parameter of the circuit in Fig 11C (with port 2 left open). One word of warning: this won't work if the transmission line is terminated in a short circuit.

Another approach is to proceed as above, but using Y parameters. Then Y_{11} would be the input admittance of a two-port network with port 2 terminated in a short circuit. Correspondingly, this approach will not work if the stub is terminated in an open circuit.

Connecting the Stub

Now that we have the stub impedance or admittance, what do we do with it? Since the stub is now a one-port network, we can connect it just like any other. For example, we could use the rules in Table 4 to connect the stub inside a two-port box. Fig 11D shows what the stub impedance would look like connected in shunt. This is the usual connection for microstrip lines. If we were to convert the matrix of the shunt stub to ABCD parameters and multiply it by the ABCD parameters of the amplifier analyzed by TWOP, we could use the stub to tune the amplifier.

Fig 11E shows what the stub would look like if its admittance were connected in series inside the two-port box. A series stub is virtually impossible to realize in microstrip. The series stub is used when building a matching network out of, say, twin lead transmission line.

Microstrip Parameters

Microstrips are used so often in microwave circuits that a great deal of work has been done to find closed form expressions for microstrip impedance and effective dielectric constant. These allow the computer to calculate transmission line impedance and effective dielectric constant. A cross section of a microstrip line is shown in Fig 12. With the dimensions W and h, and the relative dielectric constant of the substrate, ϵ_{rel}, we can calculate ϵ_{eff} and the characteristic impedance.

$$\epsilon_{eff} = \frac{\epsilon_{rel} + 1}{2} + \frac{\epsilon_{rel} - 1}{2} \left(1 + \frac{10}{u}\right)^{-ab} \qquad \text{(Eq 2)}$$

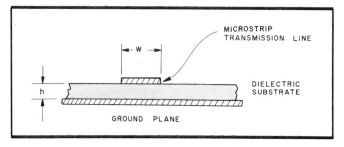

Fig 12—Cross section of a microstrip line.

where

ϵ_{eff} = effective dielectric constant
ϵ_{rel} = dielectric constant of substrate
$u = W/h$
W = width of line
h = thickness of substrate

$$a = 1 + \frac{1}{49} \ln\left(\frac{u^4 + (u/52)^2}{u^4 + 0.432}\right) + \frac{1}{18.7} \ln\left[1 + \left(\frac{u}{18.1}\right)^3\right]$$

$$b = 0.564 \left(\frac{\epsilon_{rel} - 0.9}{\epsilon_{rel} + 3}\right)^{0.053}$$

$$Z_0 = \frac{\eta_0}{2\pi \sqrt{\epsilon_{eff}}} \ln\left[\frac{f}{u} + \sqrt{1 + \left(\frac{2}{u}\right)^2}\right]$$

where

$\eta_0 = 376.73$ ohms
$$f = 6 + (2\pi - 6) \exp\left[-\left(\frac{30.666}{u}\right)^{0.7528}\right]$$

The equations are a bit involved, but in return they provide answers to within a fraction of a percent of the true values for frequencies up to the point where the thickness of the dielectric becomes a fraction of the wavelength. At this point, our model starts to break down as the dielectric constant and characteristic impedance become functions of frequency—the line is dispersive. For most circuits, if a microstrip line becomes dispersive, it is best to use a thinner substrate.

NODAL ANALYSIS

We have looked at one-port and two-port networks. The next logical step is to examine multi-port networks. The technique we will use to approach multi-port networks is called nodal analysis. Nodal analysis defines a circuit in terms of nodes, a node being a point where components of a circuit join together. Every terminal of each component must be connected to a node. The nodes are usually numbered with ground as node 0.

Fig 13 shows the circuit of Fig 9B with all nodes labeled. Node 0, ground, is not labeled. Ideally we would input a description of each circuit element, and indicate which nodes each element is connected between. For example, the source feedback impedance (a one-port network with two terminals) would be connected

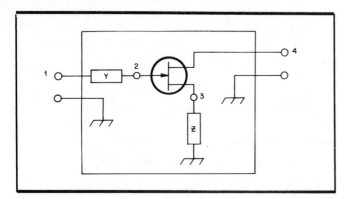

Fig 13—The circuit of Fig 9B with all nodes labeled and ready for analysis.

between nodes 3 and 0. The transistor (a two-port device with three terminals) would be connected between nodes 2, 3 and 4. We also need to indicate that port 1 of the final two-port will be node 1 and that port 2 will be connected to node 4.

It is easier to describe a circuit in terms of nodal analysis than it is in terms of two-port matrices. Also, there are some circuits that simply cannot be analyzed by combining two-port networks. On the other hand, nodal analysis typically requires more time and computer memory than two-port analysis. These disadvantages can be overcome by using "sparse matrix techniques." This can be a difficult undertaking and is not discussed here.

The difficulties of nodal analysis can be ignored in favor of its ease of use and generality. We will look at nodal analysis in terms of Y parameters. A circuit with N nodes (including ground) requires an $N \times N$ Y-parameter matrix. This means that the typical 64 kbyte microcomputer will handle up to 45 or 50 nodes for a single circuit at a single frequency. Computing time in BASIC can take hours. The circuit of Fig 13 would require a 5×5 matrix.

Building a Nodal Matrix

The process of building a nodal matrix is straightforward. First calculate the Y parameters of each element to be included in the circuit. This can be done using techniques already described. The second step is to expand each Y-parameter matrix by one row and one column. This extra row and column represent ground. Add numbers in each element of the new row and column such that summing each row and column results in 0.0. One-port and two-port examples are shown next.

One-port

$$(Y) \rightarrow \begin{pmatrix} Y & -Y \\ -Y & Y \end{pmatrix}$$

Two-port

$$\begin{pmatrix} Y_{11} & Y_{12} \\ Y_{21} & Y_{22} \end{pmatrix} \rightarrow \begin{pmatrix} Y_{11} & Y_{12} & -(Y_{11} + Y_{12}) \\ Y_{21} & Y_{22} & -(Y_{21} + Y_{22}) \\ -(Y_{11} + Y_{21}) & -(Y_{12} + Y_{22}) & Y_{11} + Y_{12} + Y_{21} + Y_{22} \end{pmatrix}$$

If you have a one-port network, by all means, use the one-port equations above. Don't connect the one-port network inside a two-port network (Table 4) and use the two-port equations.

Now we are ready to load the nodal matrix. First, set all the elements of the nodal matrix to $0.0 + j\,0.0$ (remember, everything is complex). Then, look at the expanded one-port matrix as a 2×2 matrix, and let the number 1 represent the first (input) terminal and the number 2 represent the second (grounded) terminal. These numbers will be used as two-port matrix element subscripts.

If terminal 1 of the one-port network is to be connected to, say, node 3, and terminal 2 is to be connected to, say, node 5, then we take the $_{11}$ element of the expanded one-port matrix and add it to the $_{33}$ element of the nodal matrix. Next, take the $_{12}$ element of the expanded one-port matrix and add it to the $_{35}$ element of the nodal matrix. Similarly, the $_{21}$ element is added to the $_{53}$ element of the nodal matrix, and the $_{22}$ element is added to the $_{55}$ element of the nodal matrix. The key is to split up the expanded one-port matrix and add each element to the appropriate elements of the nodal matrix. The appropriate elements are determined by which nodes each terminal is to be connected to. Don't forget that node 0 is also a node to which any terminal of a one-port may be connected.

Connecting a two-port network in a nodal matrix follows the same pattern. Now there are three terminals to be connected and the expanded two-port matrix is a 3×3 matrix. Just add each element of the 3×3 matrix to the appropriate nodal matrix element, depending on how the two-port network is connected to the circuit. In fact, if we have an N-port network (N being any positive, non-zero integer) we can connect it by calculating the expanded N-port Y-parameter matrix and adding it to the nodal matrix. In fact, the N-port Y-parameter matrix could be the result of a previous nodal analysis.

Once the nodal matrix is complete, we have an option. Node 0 doesn't have to be ground anymore. We can pick any node to be ground. We might want to do this, for example, if we changed the FET data from common source to common gate. To do this, "cross out" the row and column of the matrix that corresponds to the node you want to ground. To do this on a computer, it might be best to swap both the row and column of the node to be grounded with the last row and column of the nodal matrix, and then ignore the last row and column. If node 0 is the node to be grounded, ignore the row and column corresponding to node 0.

Now we have a Y-parameter matrix. Say we want to reduce it to a two-port matrix, leaving all nodes not connected to a port open. The easiest way (assuming we have a general purpose, $N \times N$ matrix inversion routine) is to invert the Y-parameter nodal matrix and then "cross out" all the rows and columns of nodes that are not connected to ports. It may be necessary to swap some rows and columns so that the ports are in the right order.

If you are handy with matrix manipulations, there is a faster way to reduce an $N \times N$ Y-parameter matrix to, say, a two-port Y-parameter matrix. Write out Ohm's Law,

I = Y × V, in terms of the N equations. Then, pick a node that will not be connected to any external port. Let the current flowing into that node equal zero. The resulting equation can then be solved for the voltage at that node in terms of the remaining currents. Back substitute the solution for that voltage into the remaining equations. The set of matrix equations will now have been reduced by one row and one column. Continue until all unneeded nodes are removed. If you play around with the equations on paper for a while, it will become apparent how this may be done with several loops on a computer.

Nodal analysis is a powerful and general purpose means of analyzing circuits. With some effort and ingenuity, a number of ways can be found to speed up the analysis. Our discussion has been brief, and without a good working knowledge of matrix manipulations, it may have been a little confusing. Fortunately, most circuits we will encounter can be successfully analyzed using the two-port techniques already described.

NOISE FIGURE ANALYSIS

At HF (also known to microwave types as dc), the noise figure of a receiver is of little concern because atmospheric noise is usually dominant. At microwave frequencies, most of the noise usually comes from the first amplifier and thus great emphasis is placed on designing low-noise amplifiers (LNAs). To assist the designer, we will provide some equations for calculating the noise figure of an amplifier.

Data sheets for microwave transistors usually come with noise figure data. That data may be used to calculate an amplifier noise figure in the following equation:

$$F = F_{min} + \frac{R_n}{G_s} \left[\left(G_{opt} - G_s \right)^2 + \left(B_{opt} - B_s \right)^2 \right] \quad \text{(Eq 3)}$$

where

F = noise factor
F_{min} = minimum possible noise factor
G_{opt} = input conductance at which F_{min} is realized
B_{opt} = input susceptance at which F_{min} is realized
G_s = actual input conductance
B_s = actual input susceptance
R_n = noise resistance

F_{min}, G_{opt}, B_{opt} and R_n are collectively referred to as noise parameters and can frequently be found on low-noise-transistor data sheets. However, these parameters are difficult to measure and tend to vary from device to device. Thus the noise figure using the data sheet specs will not be accurate to a tenth of a dB, but it should give an answer that is in the ballpark.

The admittance seen by the transistor input, $Y_s = G_s + jB_s$ can be calculated by taking the two port network that does the input matching (the Y in the case of Fig 9B or Fig 13), and cascading a series-connected 50-ohm resistor in front of it, and converting to Y parameters. Y_{22} is then the admittance seen by the input of the transistor.

Equation 3 will not work when there is feedback (as there is in the circuit of Figs 9B and 13). The feedback actually changes the device's noise parameters. In such a case, we need to use a more general technique. See "Further Information" at the end of this chapter. The source feedback in Figs 9B and 13 is very small, so Equation 3 should give a fairly accurate answer.

OPTIMIZATION

So, we have a computer all set up to analyze our circuit: an amplifier, with an inductor and a capacitor in the input matching circuit. We want to maximize the gain of the amplifier. As a first try, we change the inductor from 1.0 nH to 1.1 nH. The gain increases. We change it to 1.2 nH. The gain increases again. Eventually we find the optimum value is 19.8 nH (by the way, it is now 2 AM). Now on to the capacitor. We change it from 1.0 pF to 1.1 pF. The gain decreases. So we try 0.9 pF. The gain increases. Eventually, we find the optimum is at 0.5 pF. Back to the inductor. Step by step, we find that the new optimum (because we changed the capacitor) is back down to 5.3 nH. Now back to the capacitor...

The above is an example of optimizing a circuit with just two variable components. Typical circuits can have a dozen or more variables to be optimized. Clearly, some form of automatic optimization is desirable. Let's let the computer do the work.

A complete "how to" description of optimization is not possible here. What we will do is give you an idea how the various kinds of optimization techniques work and what their advantages and disadvantages are.

Optimization algorithms, which are easily applied to circuits, fall into two general categories: gradient search and random search. The example at the start of this section is an example of a crude gradient search. Looking at only one variable at a time, a decision was made to increase or decrease its value, one step at a time, until no more gain could be obtained. Then the process was repeated, this time with a different variable.

This simple algorithm is called a gradient algorithm because the decision to increase or decrease component values was based on how the objective (gain) changed when we made a small change in a variable (say, the inductor). The direction (increasing or decreasing component values) in which we get the largest positive change is called the gradient. An important part of every gradient search is the line search.

In the above example, we could think of changing the inductance and evaluating the gain as searching along a line for the highest gain. This is called, of course, a line search. Once the line search is done, we can calculate the gradient for the new circuit and proceed with another line search. Evaluating the objective function (in this case, the gain) at every point along a line until we find the maximum is one of the simplest things we could do, but it also takes the most time.

A key to most line searches is the assumption that the objective function has only one optimum (unimodal). There are line searches that try to narrow down the position of the optimum by selectively calculating the objective function at a minimum number of points along the line.

Examples of these are the search by golden section and the Fibonacci line search. There are other techniques where, by considering how fast the objective function is changing at one or more points along the line, an attempt is made to locate the optimum. These techniques assume that the objective function is nice and smooth as well as unimodal. Both of these assumptions break down frequently. Ways to handle these situations are discussed shortly.

The objective function can represent just about anything, not just gain. In fact, it doesn't even have to be maximized. Say we wanted the amplifier to have flat gain over a certain range of frequencies. We subtract the actual gain (in dB, of course) from the desired gain and square the result. This is called the squared error. This is done at each frequency, and the results added. If the objective function were reduced to zero, we would have exactly the desired gain. The closer we get to zero, the closer we get to the desired gain. Say we wanted the gain to be greater than a certain value at all frequencies of analysis. Include an IF statement when calculating the squared error to exclude all results where the actual gain was higher than the desired gain. You can be very creative with the objective function. For example, you could include squared error terms for S_{11} and S_{22}, and add K factors also.

Once we determine the desired objective function, we must next calculate its gradient. In our first example, we decided to increase or decrease the value of only one variable. Things can go much faster if we change all the variables at once. To figure out how much to change the variables, first calculate the objective function for the initial circuit. Let's say we have three circuit elements to be varied. Pick a small step-size for each one. Then add that step size to the first variable only, and re-calculate the objective function. Let's say the objective function changed by 2.4. Do the same for the second and third variables. Let's say that the objective function changed by 1.2 and then -0.6. When we do the line search, change all three variables at the same time, only when you increase the first one by one step size, increase the second by half of a step-size and decrease the third by a quarter of a step-size. The ratio in which each variable is changed is called the gradient, or direction of search. If we want to minimize the objective function (a common situation) rather than maximize it, just adjust the variables in the opposite direction.

When our component values are changing in the direction of the gradient (or minus the gradient), the optimization algorithm is called "steepest descent." A more complicated—but faster—algorithm is called the conjugate gradient search. It looks at the gradient at the start of the last line search, as well as the gradient at the current point, before deciding which direction to go. There are other algorithms that consider past gradients as well as the current gradient. Unfortunately, most of the extra computing speedup is lost in the noise of a much bigger problem—not all objective functions are "nice."

All the above gradient algorithms can get "stuck" unless you are already close to the optimum. To get around this problem, we use a random search. This is simplicity

at its finest. Simply select a reasonable range for your variables (for example, 0.1 through 20 nH, and so on), then use a random number generator to come up with values for the variables randomly distributed across that range. Program the computer to run through many randomizations, and store the circuit values that give the best result.

If the circuit is not close to optimum, this is probably the best strategy. Once a random search has worked for a while, submitting the best result of the random search to a gradient optimization can quickly produce an even better result.

Remember, nature is logarithmic. When we optimize a circuit, we do not optimize the inductance, capacitance or resistance directly: we optimize their logarithms. Take as an example a single capacitor starting at 100 pF. Let's use a step of 25 pF. If the optimum is 2 pF, our line search will start at 100, then 75, then 50, then 25 and stop at 0 pF. Now let's do a line search of the logarithm of the capacitance. This time let's make a poor initial guess and start at 1000 pF. If we use a step size corresponding to one decade, the search will start at 1000 pF, then 100, then 10, then 1 pF. The logarithmic search started further from the optimum value, with a larger initial step size, but produced a more accurate answer in fewer steps.

The next step for the logarithmic search would be 0.1 pF; for the linear search, it would be -25 pF. This shows that a logarithmic search will not cross 0, frequently a desirable quality.

Optimization offers a great deal of potential help to the microwave experimenter. The next section contains useful references for further exploration.

FURTHER INFORMATION

There are a number of useful, general purpose books on microwave circuit design using computers. A good one is Gupta, Garg and Chadha.[1] This book's presentation is a bit theoretical, but does include some closed form equations for microstrip discontinuities and a chapter on matrix manipulations. There is quite a bit of information on optimization and a sample FORTRAN program (no optimization). Another book, Vlach and Singhal[2] has a good deal of information on sparse matrix techniques and a number of circuit theory topics, including optimization. A third book, Cuthbert,[3] is directed more toward matching networks and filters. It has a strong emphasis on synthesis (that is, given a desired response, what is the circuit that will achieve it) and analysis (given a circuit, what is its response). This book covers optimization as well.

If you don't have a computer, but do have a TI-59, HP-67, 91 or 41C programmable calculator, Allen and Medley[4] will be valuable. The book includes calculator program listings for HP and TI calculators. The programs are provided, so you only need to type in programs for your desired tasks. Most of the topics we have covered here (plus a few more) are handled well. There is no information on optimization, and if you want to extract the equations for use on a different calculator or computer, you will have to decode the calculator programs.

If you would like a short but illuminating book on

programming style, Kernighan and Plauger[5] is the standard. It is directed mainly toward FORTRAN, but it can help improve your style in just about any language, and is highly recommended.

The closed form equations for microstrips were taken from Hammerstad and Jensen.[6] Equations for microstrip dispersion, loss and coupled lines can also be found there. A better model for single microstrip dispersion is included in Kirschning and Jansen.[7]

A general noise figure calculation algorithm that fits in with the two-port analysis methods described in this chapter is presented by Hillbrand and Russer.[8] They describe matrices that combine in the same manner as Z, Y and ABCD matrices when constructing a circuit. When finished with the circuit, the resulting matrix can quickly provide its noise figure. It should be possible to extend the technique to nodal analysis with little difficulty. You will save a lot of effort if you also dig up the correction[9] before implementing the technique.

An excellent tutorial on microwave circuit optimization is presented by Bandler.[10] Optimization papers tend to have a great number of complicated-looking equations, but don't let that deter you. When you find the information you need, it will all come together.

An excellent, in-depth reference for modern-day microwave circuit design is Bahl and Bhartia.[11]

REFERENCES

[1]Gupta, K. C., Garg, R. and Chadha, R., *Computer-aided Design of Microwave Circuits*, Artech House, 1981.

[2]Vlach, J. and Singhal, K., *Computer Methods For Circuit Analysis and Design*, Van Nostrand Reinhold Co, 1983.

[3]Cuthbert, T. R., *Circuit Design Using Personal Computers*, John Wiley and Sons, 1983.

[4]Allen, J. L. and Medley, M. W., *Microwave Circuit Design Using Programmable Calculators*, Artech House, 1980.

[5]Kernighan, B. W. and Plauger, P. J., *The Elements of Programming Style*, McGraw-Hill, 1978.

[6]Hammerstad, E. and Jensen, O., "Accurate Models for Microstrip Computer-Aided Design," *IEEE MTT Symposium Digest* (Washington, DC), Jun 1980, pp 407-409.

[7]Kirschning, M. and Jansen, R. H., "Accurate Model for Effective Dielectric Constant of Microstrip with Validity up to Millimetre-Wave Frequencies," *Electronic Letters*, Mar 18, 1982, Vol 18, No. 6, pp 272-273.

[8]Hillbrand, H. and Russer, P.H., "An Efficient Method for Computer Aided Noise Analysis of Linear Amplifier Networks," *IEEE Transactions on Circuits and Systems*, Vol CAS-23, No. 4, Apr 1976, pp 235-238.

[9]Hillbrand, H. and Russer, P. H., "Correction to 'An Efficient Method for Computer Aided Noise Analysis of Linear Amplifier Networks'," *IEEE Transactions on Circuits and Systems*, Vol CAS-23, Nov 1976, p 691.

[10]Bandler, J. W., "Optimization Methods for Computer-Aided-Design," *IEEE Transactions on Microwave Theory and Techniques*, Vol MTT-17, Aug 1969, pp 533-552.

[11]Bahl, I. and P.Bhartia, *Microwave Solid-State Circuit Design,* John Wiley and Sons, 1988.

Appendix

Capsule Description of Programs on The ARRL Microwave Software Diskette

The ARRL Microwave Software Diskette is a companion to this *ARRL Microwave Manual*. There are 26 programs on the 5¼-inch (360K) diskette for the IBM® PC and compatible computers. The programs aid in performing various tasks, from designing antennas to circuit analysis to system design parameters. There are 25 BASIC programs written in ASCII text format and one compiled Pascal program. The diskette is copyrighted but not copy protected.

The programs on this diskette were collected by Dr James C. Rautio, AJ3K. They have been supplied by the programmers, who are identified in the following brief descriptions of the programs. Addresses are included for those programmers who agreed to have them included. The ARRL has verified that the programs run properly with appropriate input data, but does not warrant program operation or the results of any calculations.

The *Microwave Software Diskette* includes a documentation file for each program. This documentation explains the use of the program, the meaning of various terminology, and, occasionally, some theory behind the program. The documentation for each program also includes the data for one or more sample runs of the program. Such documentation significantly increases the value and utility of any software. Anyone who has explored a few of the many available "documentation-less" public domain programs will appreciate this point.

There were over 100 programs from which to choose when this diskette was put together. Selection criteria placed strong weighting in favor of programs that could be used easily with small probability of user error. Programs that require substantial documentation to use correctly were regretfully passed over.

Programs with a comfortable user interface were also given an advantage. Several important programs, which lacked such an interface, were appropriately modified, however. In addition, some attempt was made to provide some common points to the user interfaces on all programs.

A capsule description of each program follows. You will probably find some programs here that you would like to explore. If you didn't purchase the *Microwave Software Diskette* with this book, you can order it now from your local amateur equipment dealer or directly from the ARRL.

Read the documentation on the diskette associated with the programs you are interested in before using them. We believe that such documentation is critically important in using and understanding the correct operation of a program. There is an incredible amount of free public domain software available that lacks such documentation. It has been our experience that such free, undocumented software can, in fact, be very expensive. We hope you enjoy these programs.

1) "LOOPYAGI.BAS": LOOP YAGI ANTENNA WITH 27 OR 38 ELEMENTS
by M. H. Walters, G3JVL
contributed by Bob Atkins, KA1GT

This program calculates dimensions for a circular-loop Yagi antenna, based on the experimental work of G3JVL. The user must supply the frequency of operation (in MHz), the boom diameter, and the width and thickness of the material used for the circular elements. (These dimensions are given in inches.) The program will then print out the position and circumference of each element. There are two antenna choices offered—a 27-element Yagi with a gain of about 18 dBi and a 38-element Yagi with a gain of about 20 dBi.

The antenna starts with a rectangular reflecting screen, followed by a reflector loop and then a driven-element loop. The remaining elements are all directors. Construction details for this antenna are found on pp 9.59-9.61 of the *VHF/UHF Manual*, fourth edition, edited by G. R. Jessop, G6JP, published by The Radio Society of Great Britain, Hertfordshire, England, 1983.

2) "WUYAGI.BAS": DESIGN OF DL6WU YAGI ANTENNAS

by Bob Stein, W6NBI and Jerry Haigwood, KY4Z

1849 Middleton Ave   3151 Mathos Ave

Los Altos, CA 94022   San Jose, CA 95132

DL6WU has developed design rules for what may be the best currently available very long Yagi antennas for VHF and UHF. Available gain ranges from 11.8 dBd to 21.6 dBd. The equations upon which this program is based were developed by Jerry Haigwood, who curve-fitted the charts and tables published by Gunter Hoch, DL6WU, "Extremely Long Yagi Antennas," *VHF Communications*, Verlag UKW-BERICHTE, Vol 14, Autumn 1982, Edition 3, pp 130-138. The program's original name was DL6WU.BAS. The name WUYAGI.BAS was used here so the directory listing would give some indication of the program's purpose.

WUYAGI calculates the required dimensions for these antennas. Specify either desired boom length or desired gain and the element diameters. The mechanical boom-to-element construction is selected from a list of possible configurations. Physical dimensions are specified in inches, centimeters or wavelengths.

3) "MININEC.BAS": METHOD OF MOMENTS ANALYSIS OF ARBITRARY WIRE ANTENNAS

by A. J. Julian, J. C. Logan and J. W. Rockway

MININEC analyzes wire antennas by breaking the antenna into as many as 50 short segments and using a technique called method of moments. The results are the current on each of the segments, the antenna input impedance and antenna radiation pattern. Up to 50 sources may be specified. For example, a three-element phased array would have three sources. One can also specify up to 50 complex loads, such as the traps in a multiband Yagi. MININEC will also include the effect of a perfect ground.

The documentation included on the diskette for this program is a condensation of Appendix A of the 56-page MININEC manual from Naval Ocean Systems Center, San Diego, California. This manual is Technical Document 516, "MININEC: A Mini-numerical Electromagnetic Code" by A. J. Julian, J. C. Logan and J. W. Rockway. Copies of this document, with several minor corrections, are available from Sonnet Software, 4397 Luna Course, Liverpool, NY 13090 for $10 postpaid.

This version of MININEC allows only vertical wires to be attached to ground. Also, loads may not be attached directly to ground. A subsequent version, MININEC2, was published in *Microcomputer Tools for Communications Engineering* by S. T. Li, et al, Artech House, Inc, 1984. MININEC3 and The MININEC System have also since been released. These include numerous user-interface enhancements. The earlier version is included here, mainly to conserve disk space. MININEC3 is currently available for the IBM PC/XT from:

National Technical Information Services   The program
Springfield, VA 22161   comes on a
Telephone: Main Office, 800-336-4700   single disk.
         Orders, 703-487-4600

Documentation only: Order no. ADA175800, $19.95 + $3 handling. Software and documentation: Order no. ADA181681, $75 + $3 handling.

A user-friendly version of MININEC3 with documentation on disk is available from:

Brian Beezley, K6STI   The program, with graphics
507½ Taylor Street   capability, comes on a
Vista, CA 92084   single disk for $75.

The MININEC System is a series of programs prepared by the authors of MININEC3. It is a user-friendly program with graphics capability. Order from:

Artech House, Inc   The MININEC System comes
685 Canton Street   on 2 disks, plus a manual
Norwood, MA 02062   for $150.

MININEC execution starts by specifying the antenna geometry. All dimensions are in meters. The ground is the X-Y plane (Z = 0) and the Z axis goes straight up. See Figure 1. The coordinate system is right handed (point your right hand thumb in the direction of the positive Z axis and your fingers will curl the X axis into the Y axis rather than the Y into the X axis). Figure 2 shows how a T antenna, or top-loaded vertical, is specified for MININEC input.

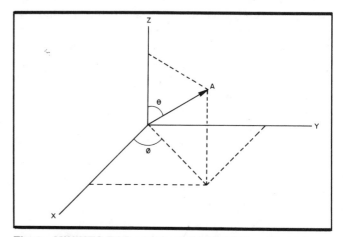

Fig 1—MININEC.BAS uses a right-handed rectangular coordinate system to specify the antenna geometry. To specify the location of point A, enter the X, Y and Z coordinates. The angles ϕ and θ represent the horizontal and vertical angles for the radiation-pattern data given by the calculations.

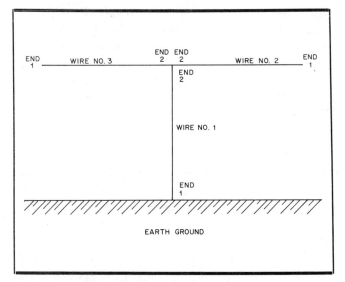

Fig 2—This figure shows how a T antenna, or top-loaded vertical is broken into three segments to specify the MININEC input.

4) "LOGANT.BAS": LOG PERIODIC ANTENNA DESIGN

by Dick Wright
Electrospace Systems, Inc
1601 N Plano Rd
Richardson, TX 75080

A log periodic antenna provides a convenient broadband directive antenna. While there are many programs for log periodic design, the one presented here ranks among the best.

To use the program, you simply select the desired antenna gain from a list of five possibilities, ranging from 5.5 dBi to 9.5 dBi. Next, the program asks for the lowest and highest operating frequencies (in MHz). The program then calculates the design parameters for five log periodic antennas. You can select one of these design choices and the program will calculate the element lengths and spacings for that antenna.

This program was described in the "Design Feature" section of *Microwaves and RF*, May 1985, pp 110 and 112.

5) "HELICAL.BAS": HELICAL ANTENNA DESIGN

by William G. Smith, W9LRG

This program is from George R. Isely, WD9GIG and William G. Smith, W9LRG, "A Helical Antenna for Space-Shuttle Communication," *QST*, December 1984, pp 14-18.

The helical antenna is an easy-to-build, high-gain antenna used at UHF and microwave frequencies. It consists of a wire helix about one wavelength in diameter fed at one end with coaxial cable. The outer conductor of the coax is connected to a flat plate, which forms a ground plane. Power fed to the antenna sets up a traveling wave, which then generates a beam in the direction of the helix's axis. The antenna has a very broad bandwidth, useful from 0.75 to 1.33 times the design center frequency.

To use this program, you specify the antenna center frequency (in MHz), the helix circumference (in wavelengths) and the helix pitch (in degrees). The program suggests the common range for these variables. HELICAL will calculate antenna dimensions, gain and input impedance.

For more information on helical antenna design, see Dr John D. Kraus, W8JK, *Antennas*, 2nd ed. (New York: McGraw Hill, 1988), Chapter 7.

6) "HELIX.BAS": HELICAL ANTENNA DESIGN

by Bob Atkins, KA1GT

This program is used to design helical antennas much as the previous program, "HELICAL.BAS." With this program, you specify whether the design is to be based on gain, bandwidth or the number of turns in the helix. The helix pitch angle is fixed at 12.8 degrees. The program then prompts you for the information needed to complete the design. The range of acceptable values is specified with each prompt. The antenna center frequency is specified in MHz.

The section on helical antenna design in Chapter 9 of *The ARRL Microwave Manual* contains more information about this program and the design philosophy it uses.

7) "DISH.BAS": PARABOLIC DISH ANALYSIS PROGRAM

by Mike Watson, W5UC

Here is a short BASIC program that allows the experimenter to calculate the gain and 3-dB beamwidth for any diameter dish at any frequency. You enter the frequency (in MHz), the dish diameter and focal length (in feet) and the required antenna efficiency. The program will also provide data necessary to lay out the chosen dish.

Next, you are asked for a support spacing (in inches). The support spacing information can be used to draw a template for the dish. If we imagine the dish pointed straight up with the center (bottom) of the dish setting on the floor of our shop, the program will print out the height of the dish above the floor at the specified support distances from the center of the dish.

For example, to build a 7-foot-diameter dish, we might want to construct the dish so that the edge (42 inches from the center, measured flat along the floor) is 10.5 inches above the floor. If you specified the distance between supports as 6 inches, the program will calculate the height of the dish every 6 inches from the center.

8) "EMEPATH.BAS": EARTH-MOON-EARTH PATH SYSTEM CALCULATION

by Dr Allen Katz, K2UYH

The earth-moon-earth path is a clearly defined communications path that can be accurately evaluated. This program performs the necessary calculations to provide an overall system signal-to-noise ratio. The program asks for the necessary system parameters and specifies the units to be used.

You are asked for the frequency (in MHz), transmit power (in watts), transmit and receive antenna gains (in dBi), transmit and receive feed line loss (in dB), antenna noise temperature (in kelvins), receiver noise figure (in dB) and system bandwidth (in Hz).

A menu at the end allows a quick change of system parameters so you can try out different systems without actually building them.

9) "SATPATH.BAS": SATELLITE SYSTEM DESIGN

by Dr Allen Katz, K2UYH

This program assists in the design of a satellite communications system. The parameters for both the earth station and the spacecraft can be changed and the program evaluates the impact of those changes on the overall link signal-to-noise ratio.

The program starts by asking for the earth station transmitter (uplink) power (in watts). The power is converted to dBm (dB referenced to 1 milliwatt) and printed out. Then after asking for the frequency (in MHz) and the distance to the satellite (in miles), the program calculates the uplink path loss. The transmitted power is attenuated by the path loss. Next, you are asked for the transmit and receive antenna gains (in dBi). The earth-station transmit-antenna gain and satellite receive-antenna gain help to compensate for the path loss. After you provide the satellite-receiver noise figure (in dB), the satellite antenna temperature (in kelvins) and the system bandwidth, the program calculates the satellite signal-to-noise ratio. The program will also calculate the downlink conditions, given similar information about the downlink system.

10) "SYSNF.BAS": SYSTEM NOISE FIGURE CALCULATION

by Dr James C. Rautio, AJ3K
based on a program by William Troetschel, K6UQH

We often have a good idea what the noise figure is for the low-noise amplifier in our receiver. SYSNF will take that information and combine it with any transmission line

loss, interstage loss and the noise figure of subsequent stages. SYSNF will then calculate the overall system noise figure. This number can be used in link budget calculations.

SYSNF can also answer questions like "Should I get lower loss coax or a mixer (or second RF amplifier) with a lower noise figure?" Just plug the numbers into SYSNF and you will know how much better a noise figure you will be getting.

11) "TROPS.BAS": TROPOSPHERIC SCATTER PATH LOSS EVALUATION

by Michael Moreken, KA2BIQ

A small portion of the power transmitted through the atmosphere is scattered by the atmosphere, much as a flashlight beam is scattered by dust in the air. Just as we can see the flashlight beam even when it is not pointed directly toward us, we can receive the scattered power by pointing our antenna at the region of the atmosphere doing the scattering. While it would be desirable to have the beam pointed directly at us (line of sight), receiving only the scattered power is a viable alternative when we are well beyond the horizon. Since most of the scattering occurs in the troposphere (the first ten miles of atmosphere), this mode is called tropospheric scatter.

The program offers you a choice of specifying the required information using Metric or US Customary units. It then prompts you for inputs such as transmit antenna height, distance between the transmitter and antenna, frequency (in MHz), antenna beamwidths and the refractive index of the air. (The refractive index usually varies between 250 and 400.) Since there is often one or more obstacles in the path between the transmitting and receiving sites, the program allows you to specify the height and location of an obstacle in the transmit path and another one in the receive path.

After you have entered the necessary information, TROPS.BAS calculates an estimate of the free space path loss, the tropospheric scatter path loss and the total path loss.

12) "PATHLOSS.BAS": PATH LOSS, CLEARANCE AND AZIMUTH CALCULATION

by Dennis Haarsager, N7DH

Given the operating frequency (in GHz) and the latitude and longitude of two sites, PATHLOSS will calculate the distance between the two sites, the direction of the second site from the first site and the free space path loss between the two sites. Given some information about the terrain between the two sites, PATHLOSS will also calculate the line of sight clearance. Since line of sight is not sufficient for a good path, PATHLOSS also calculates the Fresnel zone clearance.

13) "SUNMOON.BAS": SOLAR AND LUNAR EPHEMERIS

by David B. Shaffer, W8MIF
1742 Saddleback Court
Henderson, NV 89014

Precise knowledge of the azimuth and elevation of the moon can speed lunar acquisition during moon-bounce operations. Likewise, when evaluating antennas using the sun as a signal source, ephemeris information can be useful. The solar position is also important for HF DXing. SUNMOON will provide the coordinates of the sun and the moon when given the time, date, latitude and longitude. SUNMOON even includes a correction for the non-spherical shape of the earth as well as the offset in the lunar position due to the closeness of the moon. Calculations by SUNMOON should be accurate well into the 21st century.

14) "XFMR.BAS": TRANSMISSION LINE IMPEDANCE TRANSFORMER

by Dr James C. Rautio, AJ3K

One of the first matching circuits we learn about is the quarter-wave transformer. This is simply a transmission line a quarter-wavelength long connecting a source (such as a transmitter) to a load (such as an antenna). If the impedance of the source and load are both real, then a perfect match at a single frequency will be realized if the transmission line impedance is equal to the geometric mean of the source and load impedances.

If we don't restrict ourselves to quarter-wavelength transmission lines, then we can match many complex impedances as well. This program calculates the impedance and length of the transmission line required to match a complex load to a complex source. For more information, see T. Choinski, "Generalized Transmission Line Transformers," *Microwave Journal*, December 1983, pp 114-118.

15) "TPAD.BAS": DESIGN OF T-NETWORK RESISTIVE ATTENUATORS

by Philip C. Arnold
6719 Aqueduct Avenue
Van Nuys, CA 91406

TPAD calculates the resistances required to construct an attenuator (pad) of any desired attenuation using a T-network. Z1 and Z2 are the input and output impedances of the pad (usually 50 ohms). TPAD will calculate attenuators for any input or output impedance; the impedances can even be different. For a given attenuator, TPAD calculates the actual attenuation, input VSWR and input reflection coefficient.

This program was described in the "Design Feature" section of *Microwaves and RF*, May 1985, pp 114-115.

16) "PIPAD.BAS": DESIGN OF PI-NETWORK RESISTIVE ATTENUATORS

by Philip C. Arnold
6719 Aqueduct Avenue
Van Nuys, CA 91406

PIPAD calculates the resistances required to construct an attenuator (pad) of any desired attenuation using a PI-network. Z1 and Z2 are the input and output impedances of the pad (usually 50 ohms). PIPAD will calculate attenuators for any input or output impedance; the impedances can even be different. For a given attenuator, PIPAD calculates the actual attenuation, input VSWR and input reflection coefficient.

This program was described in the "Design Feature" section of *Microwaves and RF*, May 1985, pp 114-115.

17) "WEFILTER.BAS": WAVEGUIDE FILTER DESIGN

by M. H. Walters, G3JVL

The usual lumped-element filters are difficult to realize and tend to be exceedingly lossy at microwave frequencies. On the other hand, waveguide filters are relatively easy to build and are nearly lossless at microwave frequencies. This program provides the necessary dimensions for the construction of a waveguide filter given the desired filter response.

The program first asks for the number of cavities, center frequency and bandwidth. The filter will have an equal-ripple response in the passband. This means that the filter passband is not flat but rather smoothly ripples from zero attenuation to some small value and back again. The number of points with zero attenuation (also called "poles") is equal to the number of cavities. The bandwidth specified is the equal-ripple bandwidth. For a 0.25-dB equal-ripple filter, the equal-ripple bandwidth is defined between the points where the response falls off to 0.25 dB. Note that the 3-dB bandwidth definition (where the response falls off to 3 dB) will label a given filter with a wider bandwidth. If you can tolerate more passband ripple (say 0.5 dB), you can get more stop-band attenuation. If you don't need a lot of stop-band attenuation, then you can design a filter with less passband ripple.

If you specify a negative number for the maximum passband attenuation, the program will ignore the value of the attenuation and give you a maximally flat, or Butterworth, response. At band center, the response is as flat as possible and there is no ripple. The trade-off is that the skirts of the filter (stop band) do not fall off as quickly and the filter response at the band edges is more rounded.

18) "NBMATCH.BAS": NARROW BAND MATCHING NETWORK DESIGN

by Alan J. LaPenn

NBMATCH was written by Alan J. LaPenn and adapted from his article, "BASIC Program Computes Values For 14 Matching Networks," *RF Design*, April 1985, pp 44-47. This information and the program are included by permission of Cardiff Publishing Company.

NBMATCH synthesizes two- and three-element LC matching networks. The networks are either low-pass or high-pass types and will match any two resistive loads at a single frequency. Any of 14 different networks may be calculated, including the familiar L and Pi networks. Figure 3 shows the 14 possible networks. You will have to refer to this figure and enter the desired network by number when you run the program.

When you run the program you will first be asked for the source impedance. The source is the resistive load with the lower impedance. The load resistance, asked for next, must be higher than the source resistance. In some cases, it may be equal. The third question asks for the design frequency (in hertz). If you enter 0 at this point, all results will be given in ohms rather than farads and henrys.

Next, you will be asked for the network number that you wish to design. Select the desired network from Figure 3 in this Appendix. Network 12, for example, has a series capacitor on the input with a parallel LC combination connected in shunt on the output. This particular network has a high-pass characteristic.

To choose between several possible networks, examine the element values for the most desirable values. Also, if, for example, you are interested in reducing harmonic output, you may want to stay away from the high-pass

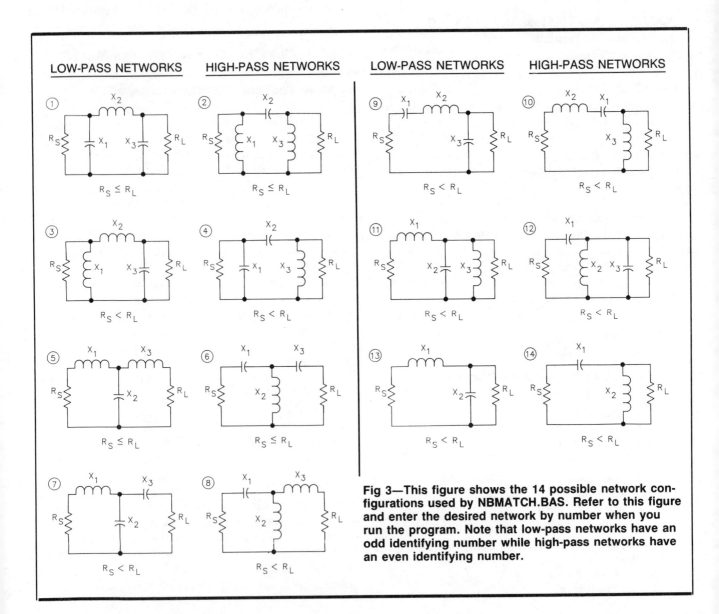

Fig 3—This figure shows the 14 possible network configurations used by NBMATCH.BAS. Refer to this figure and enter the desired network by number when you run the program. Note that low-pass networks have an odd identifying number while high-pass networks have an even identifying number.

networks. Keep in mind that you can always cascade a transformer (at VHF, a toroid will work well) and design for a different load or source impedance.

19) "ONEP.BAS": ONE-PORT ANALYSIS
by Dr James C. Rautio, AJ3K

This is the first of two programs described in the microcomputer chapter of *The ARRL Microwave Manual*. This program allows you to determine the input impedance of almost any interconnection of resistors, capacitors and inductors. See Chapter 12 of this book for more details about the structure of this program.

When you run the program you will be asked to enter the frequency (in GHz). Next you will specify the first component as a resistor, an inductor, or a capacitor and give its value, either in ohms, nanohenrys or picofarads. Then the program asks for the second component and whether you want it connected in series or parallel. You can choose to print the results of this combination, and then continue adding more components to your circuit, one at a time.

20) "TWOP.PAS": TWO PORT ANALYSIS
by Dr James C. Rautio, AJ3K

TWOP is the second program in *The ARRL Microwave Manual* microcomputer chapter. It calculates the S-parameters of a simple two-port FET amplifier. Unlike all the other programs on the software diskette, TWOP is written in Pascal. Pascal was chosen to provide a brief introduction to a language many have heard of but may never have used. The program will run under Turbo Pascal. If you don't have Turbo Pascal you can execute the compiled code, TWOP.COM, by typing "TWOP" at the DOS prompt. For more information about how to run this program and the calculations it performs, see Chapter 12 of this book.

21) "MANA.BAS": MICROSTRIP ANALYSIS AND SYNTHESIS

by Alastair Upton
4910 Joyce Place
Liverpool, NY 13090

Microstrip transmission lines are formed with printed circuit lines on top of a dielectric substrate (such as a circuit board). The bottom side of the substrate remains copper clad. The impedance of the line is selected by adjusting the line width. The wider the line, the lower the impedance. The impedance is a function of the line width and the dielectric constant of the circuit board material. To a lesser extent, the impedance is also a function of metalization thickness and frequency. The electrical length of the line is determined by the effective dielectric constant, of the

substrate and that of air (part of the field is in the dielectric and part is in air).

MANA will calculate the impedance and effective dielectric constant of a microstrip transmission line given the width, metalization thickness, substrate thickness and substrate dielectric constant. The program asks for the thickness input in terms of the microstrip width to substrate thickness (W/H) ratio and the microstrip metalization thickness to substrate thickness (T/H) ratio. Loss is also calculated (using the incremental inductance rule). Microstrip is a dispersive medium, that is, the impedance and effective dielectric constant are functions of frequency. MANA also calculates the dispersion.

In addition to analyzing the characteristics of a microstrip line, MANA can also help you design a specific line. Given the desired characteristic impedance and the substrate dielectric constant, MANA calculates the required microstrip width to substrate thickness (W/H) ratio. This calculation doesn't take frequency or metalization thickness into account, so you may want to put that data back into the analysis section of the program to verify the design at the frequency it will be used at.

22) "ATAN2.BAS": FULL 360 DEGREE ARCTANGENT WITH DIVIDE BY ZERO PROTECTION
by Dr James C. Rautio, AJ3K

This routine is similar to the arctangent routine described in *The ARRL Microwave Manual* microcomputer chapter. ATAN2 also includes divide by zero protection, and it is in the form of a subroutine rather than in-line code.

To use the routine, place the real part of the complex number in RE and the imaginary part in IM. Then use GOSUB 8 and the variable AN will be returned with the true angle (in radians) of the complex number.

23) "BBMATCH.BAS": BROADBAND MATCHING NETWORK SYNTHESIS
by Thomas R. Apel

Broadband matching network synthesis is an area that has seen a lot of research in the past few years. BBMATCH brings us some of the fruit of this research. For more detailed information on how BBMATCH works, see Thomas R. Apel, "Bandpass Matching Networks Can Be Simplified By Maximizing Available Transformation," *Microwave Systems News*, December 1983, pp 105-117. The version of the program included on *The ARRL Microwave Software Diskette* was converted from the original Commodore BASIC for use on the IBM PC and compatibles by M. A. G. Upton. The program is included by permission of Cardiff Publishing Company.

There are a number of programs (some of them are included on *The ARRL Microwave Software Diskette*) that will design circuits of various sorts to match one impedance to another. Unfortunately, the resulting circuits work only at a single frequency. Their response often deteriorates rapidly as you move away from the design frequency. This program will design a four-element (two inductors and two capacitors) bandpass network to match two resistive loads over a specified bandwidth. In addition, if one of the loads includes a series or parallel reactance, that reactance can be absorbed in the matching network. Although it won't match any impedance to every impedance over a frequency range from dc to daylight, it will handle a lot of problems that were once done by trial and error.

When you run the program, you are first asked to indicate if the load has a series or parallel inductor or capacitor. Then you are asked to specify the frequency range (in MHz) for the matching network. After specifying the impedance values (in ohms) for the high- and low-impedance ports you are asked for the network order, in multiples of four. As far as BBMATCH is concerned, the order of the network is always the number of inductors and capacitors in the network. (The true order of a network is not necessarily equal to the number of inductors and capacitors in the network.)

At this point the program will proceed to calculate the network values and print them out (with unit labels). Each component is identified as a series or parallel capacitor or inductor. The resistor values given represent the network input and output impedances.

24) "INDUCTOR.BAS": ANALYSIS AND SYNTHESIS OF A VARIETY OF INDUCTORS
by Dr Allen Katz, K2UYH

INDUCTOR calculates the inductance of straight round wires, wire straps and coils of wire. Given the inductance, INDUCTOR will also calculate the dimensions required to realize a given inductance for all the above cases as well as microstrip. This program can be used in the design of circuits as well as in their analysis. For example, if you are trying to find an equivalent model for an FET and you know the length of the wire bonds connecting the chip into the circuit, this program could be used to calculate the inductance of those wire bonds for the FET model.

When you run the program, it first asks if you are working with straight wire, strap, a coil or microstrip. Next you are asked if you want to do analysis or synthesis. If you choose analysis for a wire, for example, you are asked for the wire diameter and length (both in mils or 0.001 of an inch). The program calculates the inductance of the conductor. If you choose synthesis you are asked for conductor diameter and desired inductance. In calculating the required conductor length the program may not find a length for the exact inductance you specified, so the printout includes the calculated inductance along with the calculated length. If you choose strip, coil or microstrip, the program prompts you for the necessary input, and specifies the required dimensions.

25) "GRIDLOC.BAS": MAIDENHEAD GRID LOCATOR CALCULATIONS
by Dr James C. Rautio, AJ3K

The Maidenhead grid locator system divides the entire world into squares one degree (in latitude) by two degrees (in longitude). Each square is given a label, two letters followed by two numbers. You can determine grid locators in North America using the tables given on pages 49-50 of the January 1983 issue of *QST* or for South America using the tables given on pages 52-53 of the October 1983 issue of *QST*. If you don't have those references handy, or need a locator for some other spot around the world, just run GRIDLOC.BAS.

GRIDLOC will take any latitude and longitude and calculate the corresponding grid locator. GRIDLOC will also take any grid locator and print out the boundaries of that grid square. If you are given a grid locator, you will be able to tell approximately where that station is.

For more precise location information, the Maidenhead system also allows an optional two characters to be appended to the basic grid locator. These two letters will pin a station's location down to within several miles. GRIDLOC will handle the precise locator as well. Given the minutes of latitude and longitude (as well as the degrees), GRIDLOC will print out the precise locator. Given a precise locator, GRIDLOC will print out the boundaries of the grid square.

26) "HORN.BAS": GENERAL WAVEGUIDE HORN ANTENNA DESIGN PACKAGE
by Dr Barry Chambers, G8AGN

Horn antennas provide a simple means of obtaining a gain antenna at microwave frequencies, especially if waveguide is used as the transmission line. This program will provide the required dimensions for several different types of horn antennas given a required gain.

When you run the program, the first question it asks is whether you would like an optimal-gain horn or a sectoral horn. A sectoral horn spreads the waveguide out in only one dimension with either an E-plane or an H-plane flare. A sectoral horn will have a narrow beamwidth in the wide dimension of the horn. The optimal-gain horn spreads the waveguide out in both dimensions and will have a narrow beamwidth in both dimensions.

Next, the program asks for the frequency (in MHz) and the required gain (in dB) for your antenna. You have a choice of designing a pyramid-shaped horn antenna or a conical one. The program then proceeds to recommend a waveguide size for your antenna and asks if this choice is acceptable. Finally the program calculates the dimensions of the antenna (in cm). You can elect to display the gain and frequency data for the antenna.

About the Authors

Robert Atkins, KA1GT, was first licensed as G8EKB in 1969, and was later licensed as KA1GT in 1979. He holds a BSc and PhD in chemistry and was *QST* microwave columnist from 1981 to 1989. Robert later served as *Ham Radio* microwave columnist and enjoys building equipment, including 432-MHz EME and 10-GHz SSB systems.

Rick Banghart graduated from Michigan State University in 1970 and has worked there as an engineer for their Broadcasting Services since 1978. He received his electronics training from the Cleveland Institute of Electronics and has taught digital electronics and assembly language programming at Lansing Community College. He has written several special-application computer programs for McCurdy Radio and MSU.

Joe M. Cadwallader, K6ZMW, was licensed in 1957 and became active on VHF/UHF in 1968, starting on 50-MHz SSB and extending to 1296-MHz SSB in the early 1970s, where he helped develop West Coast 1296-MHz activity, along with notables K6UQH and N6OA. He developed and published a high-level 2C39 transverter for 1296 MHz (with AA6S), and completed the first California-Nevada and California-Utah 1296-MHz two-way QSOs (with N6CA) and the first California-Arizona 1296-MHz two-way QSO (with K7GNV) to establish an early 1296-MHz West Coast record of 400 miles before the W6-KH6 path was spanned by N6CA. Joe lives with his wife, Naida, in Los Angeles and is primarily occupied as a Senior Staff Engineer designing and building millimeter-wave subsystems and instrumentation assemblies from 18 GHz to 200 GHz at Hughes Aircraft Co, Millimeter-Wave Products, where he has been since 1977.

Dr David Davidson, W1GKM (SK), was an active amateur for over 50 years and served on the ARRL Committee on the Biological Effects of RF Radiation. He was a Senior Member of the Scientific Staff of GTE Laboratories and also served as GTE Corporate Technical Advisor on RF Bioeffects Safety and Regulations.

Keith Ericson, KØKE, was originally licensed in 1962 as WA2WMT, earned his Extra in 1967 and was issued his current call in 1972. He is currently employed by Cellular One as Project Manager; he previously worked as Engineering Manager for KOSI-FM and KEZW-AM for 15 years. Keith holds the current record for 3456-MHz EME and was involved in the construction of OSCAR 13. He is a founding member of the Colorado Front Range Microwave Society and past Vice President and member of the board of directors of the Central States VHF Society.

Dennis Haarsager, N7DH, was first licensed as WNØKKR in 1965 and upgraded to Extra Class in 1975. He holds a BS and an MA from the University of South Dakota and works as general manager of Washington State University's five public radio and television stations and its interactive video microwave system. Dennis is owner of H2A Communications, which markets a computer software package for microwave transmission engineers. He has designed and built statewide video microwave systems in South Dakota, Idaho and Washington.

David Hallidy, KD5RO, has been licensed for 24 years—first as WN2ZEA, then WB2ZEA, then WB5KVU—and holds an Amateur Extra license. He is active on all VHF/UHF/microwave bands through 10 GHz, and holds one end of the current US tropospheric distance records on 23 cm and 13 cm, as well as one end of the current world distance record on 33-cm EME. David was part of the team that put together the first EME QSOs on 3456 and 5760 MHz, in 1987, and is currently active on 70, 33, 23 and 13-cm EME. He is Chairman of the Rochester (NY) VHF Group, the oldest organized VHF/UHF club in the US.

Gunter Hoch, DL6WU, studied Communications Engineering at Daienstadt Tech and works for German Telekom as information manager and editor. He was licensed while in high school in 1950 and has held the same call ever since. He is active on 70-cm EME and has a special interest in antennas.

Maurice Johnson, W3TRR, earned a BSE from Johns Hopkins University, is a registered PE in Maryland and has held his current call since 1952. He was a pioneer in TV broadcasting from 1948-56, and was a Design Engineer with Westinghouse from 1956-85, working on communications equipment, radar and microwave design. He is currently owner of Technical Services, a consulting firm specializing in technical writing and custom electronic design.

Dr Allen Katz, K2UYH, has been a licensed radio amateur for 34 years and is currently a professor in the Electrical Engineering Department at Trenton State College and a consultant for the RF/microwave Design Group at GE Astro Space Division. He was a recipient of the first WAC (Worked All Continents) awarded for EME and is a holder of the current 10-GHz distance record. Allen also received the ARRL Technical Merit Award in 1976, the ASEE's Western Electric Fund Outstanding Engineering Educator award in 1979, the John Chambers Award in 1982, the IEEE Centennial Medal in 1984 and the GE ASD Technical Excellence Award in 1990.

Geoffrey Krauss, WA2GFP, was first licensed in 1957 and has been active on the VHF/UHF/microwave bands since 1958. He received a BSEE and MEE in RF/microwave electronics and worked as an engineer and teacher before obtaining his JD. Geoffrey is now a Patent Counsel in electronic and medical systems at GE's corporate R & D center. He has written extensively in the VHF/UHF/microwave area, writes the "VHF + Technology" column in *QEX* and builds control equipment as part of the W2SZ/1 VHF contesting group.

Carl Lodstrom, W6/SM6MOM, graduated from Polhemsgymnasiet in Goteborg, Sweden in 1975 and immigrated to the US in 1982. He worked as an engineer for Dow-Key® Microwave for several years before becoming a self-employed consultant in RF, microwave, optics and mechanics in 1987.

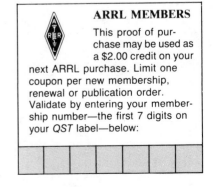

Buzz Miklos, WA4GPM, was first licensed in 1960 in Jacksonville, Florida. An avid experimenter and VHF operator, he served in the US Navy as a radioman before receiving his engineering degree from Old Dominion University in Norfolk, Virginia. Buzz is currently the manager of R & D for RF cavities and tubes at VARIAN EIMAC in Salt Lake City, Utah.

Emil Pocock, W3EP, earned his Novice license as a teenager in 1961 and earned his Extra and the call K3OKC before graduating from high school. Since 1979, W3EP has been active on the VHF/UHF bands from Indiana, Georgia and Connecticut, and has been heard from time to time on hilltops in nearly a dozen other states. He has written extensively on VHF and UHF propagation for *QST*, *QEX* and other ARRL publications and serves as an ARRL Technical Advisor and co-editor of the "VHF/UHF Contesting" column in the *National Contest Journal*. Pocock now lives with his wife, Ann, in Connecticut, where they are both members of the history faculty of Eastern Connecticut State University.

Steve Powlishen, K1FO, first licensed in 1965, was quickly drawn to the VHF bands by the lure of VHF/UHF weak-signal DX work and made his first EME QSO in 1971. Steve received a BSEE from Worcester Polytechnic Institute, specializing in RF and microwaves. He has authored numerous articles on VHF/UHF power amplifiers and antennas. His main Amateur Radio interests are EME operation and the design, development and construction of VHF/UHF arrays and equipment.

James C. Rautio was first licensed as WB2LQW in 1969, upgrading to AJ3K in 1979. He received a BSEE from Cornell in 1978, an MS from the University of Pennsylvania in 1981 and a PhD from Syracuse University in 1986. He worked as an electrical engineer for GE Space Division from 1978 to 1986, and then served as a visiting faculty member at Syracuse University until 1988 and is now founder and president of Sonnet Software, Inc, which develops and markets electromagnetic software for the microwave market.

William Sayer, WA6BAN, has been licensed since 1939 and has also held the calls W2NYY and W3KRI. He has done design and construction work on video transmitters, video stations, high-power klystrons, the first EME, and 100-kW radar trackers for MIT and the Shemya installation. William also worked on linear accelerators for the University of Hamburg and for cancer treatment. He collects, builds and tests all types of amateur equipment and enjoys working almost all bands, especially the challenge of contests and Field Day in remote areas.

David Shaffer, W8MIF/ZF2AZ, became an Amateur Radio operator in 1960 and now holds an Advanced class license. He is a radio astronomer by training, and received his PhD in astronomy from Caltech in 1974. He has observed astronomical objects with antennas ranging in size from 4 feet to 1000 feet, at frequencies from 400 MHz to 100 GHz. He is Chief Scientist at Interferometrics, a small high-tech R & D firm in Vienna, Virginia.

Dr H. Paul Shuch, N6TX, began his microwave experiments in the 1960s, with APX-6 transponders at 1215 MHz. He holds a PhD in engineering from the University of California at Berkeley, where he was a Hertz fellow and Robert H. Goddard Scholar. Paul is Professor of Electronics at the Pennsylvania College of Technology, and has written more than 50 journal articles on microwave circuit design and aviation safety. He has chaired the ARRL VHF/UHF Advisory Committee and served as Technical Director and Chairman of the Board of Project OSCAR, Inc.

William Troetschel, K6UQH, was first licensed as W7LVO in 1947 and as manager of the satellite program was instrumental in the success of the first few OSCARs. He holds a BSEE from the US Air Force Institute of Technology at Wright-Patterson AFB and is a registered professional engineer in Ohio. William has been active on SSB on the 1296-MHz and higher bands since 1956 and holds VUCC (VHF/UHF Century Club) #17 for 10-GHz SSB. His 6-meter WAS (Worked All States) took only 30 years to obtain, due to frequent address changes!

Dick Turrin, W2IMU, was first licensed in 1939 as W3IMU at age 13. His Amateur Radio activities include traffic handling, contests, DXing and EME. A graduate electrical engineer, he was a staff member of Bell Telephone Laboratories from 1955 to 1984 with the Radio Research Department at Holmdel, New Jersey, and is now retired.

James W. Vogler, WA7CJO, has been licensed since the early 1960s and has always been interested in the technical and construction aspects of Amateur Radio. Educated in physics, Jim is an independent consultant specializing in RF, microwave and fiber-optic circuit and system design. He recently assisted Tom Clark, W3IWI, and others at AMSAT with the 2-meter receiver design used in the MicroSat/PACSAT series of satellites. Jim is a founding member, along with WA7LYI and KY7B, of the Bedlam Microwave Society, a society for amateurs over the edge!

Al Ward, WB5LUA, earned a BSEE from the University of Illinois in 1973. He is presently employed by Avantek as a microwave semiconductor Field Applications Engineer. He is active on all amateur frequencies from 50 MHz through 10 GHz on CW and SSB and has been operational on EME on 144, 220, 432, 902, 1296, 2304 and 10,368 MHz. He occasionally chases DX on the HF bands.

Paul Wilson, W4HHK, has held his current call since he was first licensed in 1941. He holds an Amateur Extra as well as a First Class Radiotelegraph and General Radiotelephone Operator's license. Paul pioneered 144-MHz meteor-scatter with W2UK in the early 1950s and was part of the first 13-cm EME QSO in 1970.

MICROWAVE
MANUAL

PROOF OF
PURCHASE

INDEX

Please use this form to give us your comments on this book and what you'd like to see in future editions.

Name _____ Call sign _____

Address _____ Daytime Phone ( ) _____

City _____ State/Province _____ ZIP/Postal Code _____

Edition 1 2 3 4 5 6 7 8 9 10 11 12
Printing   2 3 4 5 6 7 8 9 10 11 12

From_____

_____

_____

Editor, The Microwave Manual
American Radio Relay League
225 Main Street
Newington, CT 06111
USA

···································· please fold and tape ·······························